ELEMENT	SYMBOL	NUMBER	WEIGHT*
Mendelevium	Md	101	(256)
Mercury	Hg	80	200.59
Molybdenum	Mo	42	95.94
Neodymium	Nd	60	144.24
Neon	Ne	10	20.183
Neptunium	Np	93	(237)
Nickel	Ni	28	58.71
Niobium	Nb	41	92.906
Nitrogen	N	7	14.0067
Nobelium	No		
Osmium	Os		0.2
Oxygen	O		5.9994
Palladium	Pd		6.4
Phosphorus	P		0.9738
Platinum	Pt		5.09
Plutonium	Pu	94	(242)
Polonium	Po	84	(210)
Potassium	K	19	39.102
Praseodymium	Pr	59	140.907
Promethium	Pm	61	(147)
Protactinium	Pa	91	(231)
Radium	Ra	88	(226)
Radon	Rn	86	(222)
Rhenium	Re	75	186.2
Rhodium	Rh	45	102.905
Rubidium	Rb	37	85.47
Ruthenium	Ru	44	101.07
Samarium	Sm	62	150.35
Scandium	Sc	21	44.956
Selenium	Se	34	78.96
Silicon	Si	14	28.086
Silver	Ag	47	107.870
Sodium	Na	11	22.9898
Strontium	Sr	38	87.62
Sulfur	S	16	32.064
Tantalum	Ta	73	180.948
Technetium	Tc	43	(99)
Tellurium	Te	52	127.60
Terbium	Tb	65	158.924
Thallium	Tl	81	204.37
Thorium	Th	90	232.038
Thulium	Tm	69	168.934
Tin	Sn	50	118.69
Titanium	Ti	22	47.90
Tungsten	W	74	183.85
Uranium	U	92	238.03
Vanadium	V	23	50.942
Xenon	Xe	54	131.30
Ytterbium	Yb	70	173.04
Yttrium	Y	39	88.905
Zinc	Zn	30	65.37
Zirconium	Zr	40	91.22

PRINCIPLES OF CHEMISTRY

DONALD C. GREGG

PROFESSOR OF CHEMISTRY

THE UNIVERSITY OF VERMONT

BOSTON

ALLYN AND BACON, INC.

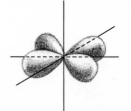

PRINCIPLES OF
Chemistry
SECOND EDITION

First printing . . . . May, 1963

Second printing . . . . September, 1963

Third printing . . . . May, 1964

Fourth printing . . . . September, 1964

Library of Congress Catalog Card Number: 63-13526

PREFACE

This second edition of *Principles of Chemistry* reaffirms the thesis that the ordinary student has a greater appreciation of the attainment, meaning, and use of facts if he studies them within a solid framework of valid principles. It seems reasonable to assume that the student who learns mere chemical facts misses much of the essence of chemistry if he does not know how to use them. Because chemistry admirably demonstrates the productivity of logical reasoning, the student's intelligence is enhanced during the study of this science as he realizes that the use of facts and ideas is a significant part of his education.

Since many students seem to need assistance in the application of ideas, this book abounds in explanations and interpretations of chemical phenomena. Because these explanations and interpretations necessarily contain both concepts and descriptions of facts, there is generally no separation of theories, principles, and facts. The blending of theory and descriptive chemistry in many sections offers a beneficial intellectual experience for the serious student.

The problems, both quantitative and qualitative, at the ends of the chapters usually require for their solution a thoughtful use of concepts and facts. Very few questions can be answered by simple recall of facts because the problems are designed to entice the student to think and reason as well as to recall facts and concepts and to follow conventional rules. Answers to most of the problems, including the qualitative problems, are given at the end of the book.

This revision contains several important features not included in the original edition: for example, a brief introduction to quantum theory and the spatial arrangement of atomic orbitals (Chapter 6); the apparent geometry of some simple covalent molecules and a detailed discussion of chemical bonding, including hybridization of atomic orbitals (Chapter 8); crystal defects and semiconductors (Chapter 10); the Boltzmann distribution principle (Chapter 14); an adequate description of the major chemistry of the halogens (Chapter 12), of the nitrogen family (Chapter 13), and of the common metals (Chapters 24 and 25). The sections on complex ions have been expanded to include their geometry and the concepts of stereoisomerism. A novel feature is Chapter 9, in which the essential aspects of the major kinds of chemical reactions are presented briefly. This unusual presentation should help the student to differentiate and integrate the various electronic phenomena that constitute chemical reactions. The concept of entropy is presented initially in the chapter on the gaseous state (Chapter 14) and again in subsequent chapters where it is appropriate. Descriptions of ion-exchange resins, chromatography, solvent extractions, and molecular distillations are included. The chapter on the physical aspects of chemical reactions includes applications of the concepts of free energy, enthalpy, and entropy. Among the sections in the expanded introduction to organic chemistry are brief descriptions of the steroids and nucleic acids (RNA and DNA).

Although this edition contains much more material than the previous edition, it is neither intended nor suggested that all sections of the text be assigned in a specific course. Teachers and students are expected to choose judiciously those portions that seem most useful and instructive for specific situations.

The suggestions and comments of those, both faculty and students, who used the first edition, the assistance of my wife, Florence, and the indulgence of my sons, Bentley and Fulton, are gratefully acknowledged.

DONALD C. GREGG

CONTENTS

7 HOW ATOMS INTERACT WITH EACH OTHER

8 CHEMICAL BONDING AND ARCHITECTURE

9 SOME COMMON TYPES OF CHEMICAL REACTIONS

27 INTRODUCTION TO ORGANIC CHEMISTRY

PRINCIPLES OF CHEMISTRY

1

MATTER

1.1 A PERSPECTIVE

Chemistry is concerned with the composition and changes of all ordinary forms of matter. In this context, matter is anything that occupies space and has mass and inertia. Ordinary matter is either solid, liquid, or gaseous.

Since chemistry is so vast, there are many different kinds of activity pertaining to the investigation of matter. Among these are the formulation and use of methods for the determination of the composition of matter. Another is the investigation of the structure of the various kinds of matter and of the forces, or bonds, that hold together the entities that constitute the material in question. Some chemists study material changes in order to ascertain how, and perhaps why, the changes occur. Others develop and use various techniques either to prepare new kinds of matter or to

isolate them from materials found in nature. In the chemical industry the chemist may develop new uses and substitutes for certain kinds of materials normally found in nature.

Since all changes of matter involve some form of energy, the chemist is continually involved with energy in its various manifestations. He obtains energy from many changes, and he expends energy to accomplish certain other changes. We shall find that the concept of energy is an extremely important aspect of any study of chemistry.

Every bit of chemical knowledge is a direct result of one or more careful and unbiased experimental observations. Most of these observations were and are made by using at least one of our five senses. Currently, however, we realize that some problems about the structure and behavior of matter may never be fully understood or solved simply by using our five senses and

3

"common sense." Although the scope and abstract character of chemistry may seem at times to be very confounding, an elementary introduction to chemistry offers an exceptional opportunity to appreciate the productivity of inductive and deductive reasoning.

Most topics presented in this book are either qualitative or quantitative. When we state that mercury is more dense than water, we are making a qualitative statement. But if we state that at a specific temperature mercury is 13.6 times as dense as water, we are making a quantitative statement. A general rule is that a qualitative statement either does not or need not contain numbers, whereas a quantitative statement always will. It will be evident that the significance of the numbers in a quantitative statement can be recognized only if the words are understood in context. Some students encounter difficulty in trying to use the numbers in a specific quantitative statement because they do not know the meanings of some of the attendant words.

Chemistry must never be considered an isolated branch of science. As time goes on, we shall realize more and more that chemistry is intimately related to physics and mathematics. Physical as well as chemical techniques must be used to investigate most of the transformations of matter. In fact, the development of our current knowledge of the structure of matter has been based upon fundamental principles of physics and upon techniques of the physicists. The modern conception of the structure of atoms, for example, can be expressed completely only by using the language of mathematics.

Prior to the twentieth century very few chemists recognized the close relationship of chemistry to physics and mathematics. Although the chemists at that time did postulate the existence of atoms, they were unaware that their chemical techniques could not yield information about the structure of atoms. For that matter, the nineteenth-century physicist did not realize that he had the keys to unlock the door to the mystery of atomic structure. Even in the twentieth century, although chemists and physicists in concert have already formulated an epic recital of man's conception of the structure of matter, the picture is far from being complete.

Biology and medicine are closely allied to chemistry. Many major advances in these fields have been and are being made through the application of chemical principles and techniques. The tremendous growth of chemotherapy in medicine attests to this fact. The fundamental relationship of chemistry to biology becomes apparent when we realize that each living organism is composed of different kinds of matter that are constantly undergoing many, perhaps hundreds of, different chemical changes.

Thoughtful organization and logical interpretation of the huge amount of chemical information and data have led to the development of many fundamental principles or concepts. These ideas, in turn, are being used in the interpretation and classification of chemical phenomena and in the prediction of the results of "new" experiments and undiscovered phenomena.

During this study of chemistry we shall attempt to describe and evaluate most of the major chemical principles and show how they may be applied. Naturally we must know some facts about matter before we can usefully apply the principles, but we would miss much of the essence of chemistry if we spent all of our time gathering facts. Although the application of principles requires logical reasoning and a strict regard for accuracy, a careful and thoughtful student can learn easily to derive the answers to many chemical questions.

1.2 DEFINITIONS

The chemist considers that all ordinary matter is composed of extremely tiny entities called *atoms*. These atoms, the chemist's building blocks of matter, consist of still smaller particles. And we may learn eventually that some of these smaller entities consist of even smaller particles. The idea that matter is atomic is the most important concept embraced by chemists.

A sample of matter is often called a *substance*. If all the atoms in a substance are nearly identical chemically, the material is called a *chemical element*. A sample of a chemical element is an elemental form of matter. Pure iron, for example, is an elemental substance because it consists solely of iron atoms. Currently 103 different chemical elements are known; hence there are at least 103 chemically different kinds of atoms. These atoms, either individually or in various combinations, compose all the known kinds of matter.

If a substance of definite and constant composition consists of the atoms of two or more different chemical elements, it is called a *compound*. Water, for example, is a compound because it consists of hydrogen and oxygen atoms in a definite and constant composition. Maple syrup, however, is not a compound because its composition varies and is indefinite.

The term *molecule* is often used to identify the smallest particle of a substance that can exhibit, under ordinary conditions, the chemical properties of the substance.   Another, perhaps better, definition is: *A molecule is any chemical entity that can maintain its identity in the ordinary fluid state of a substance.*   The number of atoms in a simple molecule is expressed by a suitable prefix.   A monatomic molecule has one atom per molecule; a diatomic molecule has two atoms per molecule; a triatomic molecule has three atoms, and so on.   If a molecule has many atoms, it is called a *polyatomic molecule.*   To cite a few examples: elemental helium, He, consists of monatomic molecules; elemental oxygen, O_2, consists of diatomic molecules at ordinary temperatures; carbon dioxide, CO_2, consists of triatomic molecules.

If two or more different substances are mixed and each retains its identity and specific properties, the result is a *mixture.*   Some mixtures are homogeneous (uniform), whereas others are hetero-geneous.   The extent of homogeneity depends on the intimacy of mixing.   Cane sugar and table salt dissolved in water yield a homogeneous mixture.   However, sugar and salt combined as solids yield a heterogeneous mixture.

Matter exists ordinarily in three physical states—the solid, the liquid, and the gaseous states.   The liquid and gaseous states are fluid states.   In many cases it is possible to transform a substance from one physical state to either of the other two.   Later we shall learn how and why the addition or removal of heat, for instance, may cause a change in the physical state of a substance.

1.3   CHANGES IN MATTER

It is obvious that material changes are quite common.   Water freezes (solidifies); ice melts (liquefies).   Wood burns in air and only a small amount of ash remains.   Iron rusts in moist air and a reddish-brown substance appears.   Since there are countless changes in matter, the chemist attempts to classify them in order to make their investigation less difficult.   The two major types of changes of matter are chemical changes and physical changes.

An *ordinary chemical change* is a process during which one or more substances lose their identity and one or more entirely different substances are produced.   Many of these changes can be attained and controlled by choosing the proper conditions.   The course of a chemical change, as well as its rate and yield of product, often can be controlled by altering the reaction conditions.

A *physical change* is any transformation of matter during which the composition of the molecules, or the smallest chemical entities in the substance, remain unchanged. In contrast to ordinary chemical changes, it is often difficult and sometimes impossible to alter or control the course of a physical change.

1.4   PROPERTIES OF MATTER

Every pure substance has at least one property that is unique to it, although it may have some properties identical to those of one or more other substances. Care must be used, therefore, in the identification of a specific substance.

Properties of substances are usually divided into two groups, chemical and physical. The *chemical property* of a substance is defined as its characteristic behavior during chemical change. It is either a description of the substance's fate during a chemical reaction or a description of its inertness (absence of change). For example, solid sulfur burns in oxygen to yield a gas. Sodium reacts vigorously with water: the sodium disappears and gaseous hydrogen is evolved. Platinum does not react with water. Each example states only one of many properties of the substance named.

The simplest definition of a *physical property* of a substance is any specific behavior or characteristic that does not describe its fate during a chemical change. The melting point and crystalline form are physical properties of a solid. The boiling point and freezing point are physical properties of a liquid. The color and density are physical properties of a gas.

1.5   QUANTITATIVE DESCRIPTIONS OF MATTER

Chemists everywhere use a uniform system of units for quantitative measurements, especially those of dimension, mass, and time. This system is usually called the *metric system*, but it is also called the *cgs* system (centimeter-gram-second). The metric system is preferred by most scientists because the units of dimension are related to each other by some integral power of ten. The units of mass in the metric system are also assigned by means of the decimal system.

The so-called *English system*, or *fps* system (foot-pound-second), is seldom used by chemists outside of the chemical industry. The units of time in the metric system are identical to those in the English system.

1.6   MASS

Whenever a quantitative statement is made about the amount or quantity of matter, we shall express the amount in terms of its *mass*. The most practical unit of mass is the *gram* (g), an arbitrarily chosen standard amount of matter. The mass of very large amounts of matter is often expressed in kilograms. One kilogram (1 kg) is equal to 1000 g. The mass of a very small quantity of matter may be expressed in milligrams. One milligram (1 mg) is equal to 0.001 g; 1 g of matter contains 1000 mg.

To place the gram in familiar settings: an ordinary dime has a mass of about 2.5 g; a teaspoonful of water contains about 5 g of liquid; a pound of bacon has a mass of 453.6 g. One kilogram is equal to 2.205 lb; 1 oz is equal to 28.35 g.

Although mass is used to express the amount of matter, it has nothing more than a mathematical significance in the true physical sense. An object's mass is intimately related to its *inertia*. The inertia of an object is its tendency to resist a change in the direction of its motion. For our purposes, we may assume that if a body is at rest, its inertia and mass remain constant no matter where the body resides.

1.7   WEIGHT

The weight of a given amount of matter, as measured on or near the earth, is the force exerted on the mass by the gravitational attraction of the earth. Since weight is a force exerted on a mass, weight and mass are not identical.

A given object would have a much smaller weight on the moon than on the earth because the gravitational attraction of the moon is much less than that of the earth. The mass and inertia of an object are the same on the earth as on the moon because the amount of matter is constant. In interstellar space an object may have no weight at all.

At any specific geographic location, objects that have the same weight have identical masses. The mass of an object is determined by weighing it, a procedure by which the object's weight is found to be identical to that of a "certain amount of standard mass." We might say, "This object weighs 10 g." This does *not* state, however, that the weight of the object is 10 g.

1.8 VOLUME

The concept of volume is used to identify the amount of space either occupied by matter or available for occupancy. We realize that the volume of a regular object or vessel may be calculated if the dimensions are known.

A unit of linear dimension in the metric system is the *meter* (m). This arbitrarily chosen unit of length is equivalent to about 39.37 in. Since the meter is a rather large unit, the centimeter (cm) is commonly used. The centimeter is equal to 0.01 meter. Another unit, the millimeter (mm) is equal to 0.001 meter. There are 10 mm in a centimeter, 100 cm in a meter, and 1000 mm in a meter. There are 2.54 cm in 1 in. Extremely small dimensions are expressed using the *Angstrom unit* (A). One Angstrom unit is equal to 1×10^{-8} cm.

The cubic centimeter (cu cm) is used commonly to indicate the volume of regular objects or vessels. Since it is difficult to determine the volume of an irregular object from its dimensions, another means for the expression of volume is available.

The chemist often uses the *liter* (l) as the unit of volume. The liter was designed originally as the volume of 1 kg of water. A slight error was made in the original assignment of the kilogram; hence the liter is actually equal to 1000.028 cu cm. For most purposes, we may consider that 1 liter is equal to 1000 cu cm, and that 1 cu cm is equal to 1 *milliliter* (ml). The milliliter is exactly 0.001 l. The capacity of an ordinary teaspoon is approximately 5 ml. One fluid ounce is equal to 29.57 ml. One quart is equal to 0.946 l, or 946 ml.

1.9 DENSITY

The compactness of a sample of matter may be expressed in terms of its density, the mass per unit volume. The density of solids and liquids is usually indicated in grams per milliliter (g/ml). Since ordinary gases are much less dense (less compact) than solids and liquids, densities of gases are usually in grams per liter. For practical purposes, density expressed in grams per milliliter is identical to that in terms of grams per cubic centimeter. The relationships of weight, mass, volume, and density are shown in Fig. 1.1.

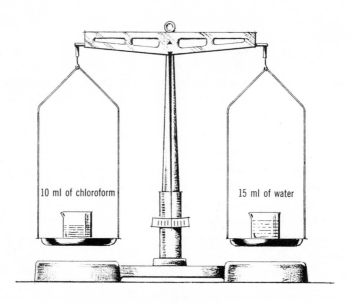

Weight of water = weight of chloroform
Mass of water = mass of chloroform
Amount of water = amount of chloroform
Volume of water is 1.5 times the volume of chloroform
Density of chloroform is 1.5 times the density of water

FIGURE 1.1 Some relationships of weight, mass, volume, and density.

Frequently it is stated that lead (density = 11.34 g/ml) is heavier than aluminum (density = 2.70 g/ml). The statement would be more exact if the word "heavier" were replaced by the words "more dense." Ten milliliters of aluminum is heavier than 2 ml of lead.

The density of a substance at constant pressure varies with the temperature. A piece of iron expands when heated and contracts when cooled. It is evident that expansion yields a decrease in density, whereas contraction results in an increase in density.

The concept of density is very useful, because the density of a substance or an object indicates the mass of one unit of volume, and it implies the volume of one unit of mass. This concept permits simple arithmetical calculation of the mass of any volume of the substance and the volume of any mass. The symbolic formulation of the concept of density is $D = M/V$, where D is density, M is mass, and V is volume.

The term *specific gravity* may be used, especially with liquids and solids, to denote the density of a substance relative to some specific standard density. Usually this standard density is 1 g/ml, the density of water at 4°C. The specific gravity of a substance has no units, because it is the ratio of the density of the substance to the density of water. If the reference density is 1 g/ml, the specific gravity of the substance is the mass of 1 ml. A notation of specific gravity such as $2.5_{4°}^{20°}$ means that the density of the substance at 20°C is 2.5 g/ml.

1.10 TEMPERATURE

When describing a sample of matter it is often necessary to note the *temperature*. A notation of temperature indicates whether something is hotter, colder, or neither hotter nor colder than something else. The temperature of a substance also indicates whether heat will flow from the material to its surroundings, or whether heat will flow from the surroundings to the material.

The concept of temperature is related intimately to the concept of *heat*. Heat is a manifestation of thermal energy. If two objects originally at different temperatures are placed in contact, heat is that which flows from the hotter to the cooler until their temperatures are identical. Because the hotter object has the greater thermal energy, energy flows from it to the cooler object.

The most common scale of temperature used internationally by scientists is the *centigrade* scale, suggested by Anders Celsius in 1742. The term *centigrade* implies that there are 100 degrees or graduations of temperature between two "fixed landmarks." These fixed points are 0°, the temperature at which water freezes under specific conditions (see p. 355) and 100°, the temperature at which water boils at standard atmospheric pressure. If an object has a temperature of 0°C, it does not mean that there is no heat or thermal energy in the object. Actually 0°C corresponds to 32° Fahrenheit.

The *Fahrenheit* scale of temperature was introduced by Gabriel Daniel Fahrenheit in 1724. In this scale there are 180 degrees between the same "fixed" points as those used to formulate the centigrade scale. (See Fig. 1.2.)

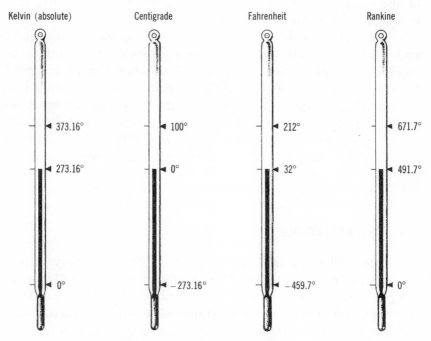

FIGURE 1.2 Common scales of temperature.

Conversion of notations of temperature from one scale to the other is possible by using the equations:

Centigrade temp. = 5/9 (Fahrenheit temp. −32)
Fahrenheit temp. = 9/5 (centigrade temp.) +32

It is well to note that each centigrade degree is equal to 9/5 Fahrenheit degree, and each Fahrenheit degree is 5/9 of a centigrade degree. The scales coincide at −40° centigrade and Fahrenheit.

It seems reasonable that the best temperature scale would be one in which zero degrees of temperature means no heat, or at least minimum energy. Such a scale is the *Kelvin* scale, often called the *absolute* scale because in using this scale zero degrees means no temperature and no heat. A temperature notation expressed in degrees Kelvin or degrees absolute has a direct relationship to the amount of heat present in a system.

A degree of Kelvin temperature is equal to a degree of centigrade temperature, and 0°K is −273°C (more accurately, −273.16°C). The temperature 0°C is the same as 273°K. To convert centigrade to Kelvin, add 273°. To convert Kelvin to centigrade, subtract 273°. The Rankine scale is an absolute temperature scale expressed in Fahrenheit degrees. (See Fig. 1.2.)

1.11 HEAT

Heat or thermal energy is one of the most important physical concepts. Energy may be defined, in a sense, as the ability of material systems to produce heat. Wherever there is molecular motion there is heat. If there is no molecular motion, there is no heat; if there is no heat, there is no molecular motion.

The importance of heat and fire was recognized very early in man's history. The earliest chemists thought that fire was one of the four fundamental material elements, the others being air, earth, and water. These four elements, either individually or in combination, were believed to compose all known forms of matter.

The role of heat during certain physical changes is evident. Because ice absorbs heat during melting, the liquid water so produced has more energy than the ice. If this energy is removed from the water, ice forms. At 0°C the amount of heat absorbed in changing 1 g of ice to 1 g of liquid water is identical to the amount of heat that must be removed from 1 g of water at 0°C to yield 1 g of ice. Heat, therefore, is not lost. Later in Chapter 4 (p. 67) we shall describe the role of heat in ordinary chemical changes.

The unit of heat in the metric system is the *calorie* (cal). Heat is measured by determining what its absorption can accomplish under specific conditions. One calorie is the amount of heat that can increase the temperature of 1 g of water from 14.5°C to 15.5°C. Although this is the definition of the calorie, we may assume for most practical purposes that a calorie can raise the temperature of 1 g of water 1° of centigrade temperature. The kilocalorie (kcal or Cal) is used to identify large amounts of heat. One kilocalorie is equal to 1000 cal. The British thermal unit (Btu) is the amount of heat necessary to raise the temperature of 1 lb of water from 39°F to 40°F. One Btu is equal to 252 cal.

The *specific heat* of a substance, measured at a specific temperature (often 20°C), is the number of calories required to increase the temperature of 1 g of the substance 1°C. By definition, the specific heat of water is 1 cal/g°C. The specific heat of gold is 0.0316 cal/g°C. This means that the absorption of 0.0316 cal of heat by 1 g of gold causes its temperature to rise 1°C. The absorption of 0.0316 cal by 1 g of water causes an increase of only 0.0316°C in the temperature of the water.

The specific heat of a substance varies with temperature, but in many cases the variation is so slight it may be disregarded. The variation in the specific heat of water is assumed to be zero between 14.5°C and 15.5°C. This is the reason for the specification of the temperature interval in the definition of the calorie.

1.12 MATTER AND ENERGY

The most common forms of energy are: heat, electromagnetic radiation (light), electricity, and kinetic, potential, and mechanical energies. Since we know relatively little about energy, we are not sure how many manifestations of energy there are. The most startling fact is that matter itself often appears to be another manifestation of energy. In fact, a physicist might argue that matter is a manifestation of energy, whereas a chemist might insist that energy is a manifestation of matter. A noted chemist has suggested that the word "mattergy" might be used to emphasize this duality.

Almost everyone has heard of the laws of the conservation of matter or mass and the conservation of energy. The first was suggested by an eminent Russian, Lomonosov, in 1756. In 1847 Hermann Helmholtz stated the second of these laws, which is, in essence, that energy can be neither created nor destroyed. Today we realize that we must combine these two laws: matter-energy can be neither created nor destroyed.

All chemical substances are sources of fantastic amounts of energy. As yet, however, man has not learned how to obtain and use most of this potential energy. In later sections we shall describe the role of several forms of energy. The role of energy is paramount because in every chemical and physical change some form of energy is involved.

Albert Einstein in 1905 proposed his classic theory that matter and energy are equivalent. A simple relationship that expressed this equivalence is $E = (2.2 \times 10^{13})(g)$, where E is the energy in calories, 2.2×10^{13} is a proportionality constant, and g is the number of grams of matter converted to energy. According to this expression, the conversion of one gram of matter to energy yields 2.2×10^{13} cal. This amount of heat could raise the temperature of 5×10^8 lb (250,000 tons) of water from 0°C to 100°C.

The term *energy* in Einstein's equation is usually called *atomic energy*. It should be recognized that the amount of this energy available in a given sample of matter is dependent only on the mass of the matter and not on the character of the matter itself.

We shall learn later (Chap. 26) that atomic energy is evolved during extraordinary chemical reactions in which atomic nuclei (those portions of atoms containing nearly all the mass) undergo compositional changes. Perhaps the term *nuclear atomic energy* would be a better way to identify this energy.

The amount of energy evolved during an ordinary chemical reaction is extremely tiny in contrast to the total mass of matter involved in the chemical change. For instance, during the combustion of 3000 tons of coal only 1 g of matter is converted to energy. This means that the loss of mass per gram of coal is 4×10^{-10} g per gram. Since this minute difference in mass cannot be detected by our most refined apparatus, the loss in mass during the ordinary burning of coal is usually ignored. We shall learn later that atomic nuclei usually do not undergo changes during ordinary chemical reactions.

1.13   A SUMMARY

Every sample of matter is composed of one or more of the currently known chemical elements and perhaps of some undiscovered elements. A chemical element consists of chemically identical atoms. Matter that has a constant composition and consists of two or more different elements is called a compound. The smallest particle of a substance that can show the chemical properties of that substance is called a molecule. Some molecules are monatomic (one atom per molecule), but most are polyatomic (more than one atom per molecule). Because some molecules, such as diamond, are so huge, they are called macromolecules.

Matter exists in three physical states: solid, liquid, and gaseous.

Conversion of a sample of matter from one physical state to another is usually a physical change accompanied by either absorption or evolution of energy. The most common form of energy involved in physical changes is thermal energy or heat. The temperature of a sample of matter is directly related to its thermal energy.

If during a phenomenon a substance completely loses its identity and one or more different substances are produced, the process is called a chemical change. The characteristic behavior of a substance during a chemical change is a chemical property of the substance.

The amount of matter in a given sample is always identified in terms of its mass, most frequently expressed in grams (g). The kilogram is 1000 g; the milligram is 0.001 g. The space occupied by a given sample of matter is called its volume. The most common unit of volume used in the laboratory is the milliliter (0.001 liter). The mass of a unit volume of matter is the density of the sample. The density of a substance varies with the temperature, due to expansion and contraction.

The unit of thermal energy (heat) is the calorie. The kilocalorie (kcal) is 1000 cal. By using an absolute scale of temperature, such as the Kelvin scale, it is possible to relate heat and temperature directly.

Problems

1. The mass of an object is 743.48 g. Express this mass in: (a) milligrams, (b) ounces, (c) pounds, (d) kilograms.

2. Six and one-half liters of an aqueous solution contain 150 g of sodium chloride dissolved in the water. (a) How many milliliters of the solution consist, in part, of 0.085 kg of sodium chloride? (b) If the water were evaporated from 940 ml of the solution, how much sodium chloride would remain? (c) A portion of the solution was heated to evaporate completely all of the water, whereupon 940 mg of sodium chloride remained. How many liters of solution were used?

3. The interior dimensions of a rectangular box are 3.5 cm × 250 mm × 45 cm. What is the capacity, in liters, of the box?

4. The temperature of an object is 65°C. What is the temperature expressed in degrees Fahrenheit?

5. The specific gravity of mercury is 13.57 regardless of whether the English system or the metric system is used. Why?

6. The density of bismuth is 9.8 g/ml and the density of hafnium is 13.4 g/ml. (a) How many milliliters of hafnium occupy the same volume as 45 g of bismuth? (b) How many grams of bismuth occupy a volume identical to that of 13.4 ml of hafnium? (c) Which contains the greater amount of matter—5 ml of bismuth or 3.5 ml of hafnium? (d) Which occupies the greater volume—2.1 ml of hafnium or 21.56 g of bismuth? (e) How many milligrams of bismuth occupy a volume the same as that of 6.7 g of hafnium? (f) How many milliliters of hafnium occupy the same volume as 0.22 liter of bismuth? (g) How many milliliters of bismuth occupy the same volume as 0.36 kg of hafnium? (h) How many grams of bismuth contain the same amount of matter as 2.6 kg of hafnium?

7. The specific gravity of a substance at 4°C is 6.2. How many milliliters of the substance contain 0.78 kg of matter?

8. When filled, a vessel contains 460 g of water at 22°C. The same vessel will hold exactly 230 g of liquid A at 22°C. What is the specific gravity of A?

9. If 49 g of bismuth is placed in a dry 50-ml graduated cylinder, how many milliliters of chloroform are needed to fill the cylinder to the 50-ml graduation?

10. (a) On what type of weighing device would one pound of matter weigh the same on the moon as it does on the earth? (b) On what type of device would one pound of matter weigh less on the moon than it does on the earth?

11. Which of the following involve chemical changes and which involve physical changes? (a) Gaseous bromine burns in an atmosphere of hydrogen. (b) Water evaporates from the ocean and returns to the earth as rain. (c) Gaseous air is liquefied. (d) An egg is fried. (e) Milk directly from a cow is homogenized. (f) A mixture of a detergent and water is shaken to yield suds. (g) A sample of sea water is left in an open pan to yield a solid residue. (h) A cube of cane sugar is dropped into a cup of tea.

12. Which of the following properties are chemical and which are physical? (a) Gold has a relatively low melting point. (b) Gold does not tarnish readily in ordinary air. (c) Gold dissolves readily in aqua regia, a mixture of acids. (d) Gold is quite malleable. (e) Gold is rather expensive. (f) Gold does not seem to dissolve in pure water. (g) Gold is often found naturally in its elemental form.

2

THE ATOMIC THEORY

2.1 CONCEPTS, LAWS, AND THEORIES

The science of chemistry is based on concepts or ideas. Chemistry is not unique in this respect, for concepts and ideas are the foundation of all intellectual activities. New concepts are suggested continually, but the more fundamental concepts on which modern chemistry is based seem well established. The validity of each fundamental concept mentioned in this book has been confirmed by the results obtained during many, sometimes hundreds of, exact quantitative experiments. Much of the material in this book consists of illustrative examples either of the use of these concepts or of the means whereby their validity is confirmed. The examples should be considered as helpful illustrations of what can be accomplished by the thoughtful reasoned application of fundamental principles. The significance of these illustrative examples must be appreciated and

18

OF MATTER

recognized because memorization without some understanding of the logical reasoning is practically worthless.

Antoine Lavoisier, a French scientist, was one of the first persons to stress the necessity of exact quantitative experimentation for substantiating the quality of a concept. This approach, he maintained, permits unbiased retention of valid concepts and the rejection of fallacious ideas. Lavoisier practiced what he preached and many of his quantitative experiments are significant milestones in the development of chemistry.

The major concepts of any science are derived from its laws and theories. A *law* or *principle* relates an established fact. An *hypothesis* is an assumption which needs further investigation for its proof. A *theory* is a reasoned, logical interpretation of a body of facts. It is often impossible to prove conclusively the validity of a theory, but if the theory is useful in the correct prediction of new facts and in the rational explanation of phenomena, the theory is retained until it fails to "fit the facts."

In the history of chemistry many theories have come and gone. A striking example is the theory suggested by John Dalton to explain the inherent character of matter. The essential aspects of this theory were considered valid for nearly 90 years during the nineteenth century. During the past 50 years, however, much of Dalton's theory has been discarded because experimentation has uncovered facts which contradict it. The failure and eventual rejection of a theory should not be considered as retrogression. Rather, all theories suggest and elicit search for new facts and ideas and in this respect all theories are successful concepts.

2.2 DALTON'S ATOMIC THEORY OF MATTER

In 1803 John Dalton, an English chemist-schoolmaster, proposed a concept about the inherent character of matter. In essence, Dalton's theory was this: All matter is composed of extremely tiny, discrete particles called atoms; all atoms of the same chemical element have the same mass; atoms of different elements have different masses; atoms do not divide into smaller particles during chemical changes.

During most of the nineteenth century, the significance of this theory was paramount because it permitted more rational predictions of undiscovered chemical phenomena and better reasoned explanations of the behavior of matter. Dalton's atomic theory probably stimulated the development of chemistry as much as any theory ever has.

In a series of articles called *A New System of Chemical Philosophy*, Dalton's theory was published during the period 1808–1810 in its entirety. However, in 1789 an English scientist, William Higgins, had published a book in which he presented an atomic theory very similar, if not essentially identical, to the theory which Dalton was to suggest several years later. Obviously Higgins had prior claim, and it is rather unfortunate that his contribution to chemistry is unrecognized today by many chemists. Chemistry, like many human endeavors, has its unsung heroes.

A concept of the atomic character of matter was recorded some time around 400 B.C. by the Greek philosopher, Democritus. Apparently this concept was conceived originally by Leucippus,

Democritus' teacher. This theory was accepted by Epicurus, but not by Plato and Aristotle. Perhaps because the theory was unacceptable to Plato and Aristotle, Leucippus' theory lay dormant for approximately 20 centuries. Robert Boyle indicated his belief in the discontinuous character of matter in his book *The Sceptical Chymist* (about 1660) and thus helped revive the doctrine of atomism.

The theories of Leucippus and Dalton have been refined considerably during the past 60 years. Today certain aspects of their theories bear little resemblance to the presently accepted atomic concept of matter. Nevertheless, the ideas of these men are classic. In a sense Leucippus planted the seed and Dalton recognized and cared for the seedling. During the first 60 years of this century, many physicists and chemists have nurtured the plant until it bloomed.

2.3 MODERN CHEMICAL ATOMIC THEORY

In subsequent sections we shall discuss the atoms from a physical viewpoint. We will realize that by performing ordinary chemical experiments we are unable to determine either the actual behavior or structure of the individual atom. The major reason for this inability is the fact that atoms are extremely small, and in order to study chemically the behavior of the atoms of a chemical element, we must use samples which contain many atoms. Therefore, whenever we discuss or note the chemical behavior of a chemical element, we must realize that the statements do not imply a knowledge of the actual behavior of an atom of that element.

Modern atomic theory is extremely complex, and a complete appreciation of it cannot be realized by using ordinary chemical techniques and concepts. Physical as well as chemical techniques must be used to investigate the ultimate character and behavior of atoms. Because this book is concerned mainly with things chemical, we shall emphasize the chemical viewpoint. The more general aspects of modern atomic theory are listed below. These concepts will be sufficient for the time being. (Following each concept a bit of experimental evidence is noted.)

a. The chemical elements are composed of extremely small, chemically discrete particles called *atoms*. Apparently for the most part these atoms retain their inherent discreteness during all ordinary chemical changes. (Atoms of the element mercury combine with the atoms in the element oxygen under appropriate conditions to form a compound, an oxide of mercury. When this oxide of mercury is thermally decomposed, elemental mercury and elemental oxygen are obtained. This oxygen appears to be identical to the oxygen used in the preparation of the oxide and the mercury appears to be identical to the mercury used.)

b. (1) The atoms which compose a given chemical element appear to have identical chemical properties, provided these properties are identified either during or after ordinary chemical transformations. (2) Atoms of different chemical elements have different chemical properties. (When 20.1 g of mercury combines with 1.60 g of oxygen under the appropriate conditions, apparently all the mercury combines with all the oxygen because the mass of the product is 21.7 g. Dry wood burns readily in the presence of oxygen, but wood never burns solely in the presence of mercury.)

c. Whenever the atoms of two or more different elements combine chemically, the atoms unite in certain simple ratios to form the smallest discrete particles of a compound. (In the compound water, hydrogen atoms and oxygen atoms are in combination in the ratio of two atoms of hydrogen to one atom of oxygen, or 2:1.)

d. In certain cases the atoms of an element unite or combine to form discrete particles. These particles are usually called molecules and each molecule of this type contains at least two identical atoms. The actual number of atoms per molecule depends on the nature of the atoms and the mode of union. (At ordinary temperatures hydrogen atoms unite to form diatomic molecules, oxygen atoms form diatomic molecules, and sulfur atoms form octatomic and hexatomic molecules. In diamond, a kind of elemental carbon, the carbon atoms are united in a polyatomic molecule, actually a macro-molecule, whose size is that of the diamond itself. Helium molecules are monatomic.)

e. The atoms of one element may combine with the atoms of another element in more than one ratio, so that more than one kind of compound may be produced. (Carbon atoms and oxygen atoms are in combination in at least three different compounds or oxides of carbon. In carbon monoxide the carbon to oxygen ratio is 1:1, in carbon dioxide this ratio is 1:2, and in carbon suboxide this ratio is 3:2.)

2.4 QUANTITATIVE RELATIONSHIPS

Now that we have some idea of the apparent behavior of atoms, it might be useful to indicate a few important generalizations based on quantitative observations.   Of course, the accuracy and validity of these observations are dependent on the apparatus used.   In most cases a major limiting factor is the sensitivity and accuracy of the balance with which masses are determined.

   a. Every pure chemical compound always contains definite, constant proportions or relative masses of the elements of which it is composed.   (This generalization is often called the *law of constant composition*.)   For example, a molecule of water always contains 2.02 parts by mass (weight) of hydrogen and 16.0 parts by mass (weight) of oxygen, or 1.01 parts of hydrogen to 8.0 parts of oxygen.

   b. Whenever different elements combine chemically to produce a compound, the elements always combine in certain definite mass proportions.   (This generalization is sometimes called the *law of reciprocal proportions*.)   For example, whenever hydrogen combines with oxygen to produce water, every 1.008 parts by mass of hydrogen combines with 8.000 parts by mass of oxygen.

   c. Whenever two elements combine to produce more than one kind of compound, the different masses of the one element which combine with a fixed mass of the second element may be expressed in a ratio of small whole numbers.   (This generalization is often called the *law of multiple proportions*.)   For example, 11.5 g of sodium combines with 16.0 g of oxygen to produce pure sodium superoxide; 23.0 g of sodium combines with 16.0 g of oxygen to produce pure sodium peroxide; 46.0 g of sodium combines with 16.0 g of oxygen to produce pure sodium oxide.   The different masses of sodium, in the order mentioned, which combine with 16.0 g of oxygen have a simple integral relationship 1:2:4.

2.5 THE SIZE AND MASS OF AN ATOM

Most people realize that atoms are infinitesimally small.   Both the actual size and the mass of an atom are actually so small they are beyond our "common-sense" conception.   This is obvious when we realize that there are 6.02×10^{23} atoms in 6.94 g of lithium, that this amount of lithium occupies a volume of 13.1 ml, and that most of this sample of solid lithium is "empty space." These facts concerning atoms need not be accepted on faith. Later, as more facts are presented, we will find that there is substantial experimental evidence to verify these statements.

It is impossible to determine the mass of an individual atom by weighing it on a balance. For that matter, we are unable to touch, taste, smell, or see an individual atom. Therefore, whenever a chemist performs ordinary chemical experiments, he uses aggregates of millions of atoms. After being informed of this fact, a layman might comment that the chemist has little, if any, definite knowledge of the chemical behavior of an individual atom. This comment implies a sound, common-sense viewpoint. However, we must beware of the use of common sense when speaking of atoms. Would anyone like to contemplate philosophically the chemical behavior of an individual atom after he is told that at least 1,000,000,000,000 of them are found in the ink used to print this page?

Late in the seventeenth century scientists were performing reasonably precise, quantitative experiments in an attempt to determine the chemical properties of the elements and to prepare new compounds. They realized that the atoms of different elements combined with each other to produce different compounds. These early workers were able to determine how much of one element combined with a definite amount of another element to form a known amount of product. They realized that they could learn very little about the chemical composition of the product until they knew how many atoms of each element were involved in the chemical transformation.

During the nineteenth century chemists assigned atomic weights to the known elements, and they did so with considerable accuracy. These assignments were made without any significant knowledge of the structure of the atoms and with no intention of assigning masses to individual atoms. The major concepts used were those listed in Section 2.4.

2.6 ATOMIC WEIGHTS

The *atomic weights* of the chemical elements are numbers on a scale, just as centigrade degrees of temperature are relative numbers on a scale. A major difference in the two scales is that the atomic weight scale has only one standard reference point. This reference is 12.00000, the assigned atomic weight of a kind of carbon atom, called carbon-12, that is found in ordinary elemental carbon. Later, in Chapter 5, we shall learn about the physically different kinds of atoms in certain chemical elements. For instance, ordinary elemental carbon consists of at least two different kinds of atoms, one called carbon-12 (99 per cent), the other called carbon-13 (about 1 per cent); sometimes a trace of carbon-14 is also found. We shall discover that ordinary oxygen consists of three different atoms, called oxygen-16, oxygen-17, and oxygen-18.

We must realize that the specific choice of carbon-12 as the standard reference atom was made in 1961 by the International Union of Pure and Applied Chemistry following a purely arbitrary decision made in 1960 by the International Union of Pure and Applied Physics. The unity of choice is the major feature of the new standard.

Prior to 1962 chemists had an atomic weight scale based on 16.00000 as the atomic weight of the element oxygen. This scale was chosen long before physicists discovered that some pure chemical elements, such as oxygen, consist of atoms having slightly different masses. The older chemical atomic weight scale which was based on natural oxygen differed slightly from the scale used by physicists. The physical atomic weight scale was based on one of the three kinds of atoms, oxygen-16, in natural oxygen, rather than on all the atoms as was the chemical scale. The chemists' scale was actually based unwittingly on a weighted average of the masses of the atoms in ordinary oxygen. When the chemical scale was established originally, everyone thought that all atoms in pure oxygen were identical; not until 1930 did scientists realize that this is not true. The difference in the two atomic weight scales prior to 1962 was not critical for ordinary chemical work because the two scales were nearly identical. To convert an atomic weight from the physicists' scale to the chemists', the physical atomic weight had to be divided by 1.000275.

When the chemists decided to use the same atomic weight scale standard as the physicists, it was necessary to recalculate the official atomic weights of 1957. The "new" atomic weights are usually less than the earlier values by 37 parts per million. This small variation results in few major numerical changes because very few atomic weights had been expressed to an accuracy such that they would be significantly affected. The physicists had to recalculate their atomic weights also; in fact, the "new" physical atomic weights differ from the "old" by at least 200 parts per million.

In Table 2.1 are listed some of the 1957 official chemical atomic weights and their 1962 counterparts. A list of the current chemical

TABLE 2.1   Some chemical atomic weights

Element	Official 1962 Value	Official 1957 Value
Aluminum	26.9815	26.98
Bromine	79.909	79.916
Carbon	12.01115	12.011
Copper	63.54	63.54
Hydrogen	1.00797	1.0080
Iron	55.847	55.85
Oxygen	15.9994	16.00000
Sulfur	32.064	32.066
Tin	118.69	118.70
Zinc	65.37	65.38

atomic weights is on the inside front cover of the text. Usually the rule for precision of an atomic weight value is that the last digit is valid to $\pm\frac{1}{2}$ digit. For example, for copper, whose atomic weight is 63.54, the value is 63.54 $\pm$ 0.005, or in the range 63.545 to 63.535. Some atomic weights are known more accurately than to $\pm\frac{1}{2}$ digit. For example, for hydrogen the observed range is ±0.00001; for carbon, ±0.00005; for oxygen, ±0.0001.

It is imperative to realize that the chemical atomic weight of carbon is 12.01115, and not 12.00000. The exact number 12 is the physical standard atomic weight of the atom called carbon-12, whose symbol is ^{12}C. Since natural carbon is about 99 per cent ^{12}C and about 1 per cent ^{13}C, with an occasional trace of ^{14}C, the chemical atomic weight (a weighted average) is slightly more than 12. The value 12.01115 $\pm$ 0.00005 varies slightly because of small variations in the composition of samples of natural carbon.

Essentially the current chemical atomic weights are based on a physical standard, whereas prior to 1962 they were based on a purely chemical standard that assumed all atoms in ordinary oxygen to be identical.

2.7 CANNIZZARO'S PRINCIPLE

One of the most important concepts upon which the atomic weight assignments are made is an idea originally suggested by an Italian, Stanislas Cannizzaro, during the middle of the nineteenth century. His principle is: Since molecules are composed of integral numbers of atoms, the smallest mass of an element that can exist in one molecule of any compound containing that element is the mass of one atom of that element.

Table 2.2 lists certain compounds containing carbon atoms, their approximate molecular weights, the percentage of carbon per

TABLE 2.2 Amount of carbon per molecule in some compounds of carbon

Compound	Molecular Weight (Experimental)	Percentage of Carbon/Molecule (by Analysis)	Amount of Carbon/Molecule
Methane	16.0 units	75.0	12.0 units
Ethane	30.0	80.0	24.0
Butane	58.0	82.8	48.0
Benzene	78.0	92.3	72.0
Naphthalene	128.0	93.7	120.0
1-Butanol	74.0	65.0	48.0
Formic acid	46.0	26.0	12.0
Methyl chloride	50.5	23.8	12.0
Ethyl chloride	64.5	37.2	24.0
Acetone	58.0	62.0	36.0

molecule, and the approximate amount of carbon per molecule. These data show that the smallest amount of carbon per molecule is 12 units, and that the amount of carbon in all other molecules is some integral multiple of 12. The conclusion is therefore that the atomic weight of carbon is 12.

2.8 QUANTITATIVE ASPECTS

Now that we know that all chemical atomic weights are based on the arbitrary choice of 12.00000 as the atomic weight of carbon-12, the question of specific mass units arises. When we identify an atomic weight, mass units are unnecessary because the atomic weight of an element is a number that simply indicates the relationship of the mass of a given number of atoms of the element to the mass of an identical number of carbon-12 atoms. For example, the atomic weight of calcium, 40.08, indicates that a given number of calcium atoms has a mass that is 40.08/12.0000 times that of an identical number of carbon-12 atoms. In other words, 40.08 mass units of calcium contains the same number of atoms as 12.0000 mass units of carbon-12.

Since each atomic weight is related to the assigned atomic weight of carbon-12, the atomic weight of each chemical element is similarly related to that of every other element. Therefore 1.00 mass unit of hydrogen, 16.0 mass units of oxygen, and 14.0 mass units of nitrogen contain identical numbers of atoms. If we had a sample of 8.0 mass units of oxygen, we should need 7.0 mass units of nitrogen to supply the same number of atoms.

The atomic weight of carbon-12 may be expressed as 12.0000 atomic mass units (12.0000 amu), where 1 amu is an amount of matter that has a mass $\frac{1}{12}$ that of a carbon-12 atom. Hence 1.008 amu of hydrogen contains the same number of atoms as 12.0000 amu of carbon-12; also, 63.54 amu of copper and 40.08 amu of calcium contain identical numbers of atoms. The chemical atomic weight of an element is the number of atomic mass units of the element that contains the same number of atoms as 12 amu of carbon-12.

If the mass unit used is the gram, we conclude, for instance, that identical numbers of atoms are present in 1.00 g of hydrogen, 16.0 g of oxygen, and 14.0 g of nitrogen. If the mass unit used is the pound, then 1.00 lb of hydrogen, 16.0 lb of oxygen, and 14.0 lb of nitrogen contain identical numbers of atoms; also, 1.00 ton of hydrogen contains the same number of atoms as 16.0 tons of oxygen. Of course, we can state that 1.0 g of hydrogen contains four times as many atoms as 4.0 g of oxygen.

2.9 THE MOLE AND THE GRAM-ATOM

Now that we know that the atomic weights of the chemical elements are numbers of mass units that contain identical numbers of atoms, we realize that we could use the number of atoms in 12.0000 g of carbon-12 as a reference standard. If you have suspected that this number is tremendous, you are correct. The number is 6.0248×10^{23} atoms—practically inconceivable. This number has always been called *Avogadro's number,* named for its very influential Italian proponent, Amedeo Avogadro. This number, which is extremely important in chemistry and physics, is called the *mole.* The mole is a number equal to the number of atoms in 12.0000 g of carbon-12. The mass of one mole (the *molar weight*) of carbon-12 atoms is 12.0000 g. A mole of oxygen atoms has the same number of atoms as a mole of carbon-12 atoms; hence the molar weight of a mole of oxygen atoms is 16.0 g. The atomic weight of an element when expressed in grams is the mass of one mole of atoms of the element.

Although knowing that a mole of atoms is a specific number of atoms is useful, the notion of the amount of matter represented by one mole of atoms has probably even more utility. The term *gram-atom* (g-atom) is used to represent the amount of matter in one mole of atoms. The g-atom is a unit of quantity specific for each element, whereas the mole is a pure number, approximately 6.02×10^{23}. One g-atom of an element is a specific bundle of matter that contains one mole of atoms of the element.

Since the mass of one mole of atoms depends on the kind of atoms, the mass of a g-atom varies from element to element. This should not be surprising because the mass of one dozen walnuts is quite different from that of one dozen grapefruit. One g-atom of calcium has a mass of 40.08 g and contains one mole of atoms (6.02×10^{23}). One-half of a g-atom of oxygen weighs 8.0 g. (See Fig. 2.1.) It is useful to keep in mind the fact that one g-atom of a

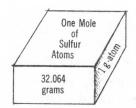
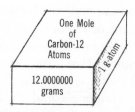
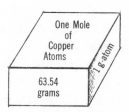

FIGURE 2.1   Each box contains one mole of atoms, an Avogadro's number of atoms, 6.02×10^{23} atoms. Each box contains one g-atom of an elemental form of matter. The amount of matter (expressed in grams) in each box is numerically equal to the atomic weight of the element inside the box, because each box contains one g-atom of an element.

given element contains the same number of atoms as one g-atom of any other element.

The terms *mole* and *g-atom* may be differentiated more readily if you recognize that (1) the mole is a specific number of things, such as a dozen, a gross, a quorum; and (2) the g-atom is a specific amount or quantity of matter, such as a bushel, a peck, a carload.

2.10   ATOMIC HEAT CAPACITIES

On page 14 we defined the *specific heat* of a substance as the number of calories (amount of heat) required to increase the temperature of one gram of the substance 1°C. The *heat capacity* of a sample of a substance is the amount of heat needed to increase the temperature of the sample 1°C.   The heat capacity of one mole of atoms of a given element is the amount of heat needed to raise the temperature of one g-atom of the element 1°C.

In 1818 two French physicists, Pierre Dulong and Alexis Petit, proposed an idea which for a while was useful in the determination of approximate values for certain atomic weights. These men noticed that the heat capacity per mole of atoms, or per g-atom, is approximately 6.1 calories per degree (6.1 cal/deg/mole), within 10 per cent, for most solid elements near room temperatures.

For iron:

55.8 g/mole $\times$ 0.112 cal/g/deg = 6.3 cal/deg/mole
molar weight $\times$ specific heat of solid = molar heat capacity
(mass of 1 mole)

For silver:

108 g/mole $\times$ 0.056 cal/g/deg = 6.0 cal/deg/mole

Since the molar heat capacity of solid elements seemed essentially constant, the concept of Dulong and Petit offered a relatively simple means of determining approximate atomic weights of certain solid elements. Remember that the mass of one mole (molar weight) of the solid element is numerically equal to the atomic weight of the element. Dulong's and Petit's concept did, on at least two occasions, resolve early uncertainties in atomic weight values.

Because one mole of atoms of an element is approximately 6.02×10^{23} atoms, we can conclude that for solid elements of relatively large atomic weights

$$\frac{6.1\,\mathrm{cal/deg/mole}}{6.02 \times 10^{23}\,\mathrm{atoms/mole}} = 1.0 \times 10^{-23}\,\mathrm{cal/atom/deg}$$

is the amount of heat needed to raise the temperature of one atom 1°C. The value, 1.0×10^{-23}, is reasonably valid for many different kinds of atoms.

2.11 A SUMMARY

Since atoms are infinitesimally small, it is impractical to identify and use the actual masses of individual atoms. Instead, an atomic weight scale is used to identify the numbers of mass units of the various elements that contain identical numbers of atoms. The standard reference atomic weight on the scale is 12.00000, the assigned atomic weight of carbon-12. The atomic weight of any given element is the number of atomic mass units of the element that contains the same number of atoms as does 12 amu of carbon-12. One atomic mass unit is an amount of matter that has a mass $\frac{1}{12}$ that of a carbon-12 atom.

A mole of atoms is approximately 6.02×10^{23} atoms, an Avogadro's number of atoms. This number, one mole, is equal to the number of atoms in 12.0000 g of carbon-12. Actually one mole of atoms of any element is a specific number of atoms, 6.02×10^{23}.

The amount of matter in one mole of atoms of a given element is called one gram-atom. The mass, in grams, of one g-atom of a given element is numerically equal to the atomic weight of the element. One g-atom of an element contains the same number of atoms as one g-atom of any other element because one g-atom is the amount of matter in one mole of atoms.

The atomic weights of the elements offer the only means of relating numbers of atoms to amounts of matter. Without the chemical atomic weights it would be impossible to attach a definite quantitative relationship to a given number of atoms.

Problems

1. What mass of elemental bromine contains the same number of atoms as 40 g of silicon?

2. The formation of a certain compound requires that the number of participating oxygen atoms be $1\frac{1}{2}$ times the number of participating aluminum atoms. If 20 g of oxygen is used, how much aluminum is necessary?

3. How many milligrams of nitrogen are needed to supply twice as many atoms as 64 ml of silicon (density, 2.0 g/ml)?

4. A pure binary compound contains twice as many atoms of oxygen as of carbon. In preparing this compound, how many grams of oxygen are needed per gram of carbon?

5. (a) Which amount of matter contains the largest number of atoms: 10 g of sodium, 36 g of bromine, or 5.0 g of boron? (b) Of these three amounts, which contains the smallest number of atoms?

6. How many grams of chlorine are needed to supply the same number of atoms as 3.4 moles of sodium atoms?

7. How many moles of iron atoms are needed to supply the same number of atoms as 40 g of carbon?

8. How many g-atoms of sulfur are needed to supply $2\frac{1}{2}$ times as many atoms as 6.3 moles of oxygen atoms?

9. How many grams of barium are needed to supply one-half as many atoms as 20.6 g of calcium?

10. What is the mass of 5.7 g-atoms of bromine?

11. How many pounds of sodium are needed to supply the same number of atoms as 63 lb of potassium?

12. What is the mass of 0.45 mole of boron atoms?

13. What is the volume, in milliliters, of 1.6 g-atoms of bismuth (density, 9.8 g/ml)?

14. How many milliliters of bismuth are needed to supply 4 times as many atoms as 7.5 g of lithium?

15. If rubidium were assigned the atomic weight 44.0, what would be the atomic weight of arsenic?

16. How many atoms of calcium are present in 10 g of the metal?

17. Assume that the specific heat of gold is 0.0316 cal/g°C. According to the concept of Dulong and Petit, what is the approximate atomic weight of gold?

18. By using the concept of Dulong and Petit, calculate the approximate specific heat of pure metallic cadmium.

3

3.1 THE SYMBOLS OF THE ELEMENTS

Since the advent of alchemy, symbols have been used in the language of chemistry in order to provide a sort of chemical shorthand. Because the alchemists knew very little about the actual character of matter, the

TABLE 3.1 Alchemical symbols

⊿ Air (element related to fire)	♂ Iron (Mars) (male)
⊽ Earth (element related to water)	♀ Copper (Venus) (female)
△ Fire (heat rises)	♯ Sulfur (stone that burns)
▽ Water (water falls)	♁ Antimony (the wolf metal)
☾ Silver (moon)	☿ Mercury (the nimble metal)
☉ Gold (sun)	♄ Lead (Saturn)

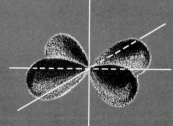

OF CHEMICAL SYMBOLS

symbols used by them may seem somewhat trivial and perhaps rather romantic. The symbols used in modern chemistry are arbitrary, and the difference between the alchemical and the modern symbols is more one of

TABLE 3.2 Element names derived from Latin

Name	Symbol
Antimony (Stibium)	Sb
Copper (Cuprum)	Cu
Gold (Aurum)	Au
Iron (Ferrum)	Fe
Lead (Plumbum)	Pb
Mercury (Hydrargyrum)	Hg
Potassium (Kalium)	K
Silver (Argentum)	Ag
Sodium (Natrium)	Na
Tin (Stannum)	Sn

degree than of kind. A few of the alchemical symbols are noted in Table 3.1.

The current symbols of the chemical elements are derived from the accepted names of the elements. Usually two letters from the name of the element are used for the symbol. Ten of these symbols are derived from the Latin name of the element, as indicated in Table 3.2, and have little, if any, relationship to the Anglo-Saxon name.

3.2 QUALITATIVE INTERPRETATIONS OF AN ELEMENTAL SYMBOL

a. The symbol of an element always signifies or represents a specific element. For example, the symbol Ar always represents the element argon.

b. The symbol of an element may also signify or represent the chemical atom or atoms of the element. The symbol Ar may in certain cases represent an argon atom.

If the symbol of an element appears in the formula of a compound substance, it indicates that the substance contains that element, or it implies that the element and one or more other elements have combined to produce the substance during a chemical transformation. For instance, the formula of sulfuric acid, H_2SO_4, indicates that the substance consists of the atoms of hydrogen, sulfur, and oxygen.

3.3 QUANTITATIVE INTERPRETATIONS OF AN ELEMENTAL SYMBOL

a. The simplest quantitative interpretation of the symbol of an element is that it represents one atom of the element. However, because this amount of the element is so extremely small, this interpretation has little practical significance.

b. A practical quantitative interpretation of the symbol of an element is that it represents a certain number of atomic mass units of the element. The number of atomic mass units (amu) represented by the symbol is numerically equal to the atomic weight of the element. For example, in the case of hydrogen, the symbol H represents 1.008 amu of hydrogen. The symbol Ca represents 40.08 amu of calcium. This quantitative interpretation is extremely useful in that any acceptable unit of mass may be used. The amount of calcium represented by Ca, for example, may be expressed in grams (40.08 g), in pounds (40.08 lb), or in milligrams (40.08 mg), depending on the problem or the experiment in question.

c. Since the gram is the most common unit of mass used in the chemical laboratory, a very useful quantitative interpretation of the symbol of an element is that it represents one g-atom of the element. You will recall that in Section 2.9 we defined a g-atom as the amount of matter represented by one mole of atoms. The mass of one g-atom of an element is therefore the mass of one mole of atoms of the element. The symbol Ca can be interpreted as one g-atom of calcium whose mass is 40.08 g. The mass of one g-atom of an element, which is always expressed in grams, is numerically equal to the atomic weight of the element.

d. The symbol of an element can be used to represent a specific number of atoms of the element, namely one mole of atoms. In Section 2.9 we introduced the mole as a specific Avogadro's number of entities, 6.0248×10^{23}. Therefore the symbol Ca may be considered as representing one mole of calcium atoms, or 6.0248×10^{23} calcium atoms. In **c** of this section we stated that this number of atoms (one mole) is a specific amount of matter, namely one g-atom. It is now evident that if the symbol Ca represents one mole of calcium atoms, it also represents one g-atom of calcium whose mass is 40.08 g.

Let us now summarize the common quantitative interpretations of the symbol of a chemical element.

The chemical symbol for the element copper is Cu. Dependent upon the implications of the problem or experiment, this symbol Cu may have any of the following quantitative interpretations:

1. One atom of copper.
2. 63.54 amu of copper. (If the mass is expressed in grams, the symbol represents 63.54 g; if the mass is expressed in pounds, the symbol represents 63.54 lb).
3. One g-atom of copper whose mass is 63.54 g.
4. One mole of copper atoms, 6.0248×10^{23} atoms, whose total mass is 63.54 g.

3.4   ARITHMETICAL PROBLEMS INVOLVING ELEMENTAL SYMBOLS

The symbol of the element palladium is Pd.   The atomic weight of Pd is 106.4.

1. What is the mass of 4.2 g-atoms of palladium?
   Since the mass of 1 g-atom is the atomic weight expressed in grams, 1 g-atom of Pd has a mass of 106.4 g.   Then 4.2 g-atoms of Pd have a mass of 446.9 g.

2. What is the mass of 6.5 lb-atoms of palladium?
   The mass of 1 lb-atom of Pd is 106.4 lb.   Then 6.5 lb-atoms have a mass of 691.6 lb.

3. How many atoms are present in 21.28 g of palladium?
   One g-atom of Pd contains N atoms, where $N = 6.02 \times 10^{23}$. Because 21.28 g is 0.2 of a g-atom of Pd, the number of atoms in 21.28 g of Pd is 1.20×10^{23} atoms.

4. How many grams of palladium contain the same number of atoms as 11.73 g of potassium?
   Since 11.73 g of potassium is 0.3 g-atom of potassium, 0.3 g-atom of palladium contains the same number of atoms as 11.73 g of potassium.   The mass of 0.3 g-atom of palladium is 31.92 g.

5. How much matter, in grams, is represented by the symbol 6Pd?
   Since the symbol Pd represents 1 g-atom of Pd or 106.4 g, 6Pd represents, in grams, 638.4 g of Pd (106.4×6).

3.5   CHEMICAL FORMULAS

The *formula* of a substance is a symbolic representation of its actual composition or formulation.   The formula of water, H_2O, for example, indicates the actual number of atoms in one unit-formula of the substance.   Since ordinary water consists almost entirely of water molecules, the formula H_2O indicates that two atoms of hydrogen and one atom of oxygen constitute the molecule of water. The symbol of a compound always contains the symbols of two or more different elements.

If the formula of a substance contains only one kind of elemental symbol, it represents the composition of the molecules that constitute the substance in question.   For example, elemental chlorine at ordinary temperatures consists of molecules that contain two atoms per molecule.   Since the formula for these molecules must indicate this fact, the formula is Cl_2.   The subscript is used to indicate the number of atoms per particle.   The symbol $2Cl$ would be incorrect in this case because $2Cl$ indicates two chlorine atoms, or two discrete particles.   The symbol Cl_2 shows that the two chlorine atoms are paired to yield one particle.

3.6 THE FORMULA OF A COMPOUND

a. The formula identifies the elements present or the elements from which the compound is formed.   (Qualitative.)

b. The formula indicates the number of atoms of each element in, or used in the formation of, one unit-formula.   (Quantitative.)

c. The formula implies the proportionate mass contributed by each element in a given amount of the compound.   For instance, the formula H_2O indicates that there are 2 moles of hydrogen atoms (2 g-atoms of hydrogen) and 1 mole of oxygen atoms (1 g-atom of oxygen) in 1 mole of H_2O molecules.   Therefore 1 mole of H_2O molecules has a mass of 18 g, because 2 g-atoms of H contribute 2 g and 1 g-atom of O contributes 16 g.

In a generalized sense, the number of atomic mass units of each constituent element present in one unit-formula of the compound is implied by the formula.   The formula H_2O indicates that there are twice as many atoms of hydrogen as of oxygen in any given amount of H_2O.   However, the number of atomic mass units of each element in one unit-formula, or any amount of H_2O, depends on the atomic weights of the element.   In the case of H_2O, the 2 H's contribute 2 amu (2×1 amu), the O contributes 16 amu. The ratio of the masses of the constituent elements is $2:16$ or $1:8$.

Let us consider the compound H_2SO_4.   Here the ratios of the numbers of atoms in a given amount of H_2SO_4 are H, $2:S$, $1:O$, 4. If these ratios are expressed in terms of amu, they become H, $2:S$, 32: O, 64.

d. The formula may represent a certain number of molecules of the compound, namely one mole (Avogadro's number) of molecules.   The formula H_2O may represent one mole of H_2O molecules, or 6.02×10^{23} molecules.

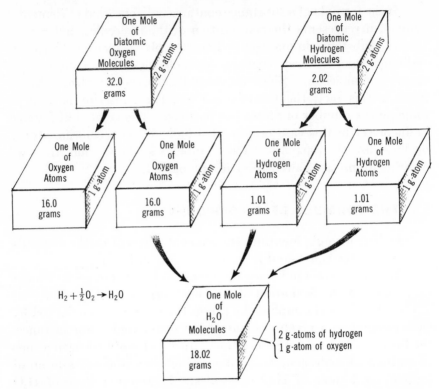

$$H_2 + \tfrac{1}{2}O_2 \rightarrow H_2O$$

FIGURE 3.1 Each box contains an identical number of chemical entities, namely one mole. Since one mole of H_2O molecules (6.02×10^{23} molecules) consists of two moles of hydrogen atoms and one mole of oxygen atoms, the production of one mole of H_2O requires one mole of H_2 molecules and one-half of a mole of O_2 molecules.

e. The formula may represent a specific amount of the compound, the mass of one mole. Therefore the formula indicates the actual number of g-atoms of each element in one mole of the compound. In the case of sulfuric acid, H_2SO_4, the formula indicates that there are 2 g-atoms of hydrogen, 1 g-atom of sulfur, and 4 g-atoms of oxygen per mole of H_2SO_4. The molar weight of H_2SO_4 is therefore 98 g.

f. The formula indicates the ratio, or ratios, of the g-atoms of the constituent elements. The formula of sulfuric acid, H_2SO_4, states that the number of g-atoms of hydrogen is twice the number of g-atoms of sulfur and one-half the number of g-atoms of oxygen. All ratios can be expressed by using many different numbers. Therefore we can state that in any given amount of H_2SO_4 the number of g-atoms of sulfur is one-fourth ($\frac{1}{4}$) the number of g-atoms of oxygen, and the number of g-atoms of hydrogen is one-half ($\frac{1}{2}$) the number of g-atoms of oxygen.

The so-called condensed, or compositional, formulas that are commonly used to identify simple compounds have evident limitations. They often indicate nothing concerning the structure of the compound or how the atoms are held together. The formula H_2SO_4 is a simple compositional formula. Later we shall learn that the arrangement of the atoms in an H_2SO_4 molecule is not what we might suspect from viewing the compositional formula. The H atoms are not attached either to each other or to the sulfur atom.

Let us now use a specific example to review the aspects that we have introduced relative to the interpretation of the formula of a compound.

The formula of ethanol is C_2H_5OH.

1. The formula indicates that the elements carbon, hydrogen, and oxygen constitute the compound.

2. The formula states that there are 2 carbon atoms, 6 hydrogen atoms, and 1 oxygen atom in one unit-formula of ethanol.

3. In a given amount of the compound, one mole, for example, there are 2 g-atoms of carbon that contribute 24 g of mass (2×12 g), 6 g-atoms of hydrogen, 6 g, and 1 g-atom of oxygen, 16 g. The total mass of 1 mole (molar weight) of C_2H_5OH is therefore 46 g. The ratios of the masses of the constituent elements are 24 units of C:6 units of H:16 units of O.

4. One mole of C_2H_5OH, 6.02×10^{23} molecules, consists of 2 moles of carbon atoms, 6 moles of hydrogen atoms, and 1 mole of oxygen atoms.

5. The mass of one mole of C_2H_5OH is the total mass contributed by 6 g-atoms of H, 2 g-atoms of C, and 1 g-atom of O.

6. In any given amount of C_2H_5OH, the number of g-atoms of carbon is twice the number of g-atoms of oxygen, but only $\frac{2}{6}$, or $\frac{1}{3}$, the number of g-atoms of hydrogen. The number of g-atoms of oxygen in any given amount of C_2H_5OH is $\frac{1}{6}$ the number of g-atoms of hydrogen and $\frac{1}{2}$ the number of g-atoms of carbon.

3.7 ARITHMETICAL PROBLEMS INVOLVING FORMULAS

(NOTE: It is imperative that you know the meaning of each term in any word problem before you attempt a solution. The terms imply the method you should use. The main task is deciding what to do with the numbers given. By themselves, the arithmetical operations are very simple.)

The formula of sulfuric acid is H_2SO_4.

1. How many g-atoms of oxygen are present in 3.30 moles of H_2SO_4? The formula shows that each mole contains 4 g-atoms of oxygen. Therefore 3.30 moles of H_2SO_4 contains 13.2 g-atoms (4×3.3) of oxygen.

2. How many grams of oxygen are present in 14.4 moles of H_2SO_4? Each mole of H_2SO_4 contains 4 g-atoms of oxygen; hence 14.4 moles contains 57.6 g-atoms of oxygen. Since the mass of 1 g-atom of oxygen is 16.0 g, the mass of 57.6 g-atoms is 922 g.

3. How many grams of sulfur might be obtained by the complete decomposition of 147 g of H_2SO_4? Since each mole of H_2SO_4 contains, and therefore would yield, 1 g-atom of S, we might first determine the number of moles of H_2SO_4 given. Because 98 g is the mass of 1 mole (molar weight) of H_2SO_4, 147 g is the mass of 1.5 moles of H_2SO_4. From 1.5 moles of H_2SO_4 we can expect 1.5 g-atoms of S.   The mass of 1 g-atom of S is 32 g; hence 1.5 g-atoms represents 48 g of sulfur.

Another solution involves knowing that 98 g of H_2SO_4 contains 32 g of S.   Therefore the amount of S in 147 g of H_2SO_4 is $32/98 \times 147$ g $=$ 48 g.

4. How many grams of calcium contain the same number of atoms as could be obtained by the complete decomposition of 1.30 moles of H_2SO_4? The key to the solution of this problem is the fact that 1 mole of calcium atoms is 1 g-atom of Ca, whose mass is 40.0 g.   We also know that the number of moles of calcium atoms sought is equal to the total number of moles of atoms available from 1.30 moles of H_2SO_4.   Each mole of H_2SO_4 contains 2 moles of H atoms, 1 mole of S atoms, and 4 moles of O atoms—a total of 7 moles of atoms.   Therefore 1.30 moles of H_2SO_4 contains 9.10 moles of atoms.   Since 9.10 moles of Ca atoms is needed to supply the same number of atoms as 1.30 moles of H_2SO_4, 9.10 g-atoms of Ca is needed.   The mass of 9.10 g-atoms of Ca is 364 g (40.0 g $\times$ 9.10).

5. How many tons of sulfur would be needed to produce 150 tons of H_2SO_4?

The formula indicates that in one unit-formula of H_2SO_4 there are 2 amu (2×1) of H, 32.0 amu of S, and 64.0 amu (4×16) of O—a total of 98.0 amu.   If mass units are in tons, then 98.0 tons of H_2SO_4 consists of 64.0 tons of O, 32.0 tons of S, and 2 tons of H.   Therefore the amount of S needed to produce 150 tons of H_2SO_4 is 49.0 tons ($32/98 \times 150$).

3.8 MOLAR AND EMPIRICAL FORMULAS

There are two types of formulas for certain compounds.   One is the *molar formula*, and the other the *empirical formula*.   The molar formula of a compound indicates the actual number of atoms of each element in one unit-formula.   It identifies the number of moles of atoms of each element in one mole of the compound.   A practical quantitative definition of the molar formula is that it is an exact statement of the number of g-atoms of each element in each mole of the substance.   The empirical formula of a compound expresses the simplest integral ratio of the numbers of atoms of the constituent elements.   In many compounds the empirical formula is identical to the molar formula, but in many others the two formulas are different.

Let us use a common compound to illustrate these definitions. The molar formula of hydrogen peroxide is H_2O_2.   This formula states explicitly that each mole of H_2O_2 consists of 2 g-atoms of hydrogen and 2 g-atoms of oxygen.   The actual ratio of the g-atoms is, of course, 2:2.   However, this ratio can be expressed by using simpler integral numbers, namely 1:1.   The empirical formula of hydrogen peroxide is therefore HO, which expresses the correct ratio of the constituent g-atoms by using the smallest integral numbers possible.

It should be noted carefully that the molar weight (mass of 1 mole) of hydrogen peroxide calculated by using the molar formula is twice that calculated by using the empirical formula (for H_2O_2, 34 g; for HO, 17 g).   Indeed if the molar formula of a compound is different from the empirical formula, the numerical value of the actual molar weight of the compound is always some integral multiple of that calculated by using the empirical formula.

There are hundreds of different compounds that consist solely of hydrogen and carbon atoms.   There is one large family of these hydrocarbons in which each different member contains twice as many hydrogen atoms as carbon atoms. Since the simplest integral expression of this ratio is $(C)1:(H)2$, each compound in this family of hydrocarbons has the identical empirical formula, CH_2. Although all of these different hydrocarbons have the same empirical formula, they have different molar (actual) formulas owing to their different molecular compositions. Since the molar weight of each of these compounds is some integral multiple of the so-called empirical formula weight, it should be easy to predict some of the formulas (some of the simpler compounds are C_2H_4, C_3H_6, C_4H_8).

One of the compounds in this family has a molar weight of 140 g. We can easily determine its formula because we know that 140 g is some integral multiple of 14 g, the empirical formula weight. Since 140 g is 10 times 14 g, the molar formula of this compound is $C_{10}H_{20}$, or 10 times CH_2.

The composition of a compound is determined by analysis. The analytical data indicate the kind of element and how much of it is present in a given amount of the compound. These data yield, by calculation, only the empirical formula. If the empirical formula is the same as the molar formula, this is purely incidental as it has nothing to do with the method of calculation.

There are many thousands of compounds whose molar formulas are identical to their empirical formulas, as in the case of water, H_2O, and sulfuric acid, H_2SO_4. However, there are enough compounds having molar formulas different from their empirical formulas to warrant being on our guard.

3.9 PERCENTAGE COMPOSITION OF A COMPOUND

The percentage composition (by mass) of a compound indicates the number of mass units of each element in 100 mass units of the compound. The percentage composition may be calculated either from the compound's molar formula or from its empirical formula. Since the formula of a compound indicates the amount of each element in one mole of the compound, it is easy to calculate the number of mass units of each element in 100 mass units of the compound.

3.10 EXPERIMENTAL DETERMINATION
OF MOLAR WEIGHTS

We have just mentioned the fact that if the molar formula of a compound is different from its empirical formula, as in the CH_2 hydrocarbons, the molar formula can be determined only if the molar weight is known. Of course, the molar weight of a substance is easily calculated if the molar formula is known, but what if it is unknown?

In this section we shall briefly describe one experimental method for the determination of molar weights of gaseous substances and any liquids and solids that can be vaporized readily without decomposition at ordinary elevated temperatures. In Chapter 14 (p. 320) we shall present more details about the principles upon which this specific method is based. Hence you are not expected at the moment to be able to solve involved problems relative to this method.

During the early part of the nineteenth century Avogadro made an extremely significant hypothesis, namely that equal volumes of gases at the same temperature and pressure contain equal numbers of molecules. In other words, gases that contain identical numbers of molecules occupy identical volumes at identical temperatures and pressures. General acceptance of this epic hypothesis did not occur until the early 1860s, but its validity and utility have been evident during the past 100 years.

Before we apply Avogadro's hypothesis, we should pause and recall the fact that the molar weights (masses of 1 mole) of two different substances differ exactly as do the masses of identical numbers of their molecules. For instance, if a certain number of molecules of A has twice the mass of an identical number of molecules of B, the molar weight of A is twice that of B. We should also recall that prior to 1962 the chemical atomic weights were based on the standard 16.0000 for the element oxygen. But since oxygen at ordinary temperatures is diatomic, its molar weight is 32 g. Therefore the molar weights of all substances were, in a sense, based on the standard 32 g, the molar weight of ordinary oxygen.

Now it is evident that the molar weight of a substance can be determined by contrasting the mass of a certain number of its molecules with the mass of an identical number of ordinary oxygen molecules. If the substance is in its gaseous state, its molar weight can be determined by contrasting the mass of a certain volume of the gas at a specific temperature and pressure with the mass of an identical volume of oxygen at the same temperature and pressure.

It is an experimental fact that the volume of 1 mole of oxygen molecules (molar volume), whose mass is 32.0 g, is approximately 22.4 liters if the gas is at 0°C and under a pressure of 1 atmosphere. But this molar volume, 22.4 l, is also the molar volume of any gas at 0°C and 1 atm because we know that equal numbers of molecules, or moles, occupy identical volumes at the same temperature and pressure. Hereafter we shall call 0°C and 1 atm the standard temperature and pressure, abbreviated as STP.

All experimental facts lead to the final conclusion that the molar weight of a given substance is the mass, in grams, of 22.4 l of the gaseous state of the substance at STP. In actual practice we can weigh small volumes, say 200 ml, of the gas at any convenient temperature and pressure and then by arithmetic calculate what would be the mass of 22.4 l at STP. We shall postpone a description of these calculations until Chapter 14, but at least we now realize that molar weights of some substances can be determined experimentally.

3.11 THE EMPIRICAL FORMULA FROM ANALYTICAL DATA

To calculate the empirical formula, we must determine the simplest integral ratio of the numbers of atoms of each element in the compound. Using the gram as the unit of mass, we determine the simplest integral ratio of the numbers of g-atoms of each element in a certain mass of the compound.

If the percentage composition of trisodium phosphate is

$$\text{Sodium (Na)} = 42.08\%$$
$$\text{Phosphorus (P)} = 18.89\%$$
$$\text{Oxygen (O)} = 39.03\%$$

what is the empirical formula of this compound?

From the percentage composition of the compound:

1. The percentage composition indicates the number of grams of each element in 100 g of the compound.
2. Therefore determine the number of g-atoms of each element in 100 g of the compound.

For sodium, 1 g-atom = 22.99 g

Therefore $\dfrac{42.08 \text{ g}}{22.99 \text{ g}} = 1.830$ g-atom of Na in 100 g of compound

For phosphorus, 1 g-atom = 30.98 g

Therefore $\dfrac{18.89 \text{ g}}{30.98 \text{ g}} = 0.610$ g-atom of P in 100 g of compound

For oxygen, 1 g-atom = 16.00 g

Therefore $\dfrac{39.03 \text{ g}}{16.00 \text{ g}} = 2.439$ g-atom of O in 100 g of compound.

3. The ratio of the g-atoms of the elements is 1.830 of Na to 0.610 of P to 2.439 of O.
4. If necessary, next determine the simplest integral ratio of the g-atoms of the elements by assuming that the smallest g-atom ratio number represents one atom of the element concerned. In this case it is 0.610 for P. (The quotients may deviate slightly from whole numbers or integers. This deviation is due either to experimental error or to the inherent nature of decimal numbers and significant figures.)

Then for Na, $\dfrac{1.830}{0.610} = 3$ (or 3 atoms of Na for each atom of P)

For O, $\dfrac{2.439}{0.610} = 4$ (or 4 atoms of O for each atom of P)

Therefore the empirical formula is Na_3PO_4.

From the masses of the elements involved:

1. Twenty-five grams of carbon combines with 66.67 g of oxygen to form a pure compound. What is the empirical formula of this compound?

No. of g-atoms of C combined with the O $= \dfrac{25.00 \text{ g}}{12.01 \text{ g}}$

$= 2.08$ g-atoms of C

No. of g-atoms of O combined with the C $= \dfrac{66.67 \text{ g}}{16.00 \text{ g}}$

$= 4.16$ g-atoms of O

Assuming that the smallest g-atom ratio number (2.08) represents one atom of carbon, there are twice as many atoms of oxygen as of carbon. Therefore the empirical formula is CO_2.

2. Five grams of iron combines with a certain amount of oxygen to produce 7.15 g of a pure compound. What is the empirical formula of this compound?

The mass of the product is 7.15 g. Therefore 2.15 g of oxygen reacted with 5.0 g of iron.

$$\text{No. of g-atoms of Fe in 7.15 g of compound} = \frac{5 \text{ g}}{55.8 \text{ g}}$$

$$= 0.0896 \text{ g-atoms of Fe}$$

$$\text{No. of g-atoms of O in 7.15 g of compound} = \frac{2.15 \text{ g}}{16.0 \text{ g}}$$

$$= 0.135 \text{ g-atoms of O}$$

Divide the larger ratio number by the smaller and find that there are 1.5 g-atoms of oxygen for each g-atom of iron. Multiply both ratio numbers by 2 to obtain the integral ratio, which is 3 of oxygen to 2 of iron. Therefore the empirical formula is Fe_2O_3.

3.12 NAMING OF INORGANIC COMPOUNDS

In this section we shall describe a systematic nomenclature used in identifying some common kinds of inorganic compounds. The nomenclature of organic compounds is described in Chapter 27.

We shall arbitrarily divide the chemical elements into two groups, the metals and the nonmetals. All the metals reside to the left of the "stairway" in the periodic chart (see inside back cover), whereas the nonmetals reside to the right of the "stairway," or in the upper right portion of the chart. Elements adjacent to the "stairway" often act as metals in some reactions and as nonmetals in others, but for the sake of simplicity let us use the stairway as the boundary.

The simplest compounds are those that consist of only two different elements. They are called *binary compounds*. The major rules used in naming binary compounds are:

a. If a binary compound consists of a metal and a nonmetal, the name of the metal appears first and the name of the nonmetal, changed to include the suffix *ide*, appears next. In the formula of the compound, the symbol of the metal appears to the left of the nonmetal. The names of the nonmetals when they are in binary compounds with the metals are:

H—hydride	F—fluoride	O—oxide
N—nitride	Cl—chloride	S—sulfide
P—phosphide	Br—bromide	Se—selenide
Te—telluride	I—iodide	C—carbide

For example: NaCl, sodium chloride; CaO, calcium oxide; BaS, barium sulfide; Al_2O_3, aluminum oxide; Li_2Se, lithium selenide.

b. If a binary compound consists of two nonmetals, the name of one of the nonmetals is left unchanged while the name of the other is changed to include the suffix *ide*. In deriving the name from the symbol of the compound, the name of the element on the left is unchanged while the name of the element on the right has the suffix *ide*. For instance, BrCl is bromine chloride. If there are two or more atoms of a given element in one unit-formula, the number of atoms is identified by using prefixes. These are: *mono*, 1; *di*, 2; *tri*, 3; *tetra*, 4; *penta*, 5; *hexa*, 6; *hepta*, 7; *octa*, 8; *nona*, 9; *deca*, 10. For example, CO_2 is carbon dioxide; PCl_5 is phosphorus pentachloride; N_2O_3 is dinitrogen trioxide; CCl_4 is carbon tetrachloride.

c. In binary compounds consisting of a metal and a nonmetal, each element is assigned a combining capacity, or *valence number*. The valence number of the metal is positive, that of the nonmetal is negative. In a given binary compound of this type, the valence numbers of the elements are additive and the algebraic sum is zero (0). For example, in $CaCl_2$, Ca has a valence number of $+2$ and Cl has a valence number of -1. Two chlorines are needed to balance the one calcium. The assigned valence numbers of some of the common elements as they occur in metal $+$ nonmetal binary compounds are listed in Table 3.3. Because many elements have var-

TABLE 3.3 Valence numbers for elements in metal $+$ nonmetal binary compounds

Li	$+1$	Ca	$+2$	F	-1
Na	$+1$	Sr	$+2$	Cl	-1
Rb	$+1$	Ba	$+2$	Br	-1
Cs	$+1$	Ra	$+2$	I	-1
Be	$+2$	Zn	$+2$	O	-2 (some exceptions)
Mg	$+2$	Cd	$+2$	S	-2
K	$+1$	Ag	$+1$	Se	-2
Al	$+3$				

iable valence numbers in such compounds, general assignments to some elements cannot be made.

d. Considering the valence numbers, it is possible to formulate names and symbols for many binary compounds consisting of a metal and a nonmetal. Let us consider as an example the compound of aluminum, Al, and chlorine, Cl. Since Al has a valence number of +3 and Cl a valence number of −1, 3 Cl's will be needed for each Al. Hence $AlCl_3$ is the formula, and aluminum chloride is the name. For the compound of barium, Ba, and sulfur, S, the formula is BaS because each valence number exactly balances the other. Silver oxide is Ag_2O because the valence number of Ag is +1, while that of oxygen is −2.

e. Because the valence numbers of many metals vary, they are not listed in Table 3.3. The valence number of such a metal in a given binary compound is usually identified in the name of the compound by using a Roman numeral. In many cases the valence number of the nonmetal is known; hence the valence number of the metal can be calculated if the formula is known. For instance, $FeCl_3$ is iron(III) chloride; iron(II) chloride is $FeCl_2$; CrO_3 is chromium(VI) oxide because the total valence number of 3 O's is −6 and Cr must therefore be +6. Mercury(II) sulfide is HgS because Hg is +2 and S is −2.

f. Some compounds consist of electrically charged molecules called *ions*. One such compound is called sodium nitrate, $Na^+NO_3^-$. If this white solid is dissolved in water, the crystals disintegrate and the resultant solution contains mobile sodium ions, Na^+, and nitrate ions, NO_3^-. Since each ion essentially maintains its identity in this fluid state, it is called a molecule. Such ions, or charged molecules, are assigned electrical charges, which for our purposes here we shall call valences or valence numbers. Table 3.4 lists the valence numbers (ionic charges) of some of the common polyatomic ions.

Some compounds that consist essentially of uncharged molecules dissociate when added to water to yield solutions that contain mobile ions. One such compound is nitric acid, HNO_3. If nitric acid is added to water, the solution contains mobile nitrate ions, NO_3^-, the same ions as those in sodium nitrate. When the nitric acid dissociates in water, the H of the molecule leaves as a hydrogen ion, H^+, and is attached to a water molecule. Left behind is the remainder of the molecule, the nitrate ion.

$$HNO_3 + HOH \leftrightarrows OH_3^+ + NO_3^-$$

$$\underset{\text{acid}}{\underset{\text{nitric}}{}} \qquad\qquad \underset{\text{ion}}{\underset{\text{nitrate}}{}}$$

All molecules that consist in part of hydrogen atoms and dissolve in water to yield negative ions are called *acids* (see p. 214).

g. If a compound consists of a metal and one of the negative ions in Table 3.4, the sum of the metal's valence number plus the

TABLE 3.4 Valence numbers of polyatomic ions

Ion	Formula	Valence*	Related Acid
Sulfate	SO_4	-2	H_2SO_4—sulfuric
Hydrogen sulfate	HSO_4	-1	H_2SO_4
Sulfite	SO_3	-2	H_2SO_3—sulfurous
Hydrogen sulfite	HSO_3	-1	H_2SO_3
Thiosulfate	S_2O_3	-2	unstable
Carbonate	CO_3	-2	H_2CO_3—carbonic
Hydrogen carbonate	HCO_3	-1	H_2CO_3
Nitrate	NO_3	-1	HNO_3—nitric
Nitrite	NO_2	-1	HNO_2—nitrous
Phosphate	PO_4	-3	H_3PO_4—phosphoric
Monohydrogen phosphate	HPO_4	-2	H_3PO_4
Dihydrogen phosphate	H_2PO_4	-1	H_3PO_4
Chromate	CrO_4	-2	H_2CrO_4—chromic
Dichromate	Cr_2O_7	-2	H_2CrO_4
Permanganate	MnO_4	-1	$HMnO_4$—permanganic
Hypochlorite	OCl	-1	$HOCl$—hypochlorous
Chlorite	ClO_2	-1	$HClO_2$—chlorous
Chlorate	ClO_3	-1	$HClO_3$—chloric
Perchlorate	ClO_4	-1	$HClO_4$—perchloric
Bromate	BrO_3	-1	$HBrO_3$—bromic
Hydroxide	OH	-1	H_2O—water
Cyanide	CN	-1	HCN—hydrogen cyanide
Cyanate	OCN	-1	$HOCN$—cyanic
Thiocyanate	SCN	-1	$HSCN$—thiocyanic
Ammonium	NH_4	$+1$	none
Silicate	SiO_3	-2	H_2SiO_3—silicic
Iodate	IO_3	-1	HIO_3—iodic

* Valence is the charge of the ion.

negative ion's valence number is zero. In the name of such a compound, the name of the metal appears first. Sodium dichromate is $Na_2Cr_2O_7$ because Cr_2O_7 has a valence number of -2 and each Na is $+1$; calcium sulfite is $CaSO_3$ because Ca is $+2$ and SO_3 is -2; iron(III) hydroxide is $Fe(OH)_3$ because Fe is $+3$ and each OH is -1.

h. Certain binary compounds of hydrogen and some of the non-metals are called acids because of their behavior when added to water.

HF—hydrofluoric acid or hydrogen fluoride
HCl—hydrochloric acid or hydrogen chloride
HBr—hydrobromic acid or hydrogen bromide
HI—hydriodic acid or hydrogen iodide

Some others that act as acids are: hydrogen sulfide, H_2S; hydrogen selenide, H_2Se; hydrogen telluride, H_2Te.

i. Some solid compounds contain loosely bound water as part of their crystalline structure. These hydrous compounds are usually called *hydrates*. The amount of water per unit of anhydrous compound is noted in the name by using the common prefixes. Anhydrous copper(II) sulfate, $CuSO_4$, yields a solid hydrate in the presence of water. The hydrate is $CuSO_4 \cdot 5H_2O$, copper(II) sulfate pentahydrate. Magnesium sulfate heptahydrate is $MgSO_4 \cdot 7H_2O$.

3.12 A SUMMARY

All chemical symbols of elements and compound substances have a qualitative and quantitative meaning. The qualitative meaning is explicit, whereas the quantitative meaning may vary as to the mass units used.

Some practical quantitative interpretations are:

a. The symbol of an element represents the number of atomic mass units numerically equal to its atomic weight. For example, the symbol Cu represents 63.54 amu of copper. It may, depending on context, represent 63.54 g (1 g-atom) of copper, 63.54 lb (1 lb-atom) of copper, 63.54 tons (1 ton-atom) of copper. The symbol of an element may thus represent one g-atom, or one lb-atom, or one ton-atom. The mass of a g-atom of any element is numerically equal to the atomic weight of that element expressed in grams.

b. One g-atom of a given element consists of one mole of atoms of the element. Since one mole of atoms is a specific number of atoms, approximately 6.02×10^{23}, one g-atom of a given element contains the same number of atoms as one g-atom of any other element. One g-atom of gold contains the same number of atoms as one g-atom of helium.

c. The formula of a compound identifies the constituent elements. The formula also indicates the number of atoms of each element in one unit-formula of the compound. The formula may represent one mole of the compound, and if so, it indicates the number of moles of atoms of each element present. For example, the formula of nitric acid, HNO_3, indicates that in one mole there is 1 mole of hydrogen atoms, 1 mole of nitrogen atoms, and 3 moles of oxygen atoms. Therefore the mole of nitric acid contains 1 g-atom of hydrogen, 1 g-atom of nitrogen, and 3 g-atoms of oxygen.

d. The mass of one mole of a substance is its molar weight expressed in grams. The molar weight is calculated from the formula by summing the masses of the g-atoms of the constituent elements. The molar weight of a gaseous substance is the mass of 22.4 liters of the gas at 0°C and 1 atmosphere of pressure (STP).

e. The molar formula of a substance indicates the exact number of g-atoms of each element present in one mole of the substance. It also indicates the ratio of the g-atoms of the constituent elements in a given amount of substance. The empirical formula expresses the ratio of the g-atoms of the elements in the simplest integral form. The molar formulas of many compounds are different from the empirical formulas.

Problems

1. How many milligrams of silicon are needed to supply the same number of atoms as in 0.3 mole of tellurium trioxide, TeO_3?

2. How many grams of mercury(II) oxide, HgO, must be decomposed to yield one-half as many atoms as there are in 140 g of argon?

3. In a specific compound, the percentage of oxygen is 18.6 per cent. There is one g-atom of oxygen in each mole of the compound. What is the molar weight of the compound?

4. In 445 g (2.5 moles) of a certain ternary compound, the number of g-atoms of sulfur is equal to the number of g-atoms of hydrogen, and the number of g-atoms of oxygen is $3\frac{1}{2}$ times greater than the number of g-atoms of hydrogen. (a) What is the empirical formula of the compound? (b) What is the molar formula?

5. Eighteen and six-hundredths grams of a binary compound of hydrogen and nitrogen contains 0.42 g of hydrogen. What is the empirical formula of the compound?

6. In a binary compound, the number of atoms of hydrogen is $2\frac{1}{4}$ times the number of atoms of carbon. One-tenth of a mole of the compound weighs 11.4 g. What is the molar formula?

7. If 21.3 g (0.05 mole) of a compound that consists solely of tantalum and oxygen is decomposed completely, 1.09 ml of tantalum (density, 16.6 g/ml) is obtained. What is the molar formula of the compound?

8. Whenever the binary compound X is decomposed completely, the amount of carbon obtained is always approximately 6 times the amount of hydrogen. One-fourth of a mole of X weighs 21 g. What is the molar formula?

9. A binary compound contains 87.5 per cent nitrogen and 12.5 per cent hydrogen. What is the empirical formula of the compound?

10. How many g-atoms of iridium contain the same number of atoms as 0.55 mole of the compound CH_3OH?

11. Sodium pyrophosphate has the formula $Na_4P_2O_7$. (a) How many g-atoms of sodium are in 3 moles of the compound? (b) How many grams of phosphorus are present in 1.25 moles of the compound? (c) How many grams of phosphorus could be obtained by the complete decomposition of 0.3 mole of the compound? (d) How many moles of the compound must be decomposed to supply a total number of atoms equal to the number of atoms in 64 g of oxygen?

12. A sample of a pure compound contains 1.452 g of germanium, 1.564 g of potassium, and 2.280 g of fluorine. What is the empirical formula?

13. One-half of a mole of a binary compound contains 18 g of carbon and $2\frac{2}{3}$ times as many g-atoms of hydrogen as g-atoms of carbon. What is the molar formula?

14. A binary compound consists of the elements Z and M. The atomic weight of Z is 14 and of M it is 42. If 0.1 mole of the compound is decomposed completely, the total number of atoms obtained is identical to the number of atoms in 12.8 g of oxygen. The amount of M obtained upon decomposition is exactly 9 times the amount of Z. What is the molar formula?

15. Calculate the percentage composition of these compounds: (a) benzene, C_6H_6; (b) hydrogen azide, HN_3; (c) potassium dichromate, $K_2Cr_2O_7$; (d) acetic acid, CH_3COOH.

16. How many tons of sulfur would be needed to produce 100 tons of sulfuric acid, H_2SO_4?

17. Write the formulas of these compounds:

(a) barium selenide

(b) aluminum sulfide

(c) manganese(III) chloride

(d) radium bromide

(e) cadmium nitrate

(f) magnesium perchlorate

(g) sodium nitrite

(h) potassium phosphate

(i) lithium permanganate

(j) calcium hydrogen carbonate

(k) calcium sulfite

(l) lead chromate

(m) cobalt(II) hydroxide

(n) iron(III) chloride

(o) sodium bromate

(p) silver sulfate

(q) nickel(II) oxide

(r) chromium(III) oxide

(s) ammonium sulfate

(t) dinitrogen pentoxide

18. Write the names of these compounds:

(a) $NaClO_2$

(b) $CsHCO_3$

(c) $Mn(OH)_3$

(d) $KClO_4$

(e) CaC_2

(f) $KOCN$

(g) $ZnCrO_4$

(h) Na_2HPO_4

(i) $Ba(CN)_2$

(j) $Na_2Cr_2O_7$

(k) $Ca(HCO_3)_2$

(l) $Ba(OCl)_2$

(m) $K_2S_2O_3$

(n) SF_6

(o) SrI_2

(p) $MgSe$

(q) $CaSiO_3$

(r) $KHSO_4$

(s) $NaHSO_3$

(t) NH_4Br

4.1 INTERPRETATIONS

The symbolic expression of a chemical reaction is called a *chemical equation*. It is a shorthand representation which expresses certain essential aspects of a chemical reaction by means of symbols and formulas. This sort of representation is called an equation because in the case of ordinary chemical reactions no new atoms are created and no atoms disappear. Using ordinary balances to determine the mass of the participating substances in what appears to be a complete chemical transformation, we find that the total mass of the reacting substances (reactants) is equal to the total mass of the product(s). In a sense, the number of atoms in the reactant system may be equated with the number of atoms in the product system, and the mass of the reactant system may be equated with the mass of the product system.

EQUATION

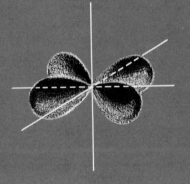

The chemical equation for the reaction between zinc and sulfur is:

$$Zn + S \rightarrow ZnS$$

or

$$Zn + S = ZnS$$

The first equation form—with an arrow separating the reactants and product—is often used, perhaps because it is more graphic and emphasizes direction of predominant change.

The general quantitative interpretations of the symbols used in the equation are the same as those noted in Chapter 3. If the gram is the unit of mass used, then the equation is interpreted as follows: each g-atom (mole) of zinc requires one g-atom (mole) of sulfur in order to produce one gram-formula (mole) of zinc sulfide.

A chemical equation, as written above, has certain distinct limitations. Perhaps it might be well to note them.

a. The equation signifies nothing concerning energy.

b. The equation does not indicate what actually happens to the atoms, and it states nothing as to how the product substance is held together.

c. The equation does not indicate the conditions under which the reaction occurs.

d. The equation does not state whether or not the reaction is complete.

e. The equation states nothing concerning the rate at which the product is produced.

f. The equation does not indicate whether the reaction occurs immediately upon mixing the reactants or whether the reactants have to be activated or excited to initiate the change.

4.2 DERIVATION OF A CHEMICAL EQUATION

To indicate how a chemical equation is derived from a written qualitative description of a reaction, we shall use the following statement: Iron(III) oxide, or ferric oxide, reacts with carbon monoxide to produce elemental iron and carbon dioxide.

a. The symbols or formulas of the reactant and product substances must be known before the equation can be written. The formulas are: iron(III) oxide, Fe_2O_3; carbon monoxide, CO; iron, Fe; carbon dioxide, CO_2.

b. Read the qualitative statement and put down the symbols or formulas in order of appearance of their names. Separate the reactants by a plus sign, use an arrow (pointing to the products) in place of the words "to produce," and then separate the products by a plus sign.

$$Fe_2O_3 + CO \rightarrow Fe + CO_2$$

c. These symbols represent a chemical equation, so the number of each kind of atom in the reactant system (left of the arrow) must equal the number of each kind of atom in the product system (right of the arrow). To arrive at the correct equation, we must "balance" it. We cannot change the formulas because this would contradict the qualitative statement. (For the moment we will have to use a trial-and-error or hit-and-miss approach in balancing chemical equations, but for certain kinds of equations, we will eventually be more systematic.) To equate the number of atoms, we put integral (whole) numbers, called coefficients, in front of the symbols and formulas of the substances. These coefficients must be the smallest numbers possible that will balance the equation. One helpful clue concerning this unbalanced equation is that no matter what we do there will always be an even number of iron atoms in the reactant system and an even number of oxygen atoms in the product system. Therefore we cannot put an odd number in front of the symbol Fe. Without undue deliberation, we should obtain the balanced equation:

$$Fe_2O_3 + 3CO \rightarrow 2Fe + 3CO_2$$

4.3 MASS RELATIONSHIPS IN CHEMICAL REACTIONS

Let us now reconsider the chemical equation presented in Section 4.2:

$$Fe_2O_3 + 3CO \rightarrow 2Fe + 3CO_2$$

This can be interpretated quantitatively as stating that whenever 1 molecule of Fe_2O_3 reacts completely with 3 molecules of CO, 2 atoms of Fe and 3 molecules of CO_2 are obtained. Since atoms and molecules are so extremely small, we shall never employ only 1 or 2 molecules of a substance. A better interpretation is: Whenever 1 mole of Fe_2O_3 molecules reacts completely with 3 moles of CO molecules, 2 moles of Fe atoms and 3 moles of CO_2 molecules are obtained. We should recall that 1 mole of particles is approximately 6.02×10^{23} of the particles.

Since the most practical quantitative relationships involve weighable amounts of matter, we shall soon realize that the concept of molar relationships is the best. Since we know that the mass of a mole of a substance, if its formula is known, may be calculated by totaling the masses of the constituent g-atoms, we can make an explicit quantitative interpretation of the equation: Whenever 1 mole (159.7 g) of Fe_2O_3 reacts completely with 3 moles (84.03 g) of CO, 2 moles (111.7 g) of Fe and 3 moles (132.03 g) of CO_2 are produced (see Fig. 4.1).

Because atomic weights are relative to a common standard and have no units, the mass relationships in a chemical reaction can be in any type of mass unit, provided the same mass unit is used throughout a specific quantitative statement. For example, when-

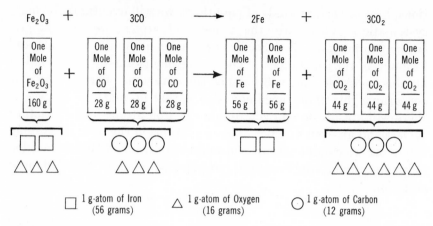

FIGURE 4.1   Each complete enclosure (rectangle, square, circle, and triangle) contains an identical number of chemical entities, namely one mole. For the complete reaction:

Number of reactant atoms = number of product atoms
Number of g-atoms of reactants = number of g-atoms of products
Mass of reactants = mass of products

ever 159.7 tons of Fe_2O_3 reacts completely with 84.03 tons of CO, 111.7 tons of Fe and 132.03 tons of CO_2 are produced. We readily accept this fact when we recall that the number of molecules in 84.03 amu of CO is identical to the number of molecules in 132.03 amu CO_2.

The arabic numerals (coefficients) preceding the chemical symbols in the equation indicate only one way of expressing the ratios of the numbers of moles of the participating substances:

$$Fe_2O_3 + 3CO \rightarrow 2Fe + 3CO_2$$

These ratios, expressed by using the smallest integral numbers, are obviously 1:3:2:3. Two of the infinite number of ways of expressing these specific ratios are: $\frac{1}{3}:1:\frac{2}{3}:1$, and $\frac{1}{2}:\frac{3}{2}:1:\frac{3}{2}$. Considering the first of these alternative expressions, we can write the statement: Whenever 1 mole of CO reacts completely with $\frac{1}{3}$ of a mole of Fe_2O_3, $\frac{2}{3}$ of a mole of Fe and 1 mole of CO_2 are produced. Also, we notice that if the reaction between Fe_2O_3 and CO is to be complete, then the number of moles of Fe_2O_3 must be at least $\frac{1}{3}$ the number of moles of CO. Furthermore, if 1 mole of Fe is produced, $\frac{3}{2}$ moles of CO_2 are produced simultaneously.

The coefficients used in the conventional chemical equations can therefore be changed, provided we retain the ratios. Two possible chemical equations that are just as true as the conventional equation, if they are interpreted in terms of moles, are:

$$\tfrac{1}{3} Fe_2O_3 + CO \rightarrow \tfrac{2}{3} Fe + CO_2$$

and

$$\tfrac{1}{2} Fe_2O_3 + \tfrac{3}{2} CO \rightarrow Fe + \tfrac{3}{2} CO_2$$

These equations as well as the conventional one (all based on one mole) enable us to determine the relative amounts of all substances involved.

4.4 VOLUME RELATIONSHIPS IN REACTIONS IN GASES

The interpretation of volume relationships in a reaction that involves gaseous participants is facilitated by using an experimental fact discovered in 1808 by Joseph Gay-Lussac (French). When Gay-Lussac made his observations, he was unable to offer a logical explanation for them. However, in 1811 Avogadro suggested what later proved to be the correct explanation (see Sec. 3.10). Avogadro's hypothesis was that *equal volumes of gases at the same temperature and pressure contain equal numbers of molecules.* At this point in our study, we find that Gay-Lussac's law is very useful. Whenever two or more gases are involved in a chemical reaction, the ratios of the volumes of these gases may be expressed by using small integral numbers, provided the gaseous volumes are measured at the same temperature and pressure. The smallest integral numbers that can be used to express the ratios of the volumes are actually the coefficients that appear in the conventional chemical equation. The volumes may be expressed in liters, milliliters, cubic feet, or in any other unit of capacity.

To illustrate the application of Gay-Lussac's law, let us consider the reaction between gaseous ethane and elemental oxygen.

$$2C_2H_6 + 7O_2 \rightarrow 4CO_2 + 6H_2O$$

Even a casual inspection of the equation reveals that the ratios of the numbers of molecules of the reaction participants are, reading from left to right, 2:7:4:6. We should also notice that the number of molecules of O_2 needed for a complete reaction is at least $3\tfrac{1}{2}$ times the number of molecules of C_2H_6 used, and the number of molecules of CO_2 produced is twice the number of molecules of C_2H_6 in the reaction.

According to Gay-Lussac's law, if the gases in this reaction are measured at the same temperature and pressure, the simplest integral expression of the ratios of the volumes of the gases is $2:7:4:6$. The identical ratios can be expressed by using different numbers:

$$C_2H_6:O_2:CO_2:H_2O$$
$$1:3\tfrac{1}{2}:2:3$$
$$\tfrac{2}{7}:1:\tfrac{4}{7}:\tfrac{6}{7}$$
$$\tfrac{1}{2}:\tfrac{7}{4}:1:\tfrac{3}{2}$$
$$\tfrac{1}{3}:\tfrac{7}{6}:\tfrac{2}{3}:1$$

If the gases are measured at the same temperature and pressure, we can use these ratios as the basis for the following statements: For each liter of C_2H_6 that reacts we must supply at least $3\tfrac{1}{2}$ liters of O_2. The reaction will yield twice as many liters of CO_2 as liters of C_2H_6 that react. The number of milliliters of O_2 that react is $3\tfrac{1}{2}$ times the number of milliliters of C_2H_6 that react. The number of liters of gaseous H_2O obtained is always $\tfrac{3}{2}$ times the number of liters of CO_2 produced.

A typical problem is: How many liters of gaseous oxygen are necessary to react completely with 43 l of C_2H_6? How many liters of CO_2 are produced? (Assume that all gases are measured at the same temperature and pressure.)

We know that the number of liters of O_2 needed is $3\tfrac{1}{2}$ times the number of liters of C_2H_6 used. (This fact is obtained by reading the equation.) Therefore the number of liters of O_2 needed is 150 l (43 l $\times$ 3.5). The number of liters of CO_2 produced is twice the number of liters of C_2H_6 that react (2 $\times$ 43 l = 86 l).

In Section 3.10 we stated that the molar volume of a gas at $0°C$ and 1 atm of pressure (STP) is approximately 22.4 l. This fact can be used to determine the volume of any gas at STP if the number of moles of the gas is known. Let us say, for instance, that during a specific reaction 150 g of C_2H_6 reacts completely in the presence of O_2. The question might be: How many liters of gaseous CO_2, measured at STP, are produced during the reaction?

$$2C_2H_6 + 7O_2 \rightarrow 4CO_2 + 6H_2O$$

According to the equation, the number of moles of CO_2 produced is twice the number of moles of C_2H_6 that react. Since 30.0 g of C_2H_6 is the mass of 1 mole of C_2H_6, 150 g represents 5 moles of C_2H_6. Therefore 10 moles (2 $\times$ 5 moles) of CO_2 will be produced.

Each mole of CO_2 occupies 22.4 l at STP. Hence 10 moles will occupy 224 l at STP. Therefore the 150 g of C_2H_6 yields 224 l of CO_2 under the conditions stated.

4.5 THEORETICAL AND ACTUAL YIELDS

Although a balanced chemical equation is a source of information about the amounts of reactants and products of a specific chemical reaction, care must be used in the interpretation of the symbols. If the yield of product expected during a chemical reaction is to be calculated by using information found in the chemical equation, the calculation must be based on a reactant that disappears completely. The mass relationships implied in chemical equations are based solely on complete reactions.

A reaction is considered to be complete if each reactant apparently disappears and only the stated product or products remain. Frequently, however, we shall encounter reactions that are incomplete under certain conditions. Some reactions are incomplete because side reactions occur; that is, the reactants interact in more than one manner and form different products. In certain cases the reverse reaction is significant; that is, the reaction or decomposition of the product(s) to form the original reactants also occurs. Occasionally the rate of formation of products is so slow that it is impractical to wait until the reaction is complete. Many times one reactant may be unable to react completely because there is present an insufficient amount of another reactant. In essence, the actual amount of a product obtained as a result of a chemical reaction depends on reaction conditions and on the inherent character of each participating substance. None of these dependent factors is even implicit in the chemical equations, so we must not read between the symbols.

We may illustrate an incomplete reaction by using the reaction of acetic acid, CH_3CO_2H, with phosphorus trichloride, PCl_3, to produce acetyl chloride, CH_3COCl, and phosphorous acid, H_3PO_3.

$$3CH_3CO_2H + PCl_3 \rightarrow 3CH_3COCl + H_3PO_3$$

Theoretically, the most practical quantitative interpretation of this chemical equation is: If a mole of acetic acid reacts completely with $\frac{1}{3}$ of a mole of PCl_3, 1 mole of acetyl chloride and $\frac{1}{3}$ of a mole of phosphorous acid are produced. Or, the number of moles of acetyl chloride obtained is equal to the number of moles of acetic acid that react completely, according to the equation.

One mole, 60.0 g, of acetic acid and the necessary amount of PCl_3 will theoretically produce 1 mole, 78.5 g, of acetyl chloride. The theoretical yield, or the amount expected according to the equation, is therefore 78.5 g of acetyl chloride. If 6.0 g of acetic acid and the necessary amount of PCl_3 were used, the theoretical yield of acetyl chloride would be 7.85 g.

The reaction for the preparation of acetyl chloride as shown here is performed by hundreds of undergraduate students every year as part of their laboratory work in organic chemistry. Even the most able and meticulous students fail to obtain the theoretical yield of acetyl chloride. The actual yield of product is usually in the neighborhood of 70 per cent of the theoretical yield. Therefore if a student started with 30.0 g of acetic acid and plenty of PCl_3, he would be fortunate if he obtained 27.5 g of pure acetyl chloride (27.5 g is 70 per cent of 39.3, the theoretical yield). The percentage of theoretical yield is the number of parts of actual yield per hundred parts of theoretical yield.

$$\frac{\text{actual yield}}{\text{theoretical yield}} \times 100 = \text{percentage of theoretical yield}$$

4.6 ARITHMETICAL PROBLEMS

The calculation of mass relationships in a chemical reaction is quite simple if the balanced chemical equation is known. This type of calculation is often called *stoichiometry*. Methods of solution of arithmetical problems are arbitrary, but the following logical pattern is suggested for those problems in which the gram is the unit of mass. This pattern may also be used, however, for any other unit of mass. You will notice that it is unnecessary to formulate algebraic equations and that no set formulas are required.

1. Calculate, if it is not given, the number of moles of the given substance.
2. Determine the number of moles of substance sought after inspecting the balanced equation, which indicates the ratio of the number of moles of the substance sought to the number of moles of the substance given.
3. Calculate the mass of one mole of the substance sought, and then, using the answer obtained in step 2, calculate the mass of the

substance sought. If the amounts of two reactants are given, it is necessary to determine the number of moles of each reactant. Then the yield of product expected is based on that reactant which could or did react completely (this can be determined only after reading the equation).

Below are some typical problems based on a specific chemical reaction. The balanced chemical equation is:

$$Fe_2O_3 + 3CO \rightarrow 2Fe + 3CO_2$$

1. How many moles of CO will be necessary to react completely with 31.94 g of Fe_2O_3?

   The number of moles of Fe_2O_3 involved in the reaction is:

   $$\frac{\text{grams of } Fe_2O_3}{\text{mass of one mole of } Fe_2O_3} = \frac{31.94 \text{ g}}{159.7 \text{ g}} = 0.2 \text{ mole}$$

   The equation states that each mole of Fe_2O_3 requires 3 moles of CO. Therefore 0.2 mole of Fe_2O_3 will require 0.6 mole of CO.

2. How many g-atoms of Fe are produced by a complete reaction between 31.94 g of Fe_2O_3 and the necessary amount of CO?

   In problem 1 we found that 31.94 g of Fe_2O_3 is 0.2 mole of Fe_2O_3. The equation states that each mole of Fe_2O_3 yields 2 g-atoms of Fe. Therefore 0.4 g-atom of Fe is produced.

3. How many grams of CO_2 are produced during the simultaneous production of 83.78 g of Fe?

   The number of g-atoms of Fe given is:

   $$\frac{\text{grams of Fe}}{\text{mass of one g-atom of Fe}} = \frac{83.78 \text{ g}}{55.85 \text{ g}} = 1.5 \text{ g-atom}$$

   The equation states that 3 moles of CO_2 are produced at the same time as 2 g-atoms of Fe, or that 1.5 moles of CO_2 are produced for each g-atom of Fe. Therefore, if 1.5 g-atoms of Fe are produced, then 2.25 moles of CO_2 are produced at the same time. The mass of one mole of CO_2 is 44.01 g. Therefore, if 2.25 moles of CO_2 are produced, the mass is 99.02 g.

4. The necessary amount of Fe_2O_3 reacted completely with 92.43 tons of CO. How many tons of Fe were produced?

   The number of ton-formulas (ton-moles) of CO given is:

   $$\frac{\text{tons of CO}}{\text{mass of one ton-mole}} = \frac{92.43 \text{ tons}}{28.01 \text{ tons}} = 3.3 \text{ ton-mole}$$

The equation states that the complete reaction of one ton-mole of CO produces $\frac{2}{3}$ of a ton-atom of Fe.   Therefore, if 3.3 ton-moles of CO are used, 2.2 ton-atoms of Fe are produced. The mass of one ton-atom of Fe is 55.85 tons.   Therefore the mass of 2.2 ton-atoms of Fe is 122.9 tons.

5. Assume that the percentage of theoretical yield of the process described by the equation is 95 per cent.   How many tons of Fe are produced during the reaction of 31.94 tons of Fe_2O_3 and the necessary amount of CO?

The number of ton-moles of Fe_2O_3 given is:

$$\frac{\text{tons of } Fe_2O_3}{\text{mass of one ton-mole}} = \frac{31.94 \text{ tons}}{159.7 \text{ tons}} = 0.2 \text{ ton-mole}$$

Theoretically, according to the equation, 0.2 ton-mole of Fe_2O_3 should yield twice as many ton-atoms of Fe.   Hence the theoretical yield of iron is 0.4 ton-atom of Fe, or 22.34 tons. However, the actual yield is given as 95 per cent of the theoretical yield.   Therefore the actual yield is 21.12 tons of Fe.

6. A mixture of 31.94 g of Fe_2O_3 is heated with 15.41 g of CO until the reaction is as complete as possible.   How much iron is obtained?

The yield of iron, Fe, must be based on the reactant that reacts completely.   Hence we must determine the number of moles of each substance given to see which, if any, is in excess.

The number of moles of Fe_2O_3 given is

$$\frac{31.94 \text{ g}}{159.7 \text{ g}} = 0.2 \text{ mole}$$

The number of moles of CO given is

$$\frac{15.41 \text{ g}}{28.01 \text{ g}} = 0.55 \text{ mole}$$

But if all of the 0.2 mole of Fe_2O_3 is to react, at least 0.6 mole of CO must be available.   (The chemical equation states that the number of moles of CO must be at least 3 times the number of moles of Fe_2O_3 for a complete reaction.)

$$Fe_2O_3 + 3CO \rightarrow 2Fe + 3CO_2$$

The yield of Fe must therefore be based on the CO.   Since the number of moles of Fe expected is $\frac{2}{3}$ of the number of moles of CO reacting, 0.367 mole of Fe, 20.5 g, is obtained.

4.7 THE ROLE OF HEAT

Thermochemical reactions are those chemical changes during which thermal energy (heat) plays a prominent role. An *exothermic* reaction is a thermochemical change during which heat is evolved. In a sense, this heat may be considered one of the products of the reaction. In all exothermic reactions, the total energy content of the product(s) is less than the total energy content of the reactant(s). An *endothermic* reaction is a thermochemical change during which heat is absorbed from the surroundings. In a sense, this heat may be considered as necessary as the reactant(s). In all endothermic reactions, the total energy content of the product(s) is greater than the total energy content of the reactant(s).

According to the law of conservation of matter and energy, there must be an energy balance just as there must be a material balance. If heat is evolved during a chemical reaction, the source of the energy is the reactant(s). If heat is absorbed during a chemical reaction, the eventual residence of most of this energy is within the product(s).

Qualitative descriptions of the role of heat in chemical reactions are common. Usually the symbol used to represent heat is the alchemical symbol of fire, Δ.

A specific qualitative notation of the role of heat is:

$$2HgO + \Delta \rightarrow 2Hg + O_2$$

This means that the reaction is endothermic, that heat must be supplied continually in order to decompose the mercury(II) oxide, HgO, and that collectively the mercury and oxygen so produced have a higher energy content than the mercury(II) oxide.

The reverse of the above reaction is a familiar chemical change:

$$2Hg + O_2 \rightarrow 2HgO + \Delta$$

This means that the reaction is exothermic, and that the mercury(II) oxide has a lower energy content than the total energy content of the mercury and the oxygen.

Since there must be an energy balance, there is another important interpretation regarding these reactions. The amount of heat absorbed in the first reaction is equal to the amount of heat evolved in the second reaction, if both reactions are complete, if the reaction conditions are such that no useful work is done, and if the physical state of each substance is the same in both reactions.

An endothermic reaction in which a substance is decomposed is called a *pyrolysis*. Some typical pyrolyses are:

$$2K^+ClO_3^- + \Delta \rightarrow 2K^+Cl^- + 3O_2$$

potassium   potassium   oxygen
chlorate   chloride

$$Ca^{++}CO_3^{--} + \Delta \rightarrow Ca^{++}O^{--} + CO_2$$

calcium   calcium   carbon
carbonate   oxide   dioxide

$$2Na^+NO_3^- + \Delta \rightarrow 2Na^+NO_2^- + O_2$$

sodium   sodium   oxygen
nitrate   nitrite

$$H_2SO_4 + \Delta \rightarrow H_2O + SO_3$$

sulfuric   water   sulfur
acid   trioxide

$$CH_3COCH_3 + \Delta \rightarrow CH_2CO + CH_4$$

acetone   ketene   methane

Some important exothermic reactions are:

the burning of glucose in oxygen:

$$C_6H_{12}O_6 + 6O_2 \rightarrow 6CO_2 + 6H_2O + \Delta$$

the decomposition of ozone:

$$2O_3 \rightarrow 3O_2 + \Delta$$

the formation of ammonia from nitrogen and hydrogen:

$$N_2 + 3H_2 \rightarrow 2NH_3 + \Delta$$

the reduction of iron(III) oxide by aluminum:

$$Fe_2O_3 + 2Al \rightarrow Al_2O_3 + 2Fe + \Delta$$

the slaking of quicklime with water:

$$Ca^{++}O^{--} + H_2O \rightarrow Ca^{++}(OH^-)_2 + \Delta$$

the burning of chlorine in hydrogen:

$$H_2 + Cl_2 \rightarrow 2HCl + \Delta$$

The equations written here are only qualitative relative to the role of heat in the reactions represented. Later, in Chapter 18, we shall discuss the quantitative aspects of heat in thermochemical reactions.

4.8 THE ROLE OF LIGHT

Some chemical reactions either are initiated by radiant energy or continually require the absorption of radiant energy. Radiant energy, an electromagnetic radiation, is evolved during some reactions. Such reactions are called *photochemical* reactions. The radiant en-

ergy evolved or absorbed in most photochemical reactions is either visible or ultraviolet light (see Fig. 4.2). Some of these reactions are endothermic, some are exothermic. The most important photochemical reaction system is *photosynthesis*. This is part of the process whereby carbon dioxide and water are converted to carbohydrate materials, such as dextrose, cane sugar, starch, and cellulose.

Although electromagnetic radiation appears to behave as a wave when it travels through space, radiant energy is absorbed in discrete "bundles" by matter. These "bundles" of radiant energy are called *quanta*; one bundle is called a *quantum*. Because electromagnetic radiation behaves as a wave in space, a specific kind of radiation has a specific wave length and a specific frequency. The wave length, λ, is related to the frequency, v, by the expression $\lambda = c/v$, where c is the velocity of the electromagnetic radiation, 3×10^{10} cm/sec.

Radiation of a specific wave length, and therefore a specific frequency, may be absorbed by a specific substance to initiate a chemical change. If a substance absorbs a specific radiation, each unit of that radiant energy is called one quantum, hv. In the expression for the quantum, v is the frequency of the radiation absorbed, and h is *Planck's constant* (6.63×10^{-27} erg sec). The

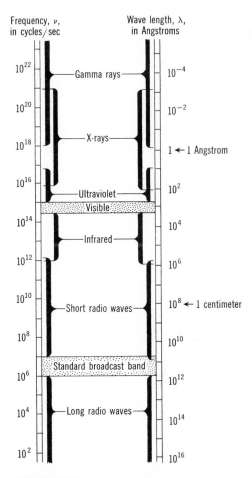

FIGURE 4.2 Electromagnetic spectrum showing frequencies and wave lengths. (Format suggested by Francis W. Sears and M. W. Zemansky, *University Physics*, Addison-Wesley, Reading, Mass., 1952.)

amount of energy in one quantum of energy is expressed in ergs. The frequency of the radiation absorbed by a substance is dependent on certain characteristics of the substance. If this radiation initiates a chemical reaction, the absorbed radiant energy has a specific frequency, and each quantum of energy absorbed has a specific value, hv, where v is a specific frequency. It must be kept in mind that only radiation of a specific frequency is absorbed by the reactant substance, and only the radiant energy that is absorbed is effective in a photochemical reaction.

One quantum of radiant energy, or one hv, as it exists in electromagnetic radiation is called a *photon*. Therefore, if a photon is absorbed by a substance, the substance gains or absorbs one quantum of radiant energy. The above statements may appear redundant, but they are made in an attempt to emphasize an extremely important concept: radiant energy is quantized.

The qualitative representation of radiant energy in chemical equations is hv. The equation that represents the photolytic decomposition of oxalic acid is:

$$(COOH)_2 + hv \rightarrow H_2O + CO + CO_2$$

Since the energy of light depends on the frequency, the light of the visible spectrum varies in energy as the wave length varies. The shorter the wave length, the greater the frequency. Therefore violet light is more energetic than red light, and green light is more energetic than yellow.

There are relatively few well-defined photochemical reactions during which visible light is evolved. A complex organic compound, 3-amino-phthalhydrazide (luminol), undergoes a chemical change in aqueous solution in the presence of potassium iron(III) cyanide or sodium hypochlorite and hydrogen peroxide. Visible light is emitted during this reaction, a striking example of chemiluminescence. Certain reactions in fireflies, railroad worms, and some microorganisms are chemiluminescent. The light emitted in most such reactions is sometimes called "cold light" because very little heat is evolved.

Triboluminescence can be demonstrated in a dark room by pulling quickly from its roll a strip of ordinary friction tape. As the tape is pulled from the roll, cleavage of chemical bonds occurs. This produces an abnormal state and as the system returns to a more normal state, energy is emitted as visible radiation. Rapid breaking of certain kinds of crystals is often accompanied by the evolution of visible light.

4.9 ELECTRICAL AND MECHANICAL ENERGY

Many kinds of chemical changes can occur in electrolytic cells by supplying electrical energy. In voltaic cells (batteries) electrical energy may be obtained as the result of chemical changes. These electrical phenomena are very important, but we shall postpone a discussion of them until we know more about the structure of matter and the role of electrons.

Since all forms of energy are interconvertible, heat, light, and kinetic energy emitted during a chemical reaction can be converted to mechanical energy. If we consider an automobile in motion, with motor running, it is obvious that chemical and mechanical energies are in concert.

Certain chemical reactions that yield gaseous products and a large quantity of heat may be used directly to do mechanical work. The exothermic combustions that occur in the cylinders of internal combustion engines produce mechanical energy. The rapid exothermic change which occurs in a rifle cartridge when the gun is fired is sufficient to give the bullet (slug) a tremendous amount of kinetic energy.

There are some rather unique chemical changes which may be initiated by mechanical means, if we assume that hitting, tapping, or jarring are mechanical means. Some of these changes are exothermic decompositions, and a few are exothermal changes in which two or more substances react with one another. The major products of these changes are gases, and because heat is evolved simultaneously, an extremely high pressure is developed if the reaction system is confined.

4.10 REVERSIBLE CHEMICAL REACTIONS

Under ordinary experimental conditions, thousands of chemical reactions are reversible. There are relatively few reactions which under ordinary conditions appear to be irreversible. It is usually assumed that every ordinary chemical reaction is inherently reversible, and that, if conditions were propitious, this reversibility could be demonstrated.

Let us now consider a well-known chemical change, and in doing so let us appreciate the relativistic character of chemical reactions.

Gaseous oxygen can be prepared in good yield by the pyrolysis of mercury(II) oxide:

$$2HgO + \Delta \rightarrow 2Hg + O_2$$

Under appropriate conditions, it is possible to prepare mercury(II) oxide by combining elemental mercury with oxygen:

$$2Hg + O_2 \rightarrow 2HgO + \Delta$$

It might be more realistic, and also more concise, to combine these equations and put a double arrow between the reactant and product systems, so that the reversibility of each reaction is emphasized.

$$2HgO + \Delta \leftrightarrows 2Hg + O_2$$

When this symbolic representation of two reversible reactions is read from left to right, it identifies the pyrolysis of mercury(II) oxide (HgO reacts to the presence of heat). When read from right to left, it represents the reaction during which mercury(II) oxide is produced from its elements. The relative significance of each reversible reaction depends on the conditions of temperature, the amount of oxygen per unit of volume, and whether the system is open or closed. The equations as written only identify the reaction participants and state explicitly that each reaction is reversible; nothing more can be inferred from the equations unless more information is given.

Let us now return to the equations.

$$2HgO + \Delta \leftrightarrows 2Hg + O_2$$

If pure HgO is heated in an open vessel sufficiently to cause pyrolysis, the gaseous oxygen and some of the mercury leave the system and enter the atmospheric air almost as soon as they are produced. Hence the reaction between the oxygen and the mercury to yield oxide is insignificant. The high temperature apparently favors the endothermic reaction.

If pure oxygen is bubbled into warm mercury in an open vessel at a temperature well below that necessary to cause appreciable decomposition of the HgO, the oxide forms, but little of it decomposes. By controlling the temperature it is possible to favor the production of oxide, the exothermic reaction.

If pure HgO is heated, say to 120°C, in a heavy-walled closed vessel, the gaseous oxygen and mercury vapor are unable to leave the reaction system. As time goes on, more and more HgO decomposes, and the numbers of molecules of mercury and oxygen gradually increase.   Therefore the chance that the reaction $2Hg + O_2 \rightarrow$ $2HgO$ can occur becomes appreciable.   If the temperature of the closed system is kept at 120°C for a sufficient period of time, eventually HgO will be produced from its elements as fast as it is decomposing to yield its elements.   In fact, the two reactions will be occurring at equal rates.   The two reactions will be in balance, with neither reaction being favored.   Such a situation is called a *state of equilibrium*.   During a given period of time each substance in the reaction system has an opportunity to act both as a reactant and as a product.   In other words, within a chemical system in equilibrium all reaction participants are both reactants and products.

It should be evident by now that it is impossible to obtain much information from equations that represent a reversible reaction until we have some facts about the physical conditions.   Since only two reactions are involved in the example used here, only three types of situations can be expected: (1) the situations that favor the decomposition of HgO, (2) those that favor the formation of HgO, and (3) those in which neither decomposition nor formation of HgO is favored.

In the discussion about the reversibility of the decomposition of HgO, we mentioned the attainment of a state of equilibrium by starting with pure HgO and heating it to a constant temperature T_1 in a closed vessel.   It is possible to attain the same state of equilibrium by heating to the constant temperature T_1 the correct amount of pure mercury and oxygen in the closed vessel.

The calculation of mass relationships in reversible reactions, especially at equilibrium, is much more complicated than the procedures mentioned in this chapter.   We shall postpone such calculations until later (Chapter 19).

4.11 A SUMMARY

A balanced chemical equation represents a chemical change only insofar as it identifies the reactants, the product(s), and the relative amount of each substance directly involved during a complete reaction in the stated direction.   In the chemical equation the number of atoms in the reactant system is equated to the number of atoms in the product system.   The coefficients (numbers) in front of the symbols of the participating substances show the ratios of the numbers of moles and/or g-atoms of the substances.   The numerical values of these coefficients may be changed, provided the ratios of the numbers of moles of the substances are kept constant.

To calculate the amount of either reactant or product involved in a chemical reaction, it is necessary to interpret the equation correctly. Suggested steps to follow are: (1) Calculate, if it is not given, the number of moles of substance given. (2) Inspect the equation and calculate the number of moles of substance sought. (3) Knowing the mass of one mole of substance sought, calculate the mass of substance sought.

The theoretical yield of a given reaction is the maximum amount of product expected during a complete reaction in which at least one, and possibly each, reactant reacts completely. The actual yield of product(s) obtained under given conditions may be much less than the theoretical yield. This actual yield is usually expressed as a per cent of theoretical yield, or percentage yield.

Some form of energy is involved in every chemical change. During exothermic reactions heat is evolved, and the total energy of the products is less than that of the reactants. During endothermic reactions heat is absorbed by the participants, and the total energy of the products is greater than that of the reactants.

During chemical changes in which radiant energy is involved, the energy is either emitted or absorbed in bundles called quanta or photons. The symbol for the energy of each photon is $h\nu$. The energy varies with the frequency of the radiation; hence blue light is more energetic than red light.

If visible light is emitted during a chemical reaction, the phenomenon is called chemiluminescence.

Problems

1. The chemical equation that represents a chemical reaction is:

$$8Al + 3Fe_3O_4 \rightarrow 4Al_2O_3 + 9Fe$$

(a) How many moles of aluminum are needed for the complete transformation of 4.8 moles of Fe_3O_4? (b) How many grams of iron are produced simultaneously with 3.33 moles of Al_2O_3? (c) How many moles of Fe_3O_4 are needed to react completely with 432 g of Al? (d) How many tons of Fe_3O_4 are needed to yield 500 tons of iron? (e) Ninety tons of aluminum are treated correctly with 270 tons of Fe_3O_4

so that reaction is as complete as possible. What is the maximum yield of iron? (f) The percentage theoretical yield was 92 per cent during a reaction in which 962 kg of aluminum was one of the reactants. What was the yield of iron, in grams?

2. Hydrogen chloride, HCl, can be prepared by treating NaCl with commercial H_2SO_4. The H_2SO_4 has a density of 1.84 g/ml and is 95 per cent (by weight) pure. The equation is:

$$NaCl + H_2SO_4 \rightarrow HCl + NaHSO_4$$

(a) What mass of commercial H_2SO_4 is needed for the production of 40 kg of HCl? (b) How many liters of commercial H_2SO_4 are needed for the production of 40 kg of HCl? (c) What is the volume, in liters, of 40 kg of HCl (gaseous) at STP? (d) If 32 g of NaCl were treated correctly with 49 g of H_2SO_4 so that reaction was as complete as possible, how many grams of HCl would be obtained?

3. Dimethyl ether, CH_3OCH_3, may be prepared by treating methyl iodide, CH_3I, with sodium methoxide, CH_3ONa. The equation is:

$$CH_3I + CH_3ONa \rightarrow CH_3OCH_3 + NaI$$

(a) If 42 g of CH_3I is treated with an excess of CH_3ONa, what is the theoretical yield of dimethyl ether? (b) A student treated 7.1 g of methyl iodide with an excess of sodium methoxide. He obtained 1.8 g of dimethyl ether. What was the percentage theoretical yield? (c) A student treated 14.2 g of CH_3I with ample sodium methoxide. He reported that his yield of dimethyl ether was 68 per cent of the theoretical yield. How many grams of the ether did he obtain? (d) A student obtained 5.6 g of dimethyl ether during an experiment using the reaction described. He stated that his percentage of theoretical yield was 65 per cent. What was the minimum amount of CH_3I that he could have used?

4. Some propane, C_3H_8, and some oxygen were put together in a vessel. The reactants were heated and the subsequent reaction was as complete as possible. The product mixture (gaseous) that remained consisted of 64.8 g of H_2O, 6 g of O_2, and some CO_2. How many grams each of propane and oxygen were put together before the reaction?

$$C_3H_8 + 5O_2 \rightarrow 3CO_2 + 4H_2O$$

5. The chemical reaction that represents the combustion of ethane (gas) in oxygen is:

$$2C_2H_6 + 7O_2 \rightarrow 4CO_2 + 6H_2O$$

(a) If 12 g of C_2H_6 reacts as completely as possible in the presence of 40 g of O_2, what is the theoretical yield of CO_2? (b) How many moles of C_2H_6 can react with 70 g-atoms of oxygen? (c) Assume that all reactants are gaseous and measured at the same temperature and pressure. How many liters of oxygen are needed for the complete combustion of 450 ml of C_2H_6? (d) How many liters of CO_2, measured at STP, can be obtained by the complete combustion of 280 g of C_2H_6? (e) If 15 l of C_2H_6 and 48 l of O_2, measured at the same temperature and pressure, are put in a closed vessel and reaction is as complete as possible, how many liters of gaseous CO_2 are produced, assuming constant temperature and pressure?

6. The atomic weight of X is one-half that of Z. Exactly 0.1 mole of X_5 and 40 g of Z_2 react completely, yielding X_5Z_4 as the sole product. (a) What is the mass of 2.5 g-atoms of Z? (b) What is the atomic weight of X? (c) If 0.1 mole of X_5 does react completely with 40 g of Z_2, how many grams of X_5Z_4 are produced?

7. Thirty grams (0.25 mole) of A_3 reacts completely with B_2 to yield 90 g of A_2B_4 as the sole product. (a) What is the atomic weight of B? (b) What is the mass of 6 moles of A atoms? (c) What is the mass of 0.1 mole of A_2B_4? (d) How many g-atoms of A are needed for the production of 35.5 moles of A_2B_4?

8. A hypothetical chemical equation is:

$$9X_3 + 10M_2 \rightarrow 6M_3X_4 + M_2X_3$$

Six grams of gaseous X_3 occupies 2.8 l at STP. This amount of X_3 reacts completely with M_2 to yield 8.3 g of M_3X_4. How many grams of M_2 react with the X_3?

9. The combustion of ethane in oxygen (see Problem 5) is exothermic, yielding 373.0 kcal of heat per mole of ethane reacting. How many calories of heat are evolved during the complete combustion of 45 g of ethane?

10. (a) How many moles of CO_2 are produced simultaneously with the evolution of 74.6 kcal of heat during the complete combustion of pure ethane in oxygen? (b) If 5.4 g of water is produced during the combustion of a pure sample of ethane, how many calories of heat are evolved?

11. Balance these equations:
(a) $SiO_2 + Mg \rightarrow Si + MgO$
(b) $PCl_5 + H_2O \rightarrow HCl + H_3PO_4$
(c) $NH_3 + O_2 \rightarrow H_2O + N_2$
(d) $Na_2S + SO_2 \rightarrow Na_2S_2O_3 + S$
(e) $FeS_2 + O_2 \rightarrow Fe_2O_3 + SO_2$

(f) $CaCO_3 + C \rightarrow CO + CaC_2$

(g) $CuO + NH_3 \rightarrow Cu + H_2O + N_2$

(h) $Ca_3(PO_4)_2 + SiO_2 \rightarrow P_4O_{10} + CaSiO_3$

(i) $C_4H_{10} + O_2 \rightarrow CO_2 + H_2O$

(j) $Hg + HNO_3 \rightarrow Hg_2(NO_3)_2 + H_2O + NO$

5

THE STRUCTURE

5.1 A PERSPECTIVE

The atomic concept of matter is one of chemistry's major contributions to man's understanding of his material environment. This atomic concept is the foundation upon which the science of chemistry is built. The chemist identifies the thousands of different varieties of matter by assuming that there are different kinds of chemical elements, and that these elements alone or in combination compose the myriad types of material entities. Each element, the chemist says, has its own singular chemical and physical properties and appears to be composed chemically of only one kind of atom. We must recognize that this concept is the chemical viewpoint; in this chapter we shall present the physical viewpoint of the atom. As we read this chapter, we must try to contrast these two different viewpoints in order to appreciate the continuity and

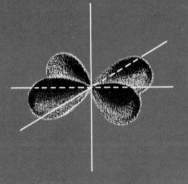

OF ATOMS

consistency of the modern conception of atomic structure.

At no time in the nineteenth century did chemists appear unduly concerned about the structures of the atoms which composed the thousands of known substances. Since the atoms in a specific element appeared to retain their essential character throughout chemical changes, perhaps there was little need to worry about their actual structures. The nineteenth-century chemists were able to be extremely productive by assuming that atoms were simple material particles. In fact, many of the most eminent chemists of the nineteenth century lived and died without realizing that atoms were not the fundamental material particles.

We recall that by using ordinary chemical techniques it is impossible to determine either the composition or the apparent structure of an atom. Since these chemical techniques were inadequate to resolve the structural character of an atom, other techniques were employed. In essence, the modern concept of the compositions and structures of the atoms is based on discoveries made by physicists using physical techniques. Of course, these physicists used the vast amount of information about the chemical composition of matter.

5.2 MATTER AND ELECTRICITY

One of the most significant phenomena used to demonstrate the nature of electricity is the discharge of electricity through a gaseous phase occupied by a relatively small number of molecules. The apparatus used is called a Crookes tube or a cathode ray tube (see Fig. 5.1). If a high potential exists between the electrodes of the Crookes tube, a quiet passage of electricity occurs between the electrodes.

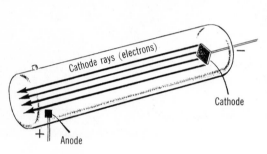

FIGURE 5.1 Simplified representation of a Crookes tube.

Because the glow within the Crookes tube appears to originate at the cathode (negative electrode), the emanations from the cathode are called *cathode rays*. One property of cathode rays is different from ordinary light: if an electric or magnetic field is placed in the vicinity of the beam of rays, the path of the beam is deflected. This indicates that the rays carry a charge. Since the rays originate at the negative electrode, they are assigned a negative charge (see Fig. 5.2).

Sir J. J. Thomson, an eminent British physicist, determined the ratio of mass to charge of the supposed particles in the beam of cathode rays and concluded correctly that the cathode rays were electrons. Since the electrons were emitted from any metallic cathode, it appeared that electrons were subatomic particles. Two familiar phenomena substantiate this concept. The *thermionic effect* (the "evaporation" of electrons from matter) is observed by heating certain metallic substances. During absorption of thermal energy many electrons gain sufficient energy to leave the metal. The metal thereby becomes less negative than before. The *photo-*

electric effect is observed when visible light is directed to some metallic surfaces. The radiant energy allows many electrons to escape from the metal, and at their point of departure the metal is less negative and more positive. The absorption of photons by the metal can therefore yield the phenomenon of electricity.

If high-energy electrons bombard a metallic target, the target emits an unusual type of radiation. When electrons collide with the target, part of the kinetic energy of the electrons is changed to electromagnetic radiation of higher energy than

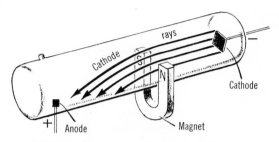

FIGURE 5.2   Path of cathode rays (electrons) is deflected by a magnetic field, indicating that electrons are negatively charged.

ultraviolet light. This phenomenon was observed originally in 1895 by Roentgen, who called the emanations from the target *x-rays*. X-rays are not deflected by a magnetic field.

5.3 THE ELECTRON

In 1909 R. A. Millikan determined the charge on an electron to be 1.602×10^{-19} coulombs. Since the ratio of charge to mass of the electron was known, the mass of the electron was computed. The mass of an electron is approximately 1/1837 of the mass of the least massive atom in elemental hydrogen. The electron, as a subatomic entity, contributes a negligible mass, 0.00054876 amu.

The apparatus used by Millikan in his classic oil-drop experiment is sketched in Fig. 5.3. Tiny drops of oil pick up one or more electrons within the upper chamber of the apparatus. These electrons have previously become separated from molecules owing to bombardment of the molecules by x-rays. The tiny oil drops, many of them charged, fall through the space between the uncharged condenser plates. The drops are watched, and since their rate of fall is related to their size, each drop's size can be calculated.

The condenser plates are subsequently charged, and the drops are observed as before. Those that carry no charge fall as if the plates were uncharged. However, if a drop is charged, its rate of fall is different from that of an uncharged drop. Some may even rise, being attracted to the oppositely charged upper plate. After watching the behavior of a drop, its electric charge can be calculated.

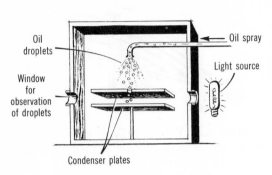

Many experiments with oil drops yield different values of charges on the drops. All these values, Millikan noticed, were integral multiples of 4.8×10^{-10} statcoulombs. He therefore concluded that this electric charge is the smallest charge possible under the conditions of his experiment. Millikan's value is within 1 per cent of the currently accepted value. The results of Millikan's experiments also yielded what is considered one of the most precise values of Avogadro's number.

FIGURE 5.3 A simplified diagram of the apparatus used by Millikan to determine the charge on the electron.

5.4 THE PROTON

After the discovery of the electron as a subatomic particle, it was inevitable that positively charged entities would be discovered. In 1886 E. Goldstein devised a tube in which the cathode was perforated. He found that positively charged entities were attracted to the cathode and passed through the perforations in the cathode (see Fig. 5.7). The least massive positively charged particle detected by using Goldstein's technique has a mass almost identical to that of the least massive atom in elemental hydrogen. This least massive positively charged particle is called the *proton*, and its charge is equal but opposite in sign to that of the electron. Its mass is 1.007595 amu.

5.5 RADIOACTIVITY

Near the turn of the century, a French physicist, Henri Becquerel, observed that compounds which contained the element uranium emitted a peculiar type of radiation without the means of any outside agency. The radiation penetrated thin opaque objects and was heterogeneous. The phenomenon wherein a substance emits radiation without the means of any external agency is called *radioactivity*.

Because Becquerel suspected that at least one element other than uranium was radioactive, he suggested a search for the element in the uranium ores. One of his most able students, Marja Sklodowska, starting with a ton of pitchblende, finally isolated 0.2 g of a substance which she called radium bromide. This material was much more radioactive than uranium bromide. Marja was assisted eventually by her husband, Pierre Curie. Their research, largely motivated by Mme. Curie, is one of the monumental epics in the history of chemistry. Today there is a permanent reminder of Mme. Curie's contribution to science—chemical element 96 is named curium.

5.6 EMANATIONS OF RADIOACTIVE SUBSTANCES

If the emanations (beam of rays) emitted by certain radioactive substances, such as radium or uranium, are passed through a magnetic field, these emanations are found to be heterogeneous. One type of emanation is positively charged, another is negatively charged, and still another is electrically neutral—it is unaffected by the magnetic field (see Fig. 5.4).

The positively charged emanation consists of a stream of material particles. This emanation is called alpha radiation, or *alpha rays*. The material particles which constitute alpha rays are called alpha particles, and each of these particles has a mass approximately four times that of the least massive atom. The positive

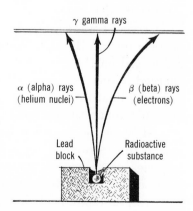

FIGURE 5.4 Effect of a magnetic field on natural radioactive emanations. Gamma radiation is not deflected, since it is uncharged; alpha radiation is positively charged; beta radiation is negatively charged.

charge of an alpha particle is twice that of the proton, because the alpha particle is a doubly positively charged helium atom, He^{++}. Since all charged atoms and molecules are called ions, the alpha particle is a helium ion.

The negatively charged emanation, *beta rays*, is a stream of electrons. These electrons constitute beta radiation and are identical to the particles in the cathode rays.

The electrically neutral emanation, *gamma rays*, is electromagnetic radiation similar to x-radiation. Most gamma radiation is much more energetic than x-radiation.

5.7　INTERNAL STRUCTURE OF AN ATOM

To discover the apparent internal structure of atoms, it is necessary either to probe into the atoms or to observe the physical behavior of atoms in known environments under specific conditions. If the process of probing into the atoms is to be successful, it seems reasonable that the probing tools should be smaller than the atoms themselves. Since electrons and protons are entities of which atoms are composed, we might expect them to be smaller than most atoms. We might also expect an alpha particle to be relatively small because its mass is only about four atomic mass units. Contrasted with an ordinary helium atom, an alpha particle is relatively tiny because, as we shall see later, an alpha particle is the nucleus of the ordinary helium atom.

In 1911 C. T. R. Wilson performed an experiment during which he observed the path of an alpha particle as it moved through a specific gaseous phase. The air in an enclosed vessel was initially saturated with water vapor, and then by sudden expansion this gaseous phase was rapidly cooled. Wilson noted that when an alpha particle moved through this gaseous phase, tiny droplets of water condensed on the ions that were left in the wake of the positively charged alpha particle. Because these tiny droplets of water formed miniature clouds, or *fog tracks*, facsimiles or modifications of Wilson's apparatus are called Wilson cloud-chambers.

Most of the so-called fog tracks observed in a cloud-chamber appear to be straight lines, and many are relatively long. The alpha particles pass through many of the molecules in the air without being deflected appreciably from a straight course. Occasionally, however, an alpha particle is deflected strongly from its apparently normal straight course, but this deflection occurs only very rarely and usually near the end of the particle's journey. This behavior of an alpha particle is explained by suggesting that an alpha particle only very infrequently encounters a positively charged entity in the air through which it passed. These positively charged entities must be extremely tiny; otherwise the alpha particles would encounter them more frequently.

During the year that Wilson made his observations of the fog tracks left by alpha particles, Ernest Rutherford performed a very informative experiment. Rutherford projected a beam of alpha particles through a thin gold foil. He used a fluorescent screen to observe their behavior as they encountered and penetrated the foil. Whenever an alpha particle strikes the surface of such a fluorescent screen, a tiny flash of light appears at the point of contact. Rutherford noticed that nearly all of those alpha particles that penetrated the foil had maintained their normal straight path while passing through the foil. He did observe that very few alpha particles were deflected sufficiently to be, in a sense, reflected by the foil.

This behavior of the alpha particles led Rutherford to believe that most of the particles passed unmolested through the atoms in the foil. He suggested that the small minority of alpha particles which were deflected, especially those deflected by more than 90°, probably had encountered other positively charged entities from which the alpha particles were repelled. Since these positively charged entities in the gold atoms were very infrequently encountered by the alpha particles, Rutherford concluded that they must comprise a very small portion of the total volume of a gold atom. (See Fig. 5.5.)

From the observations of Wilson and Rutherford, we can now appreciate the general concept of the internal structure of an atom. The atom is considered to consist of a tiny nucleus surrounded by electrons. Since there seems to be much empty space within an atom, the electrons appear to be relatively far apart and relatively far from the nucleus. Because an electron has a negligible mass relative to the mass of a proton, the nucleus (in which the protons reside) is considered to be the residence of nearly all the mass of the atom. Since all protons reside in the atomic nucleus, the nucleus is the seat of all the positive electric charge within an atom. If we assume that most of the atom is "empty space," we can logically interpret the relatively undisturbed passage of alpha particles through matter. The actual volume occupied by the nucleus is a

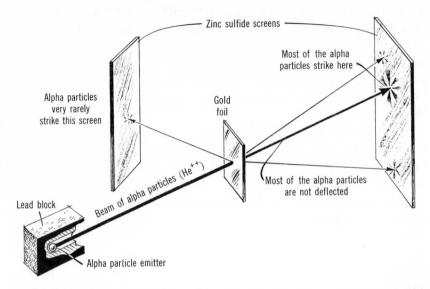

FIGURE 5.5 Simplified diagram of the experiment, performed by Rutherford, which led to the suggestion that atoms contain extremely tiny, positively charged, very dense nuclei. The collision of an alpha particle with the zinc sulfide screen produces a visible flash of light.

small fraction of the total volume of the atom itself. In the case of most atoms, the radius of the atomic nucleus is about 1/100,000 that of the atom.

5.8 ATOMIC NUMBER

In 1913 H. G. J. Moseley investigated the x-ray spectra of most of the known elements. He placed each element in its solid state on the target of an x-ray tube. Then he bombarded the target with high-energy electrons. The x-rays emitted by the bombarded element were then dispersed by passing them through suitable crystals. (These crystals disperse x-rays as an ordinary glass prism disperses visible light.) The dispersed x-rays were directed to a photographic plate. The development of the plate yielded a series of lines whose positions were dependent on the wave lengths of the x-rays. Using this technique, Moseley obtained the x-ray spectrum of an element. The formation of x-rays is shown in Fig. 5.6.

By interpreting logically and concisely the x-ray spectra of the various elements and by considering these in an appropriate succession, Moseley observed a constant increment in the square roots of the wave lengths of the individual x-radiation emitted by the elements. This constant increment appeared to be significant, and Moseley suggested that the square root of the frequency of the

FIGURE 5.6 Production of x-radiation due to the bombardment of a metallic target by high-energy electrons. The kinetic energy of the electrons is increased by increasing the electrical potential between the electrodes of the x-ray tube; the more energetic the electrons, the more energetic the x-radiation (greater frequency and shorter wave length).

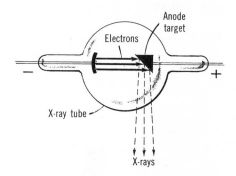

characteristic x-ray emission of an element is directly proportional to the atomic number of the element. The idea of an atomic number of an element to indicate its order number in the classification of the elements had been suggested much earlier. Moseley's important idea substantiated van den Broeck's postulation that the atomic number of an element was directly related to the positive electric charge on the nucleus of each atom of the element.

The term *atomic number* is usually identified by the letter Z, but the actual atomic number itself is represented by an integral number. The atomic number of an element is equal to the number of protons in the nucleus of each atom of the element. It is also equal to the number of electrons outside each nucleus of each uncharged atom of the element. The atomic number of an element is directly related to the nuclear charge of each atom of the element. If we assume that each proton has one unit of positive electric charge, the atomic number of an element is the nuclear charge of each atom of the element.

5.9 THE NEUTRON

In 1932 J. Chadwick discovered an uncharged nuclear particle that has a mass approximately equal to that of the proton. This particle is called the *neutron*. Neutrons do not yield fog tracks in a

Wilson cloud-chamber because they have no electric charge; they are unaffected by an electric or magnetic field. The neutron contributes mass but no charge to the nucleus of an atom. Because of the neutron's characteristics, its discovery was not an easy matter.

5.10   IONS

If an atom or a molecule loses or gains one or more electrons, a charged particle remains. Since all charged atoms and molecules are called *ions*, a process during which uncharged entities are changed to charged entities is called *ionization*. When high-energy electrons produced in a Crookes tube bombard the atoms and/or molecules in the confined gas, a high degree of ionization occurs. Many entities lose electrons to yield positive ions. (See Fig. 5.7.) For instance, if a hydrogen molecule loses an electron, a hydrogen molecule ion, H_2^+, remains.

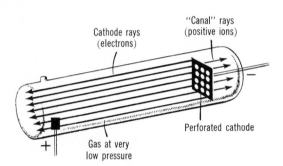

Cathode rays (electrons)

"Canal" rays (positive ions)

Perforated cathode

Gas at very low pressure

FIGURE 5.7 Production of "canal" rays in a Crookes tube. The positively charged ions in these "canal" rays are formed as electrons are knocked off uncharged atoms and molecules by the high-energy cathode rays. Positive ions can pass through the perforations in the cathode, and are attracted to the cathode because this electrode is negatively charged.

5.11   THE MASS SPECTROGRAPH

Since the mass of an ion is nearly identical to the mass of the entity from which it is formed, the mass of the ion indicates the mass of the original atom or molecule. It is therefore evident that the relative masses of the atoms of the elements may be determined by measuring the relative masses of their positive ions.

The positive ions obtained from a specific element are analyzed by a mass spectrograph, in which the positive ions are identified with respect to differences in their masses. This method of positive ion analysis was suggested originally by J. J. Thomson, but in the hands of F. W. Aston the mass spectrograph became an exceedingly useful and accurate instrument.

A complete description of a mass spectrograph would be too complex for our purposes here; we shall therefore mention only the most important aspects of its operation. (See Fig. 5.8.) The positive ions obtained from a specific element are directed through

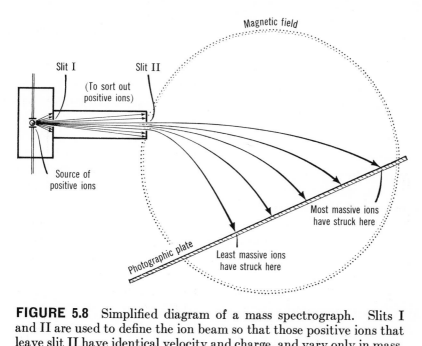

FIGURE 5.8 Simplified diagram of a mass spectrograph. Slits I and II are used to define the ion beam so that those positive ions that leave slit II have identical velocity and charge, and vary only in mass. Less massive ions are more strongly deflected than are the more massive ions. Ions of identical mass strike the photographic plate in one spot.

a system of slits and electric fields so that the ions which are finally able to leave the system have about the same velocity. These ions are then directed through a magnetic field where they are sorted with respect to their differences in mass. The positive ions having the same ratio of charge to mass (e/m) are deflected so that they all strike a specific spot on a photographic plate. As these ions collide with the photographic emulsion, they activate silver ions (Ag^+) in the emulsion. During development of the plate, a black spot appears at the point where the positive ions hit the plate. The activated silver ions are changed, during development, to silver atoms. The relative intensity of the black spot on the plate indicates the relative number of ions that hit that particular point.

5.12 NUCLIDES AND ISOTOPES

If elemental hydrogen is ionized and its ions are resolved in the mass spectrograph, an examination of the mass spectrogram reveals the existence of at least four different positive ions in the stream of positive rays. The ions of smaller mass are more strongly deflected than those of larger mass; the extent of deflection of an ion is a relative measure of its mass. Since it is known that ordinary hydrogen consists of diatomic molecules, the conclusion is that there are at least two different hydrogen atoms, one more massive than the other.

The mass spectrum of the ions obtained by the ionization of elemental oxygen yields, upon resolution in the mass spectrograph, several different ions. Three of these positive ions have masses much less than the others, and one of the three is much more abundant than the other two.

The mass spectra of several different elemental forms of matter indicate that a pure chemical element may have atoms that differ with respect to their masses. In order to formulate an atomic weight scale, the more abundant of the two kinds of atoms in ordinary carbon has been chosen as the standard reference. This atom's atomic weight is 12.00000, and the atom is called carbon-12. The two physically different atoms that exist in ordinary elemental hydrogen are assigned masses relative to this standard. Their approximate atomic weights are 1 and 2. These atoms are therefore called hydrogen-1 and hydrogen-2. In the case of elemental oxygen, the three kinds of oxygen atoms are oxygen-16, oxygen-17, and oxygen-18. The number that follows the name of the chemical element identifies the specific atom. Except for carbon-12, the number is approximately equal to the atomic weight of the atom in question. Hereafter such numbers will be called mass numbers.

Before 1962 the standard of the physical atomic weights was the most abundant kind of atom in elemental oxygen, oxygen-16. This was chosen mainly because it would allow the physical atomic weights to be most nearly coincident with the earlier assigned chemical atomic weights. You will recall from Section 2.6 that prior to 1962 the chemical atomic weights were based on the number 16 assigned to elemental oxygen. A major fault of the older atomic weight scale was that the percentage composition of oxygen, that is, the proportions of oxygen-16, -17, and -18, varied according to the source of the oxygen.   Oxygen from the atmosphere, from the ocean, and from the earth's crust differed somewhat in composition relative to these three different atoms.

Now that we realize that ordinary elemental hydrogen consists of physically different atoms, we are faced with a dilemma in regard to the word *atom*.   To speak simply about a hydrogen atom is inadequate, because someone will say, "Which one do you mean?" Because the term *atom* was used first by chemists, it is, of course, a chemical term.   But if we refer to the atoms in elemental hydrogen, we identify each atom with respect to its mass, because this is the major way that atoms differ.   (Both atoms have the same nuclear charge and the same number of extranuclear electrons.)   Since the atoms differ only in nuclear composition, it has been suggested that the term *nuclide* be used whenever specific reference is made either to an atom's nuclear mass or to its nuclear composition.   The term *nuclide* identifies a specific atom whose nucleus is different from that of every other known atom.   Elemental hydrogen therefore consists of at least two different nuclides, and elemental oxygen contains at least three different nuclides.   The name of a nuclide consists of the name of the element to which it is related followed by a mass number.   For instance, carbon-12 is one of the nuclides related to the element carbon.

The two different nuclides in ordinary hydrogen are also called *isotopes*.   The term *isotope* is used to identify those nuclides that have different masses but identical atomic numbers, or nuclear charges.   Because hydrogen-1 and hydrogen-2 are identical in one respect (same nuclear charge) but different in another (different nuclear mass), they are said to be *isotopic*.   One is an isotope of the other.   Oxygen-16, -17, and -18 are three isotopic nuclides.   When used properly, the terms *isotope* and *nuclide* are synonymous.

5.13 NAMES AND SYMBOLS OF NUCLIDES

Since an elemental form of matter may contain several different isotopes, a suitable system of nomenclature must be used.   The isotopes related to the element hydrogen have been assigned rather classic names.   All isotopes of all the other elements are named in a very systematic manner, and this scheme can also be applied to the isotopes of hydrogen.

Table 5.1 lists the atomic numbers, mass numbers, and symbols of the different isotopes related to hydrogen and oxygen. Tritium,

TABLE 5.1 Isotopes (nuclides) of hydrogen and oxygen

Atomic Number	Element	Isotope Name	Isotope Symbol	Mass Number
1	Hydrogen	Protium (Hydrogen-1)	^1_1H or H	1
		Deuterium (Hydrogen-2)	^2_1H or D	2
		Tritium (Hydrogen-3)	^3_1H or T	3
8	Oxygen	Oxygen-16	$^{16}_8O$ or ^{16}O	16
		Oxygen-17	$^{17}_8O$ or ^{17}O	17
		Oxygen-18	$^{18}_8O$ or ^{18}O	18

or hydrogen-3, is classed as an unstable isotope because it is radioactive. Only minute traces of tritium are found in nature, but it can be prepared by using suitable nuclear reactions (see Table 26.1, p. 647).

Table 5.1 reveals that part of the name of a nuclide is derived from the name of the element to which it is related. The other part of the name is the mass number of the nuclide. Thus the name oxygen-16 identifies the nuclide whose mass number is 16 and whose atomic number is 8. The nuclide whose mass number is 24 and whose atomic number is 12 is called magnesium-24 because it is related to the element magnesium whose atomic number is 12.

The symbol of a nuclide consists of the chemical symbol of the element to which it is related, a superscript number to indicate the nuclide's mass number, and a subscript number to indicate its atomic number or nuclear charge. Thus $^{54}_{24}Cr$ identifies an isotope of chromium whose mass number is 54. Since the symbol of the element implies the atomic number, the symbol for chromium-54 is also written ^{54}Cr.

A list of the known stable nuclides of some chemical elements is given in Table A.8 (p. A-11). Apparently the relative number of protons and neutrons in the atomic nucleus influences nuclear stability, because elements with odd atomic numbers usually have fewer stable isotopes than those with even atomic numbers.

There are several instances in which two different nuclides have the same mass number but different atomic numbers.   Such nuclides are called *isobars*.   Nickel-64 and zinc-64 are isobars.

5.14 NUCLEAR COMPOSITION OF A NUCLIDE

In the interest of simplicity, we shall assume that the major nuclear particles are the protons and neutrons.   These particles are often called *nucleons*.   The mass number of a specific nuclide indicates the total number of nucleons in its nucleus—protons and neutrons. The number of protons is equal to the atomic number of the element to which the nuclide is related.   For krypton-78, whose atomic number (Z) is 36, we can determine that there are 42 neutrons ($78 - 36$) in the nucleus (mass number − atomic number = number of neutrons).   The number of neutrons in a nucleus cannot be calculated if the mass number is unknown.

5.15 CHEMICAL BEHAVIOR OF ISOTOPES

Since all of the isotopes of a given chemical element have the same number of protons in their nuclei, they all have the same number of electrons outside their nuclei.   Therefore all uncharged isotopes of a specific chemical element have an identical, or at least extremely similar, extranuclear character.   Since the atomic nuclei are very tiny and the electrons surround and, in a sense, shield the nuclei, it should be easy to accept the fact that all the atoms of a given chemical element have practically identical chemical properties.   Because of this fact, the discovery, identification, and separation of the isotopes of any given element were possible only after the physical differences of the isotopes were recognized.

If elemental oxygen is ionized in a Crookes tube, the positive rays produced contain several different positive ions.   Elemental oxygen is composed of diatomic molecules.   As these molecules are bombarded by high-energy electrons or receive relatively large amounts of energy, some of the molecules are ionized (they lose electrons), and some are dissociated to yield oxygen atoms.   In the case of elemental oxygen, the group of positive ions resolved by the mass spectrograph is produced by the ionization of the atoms ^{16}O, ^{17}O, ^{18}O, and of the diatomic molecules $^{16}O^{16}O$, $^{16}O^{17}O$, $^{16}O^{18}O$, $^{17}O^{17}O$,

$^{17}O^{18}O$, and $^{18}O^{18}O$.　The approximate relative masses of these diatomic molecules, in the same order, are 32, 33, 34, 34, 35, and 36.

If elemental hydrogen is ionized, the major positive ions produced arise due to the ionization of the atoms ^{1}H and ^{2}H and of the molecules $^{1}H^{1}H$, $^{1}H^{2}H$, and $^{2}H^{2}H$.

The substance ammonia, NH_3, obviously consists of the elements nitrogen and hydrogen.　If ammonia molecules are produced by using the atoms of ordinary hydrogen and ordinary nitrogen, we should realize that several physically different ammonia molecules will be produced.　Ordinary nitrogen consists of two nuclides ^{14}N and ^{15}N, and we already know that ordinary hydrogen consists of ^{1}H and ^{2}H.　If the various possible combinations of units consisting of one N atom and three H atoms (the different NH_3 molecules) are written, we find that eight physically different NH_3 molecules exist.　Of course, they are practically identical chemically; the only differences reside in the nuclei of their constituent atoms.

5.16　SOME CHEMICAL ATOMIC WEIGHTS

Apparently elemental iodine consists of only one kind of atom, or nuclide, and that is iodine-127.　If you wonder why the chemical atomic weight of iodine is approximately 126.9 instead of 127, you should recall that the mass number is the actual atomic weight of the nuclide rounded off to the nearest integral number.　Moreover, the actual nuclear mass of the iodine-127 atom is not exactly equal to the total mass of 53 protons plus the mass of 74 neutrons.　This aspect will be discussed later in Chapter 26.

The chemical atomic weight of oxygen (15.9994) is quite close to 16.0, although there are three nuclides in elemental oxygen, because ordinary oxygen contains approximately 99.76 per cent oxygen-16, 0.04 per cent oxygen-17, and 0.20 per cent oxygen-18.

Because the chemical atomic weight of chlorine is 35.453, we should suspect that two or more isotopes of chlorine exist.　Actually, ordinary chlorine contains 77.2 per cent chlorine-35 and 22.8 per cent chlorine-37.　The weighted-average atomic weight of chlorine is approximately 35.5 $(0.228 \times 37) + (0.772 \times 35)$.

Although carbon-12 is the current standard upon which all atomic weights are based, we must be sure to remember that the chemical atomic weight of ordinary elemental carbon is 12.01115, and not exactly 12.00000. Because ordinary carbon consists of carbon-13 atoms as well as carbon-12 atoms, the weighted-average chemical atomic weight is greater than 12.

We notice, with very few exceptions, that the chemical atomic weights of the elements increase progressively with their atomic numbers (order numbers). Let us explain the exceptions.

In regard to order number, argon (at. wt, 39.948) precedes potassium (at. wt, 39.102). In this exception to the generalization previously noted, the most abundant isotope in elemental argon is argon-40 and in elemental potassium, potassium-39. Therefore the weighted-average atomic weight of argon is greater than that of potassium.

Tellurium (at. wt, 127.6) precedes iodine (at. wt, 126.9) in order number. Ordinary elemental tellurium contains 8 isotopes, but 2 of these, tellurium-128 and tellurium-130, comprise about 66 per cent of elemental tellurium. Ordinary elemental iodine contains only one nuclide, iodine-127. The weighted-average atomic weight of tellurium is 127.6, which exceeds the atomic weight of iodine. In the case of cobalt and nickel, the most abundant isotope in elemental nickel is nickel-58; elemental cobalt has only one stable isotope, cobalt-59.

We have noted that iodine-127 is the only nuclide that exists in ordinary elemental iodine; yet the chemical atomic weight of iodine is 126.9. This difference between the mass number and the chemical atomic weight is common to most elements that contain only one stable nuclide or isotope. This is due to three factors: (1) the mass number is rounded off to the nearest integral number; (2) the mass number is derived from a physical atomic weight scale; (3) the nuclear mass of the iodine-127 atom is not exactly equal to the total mass of 53 protons plus the mass of 74 neutrons.

5.17   A SUMMARY OF COMMON TERMS

Nuclide: an atom identified by physical means, relative to its nuclear composition.

Isotope: a nuclide (atom) whose nuclear charge is identical to, but whose nuclear mass is different from, that of another nuclide. (Every isotope has a nuclear charge identical to some other isotope or isotopes.)

Isobar: a nuclide (atom) whose mass number is identical to, but whose nuclear charge is different from, that of another nuclide. (Every isobar has a mass number identical to some other isobar.)

Mass number: an integral number used to indicate the approximate nuclear mass of a nuclide; the number of nucleons in the nucleus.

Nuclear mass: the mass of the nucleus of a nuclide; for practical purposes, the mass number of a nuclide on the relative, physical atomic mass scale; approximately equal to the sum of the masses of the protons plus the masses of the neutrons.

Nuclear charge: usually considered to be equal to the number of protons in the nucleus of the nuclide; the atomic number Z of the element to which the nuclide is related.

Atomic number, Z: the order number of an element; the number of protons in the nucleus of each atom of an element; the nuclear charge of an atom; the number of extranuclear electrons in an uncharged atom.

Chemical element: a pure substance all atoms of which have identical nuclear charges and identical numbers of extranuclear electrons. (In certain elements these atoms may have different nuclear masses.)

Proton: a subatomic material which has a positive electric charge and a mass of 1.007595 amu (physical scale); the nucleus of the simplest atom, the protium (hydrogen-1) atom; an entity which exists in all atomic nuclei; an entity whose symbol is p or H^+.

Neutron: a subatomic material particle that has no electric charge and has a mass of 1.008982 amu (physical scale); an entity which exists in all atomic nuclei, except the nucleus of the protium atom; an entity whose symbol is n.

Electron: a subatomic entity that has a negative electric charge (1.602×10^{-19} coulomb) and has a mass of 0.00054876 amu (physical scale), about 1/1837 the mass of a proton; an entity which appears to have material character as well as the properties of electromagnetic radiation; the principal entity in electricity; the entities (electrons) that constitute beta radiation and cathode rays; an entity that exists outside the nucleus of every atom.

Problems

1. A nuclide, YY, has 78 neutrons and 58 protons. What is its complete symbol?

2. Another nuclide, XX, is an isotope of nuclide YY in Problem 1, and has 142 nucleons. (a) What is the complete symbol of nuclide XX? (b) How many extranuclear electrons are in the triply positively charged ion of nuclide XX? (c) A nuclide, ZZ, has 82 neutrons and is an isobar of nuclide YY in Problem 1. What is the symbol of ZZ?

3. An atom loses completely two electrons, and the ion so produced has 54 extranuclear electrons. (a) What is the symbol for the atom? (b) How many protons reside in the nuclei of the ions mentioned here?

4. There are two different nuclides in ordinary elemental nitrogen, nitrogen-14 and nitrogen-15. There are two major nuclides in ordinary elemental hydrogen, hydrogen-1 and hydrogen-2. How many physically different ordinary hydrogen azide, HN_3, molecules are possible?

5. Using the table of naturally occurring stable nuclides on page A-11, indicate the number of physically different molecules of chromium(VI) oxide, CrO_3, that are possible.

6. A nuclide, WW, is transformed to a doubly negatively charged ion. In the ion there are 68 neutrons and 50 extranuclear electrons. (a) What is the complete symbol of WW? (b) An isotope of nuclide WW has 10 nucleons more than WW. How many neutrons are in the nucleus of the isotope? (c) Another nuclide is an isobar of nuclide WW, but it has 52 extranuclear electrons. What is its complete symbol?

7. Predict the approximate percentage abundance of each stable nuclide in ordinary elemental europium.

8. Although the three nuclides xenon-136, barium-136, and cerium-136 are isobaric, their nuclear compositions are obviously different. How do they differ?

9. The doubly positively charged ions of an element have 28 extranuclear electrons. What physically different nuclides can be converted to these ions?

10. The doubly negatively charged ions of an element have 36 extranuclear electrons. What physically different nuclides can be converted to these ions?

11. The isotopic composition of ordinary elemental copper is 69 per cent copper-63 and 31 per cent copper-65. What is the weighted-average atomic weight of copper?

12. A pure compound was placed in a tightly sealed flask from which nearly all the air had been removed. The gaseous phase in the flask is examined a year later and an appreciable amount of helium is detected. How is this fact explained?

13. The mass number of a nuclide is 106. An isotope of this nuclide yields an ion whose symbol is Cd^{++}. (a) What is the symbol of the nuclide? (b) What is the name of the nuclide? (c) How many extranuclear electrons are in an uncharged atom of this nuclide? (d) How many extranuclear electrons are in the Cd^{++} ion? (e) How many protons reside in the nucleus of the Cd^{++}?

14. A nuclide has the mass number 104 and has 60 neutrons in its nucleus. (a) What is the symbol of the nuclide? (b) What is its name? (c) What is its nuclear charge? (d) With what nuclide is it isobaric? (e) List by name those stable nuclides which are isotopic with the nuclide in question. (f) What is the order number of the element to which the nuclide is related?

THE ELECTRONIC

6.1 A PERSPECTIVE

The rather simplified concept of the gross structure of
an atom is insufficient to interpret the chemical behavior of an atom. An atom appears to have an extremely tiny nucleus surrounded by a relatively
voluminous envelope occupied by a certain number of
relatively tiny electrons. So we assume that this
"electronic envelope" is the chemically significant part
of an atom. If we assume that an atom has a three-
dimensional structure, we might suspect that the
character of the periphery of an atom is more important
than those interior portions of the "electronic envelope"
that are closer to the nucleus. As we develop a simplified concept of the electronic structures of the atoms,
we shall consider the entire envelope of extranuclear
electrons, but with greater emphasis on the peripheral
electrons.

STRUCTURE OF ATOMS

Since each electron—negatively charged—is situated at a considerable distance from the positively charged nucleus, each electron must have a certain amount of energy which allows it to keep away from the nucleus. Each electron is in constant motion, and a balance of forces appears to keep the electron in the immediate vicinity of the nucleus. Any attempt to identify these forces correctly in a simple mechanical manner seems to fail. The notion that each electron in an atom may be described with respect to its energy is one basis of the modern conception of the electronic structure of atoms.

6.2 ATOMIC SPECTRA

Since radiant energy is either absorbed or emitted in discrete bundles by matter, we assume that absorption and emission of radiant energy represent or reflect definite energy changes that involve extranuclear electrons. The nature of the radiation involved is a clue to the character of the electronic energy changes.

The relative energy of an extranuclear electron can be determined in part by observing what happens to it in an unexcited atom when it gains either thermal or radiant energy. Since the absorbed energy is received in discrete bundles, specific changes in the energy of the electron occur. The energy of an extranuclear electron is related to its position relative to the nucleus. The relative position of an electron changes whenever the electron's energy changes. If an electron absorbs a bundle of energy, it "jumps" from some specific *energy level* to some higher level. When the electron "drops" from the higher level to the lower level, radiant energy is emitted. The energy emitted during such changes depends on the frequency of the radiation. Since the frequency depends on the wave length, we can determine the amount of energy in each quantum of emitted radiation if we measure the wave length. In this way we identify certain energy levels which can be occupied by the electrons.

The wave lengths of the emitted radiation are measured by using a spectroscope. In this instrument the radiation is dispersed much as is a beam of white light when it is passed through a prism. The dispersed radiation forms an *emission spectrum* which reveals the various wave lengths.

Many ions of certain elements impart various colors to a Bunsen flame. Ions of lithium impart a scarlet color; of potassium, violet; of sodium, yellow; of strontium, bright red; and of barium, green. These colors are related to radiant energy of specific wave lengths. Since the different elements impart different colors to the flame, under the conditions described each element has its own emission spectrum. It seems evident that certain specific electronic changes are different in different atoms or ions. We may therefore suspect that these changes offer valuable clues to the electronic structures of the atoms.

An atom's extranuclear electrons do not lose energy continuously by radiation because radiation of continuously changing wave length is not emitted by ordinary atoms at ordinary temperatures. An ordinary atom emits radiant energy only after it has been excited (after it has absorbed energy). The spectrum of this emitted radiation is noncontinuous, that is, it consists of specific wave lengths.

The two major kinds of atomic spectra are the *emission* and *absorption spectra*. An emission spectrum of atoms is obtained either by heating liquid and solid substances in a flame or by passing an electrical charge through a gaseous substance. The spectrum appears in the spectroscope as a series of bright lines at specific wave lengths. An absorption spectrum in the visible range, for example, is obtained by placing the substance between a continuous light source and the spectroscope. Dark lines on the light background appear in the spectroscope because specific wave lengths of the radiation from the light source are absorbed by the atoms in the substance in question. The dark lines in a specific absorption spectrum of a given substance appear at the same wave length as do the bright lines of the emission spectrum of that substance. An evident conclusion is that these wave lengths of radiation are significant clues to the energy values of the excited electrons in the atoms.

6.3 THE HYDROGEN ATOM

The spectrum of hydrogen is relatively simple because hydrogen atoms contain only one electron. A thorough, logical, and consistent interpretation of this spectrum seems to be a logical departure for the examination of the spectra of more complex elements. It is beyond the scope of this text to discuss in detail the interpretation of the hydrogen spectrum, but we should note that this interpretation has served as a basis of the modern conception of the electronic structure of atoms.

In 1913 Niels Bohr proposed a theory to explain the behavior of the lone extranuclear electron in the hydrogen atom. (Note that here we may use the term *hydrogen atom* because we do not have to identify an isotope; all atoms in elemental hydrogen are identical with respect to their extranuclear character.) Bohr suggested that during excitation (absorption of energy) the lone electron in the hydrogen atom could absorb only discrete bundles of energy and consequently could occupy only certain definite energy levels. In order to conceive of a model for the hydrogen atom, Bohr also suggested that the electron can occupy only certain definite positions in space outside the nucleus. He proposed that these positions might be definite orbits in which the electron revolves around the nucleus. If an electron remains in a specific orbit, he said, it revolves around the nucleus without emission of energy. However, if the electron absorbs a discrete bundle of energy, it jumps from one orbit to another orbit farther from the nucleus. In other words, Bohr suggested that each orbit represents a specific energy level.

According to Bohr, the orbit nearest the nucleus is the one in which the electron has its minimum energy or is in its lowest energy level. This level is often called the "ground state" of the electron in the hydrogen atom. An electron in this energy level is an unexcited electron. The other possible orbits are farther from the nucleus and represent specific higher energy levels. Bohr's proposed system of specified energy levels was extended to identify the energy levels in which the electrons of more complex atoms reside.

The theory proposed by Bohr is an admirable example of logical reasoning based on experimental fact, but, as in the case of many elegant theories, Bohr's concept has had to be modified. Even though since 1913 many facts have been uncovered which cannot be explained by the original theory, Bohr's original suggestions are nevertheless considered epic ideas.

Because we realize today that it is utterly futile to try to make an accurate model or to draw a suitable picture of even the simplest atom, in this book we will not diagram any electronic configurations. We shall, however, use a simple method of electron accounting. Although this method of bookkeeping is greatly simplified, it is an excellent means of interpreting the chemical behavior of many different elements.

Let us now consider a useful viewpoint of the unexcited hydrogen atom. We know that this atom consists of a positively charged nucleus and one extranuclear electron. This lone electron seems to be a completely mobile cloud of negativity. Its average speed is 2.18×10^8 cm/sec. Although the electron's motion is random, its major motion is alternately toward and away from the nucleus. Of all the possible locations of the hydrogen atom's electron, the distance 0.53 A from the nucleus has the highest probability (see Fig. 6.1). This means that the electron effectively occupies the space within a radius of about 1 A from the nucleus. Considering other possible locations of the electron, we find that the points of high probability form a spherically symmetrical sphere surrounding the atomic nucleus. The points of highest probability are most numerous at 0.53 A from the nucleus and their number progressively decreases as the distance from the nucleus increases. The periphery of the hydrogen atom is the outer region where the probability of finding an electron is smallest (see Fig. 6.2).

The electronic configurations of more complex atoms are much more complicated than that of the hydrogen atom. However, we can imagine an atom to consist of a tiny nucleus surrounded by one or more electron clouds. The most probable positions of these electron clouds are identified by using the concept of energy levels.

The spectrum of hydrogen consists of a series of spectral lines, the Lyman, Balmer, Paschen, Brackett, and Pfund series—each named for its discoverer. Of these

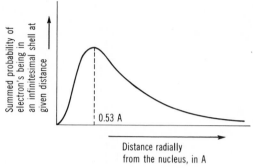

FIGURE 6.1 Distribution curve showing the radial shell probability for the 1s electron of the hydrogen atom.

the Lyman, Balmer, and Paschen series are the ones we shall identify further. The Lyman series appears whenever electrons, after prior excitation, drop from higher energy levels to the lowest, or first, energy level. The Balmer lines arise as excited electrons drop from higher energy levels to the second energy level. The Paschen series involves transitions from and to the third energy level. The Lyman series is in the ultraviolet region of the electromagnetic spectrum, the Balmer lines are in the visible-light region, and the Paschen series is in the infrared region. The Brackett and Pfund series are in the far infrared portion of the spectrum, and so are identified with difficulty (see Fig. 6.3).

FIGURE 6.2 Schematic cross section of the electron cloud surrounding the nucleus of the hydrogen atom. The density of this electron cloud is represented by dots, each dot indicating a spot where there is high probability of finding an electron. Density of the electron cloud progressively decreases with increasing distance from the nucleus (the electron cloud is spherically symmetrical).

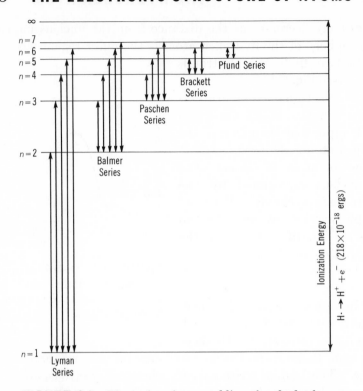

FIGURE 6.3 The series of spectral lines for the hydrogen atom based on the Bohr concept of electronic energy levels. The horizontal lines depict the principal energy levels. The notation ∞ indicates the energy level at which the electron has enough energy to escape completely from the vicinity of the atomic nucleus, thereby leaving behind the hydrogen ion, H^+.

6.4 THE WAVE-MECHANICS APPROACH

The major refinements of the Bohr theory were based originally on an extremely significant idea conceived in 1924 by the French physicist, Louis De Broglie. In essence, this idea suggested that electrons have, as material particles, certain properties identical to ordinary waves. De Broglie proposed that the wave length of an electron could be calculated, and that this wave length is inversely proportional to the electron's momentum. The wave length, 2.40×10^{-10} cm, of a stationary electron can be calculated by using the expression, $\lambda = h/mc$, where λ is the wave length, m is the rest-mass of the electron, 9.11×10^{-28} g, c is the velocity of light in vacuum, 3.00×10^{10} cm/sec, h is Planck's constant, 6.62×10^{-27} erg sec. This value is intimately related to a fraction of the length of a Bohr orbit because a stable Bohr orbit corresponds to integral numbers of De Broglie electron wave lengths. De Broglie's idea about the wave character of electrons was verified experimentally in 1927 by C. J. Davisson and L. H. Germer.

De Broglie's conception of the wave nature of material particles led to a new system of mechanics, called *wave mechanics* or *quantum mechanics*. This new system was initiated largely by the Austrian physicist-mathematician, Erwin Schrödinger. The two major features of wave mechanics are the wave character of an electron and the probability (statistical) nature of our knowledge of an electron.

In 1927 the German physicist, Werner Heisenberg, enunciated his uncertainty principle. He stated that it was impossible, by then-current experimentation, to determine accurately both the exact position and momentum (energy content) of an electron. Since the dimensions of an electron are less than the wave length of most electromagnetic radiation, the electron's position and image cannot be determined accurately by ordinary means. Radiation of shorter wave lengths has so much energy that it will markedly affect the electron's energy. Use of such radiation would therefore yield only uncertain measurements. It seems that the numerical value of Planck's constant is the current measure of uncertainty.

The second major feature of the wave-mechanics approach is the monumental wave equation (a complicated differential equation) known as the *Schrödinger equation*. This equation affords calculation of the probabilities related to the energy, or relative position, of an electron around an atomic nucleus. Since the solutions of this complex equation are extremely tedious and involved, precise calculations have been obtained only for the hydrogen atom and the singly positive helium ion, He^+. However, analogous solutions have been made for some more complex atomic systems.

A very significant and useful aspect of the Schrödinger wave equation is that it yields the definitions of four quantum numbers. These numbers identify the probabilities of location and properties of electrons in atomic orbitals and the essential character of the orbitals themselves. The atomic orbitals are related to wave functions derived from Schrödinger's equation.

6.5 QUANTUM NUMBERS

Let us now consider, in turn, the four quantum numbers that we shall use in the atomic identification of electrons. We might consider these numbers as labels which will identify the various columns in our electron bookkeeping ledger.

The principal quantum number, n, characterizes the average distance of an electron from the atomic nucleus, and its values are 1, 2, 3, 4, $\cdots$. This quantum number identifies the principal energy level in which a specific electron resides. Essentially each principal energy level identifies a specific spatial probability distribution of a "cloud" of electrons. The principal energy levels are often called *shells*, designated by K, L, M, N, $\cdots$. All electrons that have the same principal quantum number occupy the same principal energy level (see Fig. 6.4).

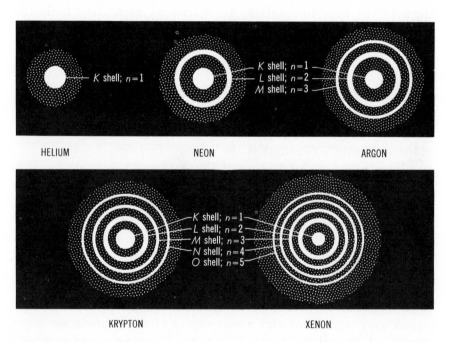

FIGURE 6.4 Cross-sectional diagrammatic representations of the electron clouds and their densities outside the nuclei of five of the inert gas atoms. Dots indicate regions of high electron density (or high probability). Electrons in the principal energy levels (shells) are most probably in spherical electron clouds that form at certain positions relative to the nucleus. The volumes of most dense clouds and the distances separating principal energy levels markedly decrease as the nuclear charge increases.

The azimuthal quantum number, l, specifies the angular momentum of the electron and also characterizes the shape of the atomic orbital. Its values are 0, 1, 2, $\cdots$, $n - 1$. If $l = 0$, the atomic orbital is spherical. If $l = 1$, the orbitals have a dumbbell shape. For higher values of l, the orbital shapes are progressively more complex. All electrons with a common value of l reside in a specific subgroup, either s, p, d, or f: for $l = 0$, an s subgroup; for $l = 1$, a p subgroup; for $l = 2$, a d subgroup; for $l = 3$, an f subgroup. The subgroups written in order of increasing energy are s, p, d, f.

The magnetic quantum number, m, characterizes the orientation of an electron cloud in a magnetic field. Attempts to explain the splitting of spectral lines in a magnetic field (the *Zeeman effect*) led to this quantum number. The values that m may have are $-l$, $\cdots$, 0, $\cdots$, $+l$, so for each value of l there are $2l + 1$ values of m.

The spin quantum number, m_s, is related to what is called the *spin of an electron*. Its values are $+\frac{1}{2}$ and $-\frac{1}{2}$. Electrons that have parallel spins have identical spin quantum numbers and

TABLE 6.1   **Quantum numbers for first and second principal energy levels**

Principal quantum number, n	1		2		
Azimuthal quantum number, l	0 ($1s$)	0 ($2s$)	1 ($2p$)		
Magnetic quantum number, m_l	0	0	-1	0	$+1$
Spin quantum number, m_s	$+\frac{1}{2}, -\frac{1}{2}$	$+\frac{1}{2}, -\frac{1}{2}$	$+\frac{1}{2}, -\frac{1}{2}$	$+\frac{1}{2}, -\frac{1}{2}$	$+\frac{1}{2}, -\frac{1}{2}$

cannot interact to yield electron pairs, whereas those that have nonparallel spins have different spin quantum numbers. Two electrons that have nonparallel spins (one electron's m_s, $+\frac{1}{2}$, the other's, $-\frac{1}{2}$) can pair.

Before using these quantum numbers, we should recall that they can be used to identify each electron in a specific atom. Since each electron should have its own specific identification, it should be easy to accept W. Pauli's exclusion principle: Each electron in a given atom has its own unique set of quantum numbers. In other words, no two electrons in a given atom can have the same set of four quantum numbers.

6.6 ELECTRONIC CONFIGURATIONS OF ATOMS

The quantum numbers which we have defined can now be used in the specification of the principal energy levels and subgroups in terms of n and l. A complete principal energy level, n, contains n subgroups, each of which contains electrons with a common value of l. A complete l subgroup contains $4l + 2$ electrons, and a complete principal energy level, n, contains $2n^2$ electrons. If an l subgroup is filled to its capacity, all electrons are paired in what are called *atomic orbitals*. The two electrons in each filled orbital have nonparallel spins, one having a quantum number $+\frac{1}{2}$, the other, $-\frac{1}{2}$. For the electron capacities of the first four principal energy levels, the subgroups and orbitals needed to accommodate the electrons in each completed or filled level are shown in Table 6.2.

TABLE 6.2 Accommodation of electrons in the first four principal energy levels

Principal Energy Level	Electron Capacity	Subgroups Involved	Orbitals (Electron Pairs) Involved
1	2	$1s$	one
2	8	$2s$	one
		$2p$	three
3	18	$3s$	one
		$3p$	three
		$3d$	five
4	32	$4s$	one
		$4p$	three
		$4d$	five
		$4f$	seven

During the orderly construction of the electronic configurations of the atoms, starting with the hydrogen atom, electrons are added progressively to these subgroups in their order of increasing energy. With a few exceptions, each subgroup of a given principal energy level is filled to its capacity before electrons are added to the next "higher" subgroup in that level. The subgroups arranged in order of increasing energy are: $1s$, $2s$, $2p$, $3s$, $3p$, $4s$, $3d$, $4p$, $5s$, $4d$, $5p$, $6s$, $4f$, $5d$, $6p$, $7s$, $5f$, and $6d$. In the more complex atoms there is some overlapping in adjacent subgroups because the energy differences between these groups becomes progressively smaller the higher their energy levels (see Fig. 6.5).

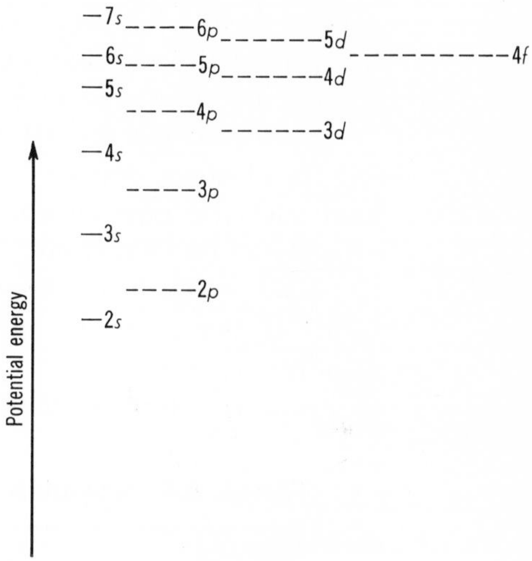

The theoretical capacities of the principal energy levels 5 and 6 have not as yet been reached because there are only 103 known chemical elements. These are listed in Table 6.3.

The principal quantum number by itself does not give an adequate description of the energy of an electron. We must break down the principal energy levels into *subgroups* which in turn are divided into *orbitals*.

The subgroups are identified by the letters, *s*, *p*, *d*, and *f*. Each subgroup has a specific electron capacity. The relationship

FIGURE 6.5 Approximate potential energy sequence for most of the atomic orbitals.

TABLE 6.3 Electron capacities of individual principal energy levels

Shell	Principal Quantum No. and Principal Energy Level	$2n^2$ (Electron Capacity)
K	1	2
L	2	8
M	3	18
N	4	32
O	5	50
P	6	72

between a subgroup and its principal energy level is indicated by placing the principal quantum number of the principal energy level in front of the letter of the subgroup. For instance, $2s$ identifies the s subgroup in which all electrons have the principal quantum number 2; $3p$ identifies the p subgroup in which all electrons have the principal quantum number 3. The subgroups arranged in order of increasing energy are: s, p, d, and f.

Spectroscopic investigations indicate that if an energy level has its electron capacity satisfied, then all electrons are paired. Each electron pair occupies an orbital; hence each orbital has a capacity of two electrons. (See Tables 6.2 and 6.4.)

Each electron apparently has a certain energy related to its spin. If two electrons have opposing spins, one positive and one negative, then they tend to pair. If an orbital is occupied by two electrons, the electrons must have opposing spins.

TABLE 6.4   Constitution of subgroups

Subgroup	Electron Capacity	Number of Orbitals
s	2	1
p	6	3
d	10	5
f	14	7

6.7   ELECTRONIC CONFIGURATIONS OF ELEMENTS 1–20

The electronic configurations of elements 1 through 20 are listed in Table 6.5. These configurations are "built" progressively by commencing with hydrogen (element No. 1), whose atoms contain one electron in the $1s$ subgroup in the first principal energy level. For helium, the second electron also enters subgroup $1s$. But for the lithium atom, the third electron must be placed in the $2s$ subgroup because the $1s$ subgroup is filled at He.

This progressive "building" of the electronic configurations, often called the *aufbau principle*, may seem more logical if we think of the space around an atomic nucleus as being a sort of energy well. As we progressively drop electrons into the "well," each electron falls as far as it can to occupy that lowest energy level in which a vacancy exists.

TABLE 6.5 Electronic configurations of the elements hydrogen to calcium*

Atomic Number	Element	Energy Levels									
		1s	2s	2p	2p	2p	3s	3p	3p	3p	4s
1	Hydrogen	(·)									
2	Helium	(··)									
3	Lithium	(··)	(·)								
4	Beryllium	(··)	(··)								
5	Boron	(··)	(··)	(·)							
6	Carbon	(··)	(··)	(·)	(·)						
7	Nitrogen	(··)	(··)	(·)	(·)	(·)					
8	Oxygen	(··)	(··)	(··)	(·)	(·)					
9	Fluorine	(··)	(··)	(··)	(··)	(·)					
10	Neon	(··)	(··)	(··)	(··)	(··)					
11	Sodium	(··)	(··)	(··)	(··)	(··)	(·)				
12	Magnesium	(··)	(··)	(··)	(··)	(··)	(··)				
13	Aluminum	(··)	(··)	(··)	(··)	(··)	(··)	(·)			
14	Silicon	(··)	(··)	(··)	(··)	(··)	(··)	(·)	(·)		
15	Phosphorus	(··)	(··)	(··)	(··)	(··)	(··)	(·)	(·)	(·)	
16	Sulfur	(··)	(··)	(··)	(··)	(··)	(··)	(··)	(·)	(·)	
17	Chlorine	(··)	(··)	(··)	(··)	(··)	(··)	(··)	(··)	(·)	
18	Argon	(··)	(··)	(··)	(··)	(··)	(··)	(··)	(··)	(··)	
19	Potassium	(··)	(··)	(··)	(··)	(··)	(··)	(··)	(··)	(··)	(·)
20	Calcium	(··)	(··)	(··)	(··)	(··)	(··)	(··)	(··)	(··)	(··)

*Each pair of parentheses represents an orbital. Each dot is an electron.

In our scheme of electron accounting, an s subgroup of any specific principal energy level is filled before the p subgroup is filled. However, in filling p subgroups, one electron is placed in each of the three p orbitals before any electrons are paired. This procedure follows Hund's rule. Apparently in the ground (unexcited) state of the atoms, the electrons remain unpaired as long as possible. Such electrons therefore appear to have parallel spins. This effect has been called the *principle of maximum multiplicity*. The electronic picture for carbon (at. no. 6) is

$$1s \quad\quad 2s \quad\quad 2p \quad\quad 2p$$
$$(\uparrow\downarrow) \quad (\uparrow\downarrow) \quad (\uparrow) \quad (\uparrow)$$

or

$$1s \quad\quad 2s \quad\quad 2p \quad\quad 2p$$
$$(..) \quad\quad (..) \quad\quad (.) \quad\quad (.)$$

For nitrogen,

$$1s \quad\quad 2s \quad\quad 2p \quad\quad 2p \quad\quad 2p$$
$$(\uparrow\downarrow) \quad (\uparrow\downarrow) \quad (\uparrow) \quad (\uparrow) \quad (\uparrow)$$

or

$$1s \quad\quad 2s \quad\quad 2p \quad\quad 2p \quad\quad 2p$$
$$(..) \quad\quad (..) \quad\quad (.) \quad\quad (.) \quad\quad (.)$$

Although arrows may imply better the relationships of the spins of the electrons, the dots are adequate. We know that if two electrons occupy an orbital, they have nonparallel spins, and that if unpaired electrons are present in an atom, each has a spin parallel to that of the other unpaired electrons.

A common abbreviated notation of atomic electronic configurations uses the principal energy level and subgroup notations and superscripts to locate the electrons. The superscripts simply indicate the number of electrons in the subgroup in question; they are not exponential numbers. Notations for some simple atoms are given below.

Hydrogen	$1s^1$
Lithium	$1s^2 \quad 2s^1$
Carbon	$1s^2 \quad 2s^2 \quad 2p^2$
Neon	$1s^2 \quad 2s^2 \quad 2p^6$
Phosphorus	$1s^2 \quad 2s^2 \quad 2p^6 \quad 3s^2 \quad 3p^3$

Observe that in each notation the sum of the superscript must equal the atomic number, or number of extranuclear electrons in the atom.

6.8 PERIODIC CLASSIFICATION OF THE ELEMENTS

By the middle of the nineteenth century, chemists had identified many of the chemical elements and their physical and chemical properties. As the number of elements increased and the various descriptions of their properties grew in number, the need for some means of classification became obvious.

In 1869 Dmitri Mendeleev, a Russian, and Lothar Meyer, a German, independently suggested a rather simple and at that time intriguing method of classification. Noting that the physical and chemical properties of the elements appeared to be periodic functions of their atomic weights, they suggested a classification of the elements based on this generalization of periodicity. Their suggestions were not immediately accepted, and until Henry Moseley suggested a modification, the explanation of this periodicity was somewhat tenuous (see Sec. 5.8). Moseley's interpretation is the basis of the so-called periodic law or periodic generalization: The physical and chemical properties of the elements are periodic functions of their atomic numbers. This generalization implies that periodicity is in some way related to the extranuclear electrons in the atoms of the elements. Now we realize that this periodicity and the physical and chemical properties of the elements are intimately related to the electronic configurations of the elements.

Other chemists had made comments about certain periodic aspects of the simple chemical elements prior to Mendeleev's publication. In 1817 Dobereiner noticed that certain elements of similar properties could be arranged in groups of three in the order of their atomic weights. In each of these triads the atomic weight of the middle member was approximately the mean of the atomic weights of the other two. For instance, in the triad Li (6.94), Na (22.99), K (39.10), the mean of the atomic weights of Li and K is 23.02, or approximately the atomic weight of Na. Only a few triads yield results as good as this.

In 1864 J. A. R. Newlands (English) suggested a systematic arrangement for some of the simple elements (omitting hydrogen) in which every eighth element had properties similar to the first. The two octaves for which this arrangement is valid are shown below.

Li	Be	B	C	N	O	F
Na	Mg	Al	Si	P	S	Cl
K	Ca					

Inspection of the current periodic chart reveals that, except for the inert gases, this is the present arrangement for the first 20 elements. Elements of closely similar chemical and physical properties are placed in a specific vertical column. That is, Li, Na, and K are in a given column or period because their chemical properties are so similar. Also Be, Mg, and Ca fall in a given period for the same reason.

In the early 1860s de Chancourtois proposed a periodic classification of the simplest elements. Because his publication appeared inconclusive, it failed to receive proper attention.

Mendeleev is usually considered the boldest original exponent of the concept of elemental periodicity. He had the courage to maintain his thesis in the face of obvious discrepancies, most of which were relatively minor. He realized that the atomic weights of tellurium (127.61) and iodine (126.91) were out of order in his periodic classification, as were those of cobalt (58.94) and nickel (58.71). However, he did not change his premise that the periodicity of chemical and physical properties was the paramount issue.

Mendeleev asserted that elements would eventually be discovered to occupy vacant places in his table. His predictions were remarkably accurate. In 1871 he predicted the eventual discovery of an element similar to silicon to fit the vacant spot below silicon in his periodic table. He called this unknown element eka-silicon, EKs, and he predicted several of its chemical and physical properties. An element, germanium, was discovered in 1886 by C. A. Winkler, and it had properties almost identical to those predicted by Mendeleev. Some of these are contrasted in Table 6.6.

Mendeleev also correctly predicted the discovery of scandium and gallium. He was unable, however, to place logically the rare earth elements and he could not predict the total number of them. Although Mendeleev did not know about the rare gases, and he did not suggest their possible discovery, these inert gases (He, Ne, Ar, Kr, Xe, and Rn) were easily placed in his table. Their general chemical behavior and indefinite valence numbers are unique. For an element (except oxygen and fluorine) in any of the long vertical columns of the periodic table, the maximum valence number is the number of the column, as shown in the modern periodic chart (see inside back cover). For example, the maximum valence number of sulfur, S, is $+6$, and S is in column 6; for germanium, Ge, it is $+4$, and Ge is in column 4.

Mendeleev's original chart was a daring and revolutionary

TABLE 6.6 **Some predicted and observed properties of germanium**

Mendeleev's Predictions of Eka-Silicon	Winkler's Experimental Observations of Germanium
Atomic weight, 72	Atomic weight, 72.3
Specific gravity, 5.5	Specific gravity, 5.47
Atomic volume, 13	Atomic volume, 13.2
Color, gray	Color, grayish white
Heat in air yields a solid, $EKsO_2$	Heat in air yields a solid, GeO_2
$EKsCl_4$, liq. of sp. gr., 1.9	$GeCl_4$, liq. of sp. gr., 1.887

suggestion. It was of inestimable help in correlating known chemical facts, in predicting properties of undiscovered elements, and in correcting certain errors in prior classifications. The contribution that Mendeleev made to chemistry is comparable in magnitude to that made by Dalton.

6.9 THE MODERN PERIODIC CHART

Since the time Mendeleev and Meyer proposed their classifications, many different types of periodic charts have been suggested. Probably the most practicable is the elongated chart that is commonly used today. It is somewhat less cumbersome than the others and is simple and very descriptive. An abbreviated chart is shown in Fig. 6.6.

The periodic chart is exceedingly useful. Once its implications are appreciated, a tremendous amount of information may be gathered from it. To use it most productively, certain facts should be known.

a. In any given vertical column in the periodic chart, each element is chemically similar to every other element in the column. A group of elements constituting a long vertical column is called a family of chemically similar elements. The 1a column (excluding H) is the alkali metal family; the 2a column, the alkaline earth metal family; the 7a column (excluding H), the halogen family; and the 8a column, the inert gas family.

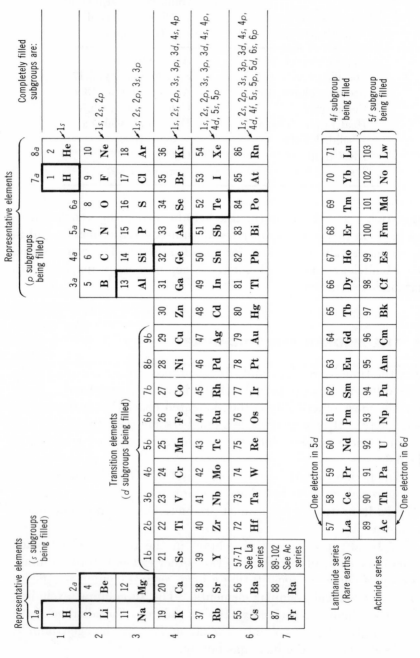

FIGURE 6.6 Periodic arrangement of the elements.

b. In any given long vertical column, the highest energy level(s) of the atoms of the elements have identical electronic configurations, except H in column 7a and He in column 8a. For example, each alkali metal atom has 1 electron in its highest energy level; each alkaline earth metal atom, 2 electrons in its highest energy level; each halogen atom, 7 electrons in its highest energy levels; each inert gas atom (except He), 8 electrons in its highest energy level.

c. Since the elements in a vertical column have similar chemical properties, it has been possible to predict correctly the chemical behavior of many elements before their discovery. Although today there are no vacancies (unknown elements) between hydrogen and element 103, the discovery of new elements will be greatly simplified because of the periodicity in the chemical behaviors of the elements.

d. The elements within each family (long vertical column) often exhibit a noticeable gradation of properties as they increase in atomic number. In Table 6.7 are listed some physical properties

TABLE 6.7 Some physical properties of the alkali metals

Element	Melting Point in °C	Boiling Point in °C	Density g/ml
Lithium	186	1335	0.534
Sodium	97.4	880	0.97
Potassium	62.3	760	0.86
Rubidium	38.5	700	1.53
Cesium	28.5	670	1.87

of the major members of the alkali metal family (Group 1a). The only discrepancy in a gradual change in properties is the density of potassium.

During subsequent discussion we shall notice many other examples in which a gradual change in properties is observed in the alkali metals. Some of these will be chemical properties. The normal boiling points of the halogens in their elemental states, for example, are: fluorine (F_2), $-187°C$; chlorine (Cl_2), $-33.7°C$; bromine (Br_2), $58.8°C$; iodine (I_2), $183°C$. The chemical activity of the halogens as oxidizing agents gradually decreases with increasing atomic number, fluorine being the most active and astatine (At) the least active.

6.10 THE PERIODIC SYSTEM AND ELECTRONIC CONFIGURATIONS

One of the most striking characteristics of the periodic classification of the elements is its manifestation of the essential harmony between the physical and chemical aspects of matter. By using the periodic table, we can correlate and interpret many physical and chemical properties of the elements because these properties are closely related to their electronic configuration. Periodicity in the elements is due to periodicity in their electronic configurations. Since we shall interpret chemical behavior in the light of electronic configurations, we must appreciate the importance of this periodicity.

In the interest of simplicity, we will here consider primarily the electronic configurations of the representative elements. These are the elements listed in the long vertical columns 1a, 2a, 3a, etc., of the periodic chart. They constitute a group of families in that the chemical behavior of each member of a given family frequently appears to be representative of every other member. The electronic configurations of these elements exhibit a striking periodicity.

The elements in the other vertical columns 1b, 2b, 3b, etc., within the main body of the periodic chart are called the *transition elements*. The remaining elements, placed below the main body of the chart, constitute two long horizontal series, the *lanthanide series* and the *actinide series*. The elements in the lanthanide series and several in the present actinide series were formerly called the rare earth elements.

Again in the interest of simplicity, we shall indicate only the electronic configurations of the highest energy levels. This seems reasonable since it is the electrons in the highest energy levels, at the periphery of the atom, that are involved in most ordinary chemical transformations. The electrons in the highest energy levels are called the *valence electrons*. In the abbreviated electronic configurations of the atoms of the representative elements, only the valence electrons will be indicated.

6.11 THE VALENCE ELECTRONS OF THE REPRESENTATIVE ELEMENTS

The configurations of the valence-electron portions of the atoms of the representative elements in the upper long horizontal row or period (Li through Ne) are the key configurations of all the other representative elements. (Helium and hydrogen are excluded from this discussion because their valence electrons reside in the first energy level.) Each element in this upper long horizontal row is the simplest member of a family of representative elements. Every other member of the family has a valence-electronic configuration identical to that of the simplest member. The valence electrons of the representative elements are tabulated in Table 6.8.

TABLE 6.8   Valence electrons of unexcited gaseous atoms of the representative elements

		Valence Electrons in Each Member of the Family	
	Family	Number	Arrangement
1a	(alkali metal)	1	1 unpaired
2a	(alkaline earth metal)	2	1 pair
3a	(boron)	3	1 pair + 1 unpaired
4a	(carbon)	4	1 pair + 2 unpaired
5a	(nitrogen)	5	1 pair + 3 unpaired
6a	(oxygen)	6	2 pairs + 2 unpaired
7a	(halogen)	7	3 pairs + 1 unpaired
8a	(inert gas)	8 (except He)	4 pairs (except He)

6.12   AN OPERATIONAL SYMBOLISM

To facilitate the representation of the number and arrangement of the valence electrons of the representative elements, we employ a system of simple symbols. These operational symbols constitute a logical scheme but do not represent the actual appearance and arrangement of valence electrons.

The operational symbols of the "key" representative elements are listed in Table 6.9. The symbols of other representative elements can be derived easily from them.

Since only the valence electrons are noted in the operational symbols of the atoms, the element symbol represents the remainder of the atom. For example, in the case of the operational symbol of the carbon atom, $\ddot{\text{C}}\cdot$, the symbol C represents everything except the valence electrons. That is, C represents the nucleus and the

TABLE 6.9   Symbols of the unexcited gaseous atoms of the "key" representative elements

Element	Operational Symbol* (Kernel and Valence Electrons)		
Lithium	Li·		
Beryllium	B̈e	or	$\overline{\text{Be}}$
Boron	B̈·	or	$\overline{\text{B}}$·
Carbon	C̈·	or	$\overline{\text{C}}$·
Nitrogen	·N̈·	or	·N̄·
Oxygen	:Ö·	or	$|\underline{\text{O}}$·
Fluorine	:F̈·	or	$|\overline{\text{F}}$·
Neon	:N̈e:	or	$|\overline{\text{Ne}}|$

* In the symbols noted, each dot represents a valence electron, and two dots placed close together represent a pair of electrons. Since in the next chapter a dash (—) will be used frequently to represent a pair of electrons, the dashes used represent pairs of electrons. Therefore there are two alternative methods to symbolize a pair of electrons, but frequently in this book, a pair of electrons is represented by a dash.

two inner electrons of the carbon atom; C is called the *kernel* of the carbon atom. The operational symbol of an atom thus represents the kernel of the atom plus its valence electrons. In the symbol ·P̈· the notation P represents the kernel of the phosphorus atom and the dots represent the valence electrons.

To write the operational symbols of the representative elements not listed in Table 6.9, we need recall only that all elements within a family of representative elements have the same number and arrangement of valence electrons. With this in mind, we readily predict the operational symbol of arsenic, which is ·Äs··.

6.13 GENERALIZATIONS

Because the electronic configurations of the representative elements are distinctly periodic and orderly, the chemical properties of these elements are fairly easily classified. However, the electronic configurations of the transition elements are somewhat less periodic and orderly, and so the chemical properties of the transition elements are less readily classified (see Table 6.10).

TABLE 6.10   Valence-electronic configurations of some transition elements

Atomic Number	Element	Orbitals in Highest Energy Levels*					
		$3d$	$3d$	$3d$	$3d$	$3d$	$4s$
21	Sc	(.)	( )	( )	( )	( )	(..)
22	Ti	(.)	(.)	( )	( )	( )	(..)
23	V	(.)	(.)	(.)	( )	( )	(..)
24	Cr	(.)	(.)	(.)	(.)	(.)	(.)
25	Mn	(.)	(.)	(.)	(.)	(.)	(..)
26	Fe	(..)	(.)	(.)	(.)	(.)	(..)
27	Co	(..)	(..)	(.)	(.)	(.)	(..)
28	Ni	(..)	(..)	(...)	(.)	(.)	(..)
29	Cu	(..)	(..)	(..)	(..)	(..)	(.)
30	Zn	(..)	(..)	(..)	(..)	(..)	(..)

* All lower electronic energy levels are complete.

In all representative elements, the valence electrons reside in the s and p subgroups of certain principal energy levels. However, some valence electrons of the transition elements either reside in or are promoted from some s subgroup, and one or more valence electrons of these elements always reside in some d subgroup.

Table 6.11 lists the subgroups and their orbitals which are progressively filled during the systematic building-up of the electronic configurations of the elements, commencing with hydrogen and terminating with element 103. The notation

Li–Ne   Representative $2s$ and $2p$

means that in progressively building up the electronic configurations

TABLE 6.11   Progressive building of electronic configurations

Series	General Class	Subgroups Filled Progressively
H–He		$1s$
Li–Ne	Representative	$2s$ and $2p$
Na–Ar	Representative	$3s$ and $3p$
K–Ca	Representative	$4s$
Sc–Cu	Transition	$3d$
Ga–Kr	Representative	$4p$
Rb–Sr	Representative	$5s$
Y–Ag	Transition	$4d$
In–Xe	Representative	$5p$
Cs–Ba	Representative	$6s$
Ce–Lu	Lanthanide	$4f$
Hf–Au	Transition	$5d$
Tl–Rn	Representative	$6p$
Fr–Ra	Representative	$7s$
Th–Lw	Actinide	$5f$

of the atoms, Li, Be, B $\cdots$ Ne, the $2s$ and $2p$ subgroups are being filled with electrons. Of course, the $2s$ subgroup is filled before electrons are placed in the $2p$ orbitals.

6.14   SPATIAL ORIENTATION OF ATOMIC ORBITALS

The three-dimensional aspects of the atomic orbitals, especially those in the highest principal energy levels, are significant. The spatial arrangements of the valence electrons characterize, in part, the nature of the chemical interactions between different atoms which yield the various types of molecular geometry. We shall elaborate on this point in subsequent chapters.

Only crude depictions of atomic orbitals are possible in two dimensions, but at least they are better than nothing (see Fig. 6.7). Electrons in an s orbital of any principal energy level are always located about the nucleus (the origin) of the atom in a spherically symmetrical manner (see Fig. 6.7). The regions of greatest probability of finding the s electron are in this spherical electron cloud.

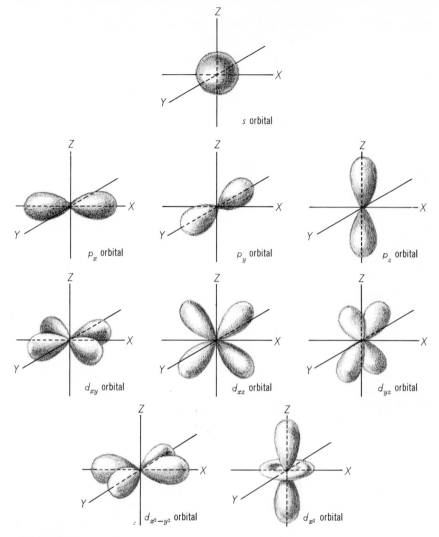

FIGURE 6.7 Diagrams of the spatial arrangements of the *s*, *p*, and *d* atomic orbitals.

The $1s$ orbital is the smallest, the $2s$ somewhat larger than $1s$, and so on.   Regardless of size, all are spherical.

Electrons in the *p* orbitals of any principal energy level are arranged along three mutually perpendicular axes *x*, *y*, and *z*, so that the regions of the probable greatest electron density are in dumbbell-shaped electron clouds whose major axes coincide with

x, y, and z. The angles between the axes through the pairs of electron clouds are 90° (see Fig. 6.7).

Since the electronic configuration of an unexcited gaseous boron atom is $1s^2\ 2s^2\ 2p^1$, the lone $2p$ electron can be in a dumbbell-shaped cloud along either the x, the y, or the z axis. The energy levels related to the x, y, and z axes have identical energies, so we cannot identify explicitly the location of the lone $2p$ electron in the unexcited boron atom.

Because there are two vacant p orbitals in the unexcited boron atom, the electronic notation is

$$
\begin{array}{c|cccc}
1s & 2s & 2p & 2p & 2p \\
(\uparrow\downarrow) & (\uparrow\downarrow) & (\uparrow) & (\ ) & (\ )
\end{array}
$$

and because of the *principle of maximum multiplicity*, it is fairly easy to excite a boron atom, thereby promoting a $2s$ electron into one of the vacant $2p$ orbitals. Therefore the configuration of the excited boron atom is

$$
\begin{array}{c|cccc}
1s & 2s & 2p & 2p & 2p \\
(\uparrow\downarrow) & (\uparrow) & (\uparrow) & (\uparrow) & (\ )
\end{array}
$$

We notice that all three valence electrons are now unpaired and that there are three partly filled atomic orbitals in the excited boron atom.

The situation relative to the carbon atom is similar to that of the boron atom. There is only one vacant p orbital in the unexcited gaseous carbon atom.

$$
\begin{array}{c|cccc}
1s & 2s & 2p & 2p & 2p \\
(\uparrow\downarrow) & (\uparrow\downarrow) & (\uparrow) & (\uparrow) & (\ )
\end{array}
$$

A carbon atom is apparently excited rather easily to yield an electronic configuration in which each p orbital has one electron. Evidently one of the $2s$ electrons is readily promoted to the vacant p orbital during the excitation.

$$
\begin{array}{c|cccc}
1s & 2s & 2p & 2p & 2p \\
(\uparrow\downarrow) & (\uparrow) & (\uparrow) & (\uparrow) & (\uparrow)
\end{array}
$$

Another notation of the electronic configuration of the excited carbon atom is

$$
1s^2 \quad 2s^1 \quad 2p_x^1 \quad 2p_y^1 \quad 2p_z^1
$$

For the unexcited nitrogen atom we see that each $2p$ orbital has one electron,

$1s$	$2s$	$2p$	$2p$	$2p$
($\uparrow\downarrow$)	($\uparrow\downarrow$)	($\uparrow$)	($\uparrow$)	($\uparrow$)

or

$$1s^2 \quad 2s^2 \quad 2p_x^1 \quad 2p_y^1 \quad 2p_z^1$$

and that each of the mutually perpendicular p atomic orbital axes has a dumbbell-shaped cloud.

Since there are five d orbitals in each of the principal energy levels above the second, we should expect that the spatial orientation of d atomic orbitals would be much more complex than that of the p atomic orbitals. Of course, we need to consider the d orbitals only when we are concerned about valence electrons of the atoms of the transition elements or when unoccupied d orbitals of representative elements beyond neon accept electrons.

Each d orbital consists essentially of four lobes around the origin. The d_{xy}, d_{xz}, and d_{yz} orbitals are aligned so that their lobes are at 45° angles between the axes specified. The d_{xy} orbital, for example, consists of four lobes placed in the plane containing the x and y axes, each lobe extending outward from the origin at a 45° angle between the axes (see Fig. 6.7). Since only five orbitals are needed in a d subgroup, we cannot have three orbitals aligned along the axes plus the three aligned between the axes. Hence only two orbitals whose lobes are on the axes are allowed. Although any of the three axial positions can be used to yield the two required orbitals, it is customary to use the $d_{x^2-y^2}$ and a sort of hybrid of the other two, called the d_{z^2} orbital (see Fig. 6.7).

In the unexcited gaseous scandium atom, Sc, the valence electronic picture is

$4s$	$3d$
($\uparrow\downarrow$)	($\uparrow$)

whereas in the excited Sc atom the valence electronic configuration is

$4s$	$3d$	$3d$
($\uparrow$)	($\uparrow$)	($\uparrow$)

In each atom the unpaired $3d$ electrons can reside in any of the d orbitals.

Since the unexcited gaseous chromium atom has one electron in each $3d$ orbital and one electron in the $4s$ orbital, the valence-electronic notation of Cr is

$$4s^1 \quad 3d_{xy}^1 \quad 3d_{xz}^1 \quad 3d_{yz}^1 \quad 3d_{x^2-y^2}^1 \quad 3d_{z^2}^1$$

Problems

1. How many paired extranuclear electrons reside in the uncharged atoms of the following elements: (a) argon, (b) potassium, (c) arsenic, (d) tellurium, (e) chlorine, (f) silicon, (g) sulfur, (h) zinc?

2. Indicate the number of valence electrons in the atoms of the elements listed in Problem 1.

3. How many pairs of valence electrons are present in the atoms of the elements listed in Problem 1?

4. How many unpaired electrons are present in the atoms of the elements listed in Problem 1?

5. How many paired electrons reside in the atomic kernels of the following elements: (a) strontium, (b) cesium, (c) lead, (d) arsenic, (e) iodine, (f) selenium, (g) antimony, (h) germanium, (i) indium, (j) astatine?

6. How many pairs of extranuclear electrons reside in the atoms of the elements listed in Problem 5?

7. Write the conventional operational symbols (valence electrons only) of the elements listed in Problem 5.

8. What is the charge of the atomic kernel of each of the elements listed in Problem 5?

9. Before element 85 was discovered, many of its physical and chemical properties were predicted correctly. (a) Why was this possible? (b) With what elements was it contrasted prior to its discovery? (c) What was the prediction as to the normal physical state and color of element 85?

10. Why did Madame Curie find that the chemical and physical properties of radium bromide were so similar to those of barium bromide?

11. Write the names of those transition elements that you have, during the past two days, seen either in their pure state or alloyed with other transition elements in their elemental state.

12. In which family of representative elements is similarity of properties manifested most strikingly?

13. Considering representative elements only, identify two atoms whose atomic kernels have an electronic configuration identical to the xenon atom.

14. Identify four entities that have the same number of extranuclear electrons in the same energy levels as Sr^{++}.

15. Considering representative elements only, identify four monatomic entities that have the same number of extranuclear electrons as the selenide ion, Se⁻⁻.

16. List five representative elements whose atomic kernels have the same number of extranuclear electrons as the kernel of the bromine atom.

17. List four different atoms whose valence-electronic configurations are identical to the valence-electronic configuration of the tellurium atom.

18. List four monatomic entities of representative elements that have electronic configurations identical to that of Ca^{++}.

19. How many representative elements have atoms consisting of at least one unpaired extranuclear electron?

20. How many representative elements have atoms that consist of at least four paired valence electrons?

21. Indicate two monatomic uncharged entities that are electronically identical to the oxygen-16 atom.

22. The density of metallic calcium is 1.55 g/ml at 20°C; of barium, 3.5 g/ml. Which of the three values, 1.40, 2.6, or 3.8, would you choose as the most likely density of strontium?

23. A striking periodicity is observed if the atomic volumes of the elements are plotted against their atomic numbers. By assuming that the atomic volume of an element is the volume of one g-atom of the element, plot for the first 40 elements the graph in which atomic volumes are on the ordinate and atomic numbers are on the abscissa. The densities (specific gravities) of the elements are listed in Table A.9 of the Appendix.

24. What are the major differences, electronically speaking, between the representative elements and the transition elements?

7

HOW ATOMS INTERACT

7.1 A PERSPECTIVE

Now that we have formulated simplified electronic configurations for some of the chemical elements, we are better equipped to understand the current ideas about how, and occasionally why, atoms interact chemically with each other.

We emphasized in Chapter 6 the number and arrangement of the valence electrons of the atoms of the representative elements and the $3d$ transition elements. It will be helpful to recall continually that apparently it is only these electrons that are directly involved in ordinary chemical changes. Since the valence electrons of atoms are such significant factors, they should appear in all symbols that we may use to depict atoms, ions, and molecules. Because the symbols are only operational, their major virtue is their utility, not their veracity.

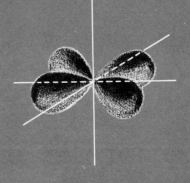

WITH EACH OTHER

This chapter will serve mainly as a brief outline of the two major ways in which atoms interact chemically to yield the two major kinds of chemical compounds. We shall postpone until Chapter 8 any detailed description of the kinds of chemical bonds and of the geometry and architecture of chemical compounds.

The actual behavior of any atom or molecule in a given situation is dependent on at least two factors: (1) the atom's or molecule's inherent characteristic electronic configuration, and (2) the environment in which the atom or molecule exists at the time of the particular change. The term *environment* includes the identity and nature of the other substances present and the nature of the physical circumstances. For example, the chemical behavior of the hydrogen atom depends, in part, on the presence of a lone valence electron, and on the tendency of the atom to attain an electronic configuration identical to the He atom. But the actual chemical behavior of the hydrogen atom in the presence of fluorine is quite different from its behavior in the presence of potassium. The hydrogen atom acts as an electron acceptor in the presence of potassium, but it acts as an electron donor in the presence of fluorine.

7.2 THE LANDMARK ELEMENTS

In starting our discussion of the chemical behavior of atoms, let us note an extremely significant fact: The inert gases (family 8*a*) exhibit little tendency to react chemically. There are few stable compounds which contain these elements, and an inert gas never reacts with another inert gas.

If we assume that chemical behavior and electronic structure are closely related, we can infer that the inert gas elements are relatively unreactive because they have a certain singular type of electronic configuration. In the case of helium, the 1*s* subgroup is filled, but in the atoms of the other inert gases, specific *s* and *p* subgroups are filled by those electrons with the relatively highest energies. These arrangements appear to be very stable and symmetrical. In helium the electrons form what is called a *stable duet;* in the other inert gases the electrons in the highest energy levels form a *stable octet.*

Since energy is involved in every chemical reaction and the inert gases are generally unreactive, it is in order to suggest that an inert gas molecule resides in a relatively low energy state. The inert gas elements appear to have little chemical potential energy.

Considering the two major aspects of the inert gas elements (their symmetrical electronic configurations and low energy states), and contrasting these with the same aspects of all other elements, we arrive at a very useful generalization: Whenever atoms react chemically with each other, they indicate a striking tendency to attain a more symmetrical, more stable electronic configuration. With the representative elements, the chemically reactive atoms usually tend to attain the same electronic configuration as some inert gas element. In the most stable electronic configurations, all electrons are paired. This situation arises because certain unfilled orbitals have accepted their quota of electrons—two per orbital. The stable electron duet in a completed orbital is just as significant as the stable electron octet.

It is an observed fact that many reactions between elemental forms of matter are exothermic. In these reactions the total energy of the product(s) is less than the total energy of the reactants; the reactant system is transformed to a system of lower energy content. Atoms tend to change to a lower energy state or to a state of greater stability. This interpretation is compatible with the idea that atoms tend to attain, if possible, a more stable electronic configuration. Of course, these two interpretations should be compatible because essentially each is based on the other.

7.3 METHOD OF ATOMIC INTERACTION

In all chemical reactions in which different elemental forms of matter are the reactants, the valence electrons of the atoms play major roles. The atoms of any given representative element either have more or less electrons than the inert gas element nearest to it in the periodic chart. It seems reasonable to suggest that the atoms of the representative element must either donate or accept electrons in an attempt to attain a more stable, symmetrical electronic configuration. Since electronic configurations are altered during a chemical change involving two chemical elements, there must be a transfer of electrons from the atoms of one element to the atoms of another. In other words, if the atoms of one element accept electrons, the atoms of another element must donate them.

From a physical standpoint, there are only two ways in which a substance may accept or donate electrons. One is by *complete transfer;* the other, by *cooperate sharing.* These two methods will be illustrated in the following sections.

7.4 COVALENT MOLECULES COMPOSED
OF IDENTICAL ATOMS

At ordinary temperatures elemental hydrogen is composed of diatomic molecules. Individual hydrogen atoms do not exist in elemental hydrogen at ordinary temperatures. Let us now attempt to explain why hydrogen atoms tend to pair and form hydrogen molecules.

The operational symbol of the hydrogen (protium) atom is $H \cdot$, where H is the kernel of the atom and the dot is the lone, unpaired electron. Apparently two hydrogen (protium) atoms combine because each atom tends to attain around its kernel the same electronic configuration as helium. If each atom shares its lone electron with another atom, then each kernel has two electrons near it, just as the helium kernel does.

In ordinary chemical reactions a hydrogen atom never donates, by complete transfer, its one electron. If it did, the entity that remained would have no electrons. According to our generalization, a hydrogen atom should tend to attain the same electronic configuration as helium, and this could never be accomplished if a hydrogen atom donated, by complete transfer, its lone electron.

The formation of the hydrogen (protium) molecule may be symbolized as follows:

$$\text{H} \cdot \; + \; \cdot \text{H} \rightarrow \text{H} : \text{H}$$

When we derived the operational symbols of the atoms of the representative elements, we suggested that each pair of electrons might be represented by a dash, —. Using this symbol, we may picture the hydrogen molecule as follows:

$$\text{H—H}$$

The shared pair of electrons between the two kernels is called a *covalent bond*—a bond because it seems to hold together the two hydrogen (protium) kernels and covalent because it is a "cooperative" composed of two valence electrons. The pair of valence electrons is placed diagrammatically between the two kernels, but the two electrons do not always reside between them. The two electrons continually roam around the vicinity of the two kernels because all electrons are in continuous motion. However, since the two electrons in a hydrogen molecule can pair, either they have or they can assume opposing spins (see Fig. 7.1).

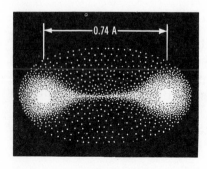

FIGURE 7.1 Cross-sectional diagram of the most probable electron distribution in the hydrogen molecule. Regions of highest electron density surround the atomic nuclei; electron density is relatively high in the region between the nuclei. The atomic nuclei continually oscillate, moving toward and then away from each other, the distance 0.74 A being the most probable time-average distance between the nuclei.

One may think of the hydrogen molecule as a sort of egg-shaped electron cloud with the two atomic nuclei imbedded therein. The spherical electron clouds of the 1s electrons of the hydrogen atoms overlap or interpenetrate to yield a resultant attraction. Although the parts of the electron cloud that do not overlap do repel each other, opposed repulsions exist in the parts of the cloud that do overlap. Therefore at the overlap the forces tend to push the molecule together. The overlap serves as a means of bonding the kernels together (see Fig. 7.2).

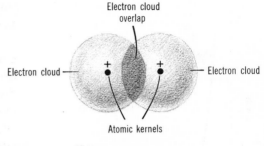

FIGURE 7.2 Diagram showing the electron cloud overlap that yields the covalent bond in the diatomic hydrogen molecule.

The pair of electrons shared by each hydrogen kernel occupies an orbital that belongs to each atom or to the entire molecule. Since each electron is in an s orbital, the covalent bond is an s—s bond, or simply a pure s bond.

Let us now consider another diagram illustrating the concept of a chemical bond between two atoms, X and Z. An examination of the graph in Fig. 7.3 reveals the relationship of the distance between the atomic nuclei of the two atoms X and Z to the total energy content of the system. At the far right side of the graph the distance between the atoms X and Z is so great that the energy of the system is not related to the interatomic distance. As the atoms move closer together, attractive forces, owing to electrostatic interactions and overlap of electron clouds, become significant. The total energy of the system gradually decreases until a minimum value is attained, the bottom of the curve. This energy minimum is related to the specific interatomic distance, d. The distance d between the X and Z atomic nuclei is considered to be the bond distance. The system, here consisting of atoms X and Z, reaches a minimum energy state when the bond is formed. We must overcome repulsive forces if we wish to push the nuclei closer together, and we must overcome attractive forces if we wish to separate the nuclei.

Early in the 1920s an eminent American chemist, G. N. Lewis, suggested an extremely useful scheme for the representation of covalent bonds as a means of identifying the structural character of covalent molecules and all entities in which atomic kernels are held together by covalent bonds. The hydrogen molecule is the simplest covalent molecule or entity and may be considered the prototype.

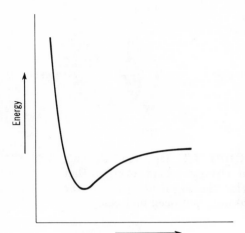

At ordinary temperature several common elemental forms of matter are composed of covalent molecules. Some of these are diatomic, such as oxygen (O_2), nitrogen (N_2), fluorine (F_2), chlorine (Cl_2), bromine (Br_2), and iodine (I_2). Apparently the individual atoms of these elements combine to form covalent molecules because they have unpaired electrons and have a strong tendency to fill incomplete orbitals by sharing electrons with each other. In each of the diatomic covalent molecules, except molecular oxygen, each kernel has an octet of electrons around it. At ordinary temperatures the oxygen molecule contains two unpaired electrons, but in the excited oxygen molecule (at higher temperatures) these two unpaired electrons form an electron pair.

FIGURE 7.3 Curves indicating the energy of interaction of two normal atoms X and Z as the atoms move toward and away from each other. The valence electron of X that interacts with that of Z has a spin opposed to the spin of the valence electron of Z.

The electronic configurations of some common diatomic covalent molecules are noted below. Such electronic configurations are only operational symbols and not descriptions of the actual molecules. These symbols should be viewed in the same light as the operational symbols of the atoms. In any given symbol the electrons are placed or localized on the basis of probability; thus a symbol implies the location of the electrons in a specific covalent molecule. Of course, the implications of a specific operational symbol should be compatible with known experimental facts about the physical and chemical behavior of a specific covalent molecule.

$$:\overset{..}{\underset{..}{O}}\cdot \ + \ \cdot\overset{..}{\underset{..}{O}}: \ \rightarrow \ :\overset{..}{\underset{..}{O}}:\overset{..}{\underset{..}{O}}: \ \text{ or } \ |\overline{\underset{.}{O}}{-}\overline{\underset{.}{O}}|$$

the oxygen molecule

$$:\!\overset{\cdot}{\underset{\cdot}{N}}\!\cdot\ +\ \cdot\overset{\cdot}{\underset{\cdot}{N}}:\ \rightarrow\ :\!N:::N:\ \text{or}\ |N\!\!\equiv\!\!N|$$

the nitrogen molecule

$$:\!\overset{\cdot\cdot}{\underset{\cdot\cdot}{F}}\!\cdot\ +\ \cdot\overset{\cdot\cdot}{\underset{\cdot\cdot}{F}}:\ \rightarrow\ :\!\overset{\cdot\cdot}{\underset{\cdot\cdot}{F}}:\overset{\cdot\cdot}{\underset{\cdot\cdot}{F}}:\ \text{or}\ |\overline{F}\!\!-\!\!\overline{F}|$$

the fluorine molecule

$$:\!\overset{\cdot\cdot}{\underset{\cdot\cdot}{Cl}}:\overset{\cdot\cdot}{\underset{\cdot\cdot}{Cl}}:\ \text{or}\ |\overline{Cl}\!\!-\!\!\overline{Cl}| \qquad :\!\overset{\cdot\cdot}{\underset{\cdot\cdot}{Br}}:\overset{\cdot\cdot}{\underset{\cdot\cdot}{Br}}:\ \text{or}\ |\overline{Br}\!\!-\!\!\overline{Br}|$$

the chlorine molecule   the bromine molecule

$$:\!\overset{\cdot\cdot}{\underset{\cdot\cdot}{I}}:\overset{\cdot\cdot}{\underset{\cdot\cdot}{I}}:\ \text{or}\ |\overline{I}\!\!-\!\!\overline{I}|$$

the iodine molecule

The shared pair of electrons of the fluorine molecule, F_2, occupies an orbital that belongs to each atom. Since the unpaired electrons of the original fluorine atoms occupied p orbitals, the electrons that form the covalent bond of the fluorine molecule are in a common p orbital. Therefore the bond in the fluorine molecule is called a p bond. The Cl_2, Br_2, and I_2 molecules are held together in the same manner as is the fluorine molecule (see Fig. 7.4).

Since two of the electrons in the oxygen molecule are unpaired, they have parallel spins and reside in two different p orbitals. The shared pair of electrons yields a p bond because the electrons in the pair were originally in p orbitals.

During the formation of a nitrogen molecule, three shared pairs are created because each nitrogen atom has three unpaired electrons. The shared electrons yield a multiple bond, in this case a triple bond.

Each dash between, or perpendicular to, the symbols of the kernels of the atoms is considered to be a shared pair of electrons (covalent bond). Each dash that is not perpendicular to a kernel is an unshared pair of electrons. Although these unshared pairs of electrons do not appear necessary to hold a molecule together, they should be included in any complete operational symbol. In many covalent molecules an unshared pair of electrons may play an important role during certain chemical reactions. After all, if an atom's chemical behavior is dependent on its electronic configuration, we should expect that a covalent molecule's chemical behavior is dependent on its electronic configuration.

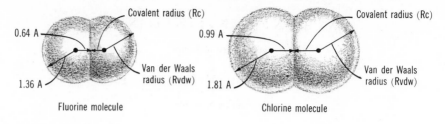

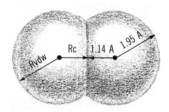

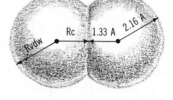

FIGURE 7.4 Relationship of the covalent radius (Rc) to the van der Waals radius in four of the halogen molecules. The van der Waals radius is nearly equal to the ionic radius of the halide (halogenide) ion. The covalent radius is half the distance between the atomic nuclei in the diatomic halogen molecule, and the van der Waals radius is the distance from the atomic nucleus to the outer edge of the electron cloud surrounding that nucleus.

At ordinary temperatures elemental sulfur (a yellow solid) is composed of octatomic molecules (S_8). However, sulfur vapor (gas) is composed of diatomic molecules (S_2).

$$8 : \overset{..}{\underset{.}{S}} \cdot \rightarrow \quad
\begin{array}{c}
\overline{S}\!-\!\overline{S} \\
|S| \qquad\quad |S| \\
| \qquad\qquad\ | \\
|S| \qquad\quad |S| \\
\overline{S}\!-\!\overline{S}
\end{array}
\quad \overset{\Delta}{\rightarrow} \ 4 \ |\overline{S}\!-\!\overline{\underset{.}{S}}|$$

White elemental phosphorus is composed of tetratomic molecules, P_4. The phosphorus kernels reside at the vertices of an imaginary three-dimensional structure; these vertices are connected by lines, or dashes, which represent covalent bonds. The dotted line is used to emphasize the three-dimensional character of the molecule.

Diamond, an elemental form of carbon, is called a macro covalent molecule because each carbon kernel is linked directly or indirectly, by a covalent bond, to every other carbon kernel. Therefore the size of this covalent entity depends on the size of the diamond itself.

$$n\text{C} \quad \rightarrow \quad \text{C}_n$$
$$\text{carbon atoms} \qquad \text{diamond}$$

where n is the number of carbon atoms. The magnitude of n depends on the size of the diamond.

Using an operational symbol, a portion of the diamond molecule may be represented:

Although the inert gases are molecular, their molecules are monatomic.

7.5 COVALENT MOLECULES COMPOSED
OF UNLIKE ATOMS

We shall now consider briefly the construction of some simple binary covalent compounds (uncharged molecules consisting of two different elements whose atomic kernels are held together by shared pairs of electrons). As we construct these covalent molecules, we shall assume that the necessary atoms are obtained from ordinary elemental forms of matter. The symbolic representations of the building of the molecules are not intended to be either complete descriptions or mechanisms of any actual chemical reactions.

Before we proceed, let us recall a few important chemical axioms.

a. The atoms of the inert gases are generally unreactive apparently because they have symmetrical electronic configurations in which all electrons are paired and all s and p orbitals of a specific principal energy level are completely filled.

b. Noninert gas atoms usually tend to attain, if possible, either an inert gas atom electronic configuration or a configuration in which all pertinent atomic orbitals are filled. The tendency is to attain stable duets which collectively may yield stable octets.

c. An uncharged gaseous atom is a potential electron donor if it can attain by electron donation a more symmetrical electronic configuration about its nucleus.

d. An uncharged gaseous atom is a potential electron acceptor if it can attain by electron acceptance a more symmetrical electronic configuration.

e. All gaseous atoms of elements to the right of the "stairway" in the periodic chart are electronically deficient relative to some inert gas atom. Hence such atoms tend to accept electrons to fill incomplete atomic orbitals.

f. If atoms of different elements to the right of the "stairway" interact with each other to yield stable compounds, any electron donation is by sharing. Since the atoms are already electronically deficient, they will hardly be expected to donate electrons by complete transfer.

g. Considering the s and p orbitals in which the valence electrons of the representative elements reside, the electrons of the p orbitals are more likely to be involved in covalent bonding than are those in the s orbital. The p orbitals can overlap more readily than the s orbitals because the p orbitals extend on specific axes outward from the nucleus farther than the s orbital. An s—p bond has a bond energy about $\sqrt{3}$ times stronger than that of an s—s bond. A p—p bond is about 3 times as strong as an s—s bond.

Elemental hydrogen reacts readily with elemental fluorine to yield hydrogen fluoride, HF. Since the gaseous atoms of both elements are electronically deficient, they share each other's odd valence electron. As a result the hydrogen atom's $1s$ orbital is filled and the fluorine's one incomplete p orbital is filled.

$$\text{H} \cdot + \cdot \overline{\text{F}}| \rightarrow \text{H} : \overline{\text{F}}| \text{ or } \text{H} \!-\! \overline{\text{F}}|$$

hydrogen
fluoride

In the covalent HF molecule, the hydrogen kernel has around it an electron duet (same as the He atom), while the fluorine kernel has a stable electron octet (same as the Ne atom). The shared pair of electrons is placed between the kernels, and the three unshared pairs (not used in bonding) are placed around the fluorine kernel, just as they were in the fluorine atom. The covalent bond is an s—p bond because s and p orbitals overlap (see Fig. 7.5).

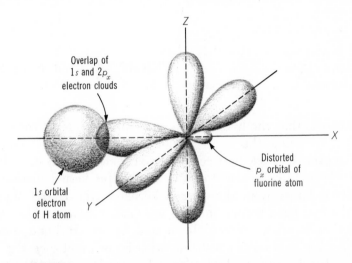

Overlap of
$1s$ and $2p_x$
electron clouds

Distorted
p_x orbital of
fluorine atom

$1s$ orbital
electron
of H atom

FIGURE 7.5   Diagram showing the electron cloud overlap that involves a $1s$ electron of a hydrogen atom and a $2p$ electron of a fluorine atom to form the hydrogen fluoride molecule, H—F.

Under appropriate conditions, hydrogen reacts with oxygen to yield water, or hydrogen oxide. Since each oxygen atom needs two electrons to complete its two incomplete p orbitals, two hydrogen atoms are necessary.

$$\begin{array}{c} \text{H} \cdot \\ \\ \text{H} \cdot \end{array} + \cdot \overline{\text{O}}| \;\rightarrow\; \begin{array}{c} \text{H} : \overline{\text{O}}| \\ \ddot{} \\ \text{H} \end{array} \;\text{or}\; \begin{array}{c} \text{H} - \overline{\text{O}}| \\ | \\ \text{H} \end{array}$$

Considering the valence electrons of a gaseous oxygen atom,

$2s$	$2p$	$2p$	$2p$
(··)	(··)	(·)	(·)

we realize that the two incomplete p orbitals are involved in electron cloud overlapping to form covalent bonds. Since these p orbitals are perpendicular to each other, we expect the angle between the covalent bonds (p bonds in this case) to be 90°. However, the actual bond angle is 104.5°. (See Fig. 7.6.) A logical explanation

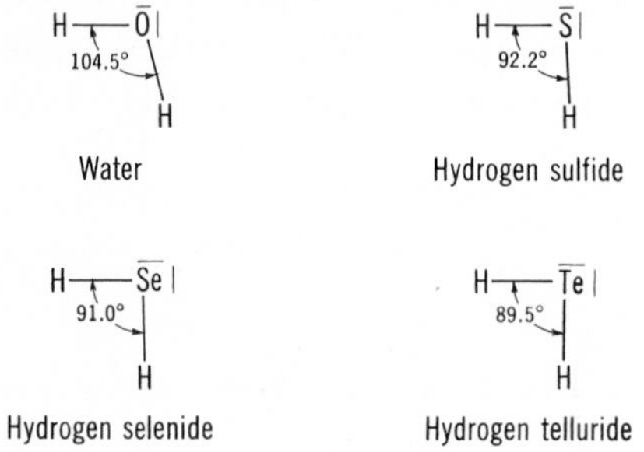

H—⊤—O̅|
104.5°⟍
H

Water

H—⊤—S̅|
92.2°|
H

Hydrogen sulfide

H—⊤—Se̅ |
91.0°|
H

Hydrogen selenide

H—⊤—Te̅ |
89.5°|
H

Hydrogen telluride

FIGURE 7.6 Bond angles in the oxygen family analogs of water.

of this fact is that the hydrogen kernels (protons) repel each other, thereby expanding the bond angle. If this reason is valid, we should expect the angle between the two covalent bonds in hydrogen sulfide, HSH, to be nearer to 90°. The sulfur kernel in the HSH molecule is larger than the oxygen kernel in the HOH molecule; hence the hydrogen kernels in HSH are farther apart and less likely to repel each other. Since the actual H—S—H bond angle is 92.2°, the explanation is consistent with known fact (see Fig. 7.6).

The bond angle in hydrogen selenide, HSeH, is 91.0°, still nearer the expected 90°. This fact strengthens the explanation because Se is larger than S. The reported bond angle in hydrogen telluride, HTeH, is 89.5 ± 1°. You may wonder why the value is less than 90°, but the experimental error, ±1°, is such that 90° is the likely value.

In Chapter 8 we shall suggest another possible explanation for the 104.5° bond angle in HOH.

When hydrogen and nitrogen react chemically, the product is ammonia, NH_3. The formula is not unexpected because each gaseous nitrogen atom has three unpaired valence electrons.

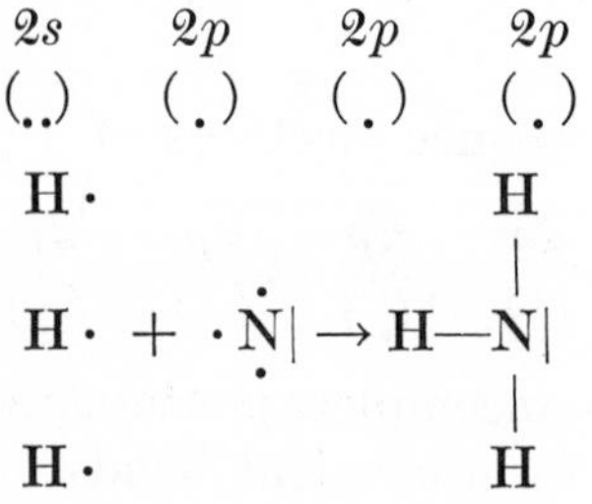

$2s$ $2p$ $2p$ $2p$

(..) (.) (.) (.)

H ·

H · + · N̄| → H—N̄|

H ·

H

|
H—N|
|
H

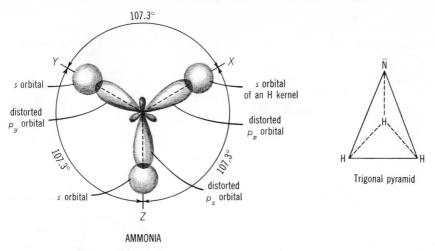

AMMONIA

FIGURE 7.7   Geometry of the ammonia molecule.

Since each of the three incomplete $2p$ orbitals in the nitrogen atom tends to be filled by accepting one electron, each covalent bond in NH_3 results from a p electron cloud overlapping with an s electron cloud.   Although the expected bond angles between the p bonds in NH_3 are 90°, the actual bond angle is 107.3°.   The molecule is a trigonal pyramid.   (See Fig. 7.7.)

If we propose the same explanation for bond angle expansion in NH_3 as that which we used in the case of HOH, we should expect the bond angles in PH_3, AsH_3, and SbH_3 to be nearer to 90°. An extension of our previous explanation seems valid because the bond angles in PH_3 are 93.3°, in AsH_3 91.8°, and in SbH_3 91.3°.

Although we shall postpone until the next chapter a discussion of more complex types of chemical bonding and molecular geometry, the current discussion should reinforce the belief that covalent bonds involving p orbitals are directional.

Figure 7.8 depicts some simple binary covalent compounds and the molecules from which their constituent atoms are obtained.

7.6   IONIC (ELECTROVALENT) COMPOUNDS

We have discussed the chemical behavior of hydrogen atoms in the presence of some atoms that have a deficiency of electrons.   Now let us consider the behavior of hydrogen atoms in the presence of atoms that have a superfluity of electrons.   Since the chemical behavior

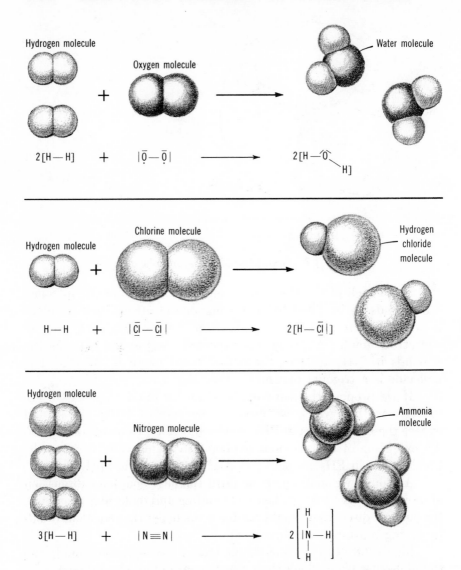

FIGURE 7.8 Three different covalent compounds, water, hydrogen chloride, and ammonia, together with the elemental molecules from which their constituent atoms are obtained.

of a hydrogen atom depends not only on its electronic configuration, but also on the nature of the substance(s) with which it is in contact, we should readily accept the fact that hydrogen atoms behave as electron acceptors in the presence of vigorous electron donors.

Under appropriate conditions, elemental hydrogen reacts with elemental lithium to produce a compound called lithium hydride. The lithium atom has one valence electron and its kernel has the same electronic configuration as helium.   Therefore it has a strong tendency to donate, by complete transfer, its one valence electron. We know that the hydrogen atom can attain, by accepting one electron, the same electronic configuration as helium.

$$\text{Li} \cdot \; + \; \cdot \text{H} \rightarrow \; \text{Li}^+ \; + \; :\text{H}^- \; \text{or } \text{Li}^+\text{H}^-$$

lithium   hydride   lithium
ion   ion   hydride

During the complete transfer of its one valence electron, the lithium atom (three protons + three electrons) becomes a positively charged particle.   This is called the lithium ion and it has the same electronic configuration as helium.

During the acceptance, by complete transfer, of one electron, the hydrogen (protium) atom (one proton and one electron) becomes a negatively charged particle called the hydride ion.   It has the same electronic configuration as helium.   In fact, the electronic configurations of the lithium and hydride ions are identical.

Lithium hydride is a compound composed of two distinct entities, lithium ions and hydride ions.   In a sense, this compound is a mixture of ions, but since the mixture has a constant and definite composition, it is called a *compound*.   Because the lithium ions and hydride ions have opposite electrical charges, they are attracted to each other by strong electrostatic (coulombic) forces.   This strong attraction creates a sort of bond between the ions which is called an *ionic* or *electrovalent bond*.

Lithium hydride is called an *ionic compound* or an *electrovalent compound*.   In fact, it is the simplest ionic compound.   At ordinary temperatures lithium hydride is a white, crystalline solid in which the individual ions are arranged in space in an orderly geometrical pattern, thus forming a crystal lattice.   (See p. 177.)

Under appropriate conditions, elemental magnesium reacts with elemental oxygen to produce magnesium oxide.   Since a magnesium atom has 12 extranuclear electrons and a neon atom 10 extranuclear electrons, a magnesium atom has a tendency to donate, by complete transfer, its two valence electrons.   An oxygen atom has a strong tendency to accept two electrons.   Therefore each magnesium atom donates two electrons to an oxygen atom, so that the ionic compound, magnesium oxide, contains magnesium ions and oxide ions in equal numbers.

$$\text{Mg}: + \cdot \ddot{\text{O}}: \rightarrow \text{Mg}^{++} + :\ddot{\text{O}}:^{--} \text{ or } \text{Mg}^{++}\text{O}^{--}$$

magnesium oxide magnesium
ion ion   oxide

Since the kernel of the magnesium atom has the same electronic configuration as the neon atom, the doubly positive magnesium ion has the same electronic configuration as neon. The oxide ion has the same electronic configuration as the magnesium ion. (See Fig. 7.9.)

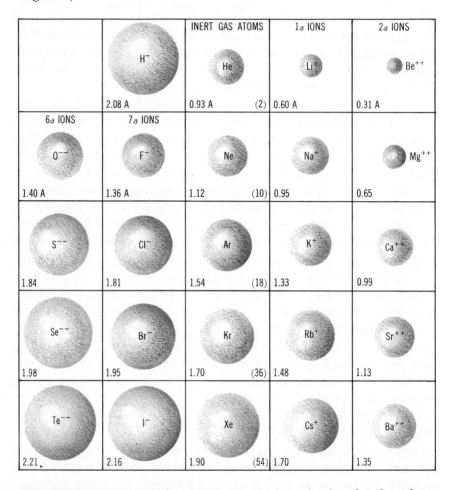

FIGURE 7.9 Inert gas atoms and common ions closely related to them. All entities in any given horizontal row have an identical number of extranuclear electrons (indicated in parentheses). Entities are drawn to scale, and the ionic radii, in Angstroms, are noted below the ions. Atomic radii of inert gas atoms are also noted.

The oxide ion and magnesium ion are isoelectronic because they have identical numbers of extranuclear electrons arranged in the same manner relative to the energy levels. Two entities are isoelectronic if they have identical electronic configurations. The entities may have different volumes, but the arrangement of the extranuclear electrons in the occupied energy levels is the same in isoelectronic entities. The ions that are isoelectronic with the neon atom are: fluoride ion, F^-; oxide ion, O^{--}; nitride ion, N^{3-}; monatomic carbide ion, C^{4-}; sodium ion, Na^+; magnesium ion, Mg^{++}; aluminum ion, Al^{3+}.

Covalent molecules may be isoelectronic provided they have the same total number of electrons about the constituent atomic

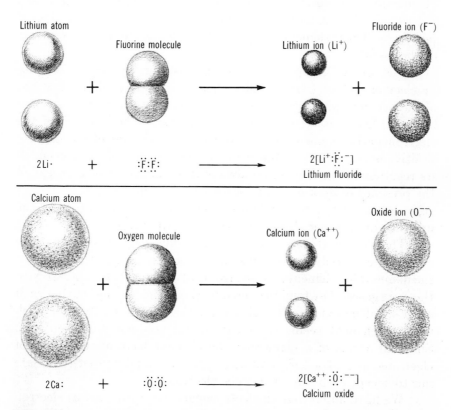

FIGURE 7.10 Formation of two different ionic compounds, lithium fluoride and calcium oxide. Each ionic compound consists of two different kinds of ions. Lithium atoms and calcium atoms have larger radii than the ions that are formed when they lose electrons. The electron clouds surrounding the oxygen kernels in the oxygen molecule expand as electrons are accepted to yield oxide ions.

nuclei. The nitrogen molecule, N_2, and the carbon monoxide molecule, CO, are isoelectronic. The sulfate ion, SO_4^{--}, is isoelectronic with the perchlorate ion, ClO_4^-.

The formations of two ionic compounds are shown in Fig. 7.10.

7.7   A RELATIVE CLASSIFICATION OF THE ELEMENTS

The elements may be classified with respect to their general chemical behavior. They are placed conventionally into two main groups. One contains those elements which, in their elemental state, nearly always donate one or more electrons per atom when they react chemically to yield stable compounds. These elements are called the *electron donors*, and their atoms tend to become positive ions if possible. These elements are also called the electropositive elements or the metals.

The second group of elements consists of the *electron-acceptor* or electronegative (nonmetallic) elements. The uncharged atoms of the electronegative elements tend to become negative ions if possible, or at least they tend to attract electrons. The behavior of the electronegative elements is not so consistent as that of the electropositive ones. Fluorine, for instance, always accepts electrons in all its reactions. Oxygen seems always to accept electrons, except in the presence of fluorine. In contrast to fluorine, oxygen is an electron donor. Oxygen and fluorine are, however, acceptors in the presence of all other elements with which they react.

The elemental state of each nonmetallic element consists either of diatomic or polyatomic covalent molecules. Since the atoms of the nonmetallic elements are electronically deficient, in contrast with the inert gases, they tend to overcome this deficiency by sharing each other's valence electrons. However, the elemental state of each metallic element seems to consist mainly of monatomic entities. Since all atoms of a given metallic element have a superfluity of electrons, in contrast with an inert gas, they tend neither to donate nor to accept each other's valence electrons.

We have noted that all electronegative elements act as electron donors in the presence of fluorine. However, whenever an electronegative element reacts with an electropositive one, the electronegative accepts electrons from the electropositive. In other words, a metallic element always donates electrons to a nonmetallic one. The relative classification of the elements is based on the fact that electropositive elements (metals) always behave as electron donors during ordinary chemical changes. Any elements that can act as electron acceptors are placed outside the group of electropositive elements. The classification indicated in Table 7.1 is rather arbitrary in some cases, but essentially it is valid.

TABLE 7.1 A relative chemical classification

Electropositive (Metallic) Elements	Electronegative (Nonmetallic) Elements
All alkali metals (1a)	All halogens (7a)
All alkaline-earth metals (2a)	All members of the oxygen family (6a)
Aluminum	
Gallium, indium, thallium	Most members of the nitrogen family (5a)
Tin	
Lead, antimony, bismuth	Carbon
All transition elements	Silicon
Lanthanides and actinides	

Hydrogen is electropositive when contrasted with the electronegative elements, but it is electronegative when contrasted with the alkali elements and most alkaline-earth metals.

In the periodic chart, we find that the electronegative elements are located for the most part in the upper right-hand corner, and that every electronegative element is a representative element.

7.8 THE RELATIVE ELECTRON AFFINITY OF ATOMS

There are several major factors which affect the acceptance and donation of valence electrons by the various elements:

a. *The atomic radius (size of the atom).* Since the valence electrons are considered to be on the periphery of the atom, the larger the atom or the greater its radius, the farther the valence electrons are from the positively charged nucleus. The force between the nucleus and a valence electron is inversely proportional to the square of the distance between them. Therefore the larger the atomic radius the weaker the attractive forces exerted by the nucleus on the valence electrons. (See Appendix.)

b. *The electrons which reside between the nucleus and the valence electrons.* Excepting the element hydrogen, the valence electrons of all atoms are shielded from the nucleus by other electrons. Since all electrons are negatively charged, these inner electrons exert a repulsive force on the valence electrons. This repulsive force tends to counterbalance, at least partially, the attractive force exerted by the nucleus.

c. *The amount of positive charge on the nucleus (atomic number).* Since the nucleus is positively charged, the attractive force exerted by the nucleus on the valence electrons depends on the number of protons in the nucleus. Therefore the larger the atomic number the greater the attractive force exerted by the nucleus on the valence electrons.

Now that we have presented the major factors which affect the attraction or repulsion of valence electrons, it is possible to derive a few important generalizations. These statements apply mainly to the representative elements, and the periodic chart is used as a means of reference (see Fig. 6.6, p. 118).

The progressive change in the electropositive character of the representative elements in a given horizontal row appears to be explicable by considering factor **c**, since electron affinity (attraction for electrons) increases as the atomic number of the element increases. Factor **b** is not significant, since in all the elements in any given horizontal row the atoms have the same number of inner or shielding electrons between their nuclei and their valence electrons.

The electropositive elements are on the left side of the chart and the electronegative elements on the right. In any given horizontal row of representative elements, the alkali metal element is the most electropositive element, and the halogen the most electronegative. Elements midway between these two extremes are relatively weakly electropositive and relatively weakly electronegative.

Considering a specific vertical column of representative elements, as we proceed from the top of the chart to the bottom, the tendency to donate electrons increases progressively and the tendency to accept electrons decreases progressively. Therefore in the alkali metal family (Li to Cs) electron-donor tendency is greatest with cesium. In the halogen family (F to At), electron-acceptor tendency is greatest with fluorine, least with astatine. Of course, astatine has a stronger electron-donor tendency than fluorine. In the oxygen family (O to Po), oxygen is an active electron acceptor, but polonium is an extremely poor one. In the carbon family

(C to Pb), carbon and silicon are weakly electronegative elements, but tin and lead have so little electronegative character we may call them electropositive.

In a given family of representative elements, factors **a** and **b** seem to explain the progressive change in electron affinity of the elements with change in atomic number and atomic radius.

7.9   ELECTRON AFFINITY

If an electronically deficient uncharged atom, such as the fluorine atom, accepts an electron by complete transfer, a negative ion is produced.

$$|\underline{\overline{F}} \cdot \; + e^- \rightarrow |\underline{\overline{F}}|^-$$

The tendency exhibited by such a gaseous atom to accept an electron (the atom's electron affinity) depends on the structure of the product ion and on the energy level which the electron enters. If the product ion is isoelectronic with some inert gas atom, the atom's electron affinity is greatly enhanced. If the additional electron enters the second principal energy level, more energy is released than if it had entered the third or fourth principal energy level. Also, an electron that enters the second principal energy level resides closer to the nucleus, and hence is bound more strongly, than if it had entered a higher principal energy level.

The electron affinity of an atom also characterizes the strength of binding of the additional electron. Therefore the energy absorbed during process 1,

$$|\underline{\overline{F}}|^- \rightarrow |\underline{\overline{F}} \cdot \; + e^- \tag{1}$$

is identical to the energy evolved, or released, during process 2,

$$|\underline{\overline{F}} \cdot \; + e^- \rightarrow |\underline{\overline{F}}|^- \tag{2}$$

The amount of energy released in process 2 and absorbed in process 1 is called the *atom's electron affinity*. The values for a few atoms are listed in Table 7.2. The electron affinities of the alkali metal atoms are frequently assumed to be zero because the values are so small. The electron affinities are zero for the inert gases. Since the determination of electron affinities is difficult, accurate values are available for only a few elements.

TABLE 7.2   Electron affinity

Element	Electron Volts*	Kcal/mole
Fluorine	3.63	83.5
Chlorine	3.78	87.3
Bromine	3.54	82.0
Iodine	3.24	75.7
Hydrogen	0.75	17.8
Oxygen†	2.20	51.0
Sulfur†	2.24	55.0

* See Table 7.3.
† Values are for gain of $1e$/atom and one mole of e/mole.

In Section 7.11 we shall relate the electron affinities of the $7a$ atoms, halogens, to the ionization potentials of some other atoms to show that it is frequently possible to make predictions as to whether a specific chemical interaction between atoms yields an ionic or a covalent compound.   In Section 8.3 we shall also relate electron affinities to ionization potentials in an attempt to identify their relationship to the nature of a covalent bond.

7.10 ATOMIC IONIZATION POTENTIALS

Let us now describe briefly a physical method that may be used to correlate the chemical behavior of an element with its tendency to retain its valence electron(s).   The energy required to remove a valence electron from an atom, or to ionize an unexcited atom in its gaseous state, is a measure of the atom's inherent tendency to retain the valence electron.   Generally the term *ionization potential* identifies the energy, in electron volts (see p. 154), needed to ionize an uncharged, unexcited gaseous atom, thereby yielding a singly positive ion.

The ionization potential of cesium is 3.9 electron volts.   This is the energy absorbed in the process:

$$\text{Cs} \quad \rightarrow \quad \text{Cs}^+ \;+\; e^-$$

one unexcited   one ion   one electron
gaseous atom

Because all atoms except hydrogen contain two or more electrons, they have two or more ionization potentials.   For example, the first ionization potential of lithium is 5.37 electron volts; its second ionization potential (removal of the second electron) is 75.28 electron volts.

$$\text{Li} + 5.37 \text{ ev} \rightarrow \text{Li}^+ + e^- \text{ (per atom)}$$
$$\text{Li}^+ + 75.28 \text{ ev} \rightarrow \text{Li}^{++} + e^- \text{ (per ion)}$$

Since the removal of an electron from the positively charged lithium ion involves the separation of an electron from a positively charged particle instead of from an uncharged atom, the second ionization potential of lithium is much greater than the first. Also, the electron separated from the lithium ion resides in the $1s$ sub-

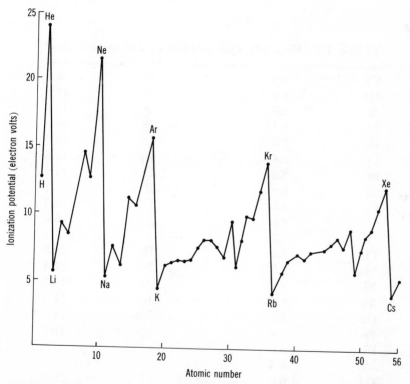

FIGURE 7.11 Energy, in electron volts, necessary to remove from the uncharged atom the first (least tightly bound) electron, plotted vs. the atomic number of the element. The alkali metal elements have the lowest ionization potentials; helium, neon, and fluorine have the highest ionization potentials.

group where it is paired with another electron. This electron is in an energy level lower than that in which lithium's valence electron resides. All three factors tend to increase the energy necessary to remove one electron from a lithium ion.

The first ionization potential of lithium is greater than the first ionization potential of cesium, mainly because the radius, 1.52 A, of the lithium atom is less than the radius, 2.62 A, of the cesium atom. Since lithium's valence electron is closer to an atomic nucleus than is cesium's, it is attracted more strongly to an atomic nucleus than is cesium's.

The first ionization potential of an atom is an individual characteristic because it is measured in the absence of any other element (see Fig. 7.11).

TABLE 7.3   First ionization potentials (in electron-volts)*

Cs	3.9	F	18.6
Rb	4.2	N	14.5
K	4.3	O	13.6
Na	5.1	H	13.5
Ba	5.2	Cl	13.0
Li	5.4	Br	11.8
Sr	5.6	C	11.2
Al	6.0	P	11.1
Ca	6.1	I	10.5
Cr	6.8	S	10.3
Sn	7.3	. . . .
Pb	7.4	He	24.5
Mg	7.6	Ne	21.5
Ni	7.6	Ar	15.7
Ag	7.6	Kr	14.0
Cu	7.7	Xe	12.1
Fe	7.9	Rn	10.7
Bi	8.0		
Sb	8.6		
Cd	9.0		
Zn	9.4		
Hg	10.4		

* An electron volt is the energy gained by an electron accelerated across a potential of one volt. $(3.8 \times 10^{-20}$ cal.) (All values are approximate.)

An element's ability to act as an electron donor is related in some way to its first ionization potential, but there seems to be no formal relationship.   An element's ability to act chemically as an electron donor must always be determined in the presence of some other chemical entity.   Therefore an element's ability as an electron donor is related to at least two factors: (1) the element's inherent tendency to donate its valence electron(s), and (2) the electron-acceptor ability of the other substance to which the element donates its valence electron(s).   We may assume generally, however, that if an element has a relatively small first ionization potential, it is classed among the active electron donors.   If an element has a relatively large first ionization potential, it is among the active electron acceptors.   Hydrogen and carbon are notable exceptions.

Table 7.3 lists the first ionization potentials of some of the more common elements.

7.11   A METHOD OF PREDICTING BOND TYPE

When two atoms X and Z interact chemically, the type of bond (ionic or covalent) that may be formed depends on the amount of energy required to remove an electron from the electron donor X and the amount of energy released (available) when the electron is accepted by Z.   If the over-all chemical interaction of the atoms to yield a product (at room temperature) releases more energy than that required to remove an electron from X, the product will be essentially ionic.   However, if the over-all chemical interaction releases less energy than that required to remove an electron from X the product will be essentially covalent.

The energy released during an ordinary chemical reaction is insufficient to remove an electron from a helium atom, a process that requires 570 kcal of energy per mole of atoms.   Hence He atoms are extremely reluctant electron donors.   The energy necessary to remove completely an electron from a hydrogen atom to yield a proton, H^+, is 315 kcal/mole of atoms.   Since this amount of energy is unavailable from ordinary chemical reactions, when hydrogen atoms react with electron-acceptor atoms the product is covalent.   The energy evolved during many chemical changes is sufficient to cause the complete removal of the lone valence electron from the sodium atom.   Therefore compounds of sodium are usually essentially ionic.   Since K, Rb, and Cs have smaller ionization energies than Na, compounds of these elements are primarily ionic. Because the ionization energy of lithium is greater than that of any other alkali metal, some compounds of lithium are more nearly covalent than those of the other 1a elements. Beryllium, Be, tends to form compounds that have covalent properties because the ionization energy of Be is even higher than that of lithium. Some ionization energies are listed in Table 7.4.

TABLE 7.4 Some ionization energies

Element	Ionization Energy (Kcal/mole)
Li	123.8
Na	120.0
K	99.7
Rb	95.9
Cs	89.4
H	315.0
I	240.8
Br	272.1
Cl	298.9
F	429.0

In the formation of a stable binary compound, the ionization energy of the electron-donor atom is usually greater than the electron affinity of the electron-acceptor atom. If the difference in the two energies is relatively small, say less than 50 kcal/mole, the deficiency is often supplied by the energy evolved during the formation of electrovalent bonds between the ions as they collectively create the crystal lattice of the ionic compound. If the deficiency is not available as the compound is formed, a covalent product is expected.

As an example, let us consider the case of sodium chloride and formulate a sort of balance sheet of the energies involved in the various processes. The equation for the over-all process is

$$Na(s) + \tfrac{1}{2}Cl_2(g) \rightarrow Na^+Cl^-(s)$$

in which the elements in their standard states at room temperature yield solid sodium chloride.

DEBITS:

Vaporization of solid Na   26.0 kcal/mole *absorbed*

$$Na(s) \rightarrow Na(g)$$

Dissociation of Cl_2 molecules   28.6 kcal/0.5 mole *absorbed*

$1/2\ Cl_2(g) \rightarrow Cl \cdot (g)$

Ionization of Na atoms   120.0 kcal/mole *absorbed*

$Na \cdot (g) \rightarrow Na^+(g) + e^-(g)$

    Total energy absorbed   174.6 kcal/mole

CREDITS:

Electron affinity of Cl   87.3 kcal/mole *evolved*

$Cl + e^- \rightarrow Cl^-$

Formation of crystal lattice   184.2 kcal/mole *evolved*
    (lattice energy)

$Na^+(g) + Cl^-(g) \rightarrow Na^+Cl^-(s)$

    Total energy available   271.5 kcal/mole

NET: $271.5 - 174.6 = 96.9$ kcal/mole

Therefore the reaction $Na(s) + \frac{1}{2}Cl_2(g) \rightarrow Na^+Cl^-(s)$ is exothermic and 96.9 kcal of energy is evolved per mole of Na^+Cl^- produced.

Although the formation of the ionic crystal lattice from its constituent gaseous ions is really much more theoretical than real, the energy released during the process is called the *lattice energy* of the ionic compound. It is usually expressed in kcal per molar weight of ionic compound. The lattice energy of a specific ionic compound may be determined indirectly by using what is called a *Born-Haber cycle*.

A typical Born-Haber cycle can be applied to sodium chloride, Na^+Cl^-. The steps in this cycle are identical to those identified on our balance sheet of energies (p. 156). It will be very helpful to refer to these values and their meaning.

$$
\begin{array}{ccc}
Na^+Cl^-(s) & \xleftarrow{\ +U\ } & Na^+(g) + Cl^-(g) \\
\downarrow{\scriptstyle -Q} & & {\scriptstyle -I}\uparrow \qquad {\scriptstyle +E}\uparrow \\
Na(s) + \frac{1}{2}Cl_2(g) & \xrightarrow[\ -S \quad -\frac{1}{2}D\ ]{} & Na(g) + Cl(g)
\end{array}
$$

The steps in the cycle are identified by letters, and the sign preceding the letter indicates whether the step is endothermic (a debit) or exothermic (a credit); positive signs indicate credits, negative signs debits.

U = lattice energy
I = ionization energy of $Na(g)$
E = electron affinity of $Cl \cdot (g)$
S = heat of vaporization of $Na(s)$
D = heat of dissociation of $Cl_2(g)$
Q = heat of formation of $Na^+Cl^-(s)$ from its elements

Since the series of different processes yields a complete cycle, the condition for the total change in energy for the cycle is zero. We can therefore formulate the expression for any alkali metal halide:

$$U - I + E - S - \tfrac{1}{2}D - Q = 0$$

To solve for U, if all other values are known:

$$U = I - E + S + \tfrac{1}{2}D + Q$$

To solve for E, if all other values are known:

$$E = I + S + \tfrac{1}{2}D + Q - U$$
(electron affinity of acceptor atom)

7.12 AN OUTLINE OF USEFUL GENERALIZATIONS

I. The alkali metal elements ($1a$).

    A. Whenever an elemental alkali metal reacts chemically with another substance to produce a stable compound, the alkali metal acts as an electron donor. Each alkali metal atom donates one electron, usually by complete transfer, thereby becoming a singly positive ion, M^+.

    B. All compounds that contain an alkali metal are ionic, and all are solid at room temperature. The alkali metal ion bears the name of the element to which it is related. Every alkali metal ion is isoelectronic with some inert gas atom, with some negatively charged monatomic halogen ion, and with some alkaline-earth metal ion. For example, Na^+ is isoelectronic with the Ne atom, the F^- ion, and the Mg^{++} ion.

II. The alkaline-earth metal elements ($2a$).

    A. Whenever an elemental alkaline-earth metal reacts chemically with another substance to produce a stable compound, the alkaline-earth metal acts as an electron donor. Each alkaline-earth metal atom donates two electrons, usually by complete transfer, thereby yielding a doubly positive ion, M^{++}.

B. Most of the compounds that contain an alkaline-earth metal ion are ionic, and all are solid at room temperature. The compounds of beryllium are usually more nearly covalent (less ionic) than those of calcium, strontium, and barium. Each alkaline-earth metal ion has an electronic configuration identical to some inert gas atom, with some negative monatomic halogen ion, and with some alkali metal ion. For example, Ba^{++} is isoelectronic with the Xe atom, the I^- ion, and the Cs^+ ion.

III. The boron family elements (3a).

A. Whenever an elemental member of the boron family reacts chemically with another substance to yield a stable compound, each 3a family atom usually donates three electrons.

B. Because the boron family ions are of $+3$ charge and are relatively tiny, they strongly attract negative ions so that most boron family compounds are more covalent than ionic.

IV. Hydrogen.

Whenever the element hydrogen reacts chemically with an electronegative element (right of "stairway"), each hydrogen atom donates by sharing its lone valence electron. The compounds produced are covalent. At room temperature several of these compounds are gaseous, some are liquid, and, except for a few hydrocarbons, none is solid. Although hydrogen acts as an electron donor if it reacts with an element to the right of the "stairway," it always acts as an electron acceptor when it reacts with a 1a or a 2a element. The singly negative hydride ion, H^-, is isoelectronic with the He atom, the Li^+ ion, and the Be^{++} ion. Alkali metal and alkaline-earth metal hydrides are ionic.

V. Fluorine.

A. Whenever elemental fluorine reacts chemically with another substance, each fluorine atom accepts one electron per atom. If the fluorine atom accepts an electron by complete transfer, the fluoride ion, F^-, produced is isoelectronic with the Ne atom, the oxide ion O^{--}, the Na^+

ion, and the Mg^{++} ion. All binary compounds of fluorine are called *fluorides*.

B. Fluorine's unusual reactivity is strikingly demonstrated by the recent preparation of stable compounds with some of the inert gases (family 8a). A few of these compounds are XeF_4, XeF_2, KrF_4, and $XeOF_3$.

VI. Oxygen.

A. Whenever elemental oxygen reacts chemically with another substance, except fluorine, the oxygen acts as an electron acceptor. Each oxygen atom accepts two electrons during the majority of the reactions. There are a few reactions during which oxygen atoms accept one electron per atom, thereby yielding compounds called *peroxides*.

B. All binary compounds of oxygen, except oxygen fluoride, OF_2, are either oxides, peroxides, or superoxides. The oxide ion is O^{--}, the peroxide ion is O_2^{--}, and the superoxide ion is O_2^{-} (see p. 263). Elements of groups 1a and 2a yield essentially ionic oxides and peroxides. The oxides of the elements to the right of the "stairway" are always covalent.

VII. Chlorine, bromine, and iodine.

A. Whenever the elemental form of one of these halogens reacts with an element to the left of the "stairway," the halogen always accepts one electron per atom. Each monatomic halogen (halide) ion is isoelectronic with some inert gas atom, with some alkali metal ion, and with some alkaline-earth metal ion.

B. Halogens may interact with each other to yield interhalogen compounds, such as ICl (called iodine chloride). Bromine chloride is BrCl; iodine bromide is IBr.

VIII. Sulfur.

Whenever sulfur reacts chemically with an element to the left of the "stairway," each sulfur atom accepts two electrons. The monatomic sulfide ion, S^{--}, is isoelectronic with the Ar atom, the chloride ion Cl^{-}, the K^{+} ion, and the Ca^{++} ion.

IX. Nitrogen.

Whenever elemental nitrogen reacts with an active electron donor (an alkali metal [1a] or magnesium or calcium), each nitrogen atom accepts three electrons. The binary compounds so produced are called *nitrides* because they consist, in part, of the nitride ion, N^{3-}. This nitride ion is isoelectronic with the Ne atom, the O^{--} ion, the F^- ion, the Na^+ ion, and the Mg^{++} ion.

Problems

1. The atoms of element 38 react with those of element 53 to yield a stable compound. What is the correct formula of the compound?

2. Atoms of element 52 react with those of element 17 to yield a stable compound. What is the correct formula of the compound?

3. A group of compounds is: CsH, AsH_3, BrCl, SO_2, SrS, MgI_2, CBr_4, Mg_3N_2, K_3FO_4, $LiClO_4$. (a) Which of these are essentially ionic? (b) Which are essentially covalent?

4. Which of the compounds listed in Problem 3 are definitely solid at room temperature?

5. List four entities that are isoelectronic with S^{--}.

6. Indicate the symbols of two different monatomic negative ions that are isoelectronic with the potassium ion, K^+.

7. Indicate the formulas of two completely different ionic compounds whose constituent ions are isoelectronic. (Be sure that the compounds have no ions in common and that all ions mentioned are isoelectronic.)

8. Of the charged molecules, ClO_3^-, BrO_3^-, NO_3^-, CO_3^{--}, SeO_3^{--}, SO_3^{--}, AsO_3^{3-}, PO_3^{3-}, which can be placed in groups of molecules such that each molecule is isoelectronic with every other molecule in the group?

9. Identify by name and symbol all probable entities that are monatomic and have 10 extranuclear electrons.

10. According to one of the accepted definitions of a molecule (see p. 6), do molecules exist in molten sodium chloride?

11. Interpret the fact that the sodium ion, Na^+, is apparently smaller than the sodium atom, whereas the fluoride ion, F^-, seems to be larger than the fluorine atom.

12. Which atomic kernels seem to be isoelectronic with the argon atom?

13. Write the most probable formula of the binary compound composed of the two elements in each of the following pairs:

(a) hydrogen and selenium
(b) hydrogen and arsenic
(c) strontium and chlorine
(d) magnesium and sulfur
(e) potassium and iodine

(f) cesium and tellurium
(g) lithium and selenium
(h) beryllium and bromine
(i) aluminum and sulfur
(j) magnesium and nitrogen

14. Which element in each of the following pairs is the better electron donor?

(a) carbon, tin
(b) magnesium, rubidium
(c) sodium, cesium
(d) iodine, chlorine
(e) nitrogen, fluorine

(f) sulfur, tellurium
(g) aluminum, indium
(h) phosphorus, chlorine
(i) carbon, nitrogen
(j) phosphorus, bismuth

15. Which element in each of the following pairs is the better electron acceptor?

(a) selenium, bromine
(b) phosphorus, arsenic
(c) silicon, chlorine
(d) fluorine, nitrogen
(e) neon, fluorine

(f) iodine, astatine
(g) carbon, silicon
(h) sulfur, tellurium
(i) arsenic, selenium
(j) carbon, nitrogen

16. What uncharged diatomic molecule is isoelectronic with the peroxide ion, O_2^{--}?

17. (a) Which of the compounds listed in Problem 13 are essentially ionic?   (b) Which are essentially covalent?

8

CHEMICAL BONDING

8.1 A PERSPECTIVE

Whenever chemical compounds are produced by chemical combination of elemental forms of matter, the electronic configurations of the atoms are altered. Since electrons are defined physical entities, every chemical phenomenon has distinct physical overtones. The acceptance and donation of electrons by the elements are physical phenomena apparently occurring in only two different ways—sharing and complete transfer.

These phenomena yield two main types of structural architecture of compound substances. One, the result of electron sharing, is exhibited by the covalent compounds; the other, the result of complete transfer of electrons, is exhibited by the ionic compounds. In many compounds these two structural types overlap; that is, both ionic and covalent architecture are found in a given compound.

AND ARCHITECTURE

In all ionic compounds the chemically individual entities are charged particles or ions. Every ionic compound contains two or more different ions, and the net charge of the positive ions is equal to that of the negative ions. Because of strong interionic attractive forces, the ions arrange themselves in space to form an orderly pattern. Interionic repulsive forces are also significant. (See Fig. 8.1.)

In most covalent compounds the major chemically definitive entities are uncharged particles composed of aggregates of atoms, the kernels of which are held together by covalent bonds (see Fig. 8.2). If the covalent compound is liquid or solid, the aggregate of molecules is held together by intermolecular forces, usually much weaker than interionic forces which hold together an ionic compound in its solid state.

Now that we recognize the general structural differences between ionic and covalent compounds, let us note three important generalizations. In these statements a pressure of 1 atmosphere is assumed.

a. Generally, all pure ionic compounds are solids at room temperature. Ionic compounds are solid at room temperature because the average kinetic energy of the ions is insufficient to counterbalance the strong interionic attractive forces.

b. Generally, all pure compounds that exist either in the gaseous or liquid state at room temperature are covalent compounds. In other words, at room temperature all pure gaseous and all pure liquid compounds are covalent compounds. Many covalent compounds are solids at room temperature. The relatively weak intermolecular attractive forces in some covalent compounds allow them to be gaseous at room temperature.

c. When we consider the liquid states of various covalent and ionic compounds, we find that one of their most striking differences, other than temperature, is their behavior in an electrical circuit. In their liquid (molten) state, all ionic compounds are good electrical conductors. Most covalent compounds in their liquid states are extremely poor electrical conductors, if they conduct at all. Ionic compounds in their molten state contain mobile ions; covalent compounds contain very few, if any, ions in their liquid state. It seems logical to suspect that mobile ions can assist in the transport of an electrical current.

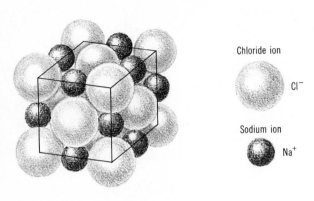

Chloride ion

Cl^-

Sodium ion

Na^+

FIGURE 8.1 Schematic representation of a portion of a sodium chloride crystal, showing the face-centered cubic arrangement of the crystal lattice. In the interior of a sodium chloride crystal, each chloride ion is surrounded by six sodium ions, and each sodium ion is surrounded by six chloride ions. The common crystal lattices of all the alkali metal halides, except cesium chloride, bromide, and iodide, are identical to that of sodium chloride.

8.2 CHEMICAL PROPERTIES

Since a pure covalent compound consists essentially of identical molecules, a specific chemical behavior of a covalent compound

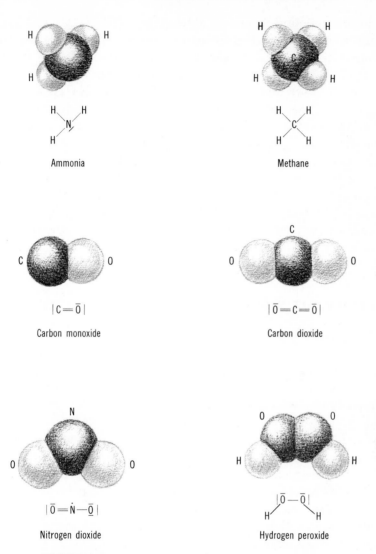

Ammonia

Methane

$|C{=}\bar{O}|$

Carbon monoxide

$|\bar{O}{=}C{=}\bar{O}|$

Carbon dioxide

$|\bar{O}{=}\dot{N}{-}\underline{\bar{O}}|$

Nitrogen dioxide

$\underset{H}{|\bar{O}}{-}\underset{H}{\bar{O}|}$

Hydrogen peroxide

FIGURE 8.2 Some common covalent molecules.

seems to be a property of all the constituent molecules. This general chemical behavior is not as simple in the case of ionic compounds.

Since a pure ionic compound consists of at least two chemically and physically different charged particles, a specific chemical behavior of an ionic compound very often is a property of only one of the constituent ions. We should be prepared to expect this since the ionic compound consists of at least two different types of entities. Many of the chemical properties of the compounds of the alkali metal elements in aqueous solution are properties solely of the negative ions which accompany the alkali metal ions.

Let us take sodium hydrogen carbonate, $Na^+HCO_3^-$, as an example. If this compound is heated, water and carbon dioxide are evolved and sodium carbonate, $(Na^+)_2CO_3^{--}$, remains. During the pyrolysis (decomposition by heating) apparently nothing happens to the sodium ions. This decomposition of hydrogen carbonate ion is not, therefore, strictly a property of the entire compound. Also, if sodium hydrogen carbonate is added to vinegar, carbon dioxide is evolved. In this case only the negative ions undergo chemical change. Here again the behavior of the compound is solely that of the negative ion, or only part of the compound.

8.3 COVALENT BONDS

According to a concept introduced in the previous chapter, a pair of electrons shared by two atomic kernels acts as a means of bonding together the kernels in question. Because the shared electrons are paired, they have opposed (nonparallel) spins and each pair fills completely some atomic orbital. The clouds of a given pair of bonding electrons overlap as the bond forms, and this overlapping creates a maximum electron density between the atomic kernels. This more dense electron cloud between the kernels apparently exerts an electrostatic attraction on the flanking atomic nuclei.

In the context of wave mechanics, the covalent bond is a result of overlapping of the wave functions of two electrons that have opposed spins. Bonding seems to occur to yield maximum overlapping of wave functions. In other words, the greater the overlap of the wave functions of the participating electrons, the stronger the bond. The electrons in a given bonding pair tend to overlap with each other and not with electrons of other atoms. Therefore an electron in a p orbital will tend to participate in bond formation so that the greatest concentration of electrons is in the p orbital. Such a bond will be directional, just as is the spatial orientation of the p orbital. The directional character of the covalent bonds in water and in ammonia was described in Section 7.5. We shall extend these descriptions in Section 8.11.

A specific covalent bond in a covalent entity can always be

identified simply as a shared pair of electrons. The exact nature of a covalent bond often has nothing whatsoever to do with its mode of formation or with what might be called its past history. There are thousands of covalent entities whose covalent bonds may be formed in at least two different ways.

To illustrate this point, let us consider the covalent bond in a hydrogen bromide molecule, H—Br. There are three ways in which this covalent bond can be formed to yield electronically identical hydrogen bromide molecules. Therefore it is evident that the mode of formation, or past history, of the covalent bond is an irrelevant factor in a consideration of the structure of an HBr molecule.

1.
$$H \cdot + \cdot \overline{Br|} \rightarrow H - \overline{Br|}$$

Each atom brings one electron to form the shared pair.

2.
$$H^+ + \left[\overline{Br|} \right]^- \rightarrow H - \overline{Br|}$$

proton   bromide
            ion

One unshared pair of the Br⁻ becomes the shared pair.

3.
$$H|^- + \left[\overline{Br|} \right]^+ \rightarrow H - \overline{Br|}$$

hydride   brominium
ion   ion

The unshared pair of the $H|^-$ becomes the shared pair.

Methods 1 and 2 are common means of producing hydrogen bromide. Although method 3 is rather exotic, the hydride ion is known and the brominium ion, or bromine(I) ion, is considered to be either free or incipient in many systems containing elemental bromine.

This discussion of the formation of a covalent bond can be extended to many thousands of examples. But before we go further into a discussion of chemical bonding, we should pause to reflect on the fact that the concept of a covalent bond is simply a convenient device to assist us in interpreting and identifying a specific kind of intramolecular force. The real problem arises the moment we try to identify or depict the bond.

In regard to the reality of a covalent bond, we must admit that it is, in essence, similar to the bond between two close friends or between a mother and her child. The bonds that hold together a happy family are just as real as those that hold together a stable covalent molecule.

According to our concept of molecular structure, the atomic kernels of the constituent atoms are held together by shared pairs of electrons or covalent bonds. In the case of a "pure" covalent bond, the pair of electrons is shared equally by the two atomic kernels. Consequently, no electric charge separation exists at this type of covalent bonding.

A covalent bond between identical atomic kernels is called a *nonpolar bond* because there is only a slight tendency for electrical charge separation, or creation of poles. In a sense the kernels have no tendency to act as ions. The pair of electrons is shared equally in the true nonpolar bond. If two different atomic kernels at a covalent bond have nearly equal tendencies to attract the shared pair, the bond is nonpolar. An example of this type is the carbon-sulfur bond, C—S.

Each covalent bond in molecules such as hydrogen (H_2), fluorine (F_2), chlorine (Cl_2), bromine (Br_2), iodine (I_2), sulfur (S_8), phosphorus (P_4), and diamond (C_n) is essentially nonpolar (see Sec. 7.4).

A covalent bond in which the pair of electrons is shared unequally is called a *polar bond*. In this type of bond there is an appreciable electrical charge separation. One atomic kernel pulls the electron pair closer toward it, thereby creating an electrical unbalance. The greater the inequity of sharing, the greater the polarity. The polar bond is said to have ionic-bond character.

Because of the charge separation at the bond site, each atom gains an incipient ionic status. The bond in the hydrogen fluoride molecule, H—F, is quite polar because the fluorine kernel has a marked tendency to attract the electron pair to it.

The polarity, or ionic-bond character, of a covalent bond depends on the nature of the atomic kernels that share the pair of electrons. The tendency shown at a covalent bond by an element's atomic kernel to attract the shared pair of electrons is said to be a measure of the electronegativity of the element. Fluorine has, according to the concept of Linus Pauling, the greatest electronegativity. This means that a fluorine kernel at a

NONPOLAR BONDS		POLAR BONDS	
Between identical kernels		Between nonidentical kernels (Z more electronegative than X)	
$X:X$	$X-X$		
Between different kernels		$X:Z$	$X^{\oplus}-Z^{\ominus}$
$X:T$	$X-T$	$X^{\delta+}-Z^{\delta-}$	
H—H	C—S	$C^{\delta+}-O^{\delta-}$	$H^{\oplus}-F^{\ominus}$
F—F	P—H	$Cl^{\delta-}-P^{\delta+}$	$N^{\ominus}-H^{\oplus}$

FIGURE 8.3 Various representations of polar and nonpolar covalent bonds.

covalent bond shows the strongest tendency to attract toward it the shared pair of electrons. In the relative electronegativity scale of the elements as conceived by Pauling, fluorine is assigned the highest value, 4.0. The electronegativities of some other elements are given in Table 8.1 (p. 173).

Pauling's concept of electronegativity is based on the notion that the amount of ionic-bond character in a specific covalent bond is closely related to the bond's energy. The greater the bond energy, the greater the ionic-bond character and the greater the polarity of the bond. In this context the bond energy of a covalent bond is the energy, in kcal/mole, required to dissociate thermally one mole of the bonds to yield uncharged atoms. This type of bond cleavage is often called *homolytic fission*.

$$X \overset{\cdot\cdot}{\underset{\cdot\cdot}{\diagup}} T + \Delta \rightarrow X\cdot + \cdot T$$

Let us start with the assumption that the expected bond energy of the nonpolar bond $X—T$ between the kernels X and T is the arithmetic mean of the bond energies of the $X—X$ bond and the $T—T$ bond.

(Bond energy of $X—X$ + Bond energy of $T—T$) ÷ 2

$$= \text{Bond energy of } X—T$$

(Pauling noticed that use of a geometric mean yielded more consistent values for the expected bond energies. The geometric mean of the bond energies of the $X—X$ and $T—T$ bonds is the square root of the product of the bond energies.)

Let us now apply this idea to a specific bond, such as that in the hydrogen fluoride molecule. If the H—F bond were nonpolar, the expected bond energy is

(Bond energy of H—H bond + Bond energy of F—F bond) ÷ 2

$$= \text{Bond energy of H—F bond}$$

(104.2 kcal/mole + 36.6 kcal/mole) ÷ 2 = 70.4 kcal/mole

However, the actual bond energy of the H—F bond is 134.6 kcal/mole, not the arithmetic mean, 70.4 kcal/mole. A logical conclusion is that the "extra" bond energy, 64.2 kcal/mole, is due to the ionic-bond character of the H—F bond. The thermal homolytic dissociation of the H—F bond requires more energy than would be expected were the bond nonpolar, because the maximum electron concentration between the atomic kernels is on the average closer to the F kernel than to the H kernel.

$$H \;\; \overline{\underline{F}}| \rightarrow H \cdot \; + \; \cdot \overline{\underline{F}}|$$

This requires 134.6 kcal/mole, whereas the nonpolar bond, if it existed,

$$H \;\; \overline{\underline{F}}| \rightarrow H \cdot \; + \; \cdot \overline{\underline{F}}|$$

would be expected to require only 70.4 kcal/mole.

The "extra" bond energies, in kcal/mole, due to ionic-bond character in the hydrogen halides are: H—F, 64.2; H—Cl, 22.1; H—Br, 12.3; H—I, 1.2. Since these values indicate a trend exactly as do the electronegativity values of the halogens (see Table 8.1), we can see evidence for the relationship between electronegativity differences and amount of ionic-bond character.

Since the kernel of each halogen atom has a +7 charge, you may wonder why the electronegativities of the halogens decrease progressively from fluorine to iodine. The fluorine kernel's charge density is greater than that of any other halogen atom's kernel; hence its tendency to pull toward it a shared pair of electrons is greater than that of any other halogen kernel.

Although the fluorine kernel is approximately the same size as the oxygen kernel, the fluorine kernel's +7 charge is greater than the oxygen kernel's +6 charge. Therefore the fluorine kernel's greater charge density yields a stronger tendency to pull to it a shared pair of electrons.

The electronegativity of hydrogen is 2.1, whereas that of tellurium is 2.2. Although the charge of the hydrogen kernel is only +1 in contrast to the tellurium kernel's +6, the tiny size of the H kernel evidently yields a charge density comparable to that of the much larger Te kernel.

R. S. Mulliken reported that electronegativity values can be related to an "average" of the ionization energy and electron affinity of the element (see Sec. 7.11). In the case of fluorine, for instance, the sum of the ionization energy plus the electron affinity divided by 125 yields a value of 3.9. This value agrees well with 4.0, the value obtained by using the bond energy approach. From Mulliken's approach, electronegativity values of some other elements are: Cl, 3.10; Br, 2.86; I, 2.54; H, 2.66; Li, 1.01; Na, 0.96. Since electron affinity values are uncertain, any comparison with values obtained by Pauling should be temperate.

There are several means of estimating the percentage of ionic character of a specific covalent bond by using the difference in the electronegativities of the elements in question. An equation that yields a fair estimation is

$$[0.16 \text{ (diff)} + 0.035 \text{ (diff)}^2] \times 100 = \% \text{ ionic character}$$

where diff is the difference in the electronegativities of the elements in question (larger − smaller). For the C—F bond, diff = 4.0 − 2.5 = 1.5.

$$[(0.16)(1.5) + (0.035)(2.3)] \times 100 = 32\% \text{ ionic character}$$

A covalent bond that involves atomic kernels of two elements having appreciably different electronegativities is a polar bond. The greater the difference in electronegativities, the greater the polarity and ionic-bond character. Generally, if the difference in the electronegativities of the two elements is 1.7, the bond is said to have 50 per cent ionic-bond character. If the difference is greater than 1.7, the bond is distinctly polar and has much ionic character. If the difference is less than 1.7, the bond is essentially covalent.

Inspection of Table 8.1 reveals the fact that in the compound cesium fluoride, Cs^+F^-, the bonds have minimum covalent character and maximum ionic character. In other words, of all ions the ions in cesium fluoride have the strongest tendency to maintain their ionic character. The bonds between these ions exhibit maximum polarity. The other alkali metal halides are usually considered more ionic than covalent.

TABLE 8.1   Electronegativity values of elements

H					
2.1					
Li	Be	C	N	O	F
1.0	1.5	2.5	3.0	3.5	4.0
Na	Mg	Si	P	S	Cl
0.9	1.2	1.8	2.1	2.5	3.0
K	Ca	Ge	As	Se	Br
0.8	1.0	1.7	2.0	2.4	2.8
Cs	Ba			Te	I
0.7	0.9			2.2	2.5

A binary compound consisting of a strongly electropositive element and a strongly electronegative one is a substance in which charge separation is evident in the highest degree. Hence ionic forces are the major structural bonds.   A binary compound derived from the combination of two electronegative elements is usually distinctly covalent.   A weakly electronegative element and a weakly electropositive one will usually yield a covalent molecule.

We must realize that every covalent bond has some ionic character, and that every ionic bond in an ionic compound has some covalent character.

8.4   IONIC (ELECTROVALENT) BONDS

Whenever we consider an ionic compound, we must recall continually that any pure sample of it consists of at least two different charged molecules.   In solid and in molten sodium chloride, for instance, we are unable to identify any sodium chloride molecules. However, sodium chloride is molecular in the sense that it consists of molecules of Na^+ and of Cl^-.   Therefore one mole of Na^+Cl^- consists of one mole of sodium ions and one mole of chloride ions. The molar weight of sodium chloride is the sum of the masses of the moles of the constituent ions, as is the molar weight of any ionic compound.   One mole of Na^+ has a mass of 23 g, and one mole of Cl^- has a mass of 35.5 g.   The molar weight of Na^+Cl^- is therefore 58.5 g.

We have mentioned previously that the ions of an ionic compound at room temperature are arranged spatially to yield an orderly crystal lattice.   The question as to what sort of bonds exist between the ions in the crystal is easily answered if we conclude simply that the bonds are electrostatic attractions and repulsions. Here we shall attempt a simplified interpretation.

We realize that, regardless of ionic charge, the atomic nuclei of two ions repel each other at short distances.   The electron clouds of two ions also repel each other regardless of ionic charge.   We therefore expect that ions of opposite charge will not be drawn very close together, although they are attracted to each other.   Since ions of identical charge are always mixed with ions of opposite charge, repulsive forces between ions of identical charge exist in the crystal.   The net result in the crystal lattice is a balance of attractive and repulsive forces.

The attractive force, electrostatic in character, between two separate ions of opposite charge is inversely proportional to the square of the distance apart.   This attractive force may be called an ionic (electrovalent) bond, but care must be used in judging the significance of the term.

If we consider the sodium chloride crystal (see p. 166), we notice that each sodium ion within the crystal lattice is surrounded by six chloride ions, each of which in turn is surrounded by six sodium ions.   Any consideration of bonding yields the obvious conclusion that each Na^+ inside the crystal is bonded equally to six Cl^-, and each Cl^- is bound equally to six Na^+.   Because no Na^+ is bonded specifically to a given Cl^-, there is no specific direction in which a given Na^+ attracts a given Cl^-.   If we use the concept of chemical bonding, we can state that the ligancy of each ion is six in the Na^+Cl^- lattice.   The term *ligancy* is used to identify extent of apparent bonding, the ligancy of a given ion being the number of apparent bonds to other entities.

Since cesium chloride, Cs^+Cl^-, forms a body-centered cubic lattice (see Fig. 8.4), it is evident that a given Cs^+ is bonded equally

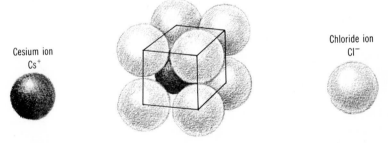

Cesium ion
Cs^+

Chloride ion
Cl^-

FIGURE 8.4 Schematic representation of a portion of a cesium chloride crystal, showing the body-centered cubic arrangement of the crystal lattice.   In a cesium chloride crystal, each cesium ion is surrounded by eight chloride ions.   Cesium bromide and cesium iodide have lattices identical to that of cesium chloride.

to eight chloride ions.   Each chloride ion is bonded equally to eight cesium ions.   Therefore the ligancy of the ions is eight in the cesium chloride lattice.

The major difference between ionic and covalent bonds is in their apparent utility.   The ionic bonds in ionic compounds are intermolecular attractive forces which hold together aggregates, or communities, of molecules.   The intramolecular forces (covalent bonds) hold together the atomic kernels of individual molecules.

Every ion in every ionic crystal is bonded directly to several other ions, but every atom in a covalent entity is not bonded directly to several other atoms. For example, each Na^+ and each Cl^- in solid Na^+Cl^- is bonded directly to six other ions, but in carbon tetrachloride, CCl_4, each chlorine kernel is bonded directly to only one carbon kernel.

The intermolecular forces in ionic compounds are between charged molecules, whereas those in covalent compounds are between uncharged molecules. Electrostatic forces between uncharged molecules are always weaker than those between charged molecules, or ions. To melt a solid, enough energy must be available to counterbalance the intermolecular attractive forces and thereby to yield a fluid system of mobile entities. To boil a liquid, enough energy must be available to overcome the intermolecular attractive forces to allow the molecules to escape from the liquid and create bubbles of the gaseous phase in the liquid. The melting and boiling points of pure ionic compounds are always therefore much higher than those of covalent compounds of comparable molar weight. The melting point of lithium fluoride (mol wt, 26 g) is 870°C, whereas that of hydrogen chloride (mol wt, 36.5 g) is only −111°C. The boiling point of lithium fluoride is 1670°C, that of hydrogen chloride −85°C. (See Table 8.2 to make further contrasts.)

TABLE 8.2 Melting and normal boiling points, in °C, of some alkali metal halides

Alkali Metal	Fluoride		Chloride		Iodide	
	Mp	Bp	Mp	Bp	Mp	Bp
Lithium	870	1670	614	1360	446	1190
Sodium	992	—	800	1413	651	1300
Potassium	880	1500	790	1500	723	1330
Cesium	683	1250	646	1290	621	1280
. . . .						
Hydrogen	−83	+19.4	−111	−85	−51	−36
Phosphorus tri-	−160	−95	−112	+76	+61	decomp.

We mentioned the concept of lattice energy in Section 7.11 (p. 157). The lattice energy of a solid ionic compound is the amount of energy released, in kcal per mole, when the gaseous ions of one mole of the compound form the crystal lattice. This energy is considerable in certain cases, and these values indicate that the more bonds that specific molecules can form and the lower the energy state to which they fall, the greater the amount of energy released. The multiplicity of bonding in ionic crystals is undoubtedly responsible for their unusual thermal stability. The

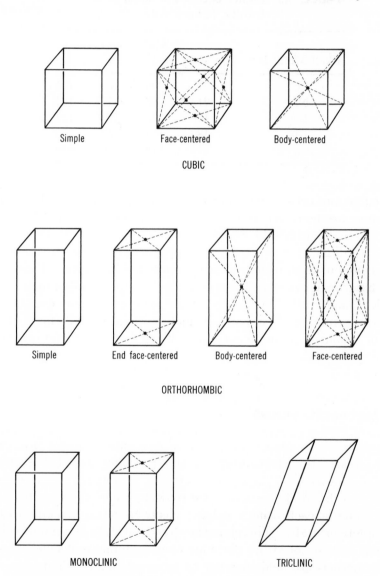

| Simple | Face-centered | Body-centered |

CUBIC

| Simple | End face-centered | Body-centered | Face-centered |

ORTHORHOMBIC

MONOCLINIC   TRICLINIC

FIGURE 8.5 Diagrams of some types of crystal lattice unit cells.

lattice energies of the alkali metal halides are given in Table 8.3.

The stability of a specific crystal lattice is intimately related to its lattice energy, but it is also dependent on the spatial arrangement of the ions. The alkali metal halides usually yield lattices

TABLE 8.3   Lattice energies of alkali metal halides, in kcal/mole

| Alkali Metal Ion | Halide Ions | | | |
	F^-	Cl^-	Br^-	I^-
Li^+	240	200	189	174
Na^+	213	183	175	164
K^+	190	165	160	151
Rb^+	182	161	154	145
Cs^+	174	152	146	139

with cubic unit cells. Some of these are face-centered (see Fig. 8.1), and some are body-centered (see Fig. 8.4). Other kinds of crystal lattices are diagramed in Fig. 8.5.

At ordinary temperatures the oppositely charged ions of some ionic compounds show a tendency to produce ion pairs. These ion pairs have no net electrical charge and behave physically much as do covalent molecules. Generally, if an ionic compound contains a significant number of ion pairs, its melting point is much lower than that of an ionic compound of comparable molar weight that contains few or no ion pairs.

8.5   METALLIC BONDS

In Section 7.7 we placed the chemical elements generally into two main classes: the electronegative (nonmetallic) and the electropositive (metallic). Since the atoms of a nonmetallic element, relative to the inert gases, are electronically deficient, they tend to share some of each other's valence electrons in an attempt to fill incomplete orbitals. Therefore the elemental state of a nonmetallic element consists of either diatomic or polyatomic molecules whose atomic kernels are held together by covalent bonds. This general picture is quite different in the case of the metallic elements.

Since the atoms of a metallic element have, relative to the inert gases, a superfluity of electrons, they have little tendency to form covalent bonds with each other. Each atomic kernel in the elemental state of a metal is held or bonded to many other kernels by many unlocalized electrons. The atomic kernels seem to be imbedded in a mobile "sea" of loosely held valence electrons. In a sense, the metallic bond is polyelectronic and multidirectional, whereas the covalent bond is bielectronic and unidirectional.

The atoms of a pure metal tend to aggregate in the crystal lattice to form the most compact packing possible. In the close-packed lattices each atomic kernel is surrounded by several of its nearest neighbors. The atoms are essentially spherical so that the metallic crystals are either body-centered cubic (each kernel with 8 nearest neighbors), face-centered cubic (12 nearest neighbors), or close-packed hexagonal (12 nearest neighbors). The metal atoms seem to pack as compactly as possible, just as golf balls or any ordinary spheres can be packed. Body-centered cubic and face-centered cubic lattices are shown in Fig. 8.5; a close-packed hexagonal is shown in Fig. 8.6.

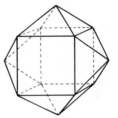

FIGURE 8.6 Diagram of a close-packed hexagonal lattice unit cell.

The forces that hold together a metallic lattice are, as we mentioned previously, neither ionic nor covalent. If we consider metallic copper, whose valence electron structure is $3d^{10}4s^1$, we discover that it yields a face-centered cubic lattice. Apparently the lone unpaired valence electron of a given copper atom is shared equally with 12 other copper atoms, so that each atom actually shares $\frac{1}{12}$ of an electron with each of its nearest neighbors. Since each copper atom donates the equivalent of $\frac{1}{12}$ of an electron to each of the other atoms, the equivalent of $\frac{2}{12}$, or $\frac{1}{6}$, of an electron acts as a bond between nearest neighbors.

Since the atoms in metallic cadmium are arranged in the close-packed hexagonal system, each cadmium atom has 12 nearest neighbors.   Since each cadmium atom has two valence electrons, the equivalent of $\frac{1}{6}$ of an electron is donated by each cadmium atom to each of its nearest neighbors.   Therefore the equivalent of $\frac{2}{6}$, or $\frac{1}{3}$, of an electron acts as a bond between two nearest neighbors.

As we review the nature of metallic bonds, we might expect that the bonds in a monovalent metal are weaker than those in a bivalent metal.   Perhaps this is why each alkali metal is much softer and has a lower melting point than its closest alkaline-earth metal neighbor.

Although the so-called electron-sea model that we presented earlier is an attractive interpretation of metallic structure, it is considered by many to be a simple-minded approach to the actual picture.   It seems adequate, however, for most elementary approaches to the structure of metals.

The loosely held, unlocalized electrons in a metal make electronic conductance possible.   The conduction of electricity and the reflection of incident light, giving the metals their *luster*, are obvious manifestations of the unique electronic structures of the metals. Metals are ductile and malleable because of the mobility of the valence electrons.   As old bonds break, new ones of identical type are formed.

The alkali metals have only one valence electron per atomic kernel.   These metals are relatively soft and have low melting points.   In some other metals the bonding is much stronger than in the alkali metals, and this is manifested by high melting points and appreciable hardness.

The formation of an alloy by mixing two or more metals often yields a solid solution.   The atomic kernels of the different metals intermingle in the common mobile sea of valence electrons.   The structure of many alloys is so complicated that a simple description is impossible.   The compositions of some common alloys are given on page A-2.

8.6   COVALENCY OF AN ELEMENT

The covalency of an element in a specific covalent entity is the number of pairs of electrons that are apparently shared by an atomic kernel of the element.   The covalency of an element may vary considerably, depending on the nature of the covalent molecule. In the hydroxide (hydroxyl) ion, O—H$^-$, the covalency of oxygen is 1; in water, HOH, it is 2; in the oxonium ion, H_3O^+, it is 3.   The most common covalences of some of the familiar elements in their uncharged compounds are: fluorine, 1; oxygen, 2; hydrogen, 1; nitrogen, 3; carbon, 4.   The maximum covalency of hydrogen is 1; of nitrogen, 4; of carbon, 4; of fluorine, 1; of oxygen, 4.

An electronic structure written to represent a covalent compound should indicate all of the valence electrons of the constituent atoms.   Nonvalence electrons are not represented.   The number of shared pairs of electrons used in writing electronic formulas is, in part, dictated by the knowledge of the covalency of the elements involved.   If we have some knowledge about these covalences, it will be much easier to write electronic formulations.

If the covalency of a specific element in an uncharged compound is increased by the addition of a positive ion, say a H^+, the resultant ion is always called an *-onium ion*.   Some examples in which the covalency of the central atomic kernel increases from 3 to 4 are:

$$NH_3 + H^+ \rightarrow \ NH_4^+$$
ammonia   ammonium
                             ion

$$PH_3 + H^+ \rightarrow \ PH_4^+$$
phosphine   phosphonium
                             ion

$$C_2H_4 + H^+ \rightarrow \ C_2H_5^+$$
ethene   ethyl
                             carbonium
                             ion

Some examples in which a covalency changes from 2 to 3 are

$$(CH_3)_2S + CH_3^+ \rightarrow \ (CH_3)_3S^+$$
dimethyl sulfide   trimethyl sulfonium ion

$$H_2O + H^+ \rightarrow \ H_3O^+$$
                             oxonium ion

$$(C_2H_5)_2O + H^+ \rightarrow \ (C_2H_5)_2OH^+$$
diethyl oxide   diethyloxonium ion

Below are some electronic structures of common compounds, under which are the covalences of the constituent elements.

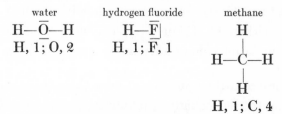

water   hydrogen fluoride   methane

H—$\overline{\text{O}}$—H   H—$\overline{\text{F}}$| H
H, 1; O, 2   H, 1; F, 1 |
                                  H—C—H
                                     |
                                     H
                             H, 1; C, 4

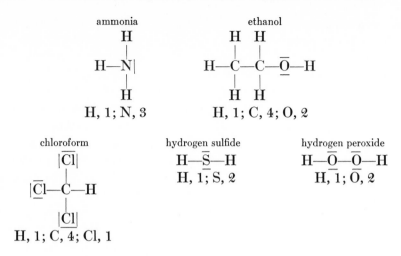

ammonia

H
|
H—N|
|
H

H, 1; N, 3

ethanol

H H
| |
H—C—C—Ō—H
| |
H H

H, 1; C, 4; O, 2

chloroform

|C̄l|
|
|C̄l—C—H
|
|C̄l|

H, 1; C, 4; Cl, 1

hydrogen sulfide

H—S̄—H

H, 1; S, 2

hydrogen peroxide

H—Ō—Ō—H

H, 1; O, 2

8.7 UNLOCALIZED ELECTRON PAIRS

Whenever we write a specific electronic structure for a covalent compound, we usually localize the electrons in pairs. We also make certain that the appropriate pairs are placed between the atomic kernels to represent covalent bonds. We keep in mind the probable covalency of each constituent element. A single electronic structure implies that the bonding electrons are localized. This is often misleading because in many covalent compounds some pairs of electrons cannot be localized to yield a logical representation. The single formula therefore is often only one of two or more possible representations.

Let us use carbon monoxide as an example. One possible electronic formulation is $|C\equiv O|$. This structure is electronically symmetrical, and each atomic kernel has eight electrons in its immediate neighborhood. There are, however, at least two other representations that are perhaps equally significant. These are $|C=\bar{O}|$ and $|C-\bar{O}|$. By using physical chemical methods, carbon monoxide is found to be less symmetrical than would be predicted by the structure $|C\equiv O|$ but more symmetrical than would be predicted by either $|C=\bar{O}|$ or $|C-\bar{O}|$ alone. Evidently a single electronic formulation cannot adequately represent the carbon monoxide molecule.

In the case of carbon dioxide, at least three electronic formulations appear to be equally probable. These are $|\bar{O}=C=\bar{O}|$,

|O≡C—O̅|, and |O̅—C≡O|. Other possibilities are |O̲—C═O̅| and |O̅═C—O̲|. Actually there are no double bonds and no triple bonds in the carbon dioxide molecule, because some of the electrons are unlocalized.

For sulfur dioxide, two equally important electronic structures are evident. These are

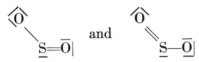

Physical studies indicate that the two sulfur-oxygen bonds in the sulfur dioxide molecule are identical. Hence both formulations are inadequate owing to the existence of unlocalized electrons.

For sulfur trioxide, the most likely formulations are:

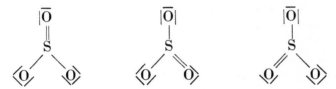

Of these, none is correct, because all bonds are identical. In this case, as in all those compounds for which multiple bond structures may be written, unlocalization of electrons makes it impossible to represent the electronic structure by using a single formulation.

Since theoretically only one shared pair of electrons is needed to hold together any two atomic kernels in a given covalent molecule, any other electrons are in a sense structurally superfluous. The placement of pairs of electrons not localized in bonding can therefore be a problem.

The electronic representations of the simple oxides mentioned in this section are given to emphasize the inadequacy of the conventional method used in writing covalent bond structures. This deficiency in the method should be expected since polyatomic molecules are much more complex than their constituent atoms. You will recall that we mentioned earlier (p. 104) that any attempt to picture an atom correctly is bound to fail.

We must also realize that the concept of the covalent bond is simply a convenient device to help us interpret a specific kind of intramolecular force. We wish to explain why two or more atomic kernels may be held together in a covalent molecule. It seems natural for us to suspect that some sort of a bond exists between these atomic kernels. The problem arises the moment we try to identify this bond.

8.8 RADICALS

In most covalent molecules, all electrons are paired. There are a few molecules, however, that contain at least one unpaired electron; these are called *radicals*. Since covalent radicals are relatively uncommon, they are often called *odd molecules*. This term is appropriate because most radicals contain an odd number of electrons. Most radicals are colored, but two of the simplest, oxygen and nitrogen monoxide, are colorless. Because many positive ions of the transition elements contain one or more unpaired electrons, they are radicals.

All radicals are paramagnetic; that is, they are attracted to a magnet more strongly than are entities in which all electrons are paired. The paramagnetism of radicals is a property often used in their identification.

Spectroscopic evidence and the fact that molecular oxygen is paramagnetic indicate that, at ordinary temperatures, oxygen molecules are biradicals; that is, each oxygen molecule has two unpaired electrons. If conventional symbolism is used, an explicit localization of the unpaired electrons is impossible. If we follow the pattern used in previous chapters, a dot will represent an unpaired electron, and a dash a pair of electrons. Among the possible electronic structures for the oxygen molecule are

$$|\overline{\text{O}}{-}\overline{\text{O}}| \qquad\qquad |\overline{\text{O}} \cdot\cdot\cdot \underline{\dot{\text{O}}}| \qquad\qquad |\underline{\dot{\text{O}}} \cdot\cdot\cdot \overline{\text{O}}|$$

Nitrogen monoxide, NO, a colorless gas, is one of the most stable radicals. There are eleven valence electrons to be represented: five from the nitrogen atom and six from the oxygen atom. Among the possible electronic formulas for NO are

$$\cdot \text{N}{=}\overline{\text{O}}| \quad |\overline{\text{N}}{=}\dot{\text{O}}| \quad \cdot \text{N}{-}\overline{\text{O}}| \quad |\underline{\text{N}}{-}\dot{\text{O}}| \quad |\overline{\text{N}} \cdot\cdot\cdot \overline{\text{O}}|$$

Nitrogen dioxide, NO_2, a reddish-brown gas, is a rather simple radical. Its four possible electronic structures are

This compound may be obtained by the pyrolysis (thermal decomposition) of lead nitrate.

$$2Pb(NO_3)_2 \rightarrow 2PbO + 4NO_2 + O_2$$

If nitrogen dioxide, at 1 atm, is cooled to at least $-10°C$, a liquid is obtained. This liquid is dinitrogen tetroxide, N_2O_4, the dimer (see p. 188) of nitrogen dioxide. The dimerization of nitrogen dioxide is reversible:

$$2NO_2 \leftrightarrows N_2O_4 + \Delta$$

At ordinary temperatures the two gases exist in an equilibrium mixture. At room temperature this equilibrium contains about 20 per cent of the monomer NO_2; at 135°C, 99 per cent of the mixture is monomer.

In the dinitrogen tetroxide molecule, all electrons are paired; hence it is not paramagnetic. During pyrolysis, the molecule undergoes homolytic fission. (Homolytic fission is that phenomenon in which a covalent bond is ruptured in such a way that each atomic kernel at the bond retains one electron of the original shared pair.)

Chlorine dioxide, ClO_2, a reddish-yellow gas, is a radical, or odd molecule. This substance is quite unstable and tends to decompose explosively to yield chlorine and oxygen. One possible electronic structure of chlorine dioxide is

The unpaired electron is unlocalized.

8.9 POLARITY AND DIPOLE-DIPOLE INTERACTIONS

The covalent bonds in the water molecule are polar and separated at an angle of 105°. Hence the water molecule is nonlinear and electronically unsymmetrical. There is a charge separation in the molecule: one seat more positive than another more negative one. For this reason the water molecule is said to be a *dipole*.

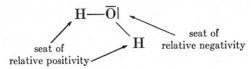

Since each water molecule is a dipole, the molecules in liquid water tend to orient themselves so that the more negative portion of a molecule is closely adjacent to the more positive portion of another molecule.   A possible orientation of dipoles is:

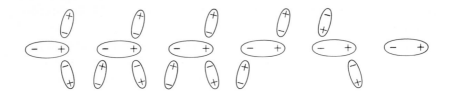

This intermolecular orientation is a result of electrostatic forces between the dipoles.   The electrostatic forces between the molecules are intermolecular attractive forces; they are much stronger than the ordinary van der Waals forces (p. 329) between relatively nonpolar molecules.   In liquid water and ice, the dipole-dipole interactions greatly increase the strength of the intermolecular attractive forces.   They are so strong that water is usually called an associated liquid because every molecule is very intimately associated with at least one other molecule. A dipole-dipole interaction creates a sort of bond between two molecules, but this bond is weaker than an ordinary covalent one.

8.10   HYDROGEN BONDS

The dipole-dipole interactions between the molecules in water and in ice are of a specific nature because they involve certain definite portions of the water molecules.   At least one hydrogen kernel (seat of positivity) of each water molecule is apparently rather strongly attracted to the oxygen kernel (in the region of negativity) of another water molecule.   This concept implies that no free, individual water molecules exist in water, since each molecule is "bonded" to at least one other molecule.   A random arrangement

of the molecules as they exist in liquid water is rather crudely
depicted below.

$$
\begin{array}{c}
\text{H} \qquad\qquad \text{H} \qquad\qquad \text{H} \\
\diagup \qquad\qquad \diagup \qquad\qquad \diagup \\
\text{H--O}\cdots\text{H--O}\cdots\text{H--O}| \qquad \text{H--O} \\
\vdots \qquad \diagdown \qquad \diagdown \qquad\qquad \diagdown \\
|\text{O--H} \qquad\qquad \text{H} \qquad\quad \text{H--O} \\
\diagup \qquad\qquad\qquad \vdots \qquad\qquad \diagdown \\
\text{H} \qquad\qquad \text{O--H} \qquad\qquad \text{H} \\
\vdots \qquad\qquad \diagup \qquad\qquad \vdots \\
|\text{O--H} \qquad \text{H} \qquad |\text{O--H} \\
\diagup \qquad\qquad\qquad\qquad \diagup \\
\text{H} \qquad\qquad\qquad \text{H}
\end{array}
$$

The dotted lines indicate the intermolecular "bonds." These are
called hydrogen bonds because hydrogen kernels seem to serve as
"bridges" between the oxygen kernels of adjacent water molecules.
By using the specific term, hydrogen bond, instead of the general
term, dipole-dipole interaction, we can say that water is a highly
associated liquid in which each water molecule is rather strongly
held by one or more hydrogen bonds to one or more water molecules.
The hydrogen bonds link the individual water molecules together
to form a huge, rather tightly knit, molecular aggregate.

Since the hydrogen kernel is relatively tiny and is a seat of
positivity, it is an important factor in the specific kind of dipole-
dipole interaction called the hydrogen bond. A hydrogen kernel
can apparently serve as an intermolecular bridge between the kernels
of such strongly electronegative atoms as oxygen, nitrogen, and
fluorine. Covalent compounds containing the groupings O—H,
N—H, F—H usually associate, by hydrogen bonding, with each
other and with most other covalent entities containing an oxygen,
nitrogen, or fluorine atom. The extent of association depends on
the size and geometric arrangement of the individual molecules.

There are many covalent compounds that contain the hydroxyl
group —O—H. This structural unit is distinctly polar, and the
hydrogen kernel serves as an intermolecular bridge between the
oxygen kernels of two different hydroxyl groups. Many liquids
whose molecules contain one or more hydroxyl groups are, as is
water, highly associated liquids. Two common examples are
methanol, CH_3OH, and ethanol, C_2H_5OH. These liquids are completely miscible with water because of extensive hydrogen bonding.
Acetic acid, CH_3COOH, and formic acid, $HCOOH$, are somewhat
unusual in that each compound forms a rather stable entity in which

two identical molecules are linked together by two hydrogen bonds. These entities are called *dimers* because two individual molecules (two monomers) associate to form a single entity (the dimer).

$$
\begin{array}{cc}
\text{O}\cdots\text{H—O} & \text{O}\cdots\text{H—O} \\
\end{array}
$$

H—C $\diagup\diagdown$ C—H H_3C—C $\diagup\diagdown$ C—CH_3

$$
\begin{array}{cc}
\text{O—H}\cdots\text{O} & \text{O—H}\cdots\text{O} \\
\end{array}
$$

formic acid dimer   acetic acid dimer

Hydrogen fluoride, $H—\overline{F}|$, is a highly associated substance. Very few if any individual molecules of hydrogen fluoride exist in the gaseous state at ordinary temperatures and pressures. At 0°C hydrogen fluoride is completely miscible with water. Liquid ammonia, NH_3, is an associated liquid, but much less so than water. Gaseous ammonia is very soluble in water. Formamide, $H—CONH_2$, and acetamide, $CH_3—CONH_2$, are highly associated substances; each is completely miscible with water.

In Section 15.5 (p. 352) we state that the normal boiling points of covalent compounds of comparable molar weights are indications of the relative strengths of the intermolecular attractive forces in the liquids. In associated liquids where hydrogen bonding between the molecules is extensive, the intermolecular attractive forces are much stronger than in those unassociated liquids in which much weaker van der Waals forces (see p. 329) are the predominant intermolecular attractive forces. Hence the boiling points of associated liquids are much higher than those of unassociated liquids of comparable molar weight. The relative significance of hydrogen bonding in two different associated liquids is usually evident from a comparison of the boiling points. Table 8.4 lists the normal boiling points, melting points, and molar weights of some typical covalent compounds. You will be able to identify those liquids in which hydrogen bonding is most extensive.

Two different associated liquids of comparable molar weights are usually miscible (very soluble in each other) because the two different kinds of molecules can hydrogen-bond with each other. An unassociated liquid, however, is often only very slightly soluble in an associated liquid. Because the molecules of the unassociated liquid apparently cannot hydrogen-bond with those of the associated liquid, they are unable to break into the "association." Two different unassociated liquids of comparable molar weight are usually miscible.

TABLE 8.4   Physical constants of some covalent compounds

Compound	Molar Weight	Normal Boiling Point, °C	Melting Point, °C
Water	18.02	100	0
Ammonia, NH_3	17.03	−33.4	−77.7
Methane, CH_4	16.04	−161.5	−182.5
Hydrogen fluoride, HF	20.01	19.4	−83
Phosphine, PH_3	33.99	−85	−132.5
Hydrogen chloride, HCl	36.51	−85	−111
Methanol, CH_3OH	32.04	64.7	−97.8
Methyl fluoride, CH_3F	34.03	−78.4	−142
Carbon monoxide, CO	28.01	−191.5	−207
Formaldehyde, CH_2O	30.03	−21	−92
Formic acid, H_2CO_2	46.03	100.8	8.4
Formamide, $HCONH_2$	45.04	193	2.6
Ethylene glycol, $C_2H_6O_2$	62.07	197.9	−15.6
Ethyl chloride, C_2H_5Cl	64.52	12.3	−138

8.11   HYBRID COVALENT BONDS

We described in Section 7.5 a plausible interpretation of the geometry of the water and ammonia molecules. Since the covalent bonds in these molecules involve overlapping of electron clouds in p orbitals, we tried to account for the fact that the bond angles in the molecules are greater than those anticipated. In this section we shall consider certain aspects that may help to eliminate our doubts.

The protons in the ammonia molecule, for instance, might be expected to arrange themselves geometrically to yield the lowest possible energy state for the molecule. If we considered the ammonia molecule to be essentially spherical, we might place the protons and the one unshared pair of electrons on the surface of the sphere so that these entities are equidistant from each other and from the nitrogen kernel in the center of the sphere. If we mentally connect the protons and the unshared pair of electrons, we recognize a tetrahedral arrangement. The imaginary regular tetrahedron has the nitrogen kernel at its center, one hydrogen kernel at each of three corners and the unshared pair of electrons at the fourth corner. Since all bonds from the nitrogen kernel are oriented to the corners of the tetrahedron, the H—N—H bond angles are 109°28'. This bond angle is much closer to the true value of 106.8° than is the expected (theoretical) angle (90°) based on the assumption that the bonding electrons occupy only p orbitals of the nitrogen atom.

The previous discussion is not intended to be an assertion about the actual structure of the ammonia molecule. However, a fact that enhances the attraction of the above suggestion is the nature of the bonds in the ammonium ion, NH_4^+. This ion is formed readily by the reversible attachment of a proton to an ammonia molecule.

$$
\begin{array}{c} H \\ | \\ H-N| \\ | \\ H \end{array} + H^+ \rightleftharpoons \left[\begin{array}{c} H \\ | \\ H-N-H \\ | \\ H \end{array} \right]^+
$$

ammonium ion

All the covalent bonds in the ammonium ion are identical (equivalent), the molecule is tetrahedral, and all bond angles are 109°28'. If the proton simply added to a trigonal pyramidal ammonia molecule (see p. 143) without altering the three covalent bonds already there, the "new" N—H bond would be an s bond, quite different from the p bonds of the rest of the molecule. However, all bonds are identical in the ammonium ion. Apparently a marked change occurs in the ammonia molecule during the acceptance of the proton.

The current explanation of the equality of the covalent bonds in the ammonium ion is that the four pairs of shared electrons are in four identical atomic orbitals. These orbitals are called *hybrid orbitals* because they result from the mixing of an s orbital and the three p orbitals. This mixing of s and p orbitals produces a more local concentration of electrons to yield stronger bonds. The hybrid orbitals are oriented or inclined at the tetrahedral angle of 109°28'. The specific bonds in ammonium ion are called sp^3 bonds because they are a result of the hybridization of one s and three p orbitals. The sum of the superscripts in a notation such as sp^3 indicates the total number of orbitals involved in producing the identical hybrid bonds. The notation sp^3 states that four orbitals are hybridized to yield four identical bonds. All sp^3 bonds, no matter what the molecule is, are oriented from the central atomic kernel to the corners of an imaginary regular tetrahedron. Therefore sp^3 bonds imply a tetrahedral molecular geometry.

The explanation of the nature of the bonding in the ammonium ion is used to interpret a type of bonding occurring in thousands of different molecules.   Most covalent bonds in molecules of three or more atoms are formed by the hybridization of atomic orbitals.

The assignment of a tetrahedral structure to the water molecule is not at all illogical.   The two protons could each occupy one corner of the tetrahedron, while the two unshared pairs of electrons could occupy the other two corners.   The angle between the two sp^3 O—H bonds would be 109°28′, a value fairly close to the actual angle of 105°.   Because water molecules readily add a proton reversibly, we would therefore assign to the resultant ion, H_3O^+ (oxonium ion), a tetrahedral structure.

The compounds of beryllium and boron consist of more covalent bonds than might be expected after a casual inspection of their valence-electron configurations.   The most logical explanation of this fact is that hybrid covalent bonds exist in most compounds of beryllium and boron.

Before we discuss the compounds in question, let us reconsider the valence-electron configurations of the elements as they were identified in Chapter 6.   These electron configurations are for unexcited gaseous atoms, so we should not be surprised to learn that they pertain to specific conditions only.   It seems very probable that a given valence-electron configuration is altered appreciably by the presence of other different atoms, especially at the start of and during a chemical reaction.   Also, at the start of many reactions the atoms or molecules become excited either because of an elevated temperature or the absorption of radiant energy.

Let us now consider the valence-electron configurations of the beryllium atom.

	$2s$	$2p$
unexcited Be atom	(..)	( )
excited Be atom	(.)	(.)

We notice that if the $2s$ and $2p$ orbitals hybridize in the excited Be atom at the time of a chemical reaction, the result is two hybrid orbitals that yield two identical sp bonds. Because the sp bonds are linear, the bond angle is 180°.

If the orbitals did not hybridize, we would expect two different covalent bonds (one an s bond, the other a p bond) in molecules such as $BeCl_2$, beryllium chloride. But since the two bonds in this compound are identical, the only valid conclusion is that the bonds are hybrids.

$$\overset{\overset{\displaystyle sp\text{ bonds}}{\swarrow\searrow}}{|\overline{Cl}—Be—\overline{Cl}|}$$

Compounds such as BeF_2, $BeBr_2$, and BeI_2 are linear. Among other linear binary covalent molecules that contain sp hybrid bonds are $HgCl_2$, $HgBr_2$, HgI_2, and Hg_2Cl_2.

$$\text{F—Be—F} \qquad \text{Cl—Hg—Cl}$$
$$\text{beryllium fluoride} \qquad \text{mercury(II) chloride}$$

The valence-electron configurations of the boron atom are

	$2s$	$2p$	$2p$
unexcited B atom	(..)	(.)	
excited B atom	(.)	(.)	(.)

It is evident that in the excited boron atom there are three un-paired electrons in three orbitals. Since the bonds in compounds such as BCl_3 (boron trichloride) are identical, we must conclude that the s orbital and the two p orbitals hybridize to yield three identical sp^2 hybrid bonds. The three sp^2 bonds are coplanar (in the same plane), and they are directed at 120° from each other toward points on an imaginary circle. This is expected because mutual repulsion of the three orbitals in a plane is minimum if they are 120° apart. The boron trichloride molecule is triangular and planar (see Fig. 8.7).

If copper(II) chloride is crystallized from an aqueous solution, green rhombic crystals of the dihydrate, $CuCl_2 \cdot 2H_2O$, are obtained. The chlorine kernels (in chloride ions) and the water molecules

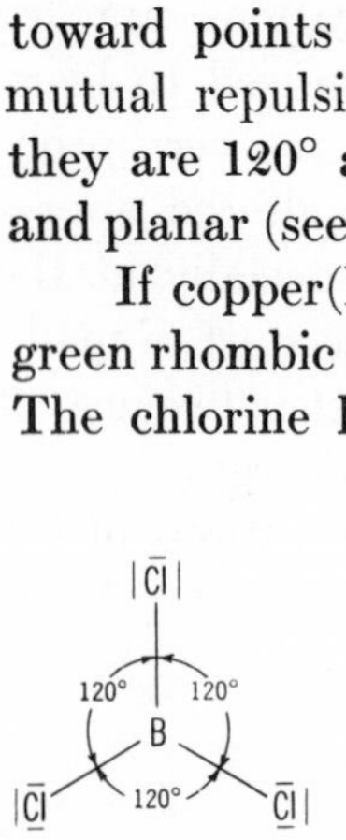

FIGURE 8.7 Diagram of the boron trichloride molecule with its sp^2 hybrid bonding.

are held to the copper kernel [copper(II) ion] by identical dsp^2 hybrid bonds to yield a square planar arrangement. In other words, the dsp^2 bonds are directed outward from the copper ion toward the corners of a square.

$$
\begin{array}{c}
\text{Cl} \text{------} \text{OH}_2 \\
\diagdown \quad \diagup \\
\text{Cu} \\
\diagup \quad \diagdown \\
\text{H}_2\text{O} \text{------} \text{Cl}
\end{array}
\quad dsp^2 \text{ bonds}
$$

Let us consider the valence-electron configurations of the copper atom (p. 123) and the copper(II) ion.

	$3d$	$3d$	$3d$	$3d$	$3d$	$4s$	$4p$	$4p$	$4p$
unexcited Cu atom	(..)	(..)	(..)	(..)	(..)	(.)	( )	( )	( )
copper(II) ion, Cu^{++}	(..)	(..)	(..)	(..)	(.)	( )			
"rearranged" Cu^{++}	(..)	(..)	(..)	(..)	( )	( )	( )	( )	(.)

used in bonding

The promotion of the unpaired electron to a $4p$ orbital may not seem so unlikely if we recall the relative proximity of the $3d$ and $4p$ subgroups (p. 111).

Elemental iron interacts with carbon monoxide, CO, to yield yellow liquid (boiling point, 103°C) whose formula is $Fe(CO)_5$. Each carbon monoxide molecule (p. 182) is bonded identically and covalently to the iron atom. Since the five covalent bonds are identical, they involve five hybridized orbitals. The bonds are called dsp^3 bonds, and they yield a trigonal bipyramidal arrangement (see Fig. 8.8).

To interpret the bonding in iron pentacarbonyl, $Fe(CO)_5$, let us look at the valence-electron configuration of an unexcited gaseous iron atom (p. 123).

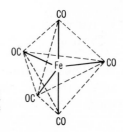

FIGURE 8.8 Diagram of the iron pentacabornyl molecule, $Fe(CO)_5$, a trigonal bipyramid having dsp^3 hybrid bonding.

	3d	3d	3d	3d	3d	4s	4p	4p	4p
unexcited iron atom	(..)	(.)	(.)	(.)	(.)	(..)	( )	( )	( )
"rearranged" Fe atom	(..)	(..)	(..)	(..)	( )	( )	( )	( )	( )

used in bonding

Apparently the five carbon monoxide molecules donate ten electrons (one pair each) to each iron atom, and in so doing "rearrange" the valence electrons of the iron atom as suggested above.

It is interesting to note that the iron atom with its 26 electrons adds ten more to yield about its nucleus an electronic configuration identical to that of the krypton atom.

Chromium carbonyl, $Cr(CO)_6$, is a colorless, readily vaporized solid that is structurally comparable to iron pentacarbonyl. The six pairs of electrons donated (by sharing) by the six carbon monoxide molecules occupy six hybridized d^2sp^3 orbitals. The six identical

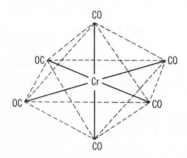

FIGURE 8.9 Diagram of the octahedral chromium hexacarbonyl, $Cr(CO)_6$, molecule with its d^2sp^3 hybrid bonding.

d^2sp^3 hybrid bonds are directed outward from the chromium atom to the corners of a regular octahedron (see Fig. 8.9). The valence-electron configurations are

	3d	3d	3d	3d	3d	4s	4p	4p	4p
unexcited Cr atom	(.)	(.)	(.)	(.)	(.)	(.)	( )	( )	( )
"rearranged" Cr atom	(..)	(..)	(..)	( )	( )	( )	( )	( )	( )

used in bonding 6 CO molecules

The acceptance of 12 electrons by the chromium atom creates an electronic configuration about the nucleus identical to that of the krypton atom.

The sulfur hexafluoride molecule, SF_6, has six identical covalent bonds that apparently are sp^3d^2 hybrids because the molecule is octahedral (see Fig. 8.10). The orbitals that hybridize are the

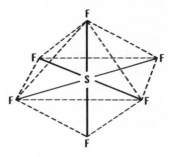

FIGURE 8.10 Diagram of the octahedral sulfur hexafluoride molecule with its sp^3d^2 hybrid bonding.

$3s$, the three $3p$ orbitals, and two of the $3d$ orbitals. Perhaps the excited sulfur atoms attain at reaction time the electronic configuration

$3s$ $3p$ $3p$ $3p$ $3d$ $3d$

(.) (.) (.) (.) (.) (.)

A summary of the types of hybrid bonds identified in this section and of those we shall describe later is given in Table 8.5.

TABLE 8.5 Hybrid covalent bonds

Bond Type	Spatial Orientation	Number of Bonds
sp, dp	linear	2
p^2, ds, d^2	angular	2
sp^2, dp^2, ds^2	planar triangle	3
d^2p	trigonal pyramid	3
sp^3, d^3s, dsp^2	tetrahedral	4
dsp^2, sp^2d	planar square	4
dsp^3, sp^3d	trigonal bipyramid	5
d^4s	tetragonal pyramid	5
d^2sp^3, sp^3d^2	octahedral	6
d^4sp	trigonal prism	6
d^4sp^3	dodecahedral	8

8.12 THE ARCHITECTURE OF SOME SIMPLE HYDROCARBONS

Because there are so many kinds of compounds of carbon, we shall postpone a lengthy discussion of them until Chapter 27. In this section, however, we shall mention a few of the simplest hydrocarbons—binary compounds consisting solely of carbon and hydrogen atoms.

Methane, CH_4, the principal component of natural gas, is the simplest stable alkane hydrocarbon. Since all the covalent bonds in methane are identical, it seems easy to accept the current belief that the bonds are sp^3 hybrids, the molecule is tetrahedral, and all bond angles are 109°28'. Therefore each hydrogen kernel occupies a corner of an imaginary regular tetrahedron. The covalency (number of covalent bonds per kernel) of carbon in methane is 4.

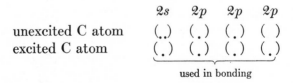

If we recall the valence-electron configuration of the carbon atom (p. 126), it should be easy to rationalize the sp^3 bonding in methane.

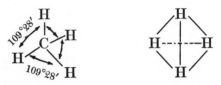

In ethane, C_2H_6, another simple alkane hydrocarbon, the six hydrogen kernels are attached individually and identically to the two carbon kernels. All bonds are sp^3 hybrids, all bond angles are 109°28', and the two tetrahedra (with carbon kernels at their centers) share a common corner (see Fig. 8.11). The covalency of carbon in ethane is 4.

Ethene, C_2H_4, also called ethylene, is classed as an unsaturated alkene hydrocarbon in contrast to ethane, C_2H_6. (Ethane is a saturated hydrocarbon because the carbon skeleton has all the hydrogen kernels it can accommodate.) A minimum number of

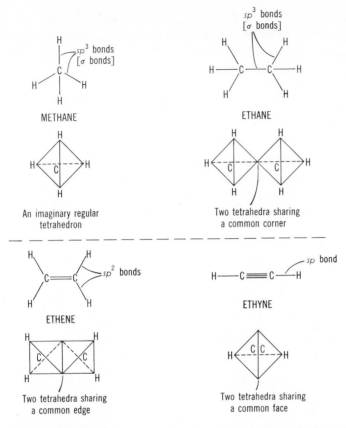

FIGURE 8.11 Diagrams showing the tetrahedral character of some simple hydrocarbon molecules.

five covalent bonds is required to hold together the ethene molecule, as evidenced by the preliminary structural formula.

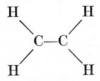

The apparent covalency of each carbon in ethene is 3, so only 3 atomic orbitals of each carbon atom are needed for covalent bonding.

	$2s$	$2p$	$2p$	$2p$
excited C atom	(.)	(.)	(.)	(.)

used in covalent
bonding

Since all the C—H bonds are identical in ethene, we classify the bonds as sp^2 hybrids. We have stated already that sp^2 bonds are coplanar and oriented at 120°. Therefore the ethene molecule is planar and all bond angles are 120° (see Fig. 8.12).

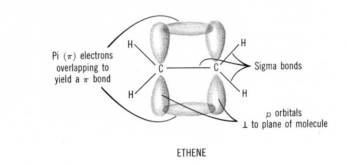

Pi (π) electrons overlapping to yield a π bond

Sigma bonds

p orbitals ⊥ to plane of molecule

ETHENE

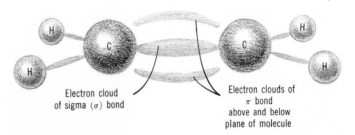

Electron cloud of sigma (σ) bond

Electron clouds of π bond above and below plane of molecule

FIGURE 8.12 Diagrams of the ethene molecule in which one sigma bond and one pi bond serve as the bonds between the two carbon kernels. Only electron clouds of bonding electrons are shown. Actually all kernels are surrounded by electron clouds.

We must not overlook the lone $2p$ electron of each carbon atom in the ethene molecule merely because it is not used in sigma bonding. The two p electrons occupy atomic orbitals oriented at right angles to the plane of the molecule, as depicted in Fig. 8.12. These p orbitals overlap to form two electron clouds, one above and one below the plane of the molecule. The p electrons apparently assist in holding together the two carbon kernels because the distance between the two carbon kernels in ethene is 1.34 A, whereas in ethane it is 1.54 A.

When p electrons do assist in covalent bonding in covalent molecules, they form what is called a *pi* (π) bond. The p electrons are called *pi electrons*. The pi bond in ethene is differentiated from the sp^2, C—C, bond by calling the sp^2 bond a *sigma* (σ) *bond*. A pi bond involves only *p* electrons, whereas a sigma bond usually results from some kind of *s* and *p* hybridization.

The ethene molecule is often depicted with two dashes between the carbon kernels, but one dash is a hybrid bond, actually a sp^2 sigma bond, and the other dash is a pi bond whose electrons *never* reside between the carbon kernels.

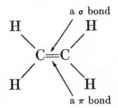

About the only virtue of the double bond notation is that it does identify a specific site, or seat, of unsaturation. At the site of the unsaturation, hydrogen atoms, for instance, can add to yield a saturated structure. Catalytic hydrogenation of ethene yields ethane.

$$\underset{\text{ethene}}{\underset{H}{\overset{H}{\diagdown}}C=C\underset{H}{\overset{H}{\diagup}}} \quad \overset{H_2}{\underset{(Pt)}{\longrightarrow}} \quad \underset{\text{ethane}}{\underset{H}{\overset{H}{\diagdown}}H-C-C-H\underset{H}{\overset{H}{\diagup}}}$$

The simplest stable hydrocarbon consisting of two carbon atoms is called ethyne, C_2H_2 (also called acetylene). Here a minimum of three covalent bonds is needed to hold together the molecule. A preliminary structure is

$$\text{H—C—C—H}$$

Since 2 is the apparent covalency of each carbon, only 2 atomic orbitals of each carbon are needed for ordinary bonding.

	2s	2p	2p	2p
excited C atom	(.)	(.)	(.)	(.)

used in covalent bonding

Because the two C—H bonds are identical, they are *sp* hybrids. Since *sp* hybrids are oriented at 180°, the ethyne molecule is linear, all kernels being in a straight line (see Fig. 8.13).

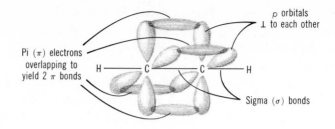

ETHYNE

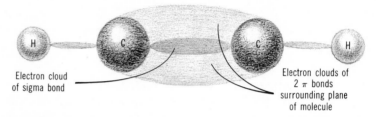

FIGURE 8.13 Diagrams of the ethyne molecule in which one sigma bond and two pi bonds serve as the bonds between the two carbon kernels. Only bonding electron clouds are shown. Actually all kernels are surrounded by electron clouds.

The two p electrons per carbon atom not used in sigma bonding in ethyne are located in a cylindrical electron cloud surrounding (but not in) the line through the carbon and hydrogen kernels. These four p electrons, also called *pi* electrons, create two pi bonds. Therefore the carbon kernels are held together in ethyne by one *sp* sigma bond and by two pi bonds. A formula of ethyne such as H—C≡C—H does not depict three identical bonds between the carbon kernels; only one is a true sigma bond.

The ethyne molecule is more unsaturated than ethene because the covalency of each carbon kernel can be increased from 2 to 4. Four hydrogen atoms can be added per ethyne molecule.

$$H\!-\!C\!\equiv\!C\!-\!H \quad \xrightarrow[\text{(Pt)}]{H_2} \quad \begin{array}{c} H \\ \diagdown \\ C\!=\!C \\ \diagup \qquad \diagdown \\ H \qquad\quad H \end{array} \quad \xrightarrow[\text{(Pt)}]{H_2} \quad \begin{array}{c} H \qquad\quad H \\ \diagdown \qquad \diagup \\ H\!-\!C\!-\!C\!-\!H \\ \diagup \qquad\quad \diagdown \\ H \qquad\qquad H \end{array}$$

ethyne   ethene   ethane

Although there are hundreds of other saturated and unsaturated molecules, space does not permit a lengthy discussion here. Later we shall be more definitive about the hydrocarbons.

8.13   A SUMMARY

It is evident that two or more atoms may combine and become held together, or bonded, to yield a polyatomic molecule. We also know that molecules themselves are attracted to each other to yield solids and liquids. We have suggested that a polyatomic molecule is held together by intramolecular attractive forces, and we have called these forces covalent bonds. Molecules are attracted to each other by intermolecular attractive forces. If these forces are between nonpolar (electrically symmetrical) molecules, they are called van der Waals forces (see p. 329). If the intermolecular forces are between polar molecules consisting of protons covalently bonded to oxygen, nitrogen, or fluorine kernels, they are called hydrogen bonds. Molecules that can hydrogen-bond with each other yield what are called associated liquids and solids at ordinary temperatures. The electrostatic forces between the ions (charged molecules) in an ionic compound are usually much stronger than those between uncharged polar and nonpolar molecules. Mainly for this reason all pure ionic compounds are solids at room temperature.

The covalent bond is considered to be a pair of electrons shared by two atomic kernels. If the two atomic kernels are identical, the sharing is nearly equal. Such a covalent bond is said to be nonpolar. If two different atomic kernels have nearly equal tendencies to attract a pair of electrons, the covalent bond between is nonpolar. If sharing of the electron pair is unequal between two different atomic kernels, a polar covalent bond results. In the case of a polar covalent bond, there is a charge separation at the site of the bond.

The electronic formula of a covalent molecule includes the symbols of the atomic kernels of the constituent atoms and their valence electrons. The covalency of an element in a specific molecule is the total number of pairs of electrons shared by each atomic kernel of the element.

It is impossible in the case of many covalent molecules to formulate a single electronic formula that logically represents the molecule in question. Some of the electron pairs in such molecules are unlocalized, and two or more electronic formulas can be written. In many cases three or more of these may have equal significance. It is evident that for many molecules their actual electronic formulas cannot be written by using conventional symbols.

Covalent molecules consisting of unpaired electrons are called radicals. Such molecules are paramagnetic, and they often associate to yield dimers, trimers, etc., in which all electrons are paired.

Problems

1. Which of the following compounds are essentially ionic and which are essentially covalent?

(a) RbCl	(e) IBr	(h) NaN_3
(b) NO_2	(f) RaO	(i) KH
(c) PH_3	(g) SiF_4	(j) SO_3
(d) BaSe		

2. Which bond in each of the following pairs is the more polar?

(a) C—O, N—O	(e) S—F, S—Br	(h) C—S, P—Cl
(b) H—O, S—O	(f) P—Cl, P—I	(i) C—H, N—Cl
(c) H—O, H—S	(g) P—O, S—O	(j) N—H, H—F
(d) Si—F, S—Br		

3. Which bond in Problem 2 has the least ionic bond character?

4. Which bond in Problem 2 has the largest percentage of ionic bond character?

5. Which bond in Problem 2 has the largest percentage of covalent bond character?

6. Draw all the probable electronic arrangements for the nitrogen dioxide molecule.

7. Phenol, C_6H_5OH, resorcinol, $C_6H_4(OH)_2$, toluene, $C_6H_5CH_3$, and anisole, $C_6H_5OCH_3$ are related organic compounds. Predict which (a) is the most associated substance; (b) is the least associated molecule; (c) has the highest boiling point; (d) has the lowest boiling point; (e) has the smallest number of polar bonds; (f) has the largest number of polar bonds.

8. Write the probable electronic formulas of (a) deuterium oxide, D_2O; (b) deuterium chloride, DCl; (c) sodium deuteride, Na^+D^-; (d) deuteromethane, CD_4; (e) deuteroammonia, ND_3; (f) deuteroammonium ion, ND_4^+; (g) deuteroarsine, AsD_3; (h) deuterium selenide, D_2Se.

9. Predict the geometry of the covalent molecules mentioned in Problem 8.

10. Draw graphic electronic representations for the following covalent compounds. Be sure to indicate unshared pairs of electrons.

(a) CS_2	(e) CCl_4	(h) NCl_3
(b) SiF_4	(f) SF_6	(i) BrCl
(c) PCl_3	(g) H_2Te	(j) $HCCl_3$
(d) PH_3		

11. Indicate the number of pairs of unshared electrons in each of the compounds listed in Problem 10.

12. In which of the molecules listed in Problem 10 are the bond angles very probably 109.5°?

13. In which of the molecules listed in Problem 10 are the bonds very probably sp^3 bonds?

14. Predict the geometry of each molecule listed in Problem 10.

15. In which one of the molecules listed in Problem 10 is bond hybridization least likely?

16. Which compounds listed in Problem 1 are definitely solids at room temperatures?

17. Predict the geometry and type of covalent bonding in the following molecules:
(a) $SiCl_2H_2$
(b) SiF_6^{--}
(c) $GaCl_3$
(d) C_2D_2
(e) $N_2H_6^{++}$
(f) C_2D_4

18. Predict which substance in each of the following pairs has the higher melting point.
(a) potassium oxide, selenium dioxide
(b) carbon bisulfide, barium sulfide
(c) nitrogen trichloride, calcium chloride
(d) phosphorus tribromide, phosphorus pentabromide
(e) selenium fluoride, rubidium fluoride

19. Which type of bonds (inter- or intramolecular) would you expect to predominate in the solid state of each of the following compounds?
(a) potassium hydride
(b) calcium carbide
(c) silicon tetrafluoride
(d) phenol, C_6H_5OH
(e) lithium nitrate
(f) methane

20. Name and write the formula of a typical example of (a) an ionic compound, (b) a metallic solid, (c) a nonmetallic solid, (d) a nonpolar covalent compound, (e) a polar covalent compound.

21. The atomic kernel of which of the following atoms has the greatest charge density: P, Se, Cl, Si, S?

22. By using the equation on page 173, calculate the percentage of ionic character of the P—Cl bond.

23. Which of the compounds mentioned in Problem 7 would you expect to be (a) most soluble in water, (b) least soluble in water?

9

SOME COMMON TYPES

9.1 A PERSPECTIVE

This chapter consists mainly of brief introductory descriptions of some common kinds of chemical reactions. Some of the types of reactions, especially oxidation-reduction and acid-base, will be discussed again in greater detail in subsequent chapters. However, because of prominence of the reaction types mentioned here, such repetition seems both warranted and beneficial.

While you study the material in this chapter, you will realize that there are relatively few major types of chemical reactions. In fact, if we consider reactions between two different reactants that yield stable products, nearly every one can be classified as either an oxidation-reduction or an acid-base reaction. Most oxidation-reduction reactions are free radical reactions because at least one reactant has, or can attain, un-

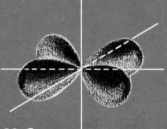

OF CHEMICAL REACTIONS

paired electrons (see Sec. 8.8). All acid-base reactions are polar reactions because electron-pairs seem to remain essentially intact as covalent bonds are either formed or broken.

Many of the radical-type reactions are chain reactions (see p. 234), such as that between hydrogen and chlorine to yield hydrogen chloride (see p. 234). The main driving force of a radical reaction is the tendency that unpaired electrons have to pair and thereby fill incomplete atomic orbitals in the reactant atoms and molecules. Many radical-type reactions are initiated either by light, by heat, or by entities that have unpaired electrons. Such reactions are frequently unaffected by a polar environment.

The discussion about the formation of covalent bonds in Section 8.3 (p. 169) will serve as a reminder that there are two different ways to create a covalent bond. One is by a free radical reaction (1), and the other is by a polar reaction (2).   Let us consider an $X : Z$ bond as an example.

$$(1) \quad X \cdot \; + \; \cdot Z \leftrightarrows X : Z \quad \text{(free radical type)}$$

$$(2) \quad X^+ + \; : Z^- \leftrightarrows X : Z \quad \text{(polar type)}$$

Since the formation of a specific bond is reversible, the cleavage (breaking) of a covalent bond may be either radical-type or polar-type.   If the cleavage of a covalent bond is by the polar-type mechanism (2), the cleavage is said to be *heterolytic*.   If the cleavage of a covalent bond is by the radical-type path (1), it is said to be *homolytic*.

During a polar-type reaction a "new" covalent bond is formed as one entity accepts, by sharing, an electron pair from some other entity.   The electron-pair acceptors are always electronically deficient, whereas the electron-pair donors seem to be, in contrast, electron-rich.   Polar-type reactions of this nature are called *acid-base reactions*.

Polar-type reactions, especially those in solutions, are often affected markedly by the presence of polar molecules.   In fact, most such reactions apparently require a polar environment, and sometimes only a trace of water is necessary.   Many polar reactions are unaffected by light and the presence of common radicals.

If the formation of ions (ionization) during a reaction between uncharged atoms or molecules involves the acceptance and donation of electrons by complete transfer (p. 145), the reaction is, very probably, a radical reaction.   Such a reaction is called an *oxidation-reduction reaction*.   The electron donor undergoes oxidation; the electron acceptor exhibits reduction.

A simple example is the reaction between elemental potassium and oxygen to produce the compound, potassium superoxide (p. 263).

$$\text{K} \cdot \; + \; |\overline{\text{O}} {-} \overline{\text{O}}| \rightarrow \; \text{K}^+ \left[|\overline{\text{O}} {-} \overline{\text{O}}| \right]^-$$

potassium superoxide

The potassium, the electron donor, undergoes oxidation; the oxygen, the electron acceptor, undergoes reduction.

The formation of a polar covalent bond by a radical-type reaction is usually called an oxidation-reduction reaction.   Let us assume that the covalent bond, $X{-}Z$, involves chemical elements that have different electronegativities (p. 173), and that X is more electronegative than Z.   Then the reaction $X \cdot \; + \; \cdot Z \rightarrow X : Z$ is oxidation-reduction, X being considered the electron acceptor and Z the electron donor.   Therefore $H \cdot \; + \; \cdot \overline{Cl}| \leftrightharpoons H : \overline{Cl}|$ is an oxidation-reduction reaction.

If the formation of ions during a reaction between uncharged molecules involves the acceptance and donation of protons by complete transfer, the reaction is an acid-base interaction, according to the concept of Brönsted and Lowry.   During a proton transfer reaction, an unshared pair of electrons of the proton-acceptor molecule (called the base) becomes a shared pair of electrons when the proton (H^+) accepts the electron pair.

Such an acid-base reaction occurs between water and hydrogen chloride molecules.

$$H{-}\overline{Cl}| \; + \; H{-}\overline{O}{-}H \leftrightharpoons \left[H{-}\underset{\displaystyle |}{\overset{\displaystyle H}{\underset{\displaystyle O}{}}}{-}H \right]^{+} \; + \; |\overline{Cl}|^{-}$$

the proton   the proton   oxonium
donor   acceptor   ion

9.2 OXIDATION-REDUCTION REACTIONS

Early in Chapter 7 (p. 133) we presented an important chemical axiom, namely that atoms of elemental substances, except some inert gases, interact chemically to attain more symmetrical electronic configurations.   The atoms of the inert gases are the acme of electronic symmetry (having all s and p orbitals filled).   Atoms of other elements interact either to accept or to donate electrons, depending on whether they have more or fewer electrons than some inert gas atom.

In Chapter 7 we also realized that atoms of the elements to the right of the "stairway" in the periodic chart always act as electron acceptors when they react chemically with an element to the left of the stairway.   All elements to the right are electronically deficient, in contrast to the inert gases, whereas atoms in families $1a$ and $2a$, for instance, are definitely electronically superfluent. Elements to the left of the stairway very rarely react chemically with each other to yield stable compounds.

Chemical reactions during which oxygen combines with another element (except fluorine) are currently called oxidations, just as they were many years before electrons were discovered.   Today we realize that in all such reactions oxygen is the electron acceptor. Because oxygen causes nearly all other entities to donate electrons to it, any process of electron donation has become synonymous with oxidation. Of course, if an electron donation occurs, a simultaneous electron acceptance occurs. Therefore an oxidation is always accompanied by a reduction; the number of electrons donated is equal to the number accepted; in other words, the extent of oxidation is identical electronically to the extent of reduction.

During an oxidation-reduction reaction, the electron donor is said to be oxidized, the electron acceptor to be reduced. The electron acceptor, which causes electron donation, or oxidation, is the *oxidizing agent*. The electron donor, which causes electron acceptance, or reduction, is the *reducing agent*. These terms may seem confusing at first glance, but after reflection on them you will see their utility.

Since elemental fluorine always acts as an electron acceptor, it is always an oxidizing agent, and it in turn is always reduced. Fluorine causes all substances with which it reacts to act as reducing agents. Whenever oxygen reacts chemically, except with fluorine, it is reduced because it always acts as an oxidizing agent.

During the complete oxidation of an element, all the valence electrons of the atoms are donated either by sharing or by complete transfer. Therefore when aluminum (three valence electrons) is oxidized completely, each aluminum atom donates three electrons to the oxidizing agent. Let us consider the reaction between aluminum and oxygen in which aluminum is oxidized completely and oxygen is reduced completely. Each aluminum atom can donate three electrons, while each oxygen atom can accept only two electrons. Therefore the number of aluminum atoms oxidized is $\frac{2}{3}$ the number of oxygen atoms used.

$$4Al \quad + \quad 3O_2 \quad \rightarrow 2Al_2O_3$$

electron donor	electron acceptor
or	or
reducing agent	oxidizing agent
or	or
substance oxidized	substance reduced

Another oxidation-reduction reaction is that between elemental sodium and chlorine.

$$2Na\cdot + |\overline{Cl}\!-\!\overline{Cl}| \rightarrow 2(Na^+ + |\overline{Cl}|^-)$$

An element is oxidized completely or is in its highest oxidation state if it donates, either by sharing or by complete transfer, all its valence electrons. For example, if a 1a-family element is to be oxidized completely, each atom must donate one electron. Complete oxidation of a $2a$-family element requires the donation of two electrons per atom; of a $3a$-family element, three electrons; and so on. In the case of fluorine, its elemental state is the highest oxidation state because fluorine cannot be oxidized. The highest oxidation state of oxygen seems to be attained by the donation, by sharing, of two electrons per atom.

To be reduced completely, the elemental state of a $7a$-family element (halogen) needs only one electron per atom because each atom has seven valence electrons. Only one more is needed for an inert gas electronic configuration. Complete reduction of the elemental states of oxygen, sulfur, selenium, and tellurium requires the acceptance of two electrons per atom; elemental nitrogen, phosphorus, and arsenic each need three electrons per atom; elemental carbon needs four electrons per atom; elemental hydrogen needs one electron.

Whenever hydrogen is combined with one or more elements to the right of the stairway, hydrogen is in its oxidized state.

Some compounds in which phosphorus is completely oxidized are P_4O_{10}, PCl_5, PBr_5, and H_3PO_4. In H_3PO_4 the four oxygen atoms have accepted eight electrons, three from the three hydrogen atoms and five from the lone phosphorus atom.

Some compounds in which nitrogen is completely reduced are NH_3, $(Cs^+)_3N^{3-}$, and $(Mg^{++})_3(N^{3-})_2$.

Elemental sulfur reacts with oxygen under certain conditions to yield sulfur trioxide, SO_3.

$$2S + 3O_2 \rightarrow 2SO_3$$

Since three oxygen atoms are involved per sulfur atom, we conclude that each sulfur atom donates six electrons because each oxygen atom apparently accepts two electrons. In this event the sulfur is completely oxidized and the oxygen is completely reduced.

If sulfur is burned in atmospheric air, the major product is sulfur dioxide, SO_2.

$$S + O_2 \rightarrow SO_2$$

Since only two oxygen atoms are involved per sulfur atom, we conclude that each sulfur atom probably donates only four electrons. In this event the sulfur is not completely oxidized because each sulfur atom has six valence electrons to donate.

Elemental potassium reacts with elemental nitrogen to yield potassium nitride, $(K^+)_3N^{3-}$.

$$3K + \tfrac{1}{2} N_2 \rightarrow (K^+)_3N^{3-}$$

Here it is evident that nitrogen is completely reduced by the potassium, while the potassium is completely oxidized by the nitrogen. Each N atom accepts three electrons, while each potassium atom donates only one.

A given molecule may act both as an oxidizing agent and as a reducing agent if it has in it an element that is neither in its completely oxidized state nor in its completely reduced state. Sulfur dioxide, SO_2, can act as an oxidizing agent and as a reducing agent because the sulfur can both donate and accept electrons.

It is possible to predict the empirical formulas of many binary compounds of representative elements produced during reactions in which oxidation and reduction are complete. For instance, if oxidation and reduction were complete during a reaction between gallium (Ga) and bromine (Br), we should predict the formula $GaBr_3$ for the product.

This brief introduction to oxidation-reduction will be greatly expanded in Chapter 20.

9.3 AUTOPROTOLYSIS REACTIONS

An important reversible chemical transformation—actually an ionization due to proton transfer—occurs continually in pure water. Because this phenomenon proceeds in the absence of any other chemical agent, it is called the *autoprotolysis* of water. The equation that represents this change is

$$\text{H}-\overline{\text{O}}-\text{H} + \text{H}-\overline{\text{O}}-\text{H} \rightleftharpoons \left[\text{H}-\overset{\displaystyle \text{H}}{\underset{|}{\text{O}}}-\text{H}\right]^+ + |\overline{\text{O}}-\text{H}^-$$

oxonium ion
or
hydronium ion   hydroxide ion

In a sample of pure water, a system in equilibrium, water molecules are interacting to yield ions at the same rate at which oxonium and hydroxide ions are interacting to yield water molecules. The relative significance of the two reactions depends just as much on the tendencies of the ions to interact with each other as it does on the tendencies of the water molecules to interact with each other. Since the concentration (density of population) of each ion in pure water is only 1×10^{-7} (0.0000001) moles per liter, we readily conclude that the reactive tendencies of the ions are much greater than those of the water molecules.

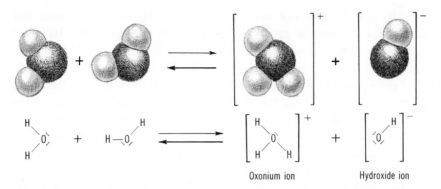

Oxonium ion   Hydroxide ion

FIGURE 9.1 Autoprotolysis of water, which occurs in pure water and in all aqueous solutions. Water molecules, oxonium ions, and hydroxide ions are always in equilibrium in all aqueous systems.

At 25°C the value of the ion product of water is approximately 1×10^{-14} because the concentration of each ion in pure water is $1 \times 10^{-7} M$, where M is called the *molarity*. (The molarity of an entity in a solution is the number of moles per liter of solution, or the number of millimoles per milliliter of solution.)

$$\underset{\text{concn of } H_3O^+}{1 \times 10^{-7} M} \times \underset{\text{concn of } OH^-}{1 \times 10^{-7} M} = 1 \times 10^{-14}$$

This expression implies that if the hydroxide ion concentration (moles/l) of a dilute (molarity not greater than 0.1 M) aqueous solution is increased 10 times, the oxonium ion concentration decreases to $\frac{1}{10}$ of the original value. Also, if the oxonium ion concentration of an aqueous solution is $1 \times 10^{-4} M$, the hydroxide ion concentration is $1 \times 10^{-10} M$.

Long before chemists were certain about the formula of water, they established arbitrary classifications of aqueous solutions. These were usually based more on the chemical behavior of the solution than on its composition. One major classification identified acidic, basic, and neutral aqueous solutions. In fact, every aqueous solution today is considered to be either acidic or basic, or neither acidic nor basic (neutral).

The current classification of aqueous solutions is based on the concentrations of the ions related to water.

a. An acidic aqueous solution is a system in which the oxonium (hydronium) ion concentration is greater than that of pure water. In other words, the H_3O^+ concentration is greater than the OH^- ion concentration, and it is greater than $1 \times 10^{-7} M$.

b. A basic aqueous solution is a system in which the hydroxide ion concentration is greater than that of pure water. In other words, the OH^- concentration is greater than the H_3O^+ ion concentration, and it is greater than $1 \times 10^{-7}\ M$.

c. A neutral aqueous solution is a system in which the H_3O^+ concentration is identical to the OH^- concentration. In other words, the OH_3^+ concentration is the same as that of pure water.

We conclude from the above classifications that an *acidic aqueous solution* can be prepared by adding directly to water either (1) oxonium ions in some compound or mixture, (2) entities that donate protons to water molecules to create oxonium ions, or (3) entities that destroy hydroxide ions. A *basic aqueous solution* can be prepared by adding directly to water either (1) hydroxide ions in some compound or mixture, (2) entities that accept protons from water molecules so that hydroxide ions appear, or (3) entities that destroy oxonium ions.

Pure sulfuric acid is a system in which autoprotolysis occurs. There is much evidence (electrical conductivity) that automatic proton transfer is more extensive in pure sulfuric acid than in pure water.

$$H_2SO_4 + H_2SO_4 \leftrightarrows H_3SO_4^+ + HSO_4^-$$

Although autoprotolysis occurs in pure liquid ammonia, it seems to be a little less extensive than that in pure water.

$$|NH_3 + |NH_3 \leftrightarrows NH_4^+ + |\overline{N}H_2^-$$

Difluoroboric acid, $H[BF_2(OH)_2]$, which is made by treating boron trioxide (B_2O_3) with hydrogen fluoride, is a liquid that has an appreciable electrical conductivity. This fact indicates that autoprotolysis occurs in the pure liquid, which boils at 160°C and is a strong monoprotic acid (p. 216).

$$\underset{\underset{\displaystyle H \quad F}{|\quad\ |}}{H-O-\overset{\overset{\displaystyle F}{|}}{B}-OH} + \underset{\underset{\displaystyle H \quad F}{|\quad\ |}}{H-O-\overset{\overset{\displaystyle F}{|}}{B}-OH} \leftrightarrows$$

$$\left[\,\underset{\underset{\displaystyle H \quad F \quad H}{|\quad\ |\quad\ |}}{H-O-\overset{\overset{\displaystyle F}{|}}{B}-O-H}\,\right]^{+} + \left[\,\underset{\underset{\displaystyle F}{|}}{H-O-\overset{\overset{\displaystyle F}{|}}{B}-OH}\,\right]^{-}$$

Although autoprotolysis (an autoionization) occurs in many pure liquids, the phenomenon in pure water is the most important example as far as our present studies are concerned.

9.4 BRÖNSTED-LOWRY ACID-BASE REACTIONS

During the early days of chemistry, certain compounds and mixtures were called *acids*, while certain others were called *bases*. If a substance acted as an acid, it did so in the presence of a base. A base acted as such only in the presence of an acid. An acidic aqueous solution could be made by adding an acid to water, just as a basic aqueous solution could be made by adding a base to water.

Today it is obvious that if an acidic solution is obtained by adding a specific substance to pure water, oxonium ions are produced as water molecules accept protons from some entity in solution. If a basic solution is obtained by adding a specific substance to pure water, hydroxide ions appear in solution as water molecules donate protons to some entity in solution.

According to a concept originally proposed independently by Brönsted (Danish) and Lowry (English) in 1923, a proton donor is classed as an acid and a proton acceptor as a base. This concept was suggested as a logical means of classifying certain compounds and their reactions, such as the behavior of hydrogen chloride, HCl, when it is added to water.

For at least a century prior to 1923, the solution obtained when pure hydrogen chloride, HCl, is added to water was called hydrochloric acid. Although the solution was called an acid, its exact composition remained essentially unknown during the nineteenth century. Not until the twentieth century were all chemists reasonably certain why the solution is acidic and what is the major acid present.

Eventually chemists verified the fact that the solution made by adding HCl to water contains ions. In fact, one of the principal ions is the chloride ion, Cl^-, the same ion that is found in all aqueous solutions of sodium chloride, Na^+Cl^-. Since pure hydrogen chloride consists solely of uncharged molecules, and since the aqueous solution of HCl is acidic, the only logical conclusion is the reversible dissociation of the HCl molecules.

$$H\!-\!\overline{\underline{Cl}}| + H\!-\!\overline{\underline{O}}\!-\!H \leftrightharpoons \left[H\!-\!\overset{\overset{\displaystyle H}{|}}{\underline{O}}\!-\!H \right]^{+} + |\overline{\underline{Cl}}|^{-}$$

the acid　　　the base　　　　the acid　　　the base

A dilute solution prepared by adding 0.01 mole of HCl to water to yield one liter of solution contains practically no HCl molecules. However, a solution made by adding 10 moles of HCl to water to yield a liter of solution does contain some undissociated HCl molecules. The relative significance of each reversible reaction evidently depends, as would be expected, on the conditions. The larger the population of the ions in the solution, the greater their tendency to react to yield HCl molecules. The smaller the ionic population, the less their tendency to interact chemically.

Hydrogen chloride is often called a Brönsted acid because it acts as a proton donor when added to water. Water acts as a base, a proton acceptor, in the presence of hydrogen chloride. We must not overlook the fact that if conditions are propitious, as in a concentrated aqueous solution of HCl, oxonium ions act as acids and chloride ions act as bases. Reflection on this statement leads us directly to an extremely significant fact, namely that the product of every Brönsted-Lowry acid-base reaction is another "new" acid and another "new" base.

Let us reconsider the reaction between hydrogen chloride and water.

$$H\!-\!\overline{\underline{Cl}}| + H\!-\!\overline{\underline{O}}\!-\!H \leftrightharpoons \left[\overset{\displaystyle H\!-\!\overline{\underline{O}}\!-\!H}{\underset{\displaystyle H}{|}} \right]^{+} + |\overline{\underline{Cl}}|^{-}$$

The base water donates, by sharing, one of its unshared pairs of electrons to the proton of the hydrogen chloride molecule, thereby affording a means of holding the proton to the water molecule.

Water is closely related to oxonium ion in that it is the base that yields an oxonium ion during proton acceptance. The chloride ion is closely related to hydrogen chloride because it yields hydrogen chloride during proton acceptance.

According to Brönsted and Lowry, every proton donor (acid) has a conjugate base, and every proton acceptor (base) has a conjugate acid. Therefore OH_3^+ is the conjugate acid of HOH, HCl is the conjugate acid of Cl^-, HOH is the conjugate base of OH_3^+, and Cl^- is the conjugate base of HCl.

If the name of an oxy Brönsted acid has the suffix -ic, the name of the conjugate base has the suffix -ate. For example, nitric acid's conjugate base is called nit*rate* ion. If the name of an oxy Brönsted acid has the suffix *-ous*, the name of the conjugate base has the suffix *-ite*. For example, hypochlorous acid's conjugate base is called hypochlor*ite* ion, ClO^-.

Every Brönsted acid has at least one covalently bound proton. Every base has at least one unshared pair of electrons. Any entity that has one or more covalently bound protons is a potential Brönsted acid. Any entity that has one or more unshared pairs of electrons is a potential base. Whether a potential proton donor acts as an acid depends, in part, on the base that is present. Whether a potential proton acceptor acts as a base depends, in part, on the acid that is present.

As we have already stated, water acts as a base in the presence of hydrogen chloride, but it acts as an acid in the presence of ammonia.

$$H-\overset{\overset{\displaystyle H}{|}}{\underset{\underset{\displaystyle H}{|}}{N}}| + H-\overline{\underline{O}}-H \leftrightarrows \left[H-\overset{\overset{\displaystyle H}{|}}{\underset{\underset{\displaystyle H}{|}}{N}}-H \right]^+ + |\overline{\underline{O}}-H^-$$

ammonium ion

A substance that can act both as an acid and as a base, especially in aqueous solutions, is called an *amphoteric substance*. In the Brönsted-Lowry sense, water is amphiprotic (a H^+ donor and acceptor).

Brönsted acids are usually classified according to the number of protons donated per molecule in the presence of water. Monoprotic acids can donate only one proton per molecule under these conditions; diprotic acids, two protons, triprotic acids, three protons; and so on.

Although acetic acid, CH_3COOH, has four covalently bound protons, only one can be donated in the presence of water. Sulfuric acid, H_2SO_4, is diprotic, as is phosphorous acid, H_3PO_3. Phosphoric (ortho) acid, H_3PO_4, is triprotic. A triprotic acid has three conjugate bases, a diprotic has two, and a monoprotic has only one.

Proton donation by diprotic and triprotic acids is by steps.

$$H_2SO_4 + HOH \leftrightarrows OH_3^+ + \underset{\substack{\text{hydrogen} \\ \text{sulfate ion}}}{HSO_4^-}$$

$$HSO_4^- + HOH \leftrightarrows OH_3^+ + \underset{\text{sulfate ion}}{SO_4^{--}}$$

It is well to keep in mind that the singly negative conjugate base of an uncharged diprotic acid is amphoteric.

Since phosphoric acid is triprotic, there are three dissociation steps.

$$H_3PO_4 + HOH \leftrightarrows OH_3^+ + \underset{\substack{\text{dihydrogen} \\ \text{phosphate ion}}}{H_2PO_4^-}$$

$$H_2PO_4^- + HOH \leftrightarrows OH_3^+ + \underset{\substack{\text{monohydrogen} \\ \text{phosphate ion}}}{HPO_4^{--}}$$

$$HPO_4^{--} + HOH \leftrightarrows OH_3^+ + \underset{\text{phosphate ion}}{PO_4^{3-}}$$

Phosphoric acid has two conjugate bases that are amphoteric, whereas sulfuric acid has only one. It might be well to recognize that the three sets of equations relative to phosphoric acid actually represent six acid-base reactions.

The proton-donor ability of a Brönsted acid is always identified by observing its behavior when it is added to water to yield a dilute solution. If all the acid molecules seem to disappear (dissociate), the substance is called a *strong acid*. However, if undissociated acid molecules remain in solution after preparation of the dilute solution, the acid is called a *weak acid*.

Hydrogen chloride is called a *strong acid* because practically all HCl molecules dissociate when added to water to yield a dilute solution. This means that chloride ions in the solution are not acting as bases although the OH_3^+ concentration is equal to the Cl^- concentration. The prominence, in dilute solutions, of the reaction reading from left to right is due to the insignificance of the reaction reading from right to left.

$$HCl + HOH \underset{\text{very prominent}}{\overset{\text{insignificant}}{\rightleftarrows}} OH_3^+ + Cl^-$$

Examinations of many monoprotic acids indicate that the conjugate base of a strong monoprotic acid never acts as a base when it is added to water. Therefore Na^+Cl^-, for example, yields a neutral solution when it is added to water. Any ion of an alkali metal (1a) element never undergoes any chemical change in dilute aqueous solutions.

Hydrogen cyanide, HCN, is a weak monoprotic acid. Therefore aqueous solutions of this acid contain HCN molecules owing to the prominence of the reaction whereby the HCN molecules are formed in solution.

$$HCN + HOH \leftrightarrows OH_3^+ + \underset{\text{cyanide ion}}{CN^-}$$

Since cyanide ions are acting as bases in the acidic solution, it should not be surprising to learn that cyanide ions act as bases when added to water. If sodium cyanide is added to water, a basic solution is obtained. Because the sodium ions are "spectators," the main reaction is

$$CN^- + HOH \leftrightarrows HCN + OH^-$$

A substance is called a strong base if it disappears (becomes completely protonated) when added to water to yield a dilute solution. Amide ion, NH_2^-, is a strong base.

$$NH_2^- + HOH \leftrightarrows NH_3 + OH^-$$

The conjugate acid of a strong base never acts as an acid when added to water.

A substance is classed as a weak base if any of its molecules remain in a dilute aqueous solution. Ammonia is a weak base because if NH_3 is added to water it is incompletely protonated.

$$NH_3 + HOH \leftrightarrows NH_4^+ + OH^-$$

The conjugate acid of a weak base always acts as an acid when added to water. Therefore $NH_4^+Cl^-$, ammonium chloride, yields an acidic solution when it is added to water. We should recall that the chloride ions are the conjugate base of a strong monoprotic acid; hence they do not react but are "spectators."

Most molecules that have hydrogen kernels (protons) covalently bound to oxygen kernels can act as Brönsted acids if conditions are propitious. Such molecules always have at least one (usually more than one) unshared pair of electrons at each oxygen kernel. Therefore they are potential bases as well as Brönsted acids. Among the compounds of carbon there are thousands that contain the element oxygen, and each is therefore a potential base.

9.5 LEWIS ACID-BASE REACTIONS

Examination of every Brönsted-Lowry acid-base reaction reveals that the base donates, by sharing, an electron pair to a proton. Hence a base can be defined explicitly as an electron-pair donor. However, an electron-pair donor, the base, acts as such only in the presence of a receptive electron-pair acceptor, the acid. These definitions are the foundation of the Lewis concept of acid-base behavior suggested by G. N. Lewis (American) in 1923.

According to the Lewis concept, an electron-pair donor is a base and an electron-pair acceptor is an acid. The proton is a Lewis acid, whereas the host molecule, of which the proton is a part, is a Brönsted acid. The major virtue of the Lewis concept is that a base is not limited to interaction with a proton. You may be less confused by the two acid-base concepts if you recall continually that every Lewis base is identical to some Brönsted-Lowry base.

Whenever a Lewis acid interacts with a base, the electron pair donated to the acid by the base serves as a covalent bond that holds the base to the acid. The initial product of every Lewis acid-base reaction is a single molecule whose molecular structure is partly that of the acid and partly that of the base.

$$LA \ + \ B \rightarrow LA\text{—}B$$

any Lewis   base   addition
acid   product

If the base is a water molecule, the initial product has all the structural characteristics of water molecules. It has obvious Brönsted acid properties.

$$LA \ + \ OH_2 \rightarrow LA\text{—}OH_2$$

any Lewis   a Brönsted
acid   acid

The Lewis concept is the only simple means of interpreting the experimentally known fact that carbon dioxide when added to water yields an acidic solution. This solution definitely contains the anions HCO_3^-, hydrogen carbonate ion, and CO_3^{--}, carbonate ion. Apparently carbon dioxide acts as an acid because an acidic solution is obtained. Since CO_2 has no covalently bound protons, it acts as a Lewis acid.

$$H\text{—}\overline{O}| \ + \ CO_2 \rightleftharpoons H\text{—}\overline{O}\text{—}CO_2 \rightleftharpoons H\text{—}\overline{O}\text{—}C\overset{O}{\underset{}{\text{—}\overline{O}\text{—}H}}$$

carbonic acid

the base   the acid   initial
product

$$H\text{—}\overline{O}\text{—}CO_2 \ + \ HOH \rightleftharpoons OH_3^+ \ + \ H\text{—}\overline{O}\text{—}CO_2^-$$

carbonic acid   hydrogen
carbonate ion

$$H\text{—}\overline{O}\text{—}CO_2^- \ + \ HOH \rightleftharpoons OH_3^+ \ + \ OCO_2^{--}$$

carbonate ion

The initial product is called carbonic acid, although it has never been identified.   It is obviously a diprotic acid, and the fact that it is weak is determined by the knowledge that the aqueous solution contains carbon dioxide molecules.

Several oxides of nonmetallic elements (to the right of the stairway) are Lewis acids, some being much stronger than carbon dioxide.

$$\text{H—}\overline{\text{O}}\text{—H} + \text{SO}_2 \leftrightarrows \text{H—}\overset{\displaystyle \text{H} \atop |}{\text{O}}\text{—SO}_2$$

sulfur
dioxide sulfurous acid
(weak, diprotic)

$$\text{H—}\overline{\text{O}}\text{—H} + \text{SO}_3 \leftrightarrows \text{H—}\overset{\displaystyle \text{H} \atop |}{\overline{\text{O}}}\text{—SO}_3$$

sulfur
trioxide sulfuric acid
(strong, diprotic)

$$\text{C}_6\text{H}_6 + \text{SO}_3 \rightarrow \qquad \text{C}_6\text{H}_5\text{SO}_3\text{H}$$

benzene benzenesulfonic acid
(strong, monoprotic)

$$3\text{H—}\overline{\text{O}}\text{—H} + \quad \text{P}_2\text{O}_5 \quad \leftrightarrows 2 \left[\text{H—}\overline{\text{O}}\text{—}\overset{\displaystyle \text{H} \atop | \atop |\text{O}|}{\underset{\displaystyle |\text{O}| \atop | \atop \text{H}}{\text{P}}}\text{—}\overline{\text{O}}| \right]$$

diphosphorus
pentoxide

orthophosphoric acid
(weak, triprotic)

$$\text{H—}\overline{\text{O}}\text{—H} + \text{N}_2\text{O}_5 \leftrightarrows 2[\text{H—}\overline{\text{O}}\text{—NO}_2]$$

dinitrogen
pentoxide nitric acid (strong)

$$\text{H—}\overline{\text{O}}\text{—H} + \text{SeO}_2 \leftrightarrows \text{H—}\overline{\text{O}}\text{—SeO}_2 \\ \underset{\displaystyle \text{H}}{\diagdown}$$

selenous acid
(weak, diprotic)

Many common bases react with Lewis acids, such as carbon dioxide, some in the presence of water, and some in the absence of any visible water.

$$H-O^- + CO_2 \rightleftharpoons HO-CO_2^-$$

hydrogen carbonate ion

$$O^{--} + CO_2 \rightleftharpoons O-CO_2^{--}$$

oxide ion   carbonate ion

$$H_3N + CO_2 \rightleftharpoons H_3N-CO_2$$

ammonia   carbamic acid

We shall refer to Lewis acid-base reactions many times in subsequent sections because there are so many polar-type reactions (p. 206) in which a covalent bond is formed by an electron-pair donation and acceptance.

9.6 ADDITION REACTIONS

The Lewis concept of acid-base behavior was introduced in the previous section. This idea identifies a type of reaction during which one or more covalent bonds are formed as one entity (the acid) accepts, by sharing, a pair of electrons from another entity (the base). The initial product of every Lewis acid-base reaction is a single molecule that is produced as the acid adds to the base. The reaction is an *addition reaction* that yields what is called an *addition compound*. The Lewis acid-base reactions are polar-type addition reactions.

A Lewis acid is said to be *electrophilic* (an electron seeker) because of its electronic deficiency. A base, in contrast, is said to be *nucleophilic* (an atomic-kernel seeker) because of its unshared electrons. Nearly all covalent compounds that have multiple bonds are electrophilic because of their unsaturated character (p. 199). Many positive ions, especially those of the transition elements, are electrophilic because of vacancies in the d orbitals. A molecule that has unshared pairs of electrons and is isoelectronic with some inert gas atom is apt to be nucleophilic.

Some addition reactions are radical-type, but since the majority seem to be polar, we shall emphasize the polar type. Because of space limitations we shall cite only a few common examples that yield relatively stable products.

Sulfur trioxide, SO_3, as we have mentioned previously (p. 219), is a strong Lewis acid. It therefore undergoes many addition reactions.

$$HOH + \overset{\displaystyle |\overline{O}|}{\underset{\displaystyle |\underline{O}|}{S}}=\overline{O}| \leftrightarrows H-\overline{O}-\overset{\displaystyle |\overline{O}|}{\underset{\displaystyle H}{\underset{\displaystyle |\underline{O}|}{S}}}-\overline{O}| \leftrightarrows H-\overline{O}-\overset{\displaystyle |\overline{O}|}{\underset{\displaystyle |\underline{O}|}{S}}-\overline{O}-H$$

sulfuric acid

$$(HO)_2SO_2 + SO_3 \leftrightarrows (HO)_2SO_2SO_3 \quad or \quad (HO)_2S_2O_5$$

disulfuric acid

$$H-Cl + SO_3 \leftrightarrows H-Cl-SO_3 \leftrightarrows Cl-SO_2(OH)$$

chlorosulfonic
acid

$$H_3N + SO_3 \leftrightarrows H_3N-SO_3 \leftrightarrows H_2N-SO_2OH$$

ammonia   sulfamic acid
(monoprotic)

Because boron trifluoride, BF_3, is an exceptionally active Lewis acid, it reacts readily to yield addition compounds. Since only six electrons reside about the boron kernel in the BF_3 molecule, the compound's electrophilicity is obvious. All other binary halides of boron, BCl_3, BBr_3, and BI_3, are active Lewis acids. All react readily with water (p. 230). Two typical reactions of boron trifluoride are

$$H_3N + \overset{\displaystyle F}{\underset{\displaystyle F}{B}}-F \rightarrow H_3N-\overset{\displaystyle F}{\underset{\displaystyle F}{B}}-F \quad or \quad BF_3-NH_3$$

boron trifluoride
ammonia

$$\overset{\displaystyle H_3C}{\underset{\displaystyle H_3C}{}}\!\!\diagdown\!\!\diagup\!\!|O| + BF_3 \rightarrow F_3B-O|\!\!\diagup\!\!\diagdown\!\!\overset{\displaystyle CH_3}{\underset{\displaystyle CH_3}{}}$$

dimethyl ether   boron trifluoride-dimethyl ether
(bp, 127°C)

Ammonia is sufficiently nucleophilic so that it yields many addition compounds. In fact, two are mentioned in the previous section. Ammonia molecules add to certain positive ions to yield relatively stable ammine complex ions.

If copper(II) sulfate, $Cu^{++}[SO_4]^{--}$, a white solid, is added to concentrated aqueous ammonia, a deep blue solution is obtained. A highly colored solid can be obtained from this solution.

$$Cu^{++}[SO_4]^{--} + aq\,NH_3 \leftrightarrows [Cu(NH_3)_4]^{++}[SO_4]^{--} \cdot H_2O$$

(white)   (excess)   (a deep blue solid)
tetramminecopper(II) sulfate-1-water

$$AgCl + aq\,NH_3 \leftrightarrows [Ag(NH_3)_2]^+ + Cl^-$$

silver   (excess)   silver ammonia
chloride   complex ion
(nearly   (in solution)
insoluble
in water)

Water participates as a base in many addition reactions to yield compounds called *hydrates*. Water adds to the positive ions of many ionic compounds to yield aquo complex ions, just as ammonia adds to certain positive ions to yield ammine complex ions.

Anhydrous copper(II) sulfate, $Cu^{++}[SO_4]^{--}$, is a white solid which dissolves readily in water to yield a blue solution. A blue solid that is hydrous (contains water) can be crystallized from the blue solution.

$$Cu^{++}[SO_4]^{--} + HOH \leftrightarrows [Cu(OH_2)_4]^{++}[SO_4]^{--} \cdot HOH$$

(white)   (excess)   (blue solid)
tetraquocopper(II) sulfate-1-water
or copper(II) sulfate pentahydrate

$$(CuCl_2)_x + 2HOH \leftrightarrows \quad \begin{array}{c} OH_2 \\ / \\ Cl-Cu-Cl \\ \backslash \\ OH_2 \end{array}$$

(brown)

(green solid)
bisaquocopper(II) chloride or
copper(II) chloride dihydrate

$$(FeCl_3)_x + 6HOH \rightarrow \quad [Fe(OH_2)_6]^{3+}(Cl^-)_3$$

(black)   (red-yellow solid)
hexaquoiron(III) chloride or
iron(III) chloride hexahydrate
or iron(III) chloride-6-water

$$(COOH)_2 + 2HOH \leftrightarrows (COOH)_2 \cdot 2HOH$$

oxalic acid   oxalic acid dihydrate
(a carboxylic
acid)

Many other examples of hydrate formation will be mentioned later (p. 406), and further discussion about complex ions appears in Chapter 23.

Many unsaturated hydrocarbons, such as the alkenes (p. 671) add certain kinds of reagents at the site of unsaturation (the double bond). Alkenes act initially as bases in the presence of strong Brönsted acids such as HCl, HBr, HI, and $(HO)_2SO_2$.

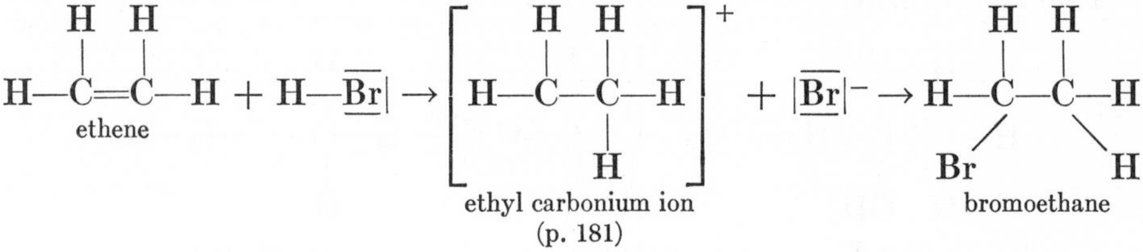

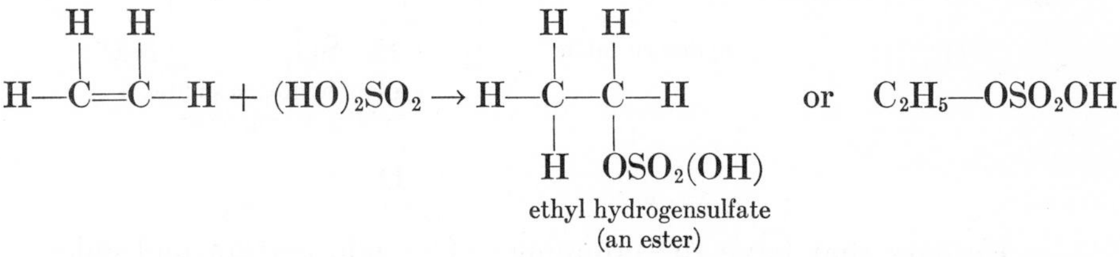

$$H{-}\underset{\underset{ethene}{}}{C}{=}C{-}H + H{-}\overline{Br}| \rightarrow \left[H{-}C{-}C{-}H \right]^+ + |\overline{Br}|^- \rightarrow H{-}C{-}C{-}H$$

ethyl carbonium ion
(p. 181)

bromoethane

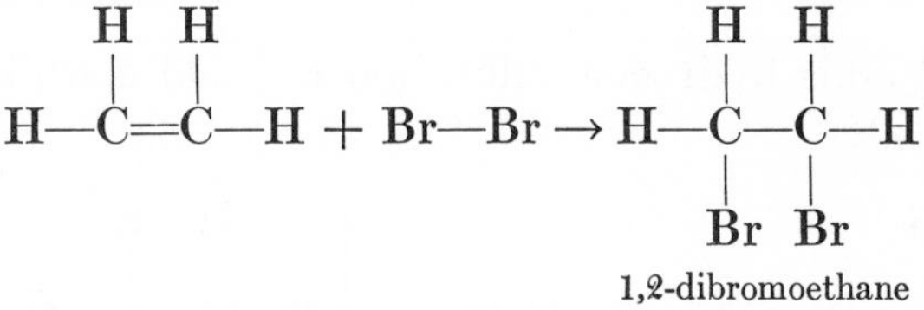

$$H{-}C{=}C{-}H + Br{-}Br \rightarrow H{-}C{-}C{-}H$$

1,2-dibromoethane

$$H{-}C{=}C{-}H + (HO)_2SO_2 \rightarrow H{-}C{-}C{-}H \qquad \text{or} \quad C_2H_5{-}OSO_2OH$$

ethyl hydrogensulfate
(an ester)

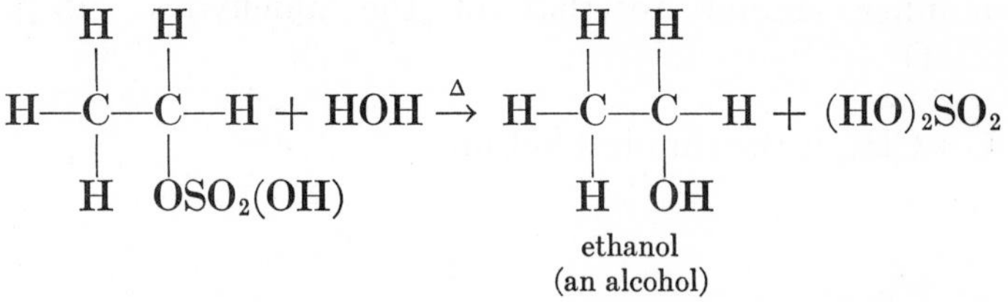

$$H{-}C{-}C{-}H + HOH \overset{\Delta}{\rightarrow} H{-}C{-}C{-}H + (HO)_2SO_2$$

ethanol
(an alcohol)

Addition of hydrogen to ethene is mentioned on page 199.

Aldehydes (compounds with the grouping $-\overset{\overset{\displaystyle H}{|}}{C}{=}O$) add many kinds of molecules because of the unsaturation of the aldehyde grouping. The carbon kernel in the grouping seems to be the electrophilic site that accepts a pair of electrons from certain bases.

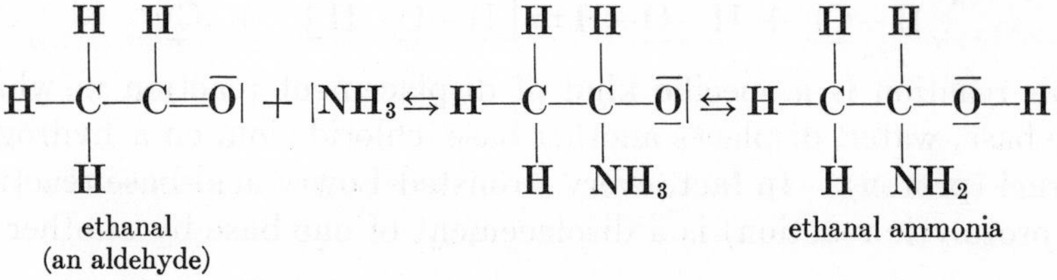

$$H{-}C{-}C{=}\overline{O}| + |NH_3 \leftrightharpoons H{-}C{-}C{-}\overline{O}| \leftrightharpoons H{-}C{-}C{-}\overline{O}{-}H$$

ethanal
(an aldehyde)

ethanal ammonia

Ethanal, a volatile liquid, may be obtained by careful oxidation of ethanol (p. 223).   Further oxidation of ethanal yields ethanoic acid (acetic acid).

$$\underset{\text{ethanol}}{H-\overset{\overset{\displaystyle H}{|}}{\underset{\underset{\displaystyle H}{|}}{C}}-\overset{\overset{\displaystyle H}{|}}{\underset{\underset{\displaystyle OH}{|}}{C}}-H} \xrightarrow{\text{oxid.}} \underset{\text{ethanal}}{H-\overset{\overset{\displaystyle H}{|}}{\underset{\underset{\displaystyle H}{|}}{C}}-\overset{\overset{\displaystyle H}{|}}{C}=O} \xrightarrow{\text{oxid.}} \underset{\substack{\text{ethanoic acid} \\ \text{(a carboxylic acid)}}}{H-\overset{\overset{\displaystyle H}{|}}{\underset{\underset{\displaystyle H}{|}}{C}}-\overset{\overset{\displaystyle O}{\parallel}}{C}-O-H}$$

Ethanal adds hydrogen sulfite ion to yield a white solid addition compound.

$$H-\overset{\overset{\displaystyle H}{|}}{\underset{\underset{\displaystyle H}{|}}{C}}-\overset{\overset{\displaystyle H}{|}}{C}=\overline{O}| + \underset{\substack{\text{sodium} \\ \text{hydrogen sulfite}}}{Na^+[O_2SOH]^-} \leftrightharpoons \left[H-\overset{\overset{\displaystyle H}{|}}{\underset{\underset{\displaystyle H}{|}}{C}}-\overset{\overset{\displaystyle H}{|}}{\underset{\underset{\displaystyle SO_3^-}{|}}{C}}-\overline{O}-H \right]Na^+$$

sodium hydrogen sulfite
addition compound

Ketones that have the grouping $-\overset{\overset{\displaystyle O}{\parallel}}{C}-$ add certain molecules in a manner similar to that of the aldehydes.   Propanone, $H_3C-\overset{\overset{\displaystyle O}{\parallel}}{C}-CH_3$, is the simplest ketone.

9.7 DISPLACEMENT REACTIONS

During the discussion of the Brönsted-Lowry acid-base concept (Sec. 9.4) we used the reaction between hydrogen chloride and water to illustrate a typical acid-base reaction.   Let us now reconsider this reaction in the light of the Lewis concept.

$$H-\overline{Cl}| + H-\overline{O}-H \leftrightharpoons \left[H-\overset{\overset{\displaystyle H}{|}}{O}-H \right]^+ + |\overline{Cl}|^-$$

This reaction is a specific kind of displacement reaction in which the base, water, displaces another base, chloride ion, on a hydrogen kernel (proton).   In fact, every Brönsted-Lowry acid-base reaction (a protolytic reaction) is a displacement of one base by another at a covalently bound proton. Another example is the reaction between sulfide ions and water.

$$|\overline{\underline{S}}|^{--} + H{-}\overline{\underline{O}}{-}H \leftrightharpoons |\overline{\underline{S}}{-}H^{-} + |\overline{\underline{O}}{-}H^{-}$$

sulfide ion   hydrosulfide
ion

In this case the sulfide ion displaces a hydroxide ion at a proton.

The displacement reactions described initially in this section are polar-type displacements. In each case covalent bonds are broken and formed so that the electron pairs seem to remain intact. In other words, bond formations and cleavages during such displacements are heterolytic.

Before we proceed, it will be well to recall that bases are said to be nucleophilic; that is, they act as atomic-kernel or atomic-nucleus seekers. Lewis acids are said to be electrophilic because they seek available (unshared) electron pairs.

There are many covalent binary compounds that consist of a halogen and a nonmetallic element (to the right of the stairway). Nearly all of these halides undergo displacement reactions in which the halogen, as halide ion, is displaced from an atomic kernel by some base. If water is the base, one or more oxygen kernels are attached to the central atomic kernel from which the halide ion is displaced. Frequently one oxygen kernel is attached for each halide ion displaced. This is exactly what happens in the case of HF, HCl, HBr, and HI (see p. 537).

$$H{-}\overline{\underline{Cl}}| + H{-}\overline{\underline{O}}{-}H \leftrightharpoons \left[H{-}\overset{\overset{\textstyle H}{|}}{\underline{O}}{-}H \right]^{+} + |\overline{\underline{Cl}}|^{-}$$

Let us now consider some common displacement reactions in which water acts as the base.

$$|\overset{\overset{\textstyle Cl}{|}}{\underset{\underset{\textstyle Cl}{|}}{P}}{-}Cl + 3HOH \rightarrow H{-}\overset{\overset{\textstyle |O|}{|}}{\underset{\underset{\textstyle |O|}{|}}{P}}{=}\overline{O}| + 3HCl$$

phosphorus   H
trichloride   phosphorous
acid

If the amount of water is limited, the products are essentially those indicated by the equation.   However, if an excess of water is used, the products are extensively dissociated.

If a limited supply of water reacts with phosphorus pentachloride, only two chloride ions are displaced to yield phosphorus oxychloride(1).   But if an excess of water is used (2), all five chloride ions are displaced.

$$(1)\quad PCl_5 \ + HOH \rightarrow \quad O\!=\!\overset{\displaystyle Cl}{\underset{\displaystyle Cl}{P}}\!-\!Cl \quad + 2HCl$$

phosphorus   (limited)
pentachloride

phosphorus oxychloride

$$(2)\qquad PCl_5 + HOH \rightarrow (HO)_3\!-\!P\!=\!O + 5HCl$$

(excess)   orthophosphoric
acid

The Brönsted acids in (2) undergo extensive dissociation.

Silicon tetrachloride, $SiCl_4$, reacts readily with water to yield SiO_2 and HCl.

$$SiCl_4 \ + 2HOH \rightarrow SiO_2 + 4HCl$$

silicon   silicon
tetrachloride   dioxide

Although $SiCl_4$ reacts readily with water at ordinary temperatures, carbon tetrachloride, CCl_4, does not.   One reason may be that the $3d$ orbitals in the silicon are available for bonding, but they are unavailable in carbon.   Hence the initial attachment of a water molecule to the silicon kernel does not require the simultaneous displacement of a chloride ion.

$$Cl\!-\!\overset{\displaystyle Cl}{\underset{\displaystyle Cl}{Si}}\!-\!Cl + HOH \leftrightharpoons Cl\!-\!\overset{\displaystyle Cl}{Si}\!\!\underset{Cl \quad OH_2}{}\!-\!Cl$$

silicon
tetrachloride

Phosgene, $COCl_2$, a poisonous gas, interacts with water to yield a solution that contains Cl^- ions.   Phosgene, a relative of carbonic acid (p. 230), is made by treating carbon monoxide with chlorine.

$$COCl_2 + 2HOH \rightarrow CO_2 + 2HCl$$

Hydroxyl groups in organic compounds (compounds of carbon)

can often be displaced by halide ions (except fluoride) from an active covalent source of halogen (see p. 63).

$$3CH_3\overset{\displaystyle O}{\overset{\|}{C}}{-}OH + PCl_3 \rightarrow 3CH_3\overset{\displaystyle O}{\overset{\|}{C}}{-}Cl + H_3PO_3$$

ethanoic acid   ethanoyl (acetyl)
or acetic acid   chloride

$$\begin{array}{c} H \\ | \\ H{-}C{-}O{-}H \\ | \\ H \end{array} + PI_3 \rightarrow \begin{array}{c} H \\ | \\ H{-}C{-}I \\ | \\ H \end{array} + H_3PO_3$$

methanol   iodomethane
(an alcohol)

$$\begin{array}{cc} H & H \\ | & | \\ H{-}C{-}C{-}O{-}H \\ | & | \\ H & H \end{array} + HBr \overset{\Delta}{\rightleftarrows} \begin{array}{cc} H & H \\ | & | \\ H{-}C{-}C{-}Br \\ | & | \\ H & H \end{array} + HOH$$

ethanol (p. 223)   bromoethane
(an alcohol)   (an alkyl halide)

Ammonia molecules can displace chloride ions from many different kinds of halogen compounds, just as they can displace these ions from hydrogen chloride.

$$NH_3(g) + HCl(g) \rightarrow NH_4^+Cl^-(s)$$

$$CuCl_2 + \text{concd aq } NH_3 \rightarrow [Cu(NH_3)_4]^{++} + 2Cl^-$$

copper(II)   tetramminecopper(II) ion
chloride

$$CH_3{-}\overset{\displaystyle O}{\overset{\|}{C}}{-}Cl + 2NH_3 \rightarrow CH_3{-}\overset{\displaystyle O}{\overset{\|}{C}}{-}NH_2 + NH_4^+Cl^-$$

acetyl   acetamide
chloride

Among the compounds of carbon that are related to methane and ethane, two alkanes (p. 667), there are many that are called alkyl halides. These are structurally similar to the alkanes except that a halogen atom replaces a hydrogen atom (p. 687). One of the simplest alkyl halides is methyl iodide, or iodomethane, CH_3I. The iodine of iodomethane is readily displaced by common bases such as OH^-, CN^-, and NH_3. Practically every reaction of an alkyl halide is a displacement reaction during which a halide ion is displaced by some base at a carbon kernel.

$$H—\underset{\underset{H}{|}}{\overset{\overset{H}{|}}{C}}—I + OH^- \rightarrow H—\underset{\underset{H}{|}}{\overset{\overset{H}{|}}{C}}—O—H + I^-$$

methyl iodide methanol

$$H—\underset{\underset{H}{|}}{\overset{\overset{H}{|}}{C}}—I + CN^- \rightarrow H—\underset{\underset{H}{|}}{\overset{\overset{H}{|}}{C}}—C≡N + I^-$$

methyl cyanide

$$H—\underset{\underset{H}{|}}{\overset{\overset{H}{|}}{C}}—I + 2NH_3 \rightarrow H—\underset{\underset{H}{|}}{\overset{\overset{H}{|}}{C}}—NH_2 + NH_4^+I^- + \text{more complicated amines}$$

methyl amine

The initial interaction of alkali metal atoms with molecules that have loosely bound protons is a type of displacement. The electron donated by the alkali metal atom displaces the base to which the proton is attached. Let us consider the reaction between water and sodium in which the base displaced is a hydroxide ion.

$$Na\cdot + H—\overline{O}—H \rightarrow Na^+ + |\overline{O}—H^- + H\cdot$$

A similar reaction occurs with methanol and an alkali metal. The initial step apparently is

$$K\cdot + CH_3OH \rightarrow K^+ + CH_3O^- + H\cdot$$
methoxide
ion

Reactions between many hydrocarbons and either chlorine or bromine are radical-type displacements. Major steps in these halogenations involve the displacement of one radical by another.

(1) $$C_2H_5\cdot + Cl—Cl \rightarrow C_2H_5—Cl + \cdot Cl$$

(2) $$Cl\cdot + C_2H_6 \rightarrow C_2H_5\cdot + H—Cl$$

In step (1) an ethyl radical, $C_2H_5\cdot$, displaces a chlorine atom at another chlorine atom, whereas in step (2) a chlorine atom displaces an ethyl radical at a hydrogen atom. Such halogenations are chain reactions (see p. 234).

Radical displacements such as in the examples given above are common, the simplest being the displacement of a hydrogen atom by a chlorine atom, and vice versa in the production of hydrogen chloride from its elements (see p. 236).

9.8 IONIZATION REACTIONS

In the perspective of this chapter we mentioned the two major kinds of ionizations: (1) the complete transfer of one or more electrons from one molecule to another (oxidation-reduction), and (2) the complete transfer of one or more protons from one molecule to another (Brönsted-Lowry acid-base). Since several examples of these types of ionizations are included in Sections 9.2 and 9.3, more will not be given in this section.

An uncharged molecule is converted into a charged molecule if an ion adds to it. This process may be called an ionization, although in this case it takes an ion to make an ion. This is different, in essence, from ionizations in which all reactant molecules are uncharged. Some examples of this type of ionization are

$$CO_2 + \underset{\text{hydride ion}}{H^-} \rightarrow \underset{\text{formate ion}}{HCO_2^-}$$

$$\underset{\substack{\text{aluminum} \\ \text{hydroxide}}}{Al(OH)_3} + OH^- \leftrightarrows \underset{\text{tetrahydroxoaluminum ion}}{Al(OH)_4^-}$$

$$\underset{\substack{\text{mercury(II)} \\ \text{chloride}}}{HgCl_2} + Cl^- \leftrightarrows \underset{\text{trichloromercury(II) ion}}{HgCl_3^-}$$

$$I_2 + I^- \leftrightarrows \underset{\text{triiodide ion}}{I_3^-}$$

Liquid sulfur dioxide has an electrical conductivity about twice that of water. This is evidence of autoionization, a phenomenon similar to autoprotolysis (p. 210).

$$SO_2 + SO_2 \leftrightarrows SO^{++} + SO_3^{--}$$

9.9 HYDROLYSIS REACTIONS

A reaction in which water molecules cause another substance to undergo a compositional change is, in the classical sense, a hydrolysis. Whenever a covalent molecule undergoes either a structural or a compositional change in the presence of water, the reaction is therefore classed as a hydrolysis. For instance, the hydrolysis of silicon tetrachloride, $SiCl_4$, in excess water yields SiO_2, OH_3^+, and Cl^-.

All displacement reactions that involve water molecules (Sec. 9.7) are hydrolyses. In fact, the reaction between hydrogen chloride and water, our model acid-base reaction, is a hydrolysis.

$$HCl + HOH \leftrightharpoons OH_3^+ + Cl^-$$

Nearly all binary covalent halides are readily hydrolyzed in the presence of water. Some of these halides are hydrolyzed at room temperature, while others require an elevated temperature. Most hydrolyses proceed more rapidly in the presence of hydroxide ions. Whenever a binary covalent halide is hydrolyzed, the halogen is displaced, as a halide ion, from the central atomic kernel. One or more oxygen kernels of one or more water molecules are thereby covalently attached to the central atomic kernel of the covalent halide. This is thus an acid-base reaction. Some examples not given earlier will serve to illustrate the general pattern.

$$\underset{\substack{\text{aluminum} \\ \text{chloride (dimer)}}}{Al_2Cl_6} + \underset{\text{(excess)}}{HOH} \leftrightharpoons \underset{\text{tetraquoaluminum ion}}{2[Al(OH_2)_4]^{3+}} + 6Cl^-$$

$$\underset{\text{boron trifluoride}}{BF_3} + 3HOH \rightarrow \underset{\text{boric acid}}{H_3BO_3} + 3HF \uparrow$$

$$\underset{\substack{\text{antimony chloride}}}{SbCl_3} + \underset{\substack{\text{(excess)} \\ -HOH}}{HOH} \leftrightharpoons Sb(OH)_2Cl \downarrow \qquad + 2OH_3^+ + 2Cl^-$$
$$\underset{\text{antimony oxychloride}}{\longrightarrow SbOCl \downarrow}$$

$$\underset{\substack{\text{tin(II) chloride}}}{SnCl_2} + \underset{\text{(excess)}}{HOH} \leftrightharpoons \underset{\text{hydroxotin(II) chloride}}{Sn(OH)Cl \downarrow} + OH_3^+ + Cl^-$$

Many oxy Brönsted acids have halogen derivatives that are called acyl halides. In each acyl halide, at least one hydroxyl group (OH) of the oxy acid is replaced by a halogen. Phosgene (carbonyl chloride), $COCl_2$ (see p. 226), may be considered the acyl chloride of carbonic acid, $CO(OH)_2$. Acyl chlorides and bromides are more common than the fluorides and iodides. Acyl halides, as a family, hydrolyze more readily than most binary covalent halides.

Sulfuric acid, $(HO)_2SO_2$, has two acyl chlorides, sulfuryl chloride, $(Cl)_2SO_2$, and chlorosulfonic acid, $(HO)SO_2Cl$ (p. 221). These two compounds are rapidly hydrolyzed at room temperature.

Because the hydrolysis of chlorosulfonic acid is violent, extreme care must be used in handling this reagent.

$$(HO)SO_2Cl + HOH \rightarrow (HO)SO_2(OH) + HCl$$

chlorosulfonic
acid   sulfuric acid

$$(Cl)_2SO_2 + 2HOH \rightarrow (HO)_2SO_2 + 2HCl$$

sulfuryl chloride

If excess water is used, the product acids are extensively dissociated. More about these acyl chlorides is presented on p. 274.

Among the oxy organic acids is a large family of carboxylic acids, each member of which has a carboxyl group ($-\overset{\displaystyle O}{\overset{\|}{C}}-OH$). The acyl halides of the carboxylic acids usually hydrolyze readily to yield the corresponding acids. Acetyl chloride, $CH_3\overset{\displaystyle O}{\overset{\|}{C}}-Cl$, the acyl chloride of acetic acid, is a typical example.

$$CH_3\overset{\displaystyle O}{\overset{\|}{C}}-Cl + HOH \rightarrow CH_3\overset{\displaystyle O}{\overset{\|}{C}}-OH + HCl$$

acetyl chloride   acetic acid
(p. 63)

Another family of oxy organic acids is the group of sulfonic acids. Each sulfonic acid has the specific group, $-SO_2OH$. A typical acyl chloride of a sulfonic acid is benzenesulfonyl chloride, $C_6H_5SO_2Cl$. This compound hydrolyzes to yield benzenesulfonic acid.

$$C_6H_5SO_2Cl + HOH \rightarrow C_6H_5SO_2(OH) + HCl$$

benzenesulfonyl   benzenesulfonic
chloride   acid

Among the thousands of negative ions there are many that are conjugate bases of weak Brönsted acids. Each such negative ion acts as a base when added to water. If the negative ion in question is accompanied by an ion of a 1*a* element, a basic aqueous solution is obtained (see p. 212).

There are many ionic compounds in which the positive ion is an alkali metal (1*a*) ion and the negative ion is the conjugate base of some weak Brönsted acid. Whenever this type of ionic compound is added to water, the negative ions act as bases and a basic solution is obtained. The positive ions simply act as "spectators."

A typical example of such a compound is sodium sulfide, $(Na^+)_2S^{--}$. The equation that identifies the fate of the reaction participants is

$$S^{--} + H-O-H \rightleftharpoons HS^- + OH^-$$

The reaction that occurs when an ionic compound such as sodium sulfide is added to water has frequently been called a hydrolysis of the compound. It is true that a chemical reaction occurs when many alkali metal compounds are added to water, but in each case it is the negative ion only that undergoes a chemical change. Hence any hydrolysis is of the negative ion only, and not of the compound in question. There are some ionic compounds, however, whose positive ions are the conjugate acids of weak bases. The positive ions of such compounds do act as acids in water. An example is ammonium ion (see p. 215).

$$NH_4^+ + HOH \rightleftharpoons NH_3 + OH_3^+$$

Let us now write a few equations to represent the reactions that occur when certain ionic compounds are added to pure water.

For $(K^+)_2SO_3^{--}$ (potassium sulfite) added to water:

$$SO_3^{--} + HOH \rightleftharpoons HSO_3^- + OH^-$$

For $Na^+NH_2^-$ (sodium amide) added to water:

$$NH_2^- + HOH \rightleftharpoons NH_3 + OH^-$$

For $NH_4^+NO_3^-$ (ammonium nitrate) added to water:

$$NH_4^+ + HOH \rightleftharpoons NH_3 + OH_3^+$$

For $NH_4^+CN^-$ (ammonium cyanide) added to water:

$$NH_4^+ + HOH \rightleftharpoons NH_3 + OH_3^+$$

and

$$CN^- + HOH \rightleftharpoons HCN + OH^-$$

In the case of ammonium cyanide, each ion reacts with water because NH_4^+ is the conjugate acid of a weak base, and CN^- is the conjugate base of a weak acid.

9.10 SOLVOLYSIS REACTIONS

The examples of hydrolysis mentioned in the previous section are reactions during which water, often acting as a solvent, initiates a chemical change. In this section we shall consider two other common liquids which are often used as solvents and which can initiate chemical changes. A reaction initiated or assisted by solvent molecules is called a *solvolysis*. Therefore a hydrolysis is a specific kind of solvolysis.

Two common liquids that initiate solvolyses are ammonia and ethanol, C_2H_5OH (p. 223). (Although ammonia is gaseous at ordinary temperatures and pressures, it is easily liquefied by cooling.) A solvolysis involving ammonia molecules is called an *ammonolysis*, whereas a solvolysis involving ethanol is usually called an *alcoholysis*. (Ethanol is an important member of a family of alcohols.) Ammonia and ethanol often act as bases during solvolyses.

Let us consider first some examples of ammonolysis.

$$HCl(g) + NH_3(g) \leftrightarrows NH_4^+Cl^-(s)$$

$$HgCl_2 + aq\ NH_3 \leftrightarrows HgNH_2Cl \downarrow + NH_4^+Cl^-$$
mercury(II)   mercury(II)
chloride   amino chloride

$$CuCl_2 + aq\ excess\ NH_3 \leftrightarrows [Cu(NH_3)_4]^{++} + 2Cl^-$$
copper(II)   tetramminecopper(II) ion
chloride

$$CH_3\overset{\displaystyle O}{\overset{\|}{C}}-Cl + NH_3 \rightarrow CH_3\overset{\displaystyle O}{\overset{\|}{C}}-NH_2 + HCl$$
acetyl chloride   acetamide

$$CH_3I + NH_3 \rightarrow CH_3NH_2 + NH_4^+I^- + other\ amines$$
methyl iodide   methyl amine

Some examples of alcoholysis (actually ethanolysis) are comparable to hydrolysis.

$$CH_3\overset{\displaystyle O}{\overset{\|}{C}}-Cl + C_2H_5OH \rightarrow CH_3\overset{\displaystyle O}{\overset{\|}{C}}-OC_2H_5 + HCl$$
acetyl chloride ethanol   ethyl acetate
          (an ester)

$$HCl(g) + C_2H_5OH \leftrightarrows C_2H_5OH_2^+ + Cl^-$$
        ethyloxonium
         ion

$$C_6H_5SO_2Cl + C_2H_5OH \rightarrow C_6H_5SO_2C_2H_5 + HCl$$
benzenesulfonyl   ethyl benzenesulfonate
chloride   (an ester)

$$CH_3-\overset{\displaystyle O}{\overset{\|}{C}}-OCH_3 + C_2H_5OH \leftrightarrows CH_3-\overset{\displaystyle O}{\overset{\|}{C}}-OC_2H_5 + CH_3OH$$
methyl acetate   ethyl acetate
(an ester)

The last reaction always yields an equilibrium mixture (see p. 73).

9.11   CHAIN REACTIONS

Most radical reactions (p. 206) appear to be chain reactions. During these reactions the initial formation of a radical (an entity having at least one unpaired electron) initiates a series of subsequent reactions. Since one reactant and one product in most of the subsequent reactions are radicals, each reaction propagates a chain of reactions. A specific chain of reactions is stopped whenever two radicals interact with each other because the continual production of radicals is necessary to maintain the chain of reactions.

A typical chain reaction occurs when elemental hydrogen and chlorine interact chemically. This reaction is described in some detail in Section 18.15.

The chlorination and bromination of certain kinds of hydrocarbons, mentioned in Section 9.12, are chain reactions.

Since oxygen molecules are biradicals (p. 184), they can participate readily in chain reactions. The peroxy linkage (O—O) in peroxides (p. 262) is a weak covalent bond that is easily cleaved homolytically to yield two radicals. Peroxides often initiate chain reactions by supplying initial radicals. Peroxides and oxygen molecules may also help to terminate chain reactions by scavenging chain propagating radicals.

The oxidation by atmospheric oxygen (often called autoxidation or auto-oxidation) of sulfite ion, SO_3^{--}, to yield sulfate ion, SO_4^{--}, is a chain reaction. Since the rate of oxidation is measurably accelerated by copper(II) ions in concentrations as low as 1×10^{-12} moles per ml, the mechanism outlined below has been suggested. Apparently a copper(II) ion (a radical ion) initiates a chain of reactions that produce thousands of sulfate ions.

$$Cu^{++} + SO_3^{--} \leftrightarrows Cu^+ + \left[\begin{array}{c} |\overline{O}| \\ | \\ \cdot S-\overline{O}| \\ | \\ |\underline{O}| \end{array} \right]^-$$

sulfite ion   copper(I)   sulfite radical

$$|\overline{\underset{\cdot\cdot}{O}}-\overline{\underset{\cdot\cdot}{O}}| + \left[\begin{array}{c} |\overline{O}| \\ | \\ \cdot S-\overline{O}| \\ | \\ |\underline{O}| \end{array} \right]^- \rightarrow \left[\begin{array}{c} |\overline{O}| \\ | \\ \cdot \overline{O}-\overline{O}-S-\overline{O}| \\ | \\ |\underline{O}| \end{array} \right]^-$$

peroxymonosulfate radical

$$\left[\begin{matrix} |\overline{O}| \\ | \\ |S-\overline{O}-H \\ | \\ |\underline{O}| \end{matrix}\right]^{-} + \left[\begin{matrix} |\overline{O}| \\ | \\ \cdot\overline{O}-\overline{O}-S-\overline{O}| \\ | \\ |\underline{O}| \end{matrix}\right]^{-} \rightarrow$$

hydrogen
sulfite ion

$$\left[\begin{matrix} |\overline{O}| \\ | \\ |S-\overline{O}\cdot \\ | \\ |\underline{O}| \end{matrix}\right]^{-} + \left[\begin{matrix} |\overline{O}| \\ | \\ H-\overline{O}-\overline{O}-S-\overline{O}| \\ | \\ |\underline{O}| \end{matrix}\right]^{-}$$

sulfite   hydrogen
radical   monoperoxysulfate ion
                    (see p. 273)

$$\left[\begin{matrix} |\overline{O}| \\ | \\ H-\overline{O}-\overline{O}-S-\overline{O}| \\ | \\ |\underline{O}| \end{matrix}\right]^{-} + \left[\begin{matrix} |\overline{O}| \\ | \\ |S-\overline{O}| \\ | \\ |\underline{O}| \end{matrix}\right]^{--} \rightarrow$$

sulfite
ion

$$\left[\begin{matrix} |\overline{O}| \\ | \\ H-\overline{O}-S-\overline{O}| \\ | \\ |\underline{O}| \end{matrix}\right]^{-} + \left[\begin{matrix} |\overline{O}| \\ | \\ |\overline{O}-S-\overline{O}| \\ | \\ |\underline{O}| \end{matrix}\right]^{--}$$

hydrogen   sulfate ion
sulfite ion

The chain propagators in this chain reaction are the sulfite radicals, $\cdot SO_3$.

The oxidation of hydrocarbons by atmospheric oxygen (autoxidations) are chain reactions in which the initial steps seem to be (1) formation of a hydrocarbon radical, (2) combination of the radical with an oxygen molecule to yield a peroxy radical, and (3) extraction of a hydrogen atom from a hydrocarbon molecule to yield a hydrocarbon radical. These reactions serve to identify probable chain propagation steps. A radical, or a source of a radical, can often initiate an autoxidation.

(1)   Initiator → radicals ($R\cdot$ or $R-\overline{O}-\overline{O}\cdot$)

(2) $R\cdot + |\overline{O}-\overline{O}| \rightarrow R-\overline{O}-\overline{O}\cdot$

     alkyl   alkyl peroxy
    radical   radical

(3) $R-\overline{O}-\overline{O}\cdot + \quad RH \quad \rightarrow R\cdot + R-\overline{O}-\overline{O}-H$

            hydrocarbon   alkyl hydroperoxide

9.12 SUBSTITUTION REACTIONS

There are many reactions, especially among the compounds of carbon, during which one atom or a group of atoms is substituted for, or replaces, a specific hydrogen atom or kernel in a given molecule. If the substitution involves replacement of a hydrogen atom, it is a radical-type (often an oxidation-reduction) reaction. If the substitution involves replacement of a hydrogen kernel, it is a polar-type (acid-base) reaction.

The simplest radical-type substitution reaction is that in which a chlorine atom is substituted for a hydrogen atom in a hydrogen molecule (see p. 437).

$$H—H + Cl_2 \rightarrow 2H—Cl$$

Radical-type substitution reactions occur during the chlorination or bromination of an alkane (saturated) hydrocarbon. These halogenations are chain reactions in which alkyl radicals seem to be chain propagators. If chlorine and ethane, C_2H_6, are alone at $120°C$, the rate of chlorination to yield chloroethane, C_2H_5Cl, is very slow. However, if 0.002 mole per cent of tetraethyl lead, $Pb(C_2H_5)_4$, is added to the system, the reaction rapidly proceeds to completion. The ethyl radicals obtained by the pyrolysis of the tetraethyl lead act as chain initiators. During the chain reaction the same ethyl radicals act as propagators.

$$Pb(C_2H_5)_4 \rightarrow Pb + 4C_2H_5 \cdot$$

$$C_2H_5 \cdot + Cl—Cl \rightarrow \underset{\text{ethyl chloride}}{C_2H_5Cl} + Cl \cdot$$

$$Cl \cdot + \underset{\text{ethane}}{C_2H_6} \rightarrow H—Cl + C_2H_5 \cdot$$

If oxygen molecules are present in the reaction system, they greatly inhibit the chain reaction. Apparently the oxygen molecules gather ethyl radicals to yield peroxyethyl radicals, $C_2H_5—\overset{..}{O}—\overset{..}{O} \cdot$. The peroxy radicals are less able than chlorine atoms to remove hydrogen atoms from ethane.

Gaseous phase halogenations of hydrocarbons seem to be entirely radical-type, as do those in nonpolar inert solvents. If the reactions are initiated by light, halogen atoms seem to be important chain initiators. If the halogenations occur in a polar environment, the reactions may be wholly or partially polar-type (acid-base).

If an aqueous solution of ammonium chloride, $NH_4^+Cl^-$, is treated with elemental chlorine for a prolonged period, nitrogen trichloride, NCl_3, is obtained. The hydrogen atoms of an ammonia molecule are replaced by chlorine atoms during the formation of a NCl_3 molecule. Nitrogen trichloride is violently explosive if heated or exposed to ultraviolet light.

Benzene, C_6H_6, and bromine undergo a substitution reaction in certain polar media to yield bromobenzene, C_6H_5Br, and HBr. The initial attack on the benzene molecules seems to be by brominium ions, Br^+, that are acting as Lewis acids. This type of substitution is therefore called an electrophilic substitution. It is polar and hence acid-base.

$$C_6H_6 + Br_2 \rightarrow C_6H_5Br + HBr$$
$$\text{benzene} \qquad \text{bromobenzene}$$

Sulfur trioxide, SO_3, molecules react as Lewis acids with benzene to yield benzenesulfonic acid, $C_6H_5SO_3H$. This is usually called an electrophilic substitution because of the attack by an electrophilic agent (Lewis acid).

$$C_6H_6 + SO_3 \rightarrow C_6H_5SO_3H$$
$$\text{benzenesulfonic acid}$$

9.13 POLYMERIZATION REACTIONS

There are many reactions during which two or more molecules, either identical or different, simply combine to yield one larger molecule. Such reactions are called *polymerizations*. However, if two molecules, each called a *monomer*, combine to form a single molecule, the process is called a *dimerization*, the product being a *dimer*. The combination of three monomers yields a *trimer;* many monomers yield a *polymer*. Many polymerizations, especially dimerizations and trimerizations, are reversible.

In this section we shall identify only a few polymerizations, but in Chapter 27 we shall describe some polymers of certain compounds of carbon.

Since all polymers are covalent, the combination of monomers creates covalent bonds. Because there are only two different types of covalent bond formation, there are only two general kinds of polymerization, the polar-type (acid-base) and the radical-type. Let us start the discussion by commenting about some polar-type polymerizations.

Many active Lewis acids either dimerize or polymerize so readily that few, if any, monomer molecules exist at room temperature. In some cases the dimer or trimer exists in the gaseous state. During the initial step in a Lewis acid polymerization, one monomer acts as an acid, the other as a base. Any Lewis acid that has either oxygen atoms or halogen atoms is a potential base because of unshared pairs of electrons.

Anhydrous aluminum chloride is a polymer in the solid state and a dimer in the gaseous state. The solid sublimes (p. 357) readily at 183°C.

$$
\begin{array}{ccccccc}
|\overline{Cl}| & & |\overline{Cl}| & & |\overline{Cl} & \overline{Cl} & |\overline{Cl}| \\
| & & | & & \diagdown & \diagup & \diagup \\
Al & + & Al & \to & Al & & Al \\
\diagup \ \ \diagdown & & \diagup \ \ \diagdown & & \diagup \ \ \diagdown & & \diagdown \\
|\overline{Cl} \quad \overline{Cl}| & |\overline{Cl} \quad \overline{Cl}| & |\overline{Cl} \quad \overline{Cl} & & |\overline{Cl}|
\end{array}
$$

The polymeric solid state is simply an extension, in three dimensions, of the dimer.

The chlorides and bromides of copper(II) and iron(III) are definitely polymeric in the solid state. In the case of copper(II) chloride the polymeric structure seems to be

$$
\begin{array}{cccccccc}
& Cl & & Cl & & Cl & & Cl \\
\diagup & & \diagdown \diagup & & \diagdown \diagup & & \diagdown \\
& Cu & & Cu & & Cu & \\
\diagdown & & \diagup \diagdown & & \diagup \diagdown & & \diagup \\
& Cl & & Cl & & Cl & & Cl
\end{array}
$$

Although sulfur trioxide (p. 183) is monomeric in the gaseous state, the liquid state contains monomers and trimers, $(SO_3)_3$. Diphosphorus trioxide, P_2O_3, monomers dimerize readily to yield P_4O_6, just as diphosphorus pentoxide, P_2O_5, yields P_4O_{10} (see Fig. 9.2).

Silicon dioxide, SiO_2, molecules polymerize to yield huge macromolecules actually manifested in ordinary quartz crystals. Each silicon kernel is in the center of an imaginary regular tetrahedron, and an oxygen kernel resides at each corner. Therefore ordinary quartz consists of SiO_4 tetrahedrons held together in a vast network, the polymer. The molar formula of silica (silicon dioxide) is $(SiO_2)_x$, where x depends on the size of the crystal. The empirical formula is SiO_2. The melting point of silica is at least 3500°C, whereas that of carbon dioxide is −57°C. This difference is not surprising since only monomer molecules exist in CO_2.

Some of the radical oxides of nitrogen undergo radical-type

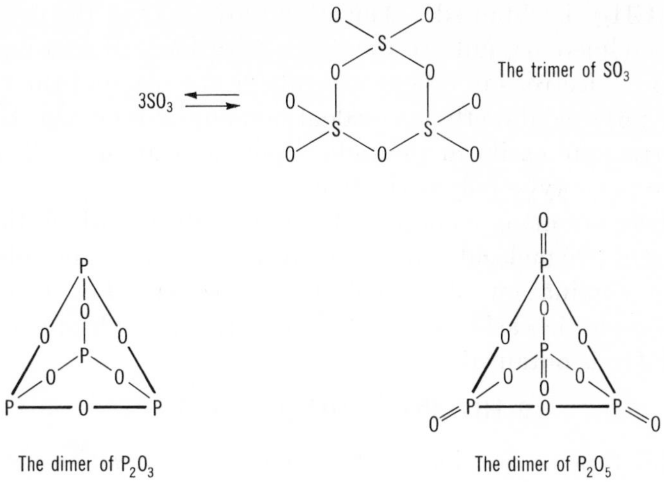

$$3SO_3 \rightleftharpoons$$

The trimer of SO_3

The dimer of P_2O_3

The dimer of P_2O_5

FIGURE 9.2 Diagrams of the S_3O_9, P_4O_6, and P_4O_{10} molecules.

dimerizations. The reversible dimerization of nitrogen dioxide has been mentioned previously (p. 185). If a mixture of nitrogen monoxide, NO, and nitrogen dioxide, NO_2 (which has a brown color) is cooled to $-21°C$, a blue liquid, dinitrogen trioxide, N_2O_3, is obtained (p. 296). Since N_2O_3 is formed by combining two different monomer molecules, it can be called a *codimer*. Polymers made by using two different monomers are called *copolymers*.

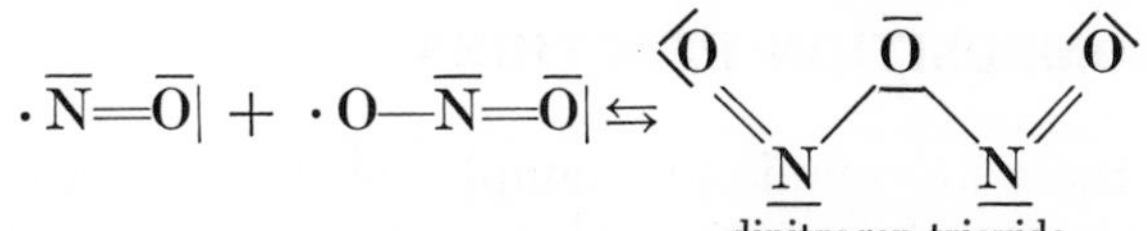

$$\cdot \overline{N}{=}\overline{O}| + \cdot O{-}\overline{N}{=}\overline{O}| \leftrightharpoons$$

dinitrogen trioxide

Gaseous sulfur at 1000°C consists mainly of diatomic molecules, S_2, but at lower temperatures these monomeric S_2 molecules polymerize. At room temperature the major form is the tetramer, S_8. At 445°C, monomers, trimers (S_6), and tetramers are present in the gaseous state.

White phosphorus consists of P_4 molecules (p. 139) that are tetrahedral. If the white (yellow) form of phosphorus is heated in the absence of air, a dark red modification is obtained. The red form, which seems to be polymeric, is less reactive than the white variety.

Alkenes, such as ethene, $H_2C{=}CH_2$, undergo radical-type polymerizations. If ethene is heated with diethylmercury, a polymeric liquid $(CH_2)_n$ is obtained.   The ethyl radicals from the pyrolysis of the diethylmercury initiate the polymerization.   If you recall that the two pi electrons in ethene are outside the plane of the molecule and are not used directly in covalent bonding, it is evident that they can participate easily in the radical polymerization.   Alkenes also undergo polar-type polymerization.

There are many examples of reactions during which the major portions of two molecules are joined to yield a single molecule following the elimination of a molecule of water.   For instance, if orthophosphoric acid is heated gently, pyrophosphoric acid, $(HO)_4P_2O_3$, is obtained.

$$2(HO)_3PO \overset{\Delta}{\leftrightharpoons} (HO)_4P_2O_3 + HOH$$

This type of reaction is often called a *condensation polymerization;* $H_4P_2O_7$ is therefore a condensation dimer.   A condensation trimer of orthophosphoric acid is $(HO)_5P_3O_5$.

$$3(HO)_3PO \overset{\Delta}{\rightarrow} (HO)_5P_3O_5 + 2HOH$$

Condensation polymerizations are currently very popular in the chemical industry; some examples, such as nylon, are mentioned in Chapter 27.   Proteins seem to be condensation polymers of amino acids (p. 707), and glycogen, starch, and cellulose are condensation polymers of sugar molecules (p. 702).

9.14 DECOMPOSITION REACTIONS

Although there are manifold examples of decomposition reactions, we shall not attempt to review them in this section.   It is sufficient to say that the major kinds of decompositions are those initiated by heat (pyrolytic), those initiated by light (photolytic), and those initiated by a difference in electrical potential (electrolytic).   The latter will be discussed in Chapter 21.   We have mentioned several examples of pyrolyses (p. 68), and the rupture of covalent bonds by radiant energy has also been considered (p. 70).

During pyrolyses and photolyses, the excitation of the molecules obviously decreases the orderliness of the bonding.   The absorption of energy ruptures bonds to yield the decomposition products.   The products of a specific decomposition may be varied and unexpected, mainly because such disorder existed during the decomposition.

Problems

1. Identify the oxidizing agents and the reducing agents in the following equations.

(a) $C_2H_2 + H_2 \rightarrow C_2H_4$

(b) $C_2H_4 + Br_2 \rightarrow C_2H_4Br_2$

(c) $2Rb + H_2 \rightarrow 2RbH$

(d) $2Cs + 2CH_3OH \rightarrow 2CsOCH_3 + H_2$

(e) $Ca + 2HOH \rightarrow Ca(OH)_2 + H_2$

(f) $2In + 3Cl_2 \rightarrow 2InCl_3$

(g) $Se + O_2 \rightarrow SeO_2$

(h) $S + 3F_2 \rightarrow SF_6$

(i) $C_2H_6 + Br_2 \rightarrow C_2H_5Br + HBr$

(j) $CH_4 + 2O_2 \rightarrow CO_2 + 2HOH$

2. Each pair of elements listed below will, under correct conditions, react chemically to yield a stable compound. Identify the compound by assuming that the oxidizing agent is completely reduced and the reducing agent is completely oxidized.

(a) Cs and Br
(b) Ca and S
(c) Ga and O
(d) Te and O
(e) P and Cl

(f) As and F
(g) S and F
(h) Rb and I
(i) Ba and S
(j) Mg and N

3. (a) How many moles of oxygen, O_2, are needed to oxidize completely 45 g-atoms of barium? (b) How many moles of sulfur atoms can be reduced completely by 50 g-atoms of gallium? (c) How many moles of electrons are needed to reduce completely 60 moles of nitrogen molecules, N_2? (d) How many grams of strontium can be oxidized completely by 70 g of bromine?

4. The hydroxide ion concentration of an aqueous solution is 100 times that of water (pure). What is the oxonium ion concentration?

5. The oxonium ion concentration of an aqueous solution is 1×10^{-5} M. What is the hydroxide ion concentration? Is the solution acidic, basic, or neutral?

6. One-half of a mole of a covalent compound, HEN, was added to water to yield one liter of solution. There was 0.01 of a mole of oxonium ion in the solution, here called solution A. (a) What was the hydroxide concentration of A? (b) What molecules, charged and uncharged, were definitely present in A? (c) If the compound Na^+EN^- is dissolved in pure water to yield solution B, what, if anything, occurs chemically in the solution B? (d) Is B acidic, basic, or neutral? (e) What molecules in B are definitely acting as acids? (f) What molecules in B are definitely acting as bases? (g) What is the most abundant molecule in B that is acting as an acid in B? (h) What is the most abundant molecule that is acting as a base in B? (i) Write an equation to represent the reaction that occurs when HEN is added to pure water. (j) Write an equation representing the reaction that occurs when Na^+EN^- is added to pure water.

7. Suggest a possible reason for the fact that pure difluoroboric acid undergoes autoprotolysis more extensively than pure water.

8. Write suitable equations to represent the following reactions:
- (a) Carbon dioxide acts as an acid in the presence of methylamine, CH_3NH_2.
- (b) Hydrogen carbonate ion acts as an acid in the presence of ammonia.
- (c) Chromium(VI) oxide dissolves in water to yield a solution that contains two different kinds of negative ions plus hydroxide ion.
- (d) Thionyl chloride, $SOCl_2$, hydrolyzes in water.
- (e) Hydroxide ion acts as a base in the presence of sulfur dioxide.
- (f) Gaseous hydrogen and gaseous bromine react to yield HBr.
- (g) Bismuth trichloride, $BiCl_3$, hydrolyzes in water. (Recall that bismuth and antimony reside in the same family on the periodic chart.)
- (h) Phosgene undergoes alcoholysis in ethanol to yield an ester.
- (i) Lead(II) oxide acts as an acid in the presence of hydroxide ion.
- (j) Copper(II) chloride dissolves in aqueous ammonia to yield a dark blue solution.
- (k) Acetyl bromide reacts with methylamine, CH_3NH_2.
- (l) Sodium acetate, $Na^+CH_3COO^-$, dissolves in water to yield a basic solution.
- (m) Nitric acid, $HONO_2$, acts as a base in $HOClO_3$.
- (n) Sodium dihydrogen phosphate, $Na^+(H_2PO_4)^-$, dissolves in water to yield an acidic solution.
- (o) Ethene is treated with HI.
- (p) Mercury(II) iodide acts as an acid in the presence of I^-.

10

HYDROGEN

10.1 OCCURRENCE AND IMPORTANCE

Hydrogen stands next to oxygen in abundance if its occurrence is calculated in terms of numbers of atoms in the lithosphere, the hydrosphere, and the atmosphere. Relatively little elemental hydrogen exists in the atmosphere and the earth's crust partly because of its ability to escape and partly because it is so readily oxidized. There are more compounds that contain the element hydrogen than there are compounds of any other element. Nearly every compound that plays an important role in plant and animal life contains hydrogen.

10.2 LABORATORY PREPARATION

Practically all the combined hydrogen found in nature is in its +1 oxidation state because hydrogen in its

−1 oxidation state (either as free or incipient hydride ion, p. 145) is extremely reactive as a base and as a reducing agent. The preparation of hydrogen usually involves, therefore, either the reduction of the element from its +1 oxidation state to its zero state or the decomposition of some covalent entity. We have already mentioned the fact that all the alkali metals, barium, strontium, and calcium react with water at room temperature to yield hydrogen. At higher temperatures magnesium and iron react with steam to yield hydrogen.

$$Mg + H_2O + \Delta \rightarrow MgO + H_2$$
$$\text{(steam)}$$

$$3Fe + 4H_2O + \Delta \rightarrow Fe_3O_4 + 4H_2$$
$$\text{(steam)}$$

The most common method for the preparation of hydrogen in the laboratory involves the treatment of an active metal (a metal above hydrogen in the activity series [p. 487]) with either aqueous hydrochloric or sulfuric acid. The metal reduces the active protons to hydrogen atoms. In the case of zinc, for instance,

$$Zn + 2H^+ \rightarrow Zn^{++} + H_2$$

Aluminum also acts as a good reducing agent in aqueous basic solutions, thereby yielding gaseous hydrogen.

$$2Al + 2OH^- + 6H_2O \rightarrow 2Al(OH)_4^- + 3H_2$$

The electrolysis of water (p. 504) is used in the laboratory and commercially for the production of hydrogen.

10.3 COMMERCIAL PRODUCTION

At high temperatures (about 1000°C) superheated steam is reduced by carbon, as coke, to yield a mixture of carbon monoxide and hydrogen.

$$\underset{\text{(coke)}}{C} + \underset{\text{(steam)}}{H_2O} + \Delta \rightarrow \underbrace{CO + H_2}_{\text{(water gas)}}$$

The water gas is mixed with steam at an elevated temperature and then passed over a catalytic mixture of oxides to yield more hydrogen.

$$CO + H_2 + H_2O \rightarrow CO_2 + 2H_2$$

The hydrogen in the product mixture is separated by dissolving the carbon dioxide at high pressure in water.

The pyrolysis of methane, CH_4, and other related hydrocarbons, C_nH_{2n+2}, is a major method of producing hydrogen.

$$CH_4 + \Delta \rightarrow C + 2H_2$$

If methane is heated with superheated steam, carbon monoxide and hydrogen are obtained.

$$CH_4 + H_2O \rightarrow CO + 3H_2$$

The pyrolysis of bituminous coal yields a solid residue, coke; a tarry residue, coal tar; and coal gas which may contain as much as 50 per cent hydrogen by volume.

10.4 PRINCIPAL USES

Most of the uses of hydrogen involve its application as a reducing agent.   It acts as an oxidizing agent only in the presence of the alkali metals and some of the alkaline-earth metals.   Hydrogen molecules, as units, are poor reducing agents, but activated molecules and the individual hydrogen atoms are extremely reactive. If hydrogen is adsorbed on the surface of certain metals such as palladium, platinum, and nickel, it is very reactive, probably because the hydrogen molecules are at least partially dissociated into hydrogen atoms.   Also, some hydrogen molecules may be deformed, thereby greatly weakening the covalent bonds.

The catalytic hydrogenation of several different animal and vegetable oils utilizes a huge amount of hydrogen.   The familiar product oleomargarine is a hydrogenated vegetable oil.

The use of hydrogen in the synthesis of ammonia by the Haber process is discussed on page 457.   The estimated production of synthetic ammonia during 1962 was 5,600,000 tons.

Most of the methanol, H_3COH, produced industrially is made by the hydrogenation of carbon monoxide.   Water gas, $CO + H_2$, is heated under pressure in the presence of an oxide catalyst.

$$CO + 2H_2 \leftrightarrows H_3COH$$

Hydrogen is used to reduce small quantities of certain metal oxides to yield the free metal.   Although this reduction is used primarily in the laboratory, it is worthy of mention.   Copper(II) oxide is easily reduced by passing hydrogen over the hot oxide.

$$CuO + H_2 \rightarrow Cu + H_2O$$

10.5 THE ATOMIC HYDROGEN TORCH

The hydrogen molecule dissociates at high temperatures and during electric discharge at low pressure.

$$H\!-\!H + 103.7 \text{ kcal} \leftrightarrows 2H \cdot$$

The equation indicates that the union of two hydrogen atoms to yield the diatomic molecule is exothermic.

The atomic hydrogen torch utilizes the large amount of heat evolved when hydrogen atoms combine on a solid surface to form hydrogen molecules. In the torch hydrogen gas is initially dissociated by the high temperature of an electric arc. The hydrogen atoms so produced are directed to the surface to be cut or welded. The heat evolved at the surface of the metal produces a temperature between 4000° and 5000°C. (See Fig. 10.1.)

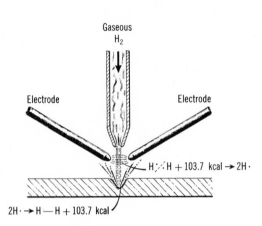

FIGURE 10.1 In the atomic hydrogen torch the hydrogen molecules dissociate endothermally at the electric arc between the electrodes. The atoms reunite exothermally to yield diatomic hydrogen molecules at the surface of the object to be heated. Temperatures up to 5000°C are attained at the object.

10.6 BINARY COMPOUNDS

a. Halides. All the hydrogen halides are gaseous at STP and each dissolves in water to yield an acidic solution (p. 534). Hydrogen fluoride has the highest standard boiling point, 19.4°C, because of extensive hydrogen bonding (p. 188). Each hydrogen halide yields a constant boiling mixture, or azeotrope (p. 382), with water.

Hydrogen reacts spontaneously with fluorine in the presence of a trace of water to produce hydrogen fluoride, HF. The moist gas reacts readily with glass to form gaseous silicon tetrafluoride and $(SiF_6)^{-2}$ ions. The glass is etched by the hydrogen fluoride. In the laboratory hydrogen fluoride is made by adding sulfuric acid to calcium fluoride, CaF_2 (fluorspar).

$$F^- + H^+ \leftrightarrows HF$$
(from
H_2SO_4)

Hydrogen reacts explosively with chlorine to yield hydrogen chloride, HCl (p. 437). Gaseous hydrogen chloride often is made in the laboratory by adding concentrated sulfuric acid to a thick paste of sodium chloride and concentrated hydrochloric acid.

$$H^+ + Cl^- \leftrightarrows HCl \uparrow$$
(from
H_2SO_4)

Hydrogen reacts with bromine vapor at slightly elevated temperatures to form hydrogen bromide, HBr. One of the best laboratory preparations is the addition of bromine to a mixture of red phosphorus and wet sand. The phosphorus tribromide produced initially is hydrolyzed to yield hydrogen bromide.

$$2P + 3Br_2 \rightarrow 2PBr_3$$

$$PBr_3 + 3H_2O \rightarrow H_3PO_3 + 3HBr$$

Hydrogen iodide is prepared by adding water slowly to a mixture of red phosphorus and iodine diluted with sand. The phosphorus triiodide hydrolyzes to form hydrogen iodide.

$$PI_3 + 3H_2O \rightarrow H_3PO_3 + 3HI$$

b. Hydrogen sulfide. Although hydrogen sulfide, H_2S, is available under pressure in cylinders, it is often prepared as needed in the laboratory by adding hydrochloric acid to iron(II) sulfide, FeS.

$$FeS + 2H^+ \rightarrow Fe^{++} + H_2S$$

Gaseous hydrogen sulfide is produced by bubbling hydrogen into boiling sulfur. If a mixture of sulfur and paraffin wax is heated, hydrogen sulfide is evolved. The gas is colorless, fairly soluble in water (0.1 M at 25°C), extremely toxic and it has the offensive odor of rotten eggs. Since it acts as a weak acid in water, it is a common source of sulfide ions (p. 543).

$$H_2S + H_2O \leftrightarrows 2OH_3^+ + S^{--}$$
$$\text{(excess)}$$

c. Hydrogen selenide. As might be expected, the gas hydrogen selenide, H_2Se, is similar to hydrogen sulfide. When contrasted with hydrogen sulfide, it is less stable, more strongly acidic, and more poisonous; it also has a more offensive odor. Hydrogen selenide is made by adding a strong acid to a metal selenide, such as Na_2Se or ZnSe. Hydrogen selenide is a good reducing agent; hence it oxidizes slowly in air to yield the red form of selenium.

$$2H_2Se + O_2 \rightarrow 2H_2O + 2Se$$

d. Hydrogen telluride. Among the binary compounds of hydrogen and the 6a elements, hydrogen telluride, H_2Te, is the strongest and the least stable acid. It decomposes when exposed to light ($H_2Te \rightarrow H_2 + Te$), but if pure it is stable in the dark. Aluminum telluride, Al_2Te_3, hydrolyzes in water to yield hydrogen telluride.

e. Ammonia. The commercial production of ammonia, NH_3, by the Haber process is described on page 457. Its uses in the chemical industry and either directly or indirectly as a fertilizer are growing steadily. In the laboratory ammonia may be produced by heating a mixture of ammonium chloride, $NH_4^+Cl^-$, and soda lime. Alkali metals dissolve in liquid ammonia to yield blue solutions; the coloration may be due to solvated electrons. If a catalytic metal is present, the alkali metal reduces hydrogen $+1$ to the elemental state. Amide ions remain in the solution with the alkali metal ion. For example,

$$2Na + 2NH_3 \rightarrow 2NH_2^- + 2Na^+ + H_2 \uparrow$$

Ammonia in the air or above a solution may be detected by using Nessler's reagent. This is prepared by dissolving mercury(II) iodide in potassium iodide solution (HgI_3^- and HgI_4^{--}) and then adding potassium hydroxide. In the presence of even tiny amounts of ammonia, the colloidal form of the substance, $Hg_2NH_2I_3$, imparts a yellow color to the reagent solution.

f. Hydrazine and hydrogen azide. Hydrazine, $H_2N—NH_2$, a liquid, is a weak base and an active reducing agent. The oxidation of ammonia by hypochlorite ion, OCl^-, yields hydrazine. The conjugate acid of hydrazine is called hydrazinium ion, $H_2NNH_3^+$.

Hydrogen azide (hydrazoic acid), HN_3, is an explosively unstable, volatile liquid weak acid. It is made by cautiously distilling an acidified solution of sodium azide, $Na^+N_3^-$. Sodium azide is produced when sodium nitrate is added slowly to molten sodium amide, $Na^+NH_2^-$.

$$3(Na^+NH_2^-) + Na^+NO_3^- \rightarrow Na^+N_3^- + 3(Na^+OH^-) + NH_3 \uparrow$$

Because lead azide, $Pb(N_3)_2$, and other "heavy" metal azides explode when struck, they are used as detonators.

g. Phosphine. The two most common binary compounds of phosphorus and hydrogen are phosphine, PH_3 (a gas), and diphosphine, P_2H_4 (a liquid). Pure phosphine is not spontaneously flammable in air at ordinary temperatures, but diphosphine is. Impure phosphine (mixed with diphosphine and hydrogen) is prepared by heating white phosphorus in a concentrated aqueous solution of sodium hydroxide.

$$P_4 + 3OH^- + 3H_2O \rightarrow 3H_2PO_2^- + PH_3 \uparrow$$
$$\text{hypophosphite}$$
$$\text{ion}$$

Phosphine and hydrogen iodide yield stable phosphonium iodide, $PH_4^+I^-$, but phosphine is too weak to act as a proton acceptor in water.

h. Arsine and stibine.   Gaseous arsine, AsH_3, is produced by adding an arsenic compound to a mixture of zinc and an aqueous strong acid.   If it is passed through a glass tube that is heated at some spot, a mirrorlike deposit of elemental arsenic is formed at that point.   This phenomenon is the basis of the Marsh test, a sensitive means for the detection of small amounts of combined arsenic.   Gaseous stibine, SbH_3,

$$Zn + 2HCl \rightarrow ZnCl_2 + H_2$$

$$12H_2 + Sb_4O_6 \rightarrow 6H_2O + 4SbH_3 \uparrow$$

(where the zinc and acid are mixed with the compound of antimony), is produced under conditions similar to those for the production of arsine.   Antimony can be detected by the Marsh test because stibine is decomposed thermally to yield elemental antimony.   An arsenic "mirror" usually is shiny black and "soluble" in a solution of sodium hypochlorite, whereas an antimony mirror usually is brownish-black and chemically inert to hypochlorite ion.   Arsine and stibine have no appreciable basic character.

i. Diborane.   The simplest of the six common hydroborons is diborane, B_2H_6, which appears to be the dimer of the unknown molecule BH_3.   Diborane is prepared by adding boron trichloride (or trifluoride) to an ionic hydride in ethereal solution.

$$6H^- + 2BCl_3 \rightarrow B_2H_6 + 6Cl^-$$

Diborane is spontaneously flammable in moist air and is rapidly hydrolyzed to boric acid and hydrogen.

An attempt to formulate a conventional covalent bond structure for diborane fails because there are only 12 available valence electrons and 14 are needed.   Of the several suggestions for possible formulations, the "three-centered bond" structure seems reasonable.

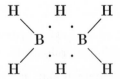

j. Ionic hydrides.   All the alkali metals and barium, strontium, and calcium react with hydrogen at elevated temperatures to yield essentially ionic hydrides, M^+H^- and $M^{++}(H^-)_2$.   These hydrides react vigorously with water to yield hydrogen and basic solutions because of the strong basicity of the hydride ion (p. 607).

$$H^- + HOH \rightarrow H_2 + OH^-$$

The hydride ion is a strong reducing agent.

Three commercially available sources of hydride ions are lithium aluminum hydride, $Li^+(AlH_4)^-$, lithium borohydride, $Li^+(BH_4)^-$, and sodium borohydride, $Na^+(BH_4)^-$. The borohydride complex ion seems to be quite stable because sodium borohydride is not decomposed by water at room temperature. Lithium aluminum hydride and lithium borohydride decompose in water.

$$AlH_4^- + 4HOH \rightarrow Al(OH)_4^- + 4H_2 \uparrow$$

Lithium aluminum hydride may be made by adding lithium hydride, Li^+H^-, to anhydrous aluminum chloride in anhydrous ether.

$$4(Li^+H^-) + AlCl_3 \leftrightharpoons Li^+(AlH_4)^- + 3(Li^+Cl^-) \downarrow$$

The complex hydride ions are good reducing agents because of the hydride ions. Reductions in aqueous solutions may be performed by using sodium borohydride; those in ethereal solutions are practical when any of the complex hydride ions are used.

Problems

1. Describe a simple apparatus to demonstrate the reduction of hot copper(II) oxide (black) by a stream of hydrogen. Remember that you want viewers to observe visually the results of the reaction.

2. (a) Contrasting all common gases at STP, why is hydrogen the least dense? (b) Is hydrogen the lightest gas under all conditions? If not, under what conditions is some other gas lighter?

3. Why is hydrogen selenide a stronger acid than hydrogen sulfide?

4. Predict what happens if phosphonium iodide is added to liquid ammonia.

5. Write the formulas of silver azide, hydrazinium hydrogen sulfate, hydroselenide ion, and sodium borohydride.

6. Elemental hydrogen is rarely found in the lithosphere, the hydrosphere, and the atmosphere, except in the outermost portions. However, large amounts of elemental hydrogen exist in the sun and many other planets and stars. Interpret these facts.

7. How many liters of hydrogen, measured at STP, are needed to reduce completely 55 g of copper(II) oxide?

8. There is on the market a solid material that when heated gently yields gaseous hydrogen sulfide. What do you suspect about its composition?

9. The directions on a can of lye, Na^+OH^-, state that the contents should not be dissolved in aluminum pots and pans. Why?

10. How many kcal of heat are evolved during the formation of 5 g of molecular hydrogen by the dimerization of the necessary hydrogen atoms?

11. How many pounds of methanol (theoretical yield) might be obtained by the proper treatment of 750 lb of carbon monoxide and 106 lb of hydrogen?

11

THE OXYGEN FAMILY

11.1 OCCURRENCE AND IMPORTANCE OF OXYGEN

Oxygen is the most abundant element, and there is at least one binary oxide of nearly every known element, except the inert gases. Its significance is great.

About 23.21 per cent by weight of dry, carbon-dioxide-free atmospheric air is elemental oxygen. There is a huge amount of combined oxygen in the hydrosphere (the bodies of water) and in the lithosphere (rocks, ores, and minerals).

The approximate percentage composition of the earth's crust with respect to the 5 most abundant elements is: oxygen, 46.4 per cent; silicon, 27.8 per cent; aluminum, 8.14 per cent; iron, 5.12 per cent; and calcium, 3.6 per cent. At least 91 per cent of the earth's crust is composed of only 5 different elements. Over 99 per cent of the earth, excluding the hydro-

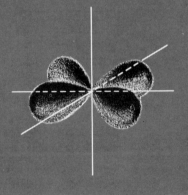

sphere, consists of only 9 different elements. Table 11.1 indicates the approximate average composition of the earth's crust, the hydrosphere, and the atmosphere.

TABLE 11.1 Approximate average composition of the earth's crust, the hydrosphere, and the atmosphere

Element	Per Cent	Element	Per Cent
Oxygen	49.2	Chlorine	0.2
Silicon	25.7	Phosphorus	0.1
Aluminum	7.4	Manganese	0.1
Iron	4.7	Carbon	0.09
Calcium	3.4	Sulfur	0.05
Sodium	2.6	Barium	0.05
Potassium	2.4	Chromium	0.03
Magnesium	1.9	Nitrogen	0.03
Hydrogen	0.9	Fluorine	0.03
Titanium	0.6	All others	0.52

Having discussed the composition of the earth, let us now consider the percentage composition of the atmosphere (dry and carbon-dioxide-free) with respect to the three gases that comprise 99.99 per cent of the atmosphere.

Gaseous Element	Atmosphere Per Cent, by Volume	Atmosphere Per Cent, by Weight
Nitrogen	78.05	75.50
Oxygen	21.00	23.21
Argon	0.94	1.28

The remainder of the atmosphere (excluding carbon dioxide and water vapor) consists of neon, helium, krypton, and xenon (listed in decreasing order of abundance). The percentage of carbon dioxide in dry country air usually varies between the limits 0.03 per cent and 0.04 per cent by volume, but in urban and industrial areas the percentage of carbon dioxide in dry air may increase to 0.07 per cent. The concentration of carbon dioxide in the atmosphere remains essentially constant because the combustion of carbonaceous matter and the respiration of animals which yield carbon dioxide are balanced by the utilization of carbon dioxide during photosynthesis in green plants (see Fig. 11.1).

We must not neglect the hydrosphere in our discussions of the elemental composition of our planetary system. The oceans constitute 98 per cent of the hydrosphere. The average percentage of oxygen in sea water is 85.8 per cent. The average percentage of dissolved solids in water from the Atlantic Ocean is 3.5 per cent. (In the Dead Sea the percentage of dissolved solids is 25 per cent.) The percentage composition of the solid residue obtained from Atlantic Ocean water is: Na^+, 30.6 per cent; K^+, 1.1 per cent; Ca^{++}, 1.2 per cent; Mg^{++}, 3.7 per cent; Cl^-, 55.3 per cent; Br^-, 0.19 per cent; SO_4^{--}, 7.7 per cent.

Let us note a few facts that eminently substantiate the conclusion that the oceans are vast chemical storehouses. The total volume of sea water is approximately 320,000,000 cubic miles. Each cubic mile contains 4×10^9 tons of sea water (a dilute aqueous solution). Each cubic mile of the Atlantic Ocean contains (in approximate amounts):

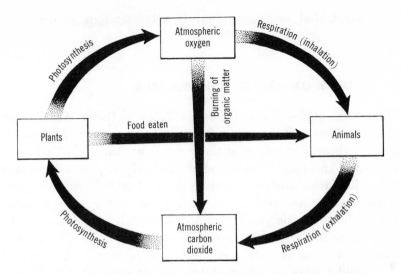

FIGURE 11.1 Natural oxygen–carbon-dioxide cycle. Respiration of animals removes oxygen from the air, and the major gaseous products of animal metabolism are carbon dioxide and water. During photosynthesis in plants, the consumption of carbon dioxide and water eventually yields carbohydrates.

4.28×10^7 tons of sodium, as sodium ion
7.7×10^8 tons of chlorine, as chloride ion
2.6×10^5 tons of bromine, as bromide ion
1.54×10^6 tons of potassium, as potassium ion
5.2×10^6 tons of magnesium, as magnesium ion
3.5×10^6 tons of sulfur, as sulfate ion

11.2 PREPARATION AND ISOLATION OF OXYGEN

In the laboratory oxygen is usually prepared by either the pyrolysis of potassium chlorate (p. 68), the electrolysis of water (p. 504), or the pyrolysis of a "heavy-metal" binary oxide, such as mercury(II) oxide (p. 72).

The atmosphere is the most convenient and economical source of oxygen. Air is liquefied, and by fractional distillation at least 99.5 per cent pure oxygen is obtained. Liquid oxygen is blue. The total mass of the atmosphere is estimated to be 5.7×10^{15} tons. Since at least 23 per cent of the atmosphere is elemental oxygen, it is evident that the atmosphere is a tremendous source of free oxygen.

11.3 BINARY OXIDES OF THE METALS

Although the oxides can be divided into classes, the lines of demarcation are unclear. If the oxides are classified according to structure, there are those that are essentially covalent, those that are essentially ionic, and those that are about as ionic as they are covalent. If the oxides are classified according to chemical behavior in aqueous solutions, some are acidic, some are basic, some are amphoteric (both acidic and basic), and a few are none of these. Some covalent oxides are reducing agents as well as oxidizing agents, because the oxidation state of the other element (not oxygen) is between the highest and lowest oxidation states of that element. Since in all binary oxides the oxidation state of oxygen is -2, the common oxides of the active metals are generally poor reducing and oxidizing agents.

Among the common oxides of the metallic elements, only the alkali metal oxides are appreciably soluble in water. The slightly soluble acidic oxides of the metals are soluble in basic solutions, the basic oxides are soluble in acidic solutions, and the amphoteric (acidic and basic) oxides are soluble in acidic and in basic solutions.

Nearly all the metal oxides, except those of the alkali metals, may be prepared by heating the appropriate metal hydroxide or carbonate. Pyrolysis of the hydroxide yields the oxide and water, whereas pyrolysis of the carbonate yields the oxide and carbon dioxide. When heated, all metal nitrates, except those of sodium, potassium, and cesium, yield the metal oxide, oxides of nitrogen and oxygen. For example,

$$2Pb(NO_3)_2 + \Delta \rightarrow 2PbO + 4NO + 3O_2$$
lead nitrate

Many metal oxides can be made by direct union of the metal and oxygen.

Among the basic metal oxides, the essentially ionic oxides are those of the alkali metals, magnesium, calcium, strontium, and barium. Each of these reacts with excess water to yield a basic solution (p. 543). The alkali metal oxides, except lithium oxide, cannot be made by the direct union of the metal and oxygen; the peroxide is produced instead (p. 262). An alkali metal oxide can be made by reduction of the nitrate by the alkali metal. For sodium oxide,

$$2NaNO_3 + 10Na \rightarrow 6Na_2O + N_2$$

The alkaline-earth metal oxides are made by heating the carbonate. For example,

$$CaCO_3 + \Delta \rightarrow CaO + CO_2$$

Each transition element has at least one slightly soluble basic oxide. Some transition elements have a basic oxide, an acidic oxide, and an amphoteric oxide. For example, chromium(II) oxide, CrO, is basic; chromium(VI) oxide, CrO_3, is acidic; chromium(III) oxide, Cr_2O_3, is amphoteric (both acidic and basic).

a. *Chromium(VI) oxide* interacts with water to yield the diprotic molecule chromic acid, $(HO)_2CrO_2$.

$$(HO)_2CrO_2 + HOH \leftrightharpoons HOCrO_3^- + OH_3^+$$

hydrogen
chromate
ion

$$HOCrO_3^- + HOH \leftrightharpoons CrO_4^{--} + OH_3^+$$

chromate
ion
(yellow)

In strongly acidic solutions, dichromate ions are formed.

$$2CrO_4^{--} + 2H^+ \leftrightharpoons HOH + Cr_2O_7^{--}$$

dichromate
ion
(orange)

b. *Beryllium oxide*, BeO, is amphoteric. Although it is only slightly soluble in water, it is soluble in both basic and acidic solutions. Other common amphoteric oxides are: aluminum oxide, Al_2O_3; chromium(III) oxide, Cr_2O_3; zinc oxide, ZnO; lead(II) oxide, PbO; tin(II) oxide, SnO; tin(IV) oxide, SnO_2; titanium(IV) oxide, TiO_2.

The most important water-soluble acidic metal oxides are *chromium(VI) oxide*, CrO_3, and *manganese(VII) oxide*, Mn_2O_7. *Vanadium(V) oxide*, V_2O_5, is a slightly soluble acidic oxide.

$$CrO_3 + H_2O \rightarrow H_2CrO_4 \text{ (chromic acid)}$$
$$Mn_2O_7 + H_2O \rightarrow 2HMnO_4 \text{ (permanganic acid)}$$
$$V_2O_5 + 3H_2O \rightarrow 2H_3VO_4 \text{ (vanadic acid)}$$

Some of the more common oxides have classical single names. A few examples are:

lithia—lithium oxide
magnesia—magnesium oxide
alumina—aluminum oxide

silica—silicon dioxide
strontia—strontium oxide
baryta—barium oxide

Many metal oxides occur in nature, and some are present in a fairly high state of purity. For example, quartz is nearly pure (silicon dioxide). Many of the minerals and ores that are the major sources of the most common metals (except the alkali metals) are either oxides or substances containing oxide complex ions. Some of these minerals are:

dolomite—$CaCO_3 \cdot MgCO_3$
bauxite—$Al_2O_3xH_2O$ (impure)
corundum—Al_2O_3 (anhydrous)
sand—SiO_2 (impure)
rutile—TiO_2
ilmenite—$FeTiO_3$
hematite—Fe_2O_3
brown hematites
  or limonites—$Fe_2O_3xH_2O$
siderite—$FeCO_3$
magnetite
  (lodestone)—Fe_3O_4

pyrolusite—MnO_2
cassiterite—SnO_2
zircon—$ZrSiO_4$
zincite—ZnO
smithsonite—$ZnCO_3$
cuprite—Cu_2O
azurite—$Cu(OH)_2 \cdot 2CuCO_3$
carnotite—$2K(UO_2)VO_4 \cdot 3H_2O$
scheelite—$CaWO_4$
wolframite—$(Fe, Mn)WO_4$
chromite—$Fe(CrO_2)_2$
pitchblende—U_3O_8

11.4 BINARY NONMETAL OXIDES

All binary oxides of the nonmetallic or electronegative elements are essentially covalent. Most of them are acids and many that are soluble in water yield acidic solutions.

The oxides of the halogens are described in Chapter 12 and those of sulfur in Section 11.11. The oxides of nitrogen, phosphorus, and arsenic are mentioned in Chapter 13 and those of carbon in Chapter 27. The chemistry of silica is described in Section 11.8.

a. *Selenium dioxide*, SeO_2, is a white solid that exists as a trimer, Se_3O_6, at room temperature. It is very soluble in water to yield an acidic solution. Evaporation of the solution yields crystalline selenous acid, $(HO)_2SeO$.

b. *Selenium trioxide*, SeO_3, is a white deliquescent solid that reacts readily with water to yield selenic acid, $(HO)_2SeO_2$, a very hygroscopic solid, mp 58°C. An aqueous solution of selenic acid may be made by treating a solution of selenous acid with permanganate ion.   Selenic acid is a strong oxidizing agent, and on heating dissolves copper and gold to yield copper(II) selenate, $CuSeO_4$, and gold(III) selenate, $Au_2(SeO_4)_3$.

11.5 HYDROGEN PEROXIDE

Hydrogen peroxide, HOOH, is the simplest covalent compound that has the peroxy group $-\overline{O}-\overline{O}-$.   Care must be used in its purification and storage because many substances either catalyze its decomposition or reduce it.   The decomposition of hydrogen peroxide is exothermic, yielding water and oxygen.   Many substances act as catalysts in accelerating its decomposition.   In animals the enzyme catalase specifically catalyzes the decomposition.

$$2H_2O_2 \rightarrow 2H_2O + O_2$$

Hydrogen peroxide acts as a weak acid in water.

$$H_2O_2 + HOH \leftrightarrows OH_3^+ + \quad O_2H^-$$
$$\text{hydroperoxide}$$
$$\text{ion}$$

Hydrogen peroxide is a colorless liquid; its density is 1.4 g/ml at 22°C; its melting point is $-0.9°C$; its normal boiling point is 152°C.

An aqueous solution of hydrogen peroxide may be prepared by carefully adding barium peroxide to dilute sulfuric acid.

$$Ba^{++}O_2^{--} + 2H^+ + SO_4^{--} \rightarrow H_2O_2 + Ba^{++}SO_4^{--} \downarrow$$

The precipitated barium sulfate is removed by filtration or centrifugation.

A commercial preparation of hydrogen peroxide developed in Germany during World War II involves the electrolysis of 50 per cent aqueous sulfuric acid.   The peroxydisulfate ion, $S_2O_8^{--}$, which appears at the anode is gently hydrolyzed to yield hydrogen peroxide.

There has been developed recently an industrial process that yields a cheaper and higher-grade product than the older electrolysis method.   In this method certain organic compounds are hydrogenated catalytically and then oxidized by oxygen to yield hydrogen peroxide.

A dilute aqueous solution of hydrogen peroxide may be concentrated to a 30 per cent solution (superoxol or perhydrol) by cautious distillation at atmospheric pressure.   Further purification either to a 98 per cent solution or to pure hydrogen peroxide involves distillation under reduced pressure. Ordinary drugstore hydrogen peroxide is 3 per cent; a 6 per cent solution is used for bleaching hair.

Hydrogen peroxide is a fairly good oxidizing agent because it is easily reduced to water. Its bleaching action is due to its behavior as an oxidizing agent. The half-reaction for the reduction of hydrogen peroxide in acidic solutions is:

$$H_2O_2 + 2H^+ + 2e^- \rightarrow 2HOH$$

Hydrogen peroxide can act as a reducing agent in the presence of strong oxidizing agents such as silver oxide, Ag_2O, and permanganate ion, MnO_4^-, in acidic solutions. In acidic solutions the half-reaction is:

$$H_2O_2 \rightarrow O_2 + 2H^+ + 2e^-$$

In basic solutions the half-reaction is:

$$OH^- + O_2H^- \rightarrow O_2 + 2e^- + HOH$$

The peroxy linkage, O—O, is found in all peroxides; it is one of the weakest covalent bonds. This O—O bond often undergoes homolytic fission to yield two radical fragments. Hydroxyl radicals, $\cdot \overline{O}$—H, are apparently formed in an aqueous solution of iron(II) sulfate and hydrogen peroxide (Fenton's reagent).

11.6 IONIC PEROXIDES AND SUPEROXIDES

The most common binary ionic peroxide is sodium peroxide, $(Na^+)_2O_2^{--}$. It is prepared by heating metallic sodium in an excess of oxygen.

$$2Na\cdot + |\overline{O}\text{—}\overline{O}| \rightarrow (Na^+)_2\left[|\overline{O}\text{—}\overline{O}|\right]^{--} \text{ or } (Na^+)_2O_2^{--}$$

Sodium peroxide is yellow, and it reacts violently with water to yield hydroperoxide ion, $(|\overline{O}\text{—}\overline{O}\text{—}H)^-$. Peroxide ion, O_2^{--}, as is oxide ion, is a strong base, relative to water:

$$O_2^{--} + HOH \leftrightarrows HO_2^- + OH^-$$

In warm water it decomposes to oxygen and hydroxyl ion. One possible fate is

$$\underset{\substack{\text{hydroperoxide} \\ \text{ion}}}{OOH^-} \rightarrow \underset{\substack{\text{oxygen} \\ \text{atom}}}{(O)} + OH^-$$

$$2(O) \leftrightarrows O_2 \uparrow$$

Lithium peroxide is difficult to prepare, but the peroxides of potassium, rubidium, and cesium are made by using an excess of the metal in the presence of oxygen. The alkali metal peroxides, except lithium peroxide, are colored. All peroxides are very active oxidizing agents because peroxide ion is easily reduced. Peroxide ion can behave as a reducing agent in the presence of certain strong oxidizing agents.

Rubidium and cesium yield pure (colored) superoxides when they react with an excess of oxygen; potassium under the same conditions yields a mixture of peroxide and superoxide.

$$Rb \cdot + |\overline{O}\text{—}\overline{O}| \rightarrow Rb^+ \left[|\overline{O}\text{—}\overline{O}| \right]^-$$

The superoxide ion, O_2^-, is a radical because it has an unpaired electron. If a superoxide is added to water, it decomposes to yield hydrogen peroxide and hydroxyl ions. The over-all reaction is

$$2O_2^- + 4HOH \rightarrow 3H_2O_2 + 2OH^-$$

It has been suggested that hydroxyl radicals, $\cdot \overline{O}H$, are initially formed and that their dimerization yields hydrogen peroxide (see p. 262).

11.7 OZONE

Ozone, O_3, is an allotropic form of oxygen (ozone and oxygen are allotropes). Gaseous ozone has a light blue color and a singular odor. The normal boiling point of ozone is —112°C; it melts at —250°C. Solid ozone has a dark violet color. Gaseous ozone is fairly soluble in carbon tetrachloride but is only slightly soluble in water.

Ozone is usually prepared by passing an electrical discharge through gaseous oxygen. The yield is rather low (usually less than 10 per cent because ozone exothermally decomposes to yield oxygen.

$$3O_2 + 68.44 \text{ kcal} \leftrightarrows 2O_3$$

The ozone molecule seems to be formed by the attachment of an oxygen atom to an oxygen molecule:

It is impossible, by using a single formulation, to represent adequately the ozone molecule because certain electrons cannot be localized (recall Sec. 8.7). Ozone is not paramagnetic because all of its electrons are paired (see Fig. 11.2).

O_3

FIGURE 11.2 Diagram of an ozone molecule, a triatomic molecule.

Ozone is an extremely active oxidizing agent. Only fluorine, oxygen fluoride, and oxygen atoms are better oxidizing agents than ozone. Ozone is therefore a better oxidizing agent than molecular oxygen. At room temperature, ozone can oxidize iodide ion to iodine and elemental silver to silver oxide; oxygen cannot. Ozone is an effective bactericide and a good bleaching agent.

Ozone is present in appreciable quantities in the upper atmosphere (15 miles above the earth) due to the photochemical conversion of oxygen to ozone. The absorption by an oxygen molecule of one quantum ($h\nu$) of far ultraviolet radiation (wave lengths 1600 A to 1800 A) causes the dissociation of the oxygen molecule to yield two oxygen atoms.

$$O_2 + h\nu \rightarrow 2|\overline{\underset{.}{O}} \cdot$$

This is immediately followed by

$$|\overline{\underset{.}{O}} \cdot + |\overline{\underset{.}{O}}{-}\overline{\underset{.}{O}}| \leftrightarrows |\overline{O} = \overline{O}{-}\overline{\underset{.}{O}}|$$

The ozone absorbs ultraviolet radiation (2400 A to 3000 A) and then dissociates photochemically to yield oxygen molecules and oxygen atoms:

$$O_3 + h\nu \rightarrow |\overline{\underset{.}{O}} \cdot + O_2$$

The photochemical formation and dissociation of ozone set up an equilibrium system. The continual absorption of ultraviolet radiation by oxygen and ozone in the "ozone layer" of the upper atmosphere removes nearly all the ultraviolet light in the solar radiation. This is, to say the least, extremely fortunate because ultraviolet radiation is so energetic that it is very destructive to living tissue.

Life as we recognize it could not exist on our planet if most of the ultraviolet light in solar radiation reached the earth.

11.8 OXY-COMPOUNDS OF SILICON

Since the elements oxygen and silicon constitute most of the earth's crust, let us now describe some of the more common substances and materials that contain oxygen and silicon.

a. Silicon dioxide (silica).   Quartz, SiO_2, is a very common mineral; most igneous rocks, such as granite, contain appreciable amounts of quartz and most types of sand have high percentages of silica.   Agate, flint, and infusorial earth (diatomaceous remains of tiny organisms called diatoms) are mainly silica.   Perhaps as much as 12 per cent of the earth's crust is silica.

Quartz is a hard, colorless substance.   It is transparent to ultraviolet radiation and thus is very useful in certain optical instruments.   (Ordinary glass is quite opaque to ultraviolet light.) Quartz (silica) has a very high melting point (1650–1700°C).   If molten silica is cooled, it undercools and forms a glass (a transparent, apparently solid, noncrystalline material).   This silica glass (quartz glass) has such a low coefficient of expansion that if a red-hot piece of it is plunged into water it will not crack.

Quartz is a macromolecule, $(SiO_2)_n$, consisting of a framework of SiO_4 tetrahedrons interconnected by polar covalent bonds.   Each silicon atom is bonded to four oxygen atoms, and each oxygen atom is bonded to two silicon atoms.   Since there are no individual SiO_2 molecules in quartz, it is evident that solid silicon dioxide is structurally quite different from solid carbon dioxide.

b. The soluble silicates.   Silica is such a weak acid it does not combine directly with water, but it will dissolve in a hot solution of sodium hydroxide to yield a concentrated solution of sodium silicate (water glass).   The silicate anions in this solution are rather complex (they are not simply SiO_3^{--} or SiO_4^{4-}, as might be expected).   Since the composition of sodium silicate is variable, it is often formulated as $Na_2O \cdot xSiO_2$, where x usually has a value between 2 and 4.   Silica dissolves in a hot solution of any alkali metal hydroxide to yield a soluble silicate.   An aqueous solution of sodium silicate may be used as an adhesive, as a fireproofing agent for wood and cloth, and as an egg preservative.

c. Hydrated silica. If an aqueous solution of a strong acid is added to a solution of an alkali metal silicate, a gelatinous precipitate is obtained. The composition of this solid is best represented by the formulation $xSiO_2 \cdot yH_2O$. If a dilute solution of a soluble silicate is added to an acidic solution, a colloidal suspension of hydrated (hydrous) silica is formed. This system soon sets to a jellylike mass. The commercial product, "silica gel," is obtained by carefully removing about 95 per cent of the water from hydrous silica. Silica gel is an efficient drying agent and is highly absorbent to many substances.

d. The silicate minerals. The minerals that are usually classed as silicates have widely varying compositions and structures. In the interest of simplicity, we shall note only a few important aspects of the silicate minerals. They are extremely important because most of the minerals in the earth's crust are silicates—we can hardly overlook them. The hundreds of different silicate minerals are often divided into three major groups: the framework (hard) minerals, the layer (soft) minerals, and the fibrous minerals.

The framework minerals usually consist of rigid three-dimensional structures built of AlO_4 and SiO_4 tetrahedrons. In the "empty" spaces of this framework are the simple monatomic cations and anions and frequently water molecules. Among these framework (aluminosilicate) minerals are ordinary feldspar (orthoclase), $KAlSi_3O_8$; chabazite, $CaAl_2Si_4O_{12} \cdot 6H_2O$; and sodalite, $Na_4Al_3Si_3O_{12}Cl$. The zeolites are also framework silicates. (See p. 610.)

The layer (sheetlike) minerals consist of planar aggregates of silicate tetrahedrons (SiO_4). In talc, $Mg_3Si_4O_{10}(OH)_2$, and in kaolinite, $Al_2Si_2O_5(OH)_4$, the planar "sheets" of silicate tetrahedrons are electrically uncharged; hence the layers readily slide over each other. In muscovite (mica), $KAl_3Si_3O_{10}(OH)_2$, the negatively charged planar frameworks of AlO_4 and SiO_4 tetrahedrons are less readily moved over each other because of the strong electrostatic forces between potassium ions and the negatively charged layers.

The fibrous minerals consist of long chainlike aggregates of SiO_4 tetrahedra. Since these solids can be readily cleaved only in directions parallel to the silicate chains, fibrous pieces (fibers) of the mineral can be separated from the main crystal. Asbestos is a mixture of the most common fibrous silicate minerals: tremolite, $Ca_2Mg_5Si_8O_{22}(OH)_2$, and chrysotile, $Mg_6Si_4O_{11}(OH)_6 \cdot H_2O$.

e. Clay. Clay is an aluminosilicate (mainly $H_4Al_2Si_2O_9$), which usually contains either sand, feldspar, iron(III) oxide, or a similar compound. Porcelain and chinaware are made by using pure, white clays, such as kaolin. The surface of the piece of ceramic may be glazed either by coating it with an easily fusible silicate (a glass) or by putting on the surface a substance that will react with the ceramic to yield a transparent, nonporous layer.

    f. Cement and concrete. Portland cement is usually made by initially pulverizing a mixture of limestone and clay, which is then heated (burned). The aluminosilicate mixture produced in the hottest part of the kiln is cooled to yield a clinker which is then finely ground to form the finished cement. The final reactions in the kiln probably involve the basic oxide, $Ca^{++}O^{--}$, and the acidic oxides, SiO_2 and Al_2O_3. These acid-base reactions form a mixture of calcium silicates, Ca_2SiO_4 and Ca_3SiO_5, and calcium aluminate, $Ca_3Al_2O_6$.

    When cement is mixed with water, a complex series of hydrolysis and hydration reactions occur. The final products of these exothermic reactions are calcium aluminosilicates which form a rigid network of crystals. If a limited amount of water is added to a mixture of cement, sand, and gravel, the mixture "sets" to yield concrete. Portland cement is often called a hydraulic cement because it can "set" under water.

    g. Glass. Most commercial glasses are brittle solutions which actually are transparent amorphous mixtures of silicates. The most common glass ("soft" or soda lime glass) is made by melting a mixture of silica, sodium carbonate, and calcium carbonate. Carbon dioxide is evolved, and a complex mixture of sodium and calcium silicates is obtained. When this molten mixture cools, its viscosity gradually increases until a brittle, undercooled solution (the glass) is obtained. Silicon and oxygen constitute about 84 per cent of ordinary ("soft") glass; the remainder is about 10 per cent sodium, 5 per cent calcium, and 1 per cent aluminum. The molten glass can be molded or blown to produce glass vessels. It can be poured onto a flat surface and then rolled to produce plate glass. Safety glass consists of two sheets of glass separated by a thin sheet of a tough plastic material.

    Pyrex glass is a boro-alumino-silicate glass. Its major constituents are silicon, oxygen, and boron. Because it has a thermal expansion about one-third that of soda lime glass, it breaks less readily when suddenly cooled or heated. Pyrex glass is more resistant to most chemical reagents than is soda lime glass, and it is not plastic at temperatures at which "soft" glass is quite easily bent or blown.

Enamels used to coat metallic surfaces are easily fusible glasses that contain either colored pigments or white solids such as titanium dioxide.

h. The silicones. The silicones are large molecules obtained by the condensation polymerization (p. 240) of certain monomer molecules containing the elements silicon, oxygen, carbon, and hydrogen. The monomer fragments are held together in the polymer by Si—O—Si bonds, just as the silicon dioxide monomers are held together in the macromolecule quartz, $(SiO_2)_n$.

A typical methyl silicone is prepared by the hydrolysis of dimethyl-dichlorosilane, $(CH_3)_2SiCl_2$. This halogen compound is made by passing gaseous methyl chloride, CH_3Cl, over elemental silicon (with copper as a catalyst).

$$2CH_3Cl + Si \rightarrow (CH_3)_2SiCl_2$$

During the hydrolysis of dimethyl-dichlorosilane, a likely intermediate is $(CH_3)_2Si(OH)_2$. Apparently these molecules condense with each other (water is simultaneously lost) to yield a silicone—a polymer whose empirical formula is $(CH_3)_2SiO$. [This formula closely resembles that of acetone, $(CH_3)_2CO$, the simplest ketone; hence the name silicone.] A portion of this silicone molecule may be represented as:

$$-\overset{\displaystyle CH_3}{\underset{\displaystyle CH_3}{Si}}-O-\left[\overset{\displaystyle CH_3}{\underset{\displaystyle CH_3}{Si}}-O\right]_n\overset{\displaystyle CH_3}{\underset{\displaystyle CH_3}{Si}}-O-$$

where the symbol within the brackets represents a monomer fragment.

In certain methyl silicone oils, the value of n is about 10 or 15. These silicone oils are extremely versatile for several reasons: they have a very low coefficient of viscosity (with temperature changes); they have high thermal stability; and they are chemically rather inert to metals and most ordinary reagents.

Rubberlike silicones (in which n may be 2000 or more) are quite useful: they retain their structural character over wide temperature ranges; they are not easily oxidized by oxygen; and they have good electrical insulating properties. "Bouncing" putty is a silicone which is somewhat fluid (it slowly flows under its own weight) and yet is very resilient to forces that are applied to it quickly.

If methyl-trichlorosilane, CH_3SiCl_3, is hydrolyzed, a cross-linked, resinous polymer is obtained. A small portion of this polymer is

$$\begin{array}{ccc}
CH_3 & & CH_3 \\
| & & | \\
-O-Si-O-Si-O- \\
| & & | \\
O & & O \\
| & & | \\
-O-Si-O-Si-O- \\
| & & | \\
CH_3 & & CH_3
\end{array}$$

By using different chlorosilanes and different reaction conditions, a wide variety of different silicones is obtained.

11.9 OCCURRENCE AND PRODUCTION OF SULFUR

A large amount of elemental sulfur occurs in the earth's crust in volcanic regions and in or near certain geologic formations associated with calcite, $CaCO_3$, deposits. Combined sulfur is in the form of metal sulfides, as hydrogen sulfide in sour gas (p. 682) and as sulfate ion in minerals such as gypsum, $CaSO_4 \cdot 2H_2O$, and barite, $BaSO_4$. A brief list of some common sulfides is in Table 11.2.

Huge quantities of elemental sulfur are mined in Louisiana and Texas by the ingenious Frasch process. A well is bored into the sulfur-bearing strata and this is fitted with concentric pipes. Air and superheated water (about 170°C) are forced into the well through two of the pipes. The sulfur (mp 113°C) is melted at the high temperature and the compressed air forces the emulsion of hot water and liquid sulfur to the surface. The sulfur obtained by the Frasch process is usually not less than 99.5 per cent pure. A typical recent annual production of sulfur in the United States is at least 5 million short tons, approximately 90 per cent of the world production.

Certain regions of North America yield a kind of natural gas that is called sour gas because it contains appreciable amounts of hydrogen sulfide. Plants are now in operation to utilize this source of sulfur.

Huge quantities of sulfur are used in the manufacture of sulfuric acid (p. 272), sulfur dioxide, and lime-sulfur sprays, and in the vulcanization of rubber (p. 705).

TABLE 11.2 Some common sulfide minerals

Name	Formula	Color
Galena	PbS	black
Sphalerite	ZnS	white-yellow-black
Cinnabar	HgS	red
Chalcopyrite	$CuFeS_2$	brass yellow
Chalcocite	Cu_2S	dark
Pyrite (fool's gold)	FeS_2	brass yellow
Cobaltite	CoAsS	dark
Pentlandite	$NiS \cdot 2FeS$	bronze yellow
Molybdenite	MoS_2	bluish gray
Argentite	Ag_2S	dark gray
Orpiment	As_2S_3	yellow
Realgar	As_2S_2	yellow
Arsenopyrite	FeAsS	light gray
Stibnite	Sb_2S_3	lead gray
Bismuthinite	Bi_2S_3	lead gray
Covellite	CuS	deep blue-black
Pyrrhotite	$FeS(S)_x$	bronze yellow

11.10 ALLOTROPY OF SULFUR

The yellow crystalline form of sulfur (brimstone) stable at temperatures below 96°C is called rhombic sulfur (mp 113°C).   If rhombic sulfur is melted and if the fluid is solidified, crystals of monoclinic sulfur (mp 119°C) are obtained.   On standing at room temperature, the monoclinic form gradually changes to the rhombic form.   If the molten sulfur is heated, it gradually darkens in color and its viscosity increases.   Rapid cooling of the viscous sulfur yields a plastic, rubbery material.   Molten sulfur boils at 445°C (1 atm). Sulfur vapor is reddish, and it condenses on a cool surface to yield solid "flowers of sulfur."

Rhombic and monoclinic sulfur consist of S_8 molecules (p. 138). During the heating of molten sulfur, the viscosity of the liquid gradually increases.   This phenomenon is apparently due to the presence of long molecular chains of sulfur atoms that entangle easily.   These chains are formed after S_8 rings rupture and the open ends of different broken rings join to yield chains of varying lengths. As the standard boiling point is reached, these long entangled chains commence to break. Then molecular size and viscosity decrease. Sulfur vapor at 445°C contains some S_2 molecules.

11.11 SULFUR DIOXIDE

Sulfur dioxide, SO_2, is a colorless gas having an irritating odor. Since its standard boiling point is $-10°C$, it is easily liquefied and shipped in the liquid state.

Sulfur dioxide is produced either by the burning of sulfur in air or during the roasting (p. 603) of sulfide ores.

$$S + O_2 \rightarrow SO_2$$
$$2CuS + 3O_2 \rightarrow 2CuO + 2SO_2$$

Certain metals reduce concentrated sulfuric acid to yield sulfur dioxide.

$$Cu + 2H_2SO_4 \rightarrow CuSO_4 + 2H_2O + SO_2$$

Huge amounts of sulfur dioxide enter the air daily in areas where much coal is burned as fuel. Of course, the amount of SO_2 evolved varies with the sulfur content of the coal.

Sulfur dioxide dissolves in water to produce sulfurous acid, H_2SO_3, weak and diprotic (yields two protons per molecule).

$$SO_2 + H_2O \leftrightharpoons H_2SO_3$$
$$H_2SO_3 + H_2O \leftrightharpoons HSO_3^- + OH_3^+$$
hydrogen
sulfite ion

$$HSO_3^- + H_2O \leftrightharpoons SO_3^{--} + OH_3^+$$
sulfite
ion

Sulfite and hydrogen sulfite ions are readily oxidized by either atmospheric oxygen, chlorine, or bromine to yield sulfate ions, SO_4^{--}. If a strong acid is added to a solution containing either hydrogen sulfite or sulfite ions, sulfur dioxide is evolved.

If a mixture of sodium sulfite and sulfur is boiled, sodium thiosulfate is produced.

$$(Na^+)_2SO_3^{--} + S \rightarrow (Na^+)_2S_2O_3^{--}$$
sodium
thiosulfate

Sodium thiosulfate (hypo) is used as a fixing agent in photography because it yields a complex silver thiosulfate ion, $Ag(S_2O_3)_2^{3-}$.

Sulfur dioxide in the presence of water is an oxidizing agent and a reducing agent. For instance, it reduces oxygen, chlorine, bromine, iodine, permanganate ion, MnO_4^-, and many colored organic compounds (dyes). Moist sulfur dioxide is used widely as a bleaching agent. It oxidizes hydrogen sulfide.

$$2H_2S + SO_2 \rightarrow 2H_2O + 3S$$

11.12 SULFUR TRIOXIDE AND SULFURIC ACID

Sulfur trioxide, SO_3, is produced readily by the oxidation of sulfur dioxide by oxygen. This occurs in the contact process.

$$2SO_2 + O_2 \leftrightarrows 2SO_3$$

It is a colorless liquid (bp 45°C), and in the solid state (mp 17°C) it exists as a dimer, S_2O_6, and a trimer, S_3O_9.

The main industrial use of sulfur trioxide is in the production of sulfuric acid by the contact process (see Fig. 11.3). Sulfur trioxide reacts vigorously with water to yield sulfuric acid, H_2SO_4 (p. 540).

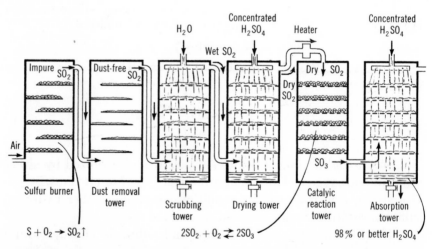

FIGURE 11.3 Contact process used to manufacture nearly 80 per cent of the sulfuric acid annually produced in the United States. Sulfur dioxide must be carefully purified before it is catalytically oxidized; otherwise certain impurities poison the catalyst. Water-soluble impurities are removed in the scrubbing tower; moist gas is dried in the drying tower; dry SO_2, in contact with the catalyst, reacts with oxygen in the reaction tower; and SO_3 is absorbed in sulfuric acid in the absorption tower, either to yield 100 per cent acid or oleum, in which SO_3 is dissolved in sulfuric acid.

$$SO_3 + H_2O \rightarrow H_2SO_4 + 21.3\,kcal$$

Sulfur trioxide is a strong acid.   It reacts with sulfuric acid to yield disulfuric acid (fuming sulfuric acid or oleum).

$$H_2SO_4 + SO_3 \rightarrow H_2S_2O_7$$
disulfuric
acid

If sulfur trioxide is treated carefully with hydrogen peroxide, peroxymonosulfuric acid (Caro's acid), H_2SO_5, is produced.

$$H_2O_2 + SO_3 \rightarrow H_2SO_5$$

Sulfuric acid is used widely in the chemical industry and in almost every other industry as well (see Fig. 11.4).   Nearly 19 million tons are produced annually in the United States.   Most of the acid is produced by the contact process (p. 272).   The lead chamber process is another industrial method (Fig. 11.5).

The commercial production of hydrochloric acid, HCl, and of nitric acid, HNO_3, utilizes large amounts of sulfuric acid.

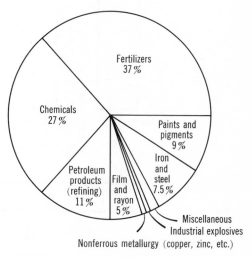

FIGURE 11.4   Typical annual consumption of approximately 19,000,000 tons of 100 per cent sulfuric acid.   Sulfuric acid is one of the most important industrial chemicals, and its consumption is considered a significant index of business activity.

$$Na^+Cl^- + H_2SO_4 \rightarrow Na^+HSO_4^- + HCl$$
salt cake

$$Na^+NO_3^- + H_2SO_4 \rightarrow Na^+HSO_4^- + HNO_3$$

If sulfuric acid is added to water, much heat is evolved because of the considerable hydration of the acid.   Hence sulfuric acid is a good dehydrating and drying agent.

11.13 ACYL CHLORIDES

Certain chlorine compounds related to sulfurous and sulfuric acids are called acid, or acyl, chlorides.   Thionyl chloride, $SOCl_2$, is the acyl chloride of sulfurous acid.   It is produced by treating sulfur

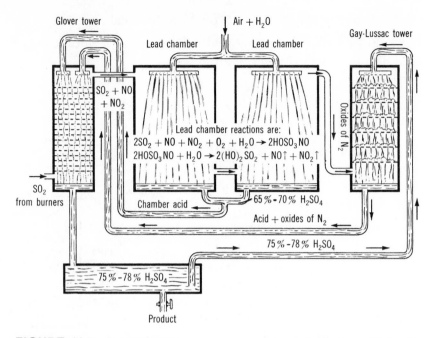

FIGURE 11.5 Lead chamber process used to manufacture 75 to 78 per cent aqueous solutions of sulfuric acid. This process yields cheaper, but less pure, acid than the contact process. Less than 25 per cent of the annual production of sulfuric acid is made by the lead chamber process. The reactions in the lead chambers first yield nitrosulfuric acid, $HOSO_3NO$, which reacts with water to yield $(HO)_2SO_2$ and oxides of nitrogen. These oxides are then recycled to react with more SO_2.

dioxide with phosphorus pentachloride. In the presence of water, thionyl chloride hydrolyzes readily to yield sulfur dioxide and hydrogen chloride.

$$SOCl_2 + 2H_2O \rightarrow H_2O + SO_2 + 2HCl$$

a. *Sulfuryl chloride*, SO_2Cl_2, is the acyl chloride of sulfuric acid. It hydrolyzes in water to yield sulfuric acid and hydrogen chloride. This acyl chloride is made by oxidizing sulfur dioxide with chlorine.

b. *Chlorsulfonic acid*, $HOSO_2Cl$, is obtained by the direct union of hydrogen chloride and sulfur trioxide. It hydrolyzes vigorously in water to produce sulfuric acid and hydrogen chloride.

If sulfuryl chloride is treated with sulfur trioxide, disulfuryl chloride, $S_2O_5Cl_2$, is obtained. This acyl chloride yields sulfuric acid and hydrogen chloride in the presence of excess water.

11.14   TEST FOR SULFATE ION

The usual test for the presence of sulfate ions, SO_4^{--}, in aqueous solutions is the addition of barium chloride, $Ba^{++}(Cl^-)_2$, and hydrochloric acid. A white precipitate of barium sulfate indicates the presence of sulfate ions.

$$Ba^{++} + SO_4^{--} \leftrightarrows Ba^{++}SO_4^{--} \downarrow$$

11.15   METAL SULFIDES

The alkali metal sulfides dissolve readily in water to form strongly basic solutions. Sulfide ion is a strong base because it is related to the weak diprotic acid H_2S (p. 541). The alkaline-earth metal sulfides also hydrolyze when added to water, but the hydroxides so produced are only slightly soluble in water. Aluminum and chromium(III) sulfides hydrolyze in water to yield the slightly soluble hydrous oxides, $Al_2O_3 \cdot xH_2O$ and $Cr_2O_3 \cdot xH_2O$.

Except for the alkali metal and alkaline-earth metal sulfides, the metal sulfides are only sparingly soluble in water. A number of these metal sulfides play important roles in some schemes of inorganic qualitative analysis. The colors and solubility characteristics of the freshly precipitated metal sulfides are used to identify the metal ions in aqueous solutions.

Among the dark-colored sulfides are those of lead, silver, bismuth, mercury(II), copper(II), tin(II), iron(II), cobalt(II), and nickel(II). Among the colored sulfides, zinc sulfide is white; chromium(III) sulfide is light green; manganese(II) sulfide is pink; cadmium, arsenic(III), and tin(IV) sulfides are yellow; antimony(III) sulfide is orange.

Some of the metal sulfides (Sb_2S_3, SnS_2, ZnS, MnS, CoS, NiS) dissolve in warm dilute hydrochloric acid. In the solution enough sulfide ions are tied up in hydrogen sulfide molecules to shift the equilibrium in the saturated solution.

$$\begin{array}{ccc} MS & \leftrightarrows M^{++} + & S^{--} \\ \text{undissolved} & & + 2H^+ \\ \text{sulfide} & & \updownarrow \\ & & H_2S \uparrow \end{array}$$

All the common metal sulfides, except mercury(II) sulfide, are soluble in hot dilute nitric acid. The sulfide ions are oxidized to elemental sulfur as well as being tied up in H_2S molecules.

$$MS \leftrightarrows M^{++} + \quad\quad \overset{S^{--}}{\underset{H_2S}{2H^+ \;\updownarrow}} \quad \Big| \quad \overset{H^+ + NO_3^-}{\underset{S^\circ \downarrow + NO \uparrow}{\updownarrow}}$$

Mercury(II) sulfide dissolves in aqua regia, a mixture of concentrated nitric and hydrochloric acids.

$$HgS \leftrightarrows \quad \underset{+\, x Cl^-}{\overset{Hg^{++}}{\underset{HgCl_4^{--}}{\updownarrow}}} \quad + \quad \overset{S^{--}}{\underset{H_2S \uparrow}{2H^+ \;\updownarrow}} \quad \Big| \quad \overset{H^+ + NO_3^-}{\underset{S^\circ \downarrow + NO \uparrow}{\updownarrow}}$$

Some of the slightly soluble sulfides are amphoteric. They dissolve in acidic solutions and in basic solutions of relatively high sulfide ion concentration. The common amphoteric sulfides are SnS_2, As_2S_3, As_2S_5, Sb_2S_5, and HgS. These sulfides form complex sulfide ions if the sulfide ion concentration is sufficient. For example,

$$\underset{\substack{\text{undissolved}\\ \text{mercury(II)}\\ \text{sulfide}}}{HgS} \;+ S^{--} \leftrightarrows HgS_2^{--}$$

$$\underset{\substack{\text{undissolved}\\ \text{tin(IV)}\\ \text{sulfide}}}{SnS_2} \;+ S^{--} \leftrightarrows SnS_3^{--}$$

The complex sulfide ions are destroyed by adding oxonium ions to the solution. As sulfide ions are tied up, the equilibrium shifts to favor reappearance of the sulfide precipitates.

11.16 SELENIUM AND TELLURIUM

The solid allotropic forms of selenium are the two red forms and a gray form that is the stable form at room temperatures. The red forms are soluble in carbon disulfide, but the gray form is not. The electrical conductivity of the gray form varies directly with the intensity of the light shining on it. Hence it is useful in photometers and in electrical circuits controlled by light. Selenium vapor contains Se_8 and Se_2 molecules among other molecular forms.

Hydrogen selenide is described on page 249. When heated, selenium combines with atmospheric oxygen to form solid selenium dioxide. Selenium trioxide is unstable. Selenium dioxide dissolves in water to yield the weak diprotic selenous acid, H_2SeO_3. This acid is a better oxidizing agent than sulfurous acid. In fact, selenous acid oxidizes sulfurous acid to sulfuric acid, thereby yielding red elemental selenium. Selenous acid is oxidized to selenic acid by strong oxidizing agents such as chlorine and lead(IV) oxide. Selenic acid, H_2SeO_4, if concentrated, is a powerful oxidizing agent, much better than sulfuric acid. The salts of selenous acid are called selenites; those of selenic acid, selenates.

Tellurium is less electronegative, therefore more nearly metallic, than selenium. The crystalline solid is silvery in appearance and very slightly soluble in carbon disulfide.

The common oxides of tellurium are TeO, TeO_2, and TeO_3. Tellurium burns readily in air to form tellurium dioxide. Although the dioxide does not dissolve readily in water, it dissolves in basic solutions to yield tellurites (TeO_3^{--}). The oxidation of tellurium by nitric acid yields the slightly soluble solid tellurous acid, H_2TeO_3. The formula of telluric acid is H_6TeO_6, weakly acidic and very slightly soluble in water.

Problems

1. Complete the equations:

(a) $Hg(NO_3)_2 + \Delta \rightarrow$

(b) $SeO_3 + OH^- \rightarrow$

(c) $Cl_2 + SO_3^{--} \rightarrow$

(d) $SOCl_2 + \text{aqueous } NH_3 \rightarrow$

(e) $SrCO_3 + \Delta \rightarrow$

(f) $Cr_2O_3 + \text{excess } OH^- \rightarrow$

(g) $V_2O_5 + OH^- \rightarrow$

(h) $BaO + H_2O \rightarrow$

(i) $Na_2O + H_2O \rightarrow$

(j) $ZnO + OH^- \rightarrow$

(k) $SeO_3 + O^{--} \rightarrow$

2. Whenever hydrogen peroxide acts as an oxidizing agent, to what substance is it transformed?

3. What is observed visually when a solution of potassium chromate, $(K^+)_2CrO_4^{--}$, is strongly acidified?

4. Suggest electronic formulas for SeO_2, SeO, O_2H^-, TeO_3^{--}, and D_2O_2.

5. What are the main reactions that occur when cobalt sulfide, CoS, dissolves in hot dilute nitric acid?

6. How many tons of mercury can be obtained from 500 tons of an ore that is 45 per cent cinnabar, if the process of metallurgy affords a yield 80 per cent of the theoretical?

7. How many moles of electrons must be accepted by 2.2 moles of super-oxide ion if reduction is complete?

8. What substances are produced when sodium peroxide is cautiously added to warm water?

9. Permanganate ion, MnO_4^-, in acidic solution (see p. 493) is reduced to Mn^{++} by hydrogen peroxide. Elemental oxygen is the product of the oxidation of the H_2O_2. Write the balanced equation.

10. Write suitable equations to illustrate the amphoteric character of beryllium oxide (p. 259).

11. Why does so-called plastic sulfur lose its plasticity so rapidly on cooling?

12. If gaseous hydrogen sulfide is added to a solution that is 0.01 M in iron(III) and OH_3^+, iron(II) sulfide precipitates. Why does the iron(II) sulfide rather than the iron(III) sulfide appear?

13. Gaseous hydrogen sulfide is added to a clear solution containing one of the common metal cations and nitrate ions. The white precipitate that appears is easily soluble in dilute HCl. What, most probably, is the metal cation in solution?

14. Considering the oxides lithia, baryta, magnesia, and alumina, (a) which is most basic, (b) least basic, (c) amphoteric, (d) soluble in dil HCl, (e) most soluble in cold water?

15. In the strict sense of the word, is the Frasch process a chemical one?

16. If 12 g of carbon is burned to carbon dioxide in oxygen, 94 kcal of heat is evolved. If 12 g of carbon is burned to CO_2 in ozone, 119.7 kcal of heat is evolved. Interpret these facts.

17. Outline a practical preparation of barium oxide starting with barium chloride. Assume that all common reagents are available.

18. Silver oxide, Ag_2O, acts as an oxidizing agent in the presence of H_2O_2. Write an equation for this reaction.

19. What is the major product of the thermal decomposition of platinum(IV) nitrate?

12

THE HALOGENS

12.1 OCCURRENCE AND COMMERCIAL PRODUCTION

The halogens (Greek, *salt formers*) never occur naturally in their elemental state because they are so easily reduced. Most of the halogens occur naturally either as metal salts in minerals or in aqueous solutions. The vast oceans, the Great Salt Lake in Utah, and the Dead Sea are aqueous solutions that contain tremendous amounts of dissolved salts, much of which consists of chloride and bromide ions (p. 257). Large amounts of bromide and iodide ions exist in solution (brine) in certain deep wells, such as those near Midland, Michigan. Chilean saltpeter, mainly sodium nitrate, also contains sodium iodate, $NaIO_3$.

Since the halogens are such good oxidizing agents, they are almost always present in nature in their -1 oxidation state. Therefore the commercial methods for

the production of the elemental halogens (except iodine from $NaIO_3$) involve, in part, the oxidation of the halide ion.

All the fluorine and most of the chlorine are produced by electrolysis (p. 502). In recent years the annual production of chlorine in the United States has been between 5.0 and 5.3 millions of tons. Major uses of chlorine include the bleaching of paper pulp and plant fibers, the purification of drinking water, and the manufacture of organic chemicals.

A large percentage of the annual production of bromine comes from sea water. Since sea water is a relatively dilute solution, the process involves the treatment of huge volumes of water. The initial steps are acidification of the sea water followed by the oxidation of bromide ions by chlorine.

$$2Br^- + Cl_2 \rightarrow 2Cl^- + Br_2$$

The bromine vapor is blown from the sea water by air and separated from the air by treatment with gaseous sulfur dioxide.

$$Br_2 + SO_2 + 2H_2O \rightarrow H_2SO_4 + 2HBr$$

The mixture of gases is scrubbed by using water in which the hydrogen bromide and sulfuric acid dissolve to yield eventually a fairly concentrated solution. The bromide ions in this solution are then oxidized by chlorine to produce a mixture much more concentrated in bromine than that obtained in the initial step of the process.

A large portion of the annual consumption of about 50,000 tons of bromine is used for the production of ethylene bromide, $C_2H_4Br_2$ (an ingredient of Ethyl gasoline), and silver bromide, an important light-sensitive material in photographic films and papers.

Ethylene bromide and lead tetraethyl, $Pb(C_2H_5)_4$, are used in compounding the antiknock agent, Ethyl fluid. The ethylene bromide deters deposition of lead in the engine during combustion of the lead tetraethyl by causing the formation of lead bromide which escapes with the exhaust gases.

The cheapest source of iodine is the sodium iodate, $Na^+IO_3^-$, that is mixed with sodium nitrate in the large deposits in Chile. The iodate ion is reduced to elemental iodine by hydrogen sulfite ion.

$$5HSO_3^- + 2IO_3^- \rightarrow I_2 + 2SO_4^{--} + 3HSO_4^- + H_2O$$

The aqueous solution is evaporated to dryness, and the iodine is separated by sublimation.

12.2 LABORATORY PREPARATION

One of the most convenient methods for making chlorine involves the oxidation of chloride ion in acidic solution by manganese(IV) oxide. The net equation is

$$MnO_2 + 4H^+ + 2Cl^- \rightarrow Mn^{++} + Cl_2 + 2H_2O$$

Usually the manganese(IV) oxide is heated with hydrochloric acid, but a mixture of sodium chloride, concentrated sulfuric acid, and MnO_2 can be heated to yield gaseous chlorine. The greenish-yellow gas is collected by the upward displacement of air. Since the gas is extremely toxic, care should be used in handling it.

Bromine and iodine may be prepared by the oxidation of bromide and iodide ions, just as chlorine is produced. For example,

$$MnO_2 + 4H^+ + 2Br^- \rightarrow Mn^{++} + Br_2 + 2H_2O$$

Bromine is a reddish-brown liquid at room temperature; hence its vapor is easily condensed. Although iodine is a black solid at room temperature, it is easily vaporized (purple vapor) and sublimed.

12.3 GENERAL CHEMICAL BEHAVIOR

The oxidation-reduction characteristics of the elemental halogens have been summarized in Section 7.12. Each halogen interacts with water—fluorine violently, iodine only slightly.

$$2F_2 + 2H_2O \rightarrow 4HF + O_2$$

Chlorine dissolves in excess water to yield an acidic solution containing chloride ions, hypochlorite ions, OCl^-, and undissociated hypochlorous acid, $HOCl$.

$$Cl_2 + 2H_2O \leftrightarrows OH_3^+ + Cl^- + HOCl$$
$$\updownarrow$$
$$H^+ + OCl^-$$

Hypochlorous acid decomposes in sunlight to yield oxygen and hydrogen chloride.

$$2HOCl \rightarrow 2HCl + O_2$$

Bromine in excess water behaves essentially as does chlorine, but not so extensively.

$$Br_2 + 2H_2O \leftrightarrows OH_3^+ + Br^- + HOBr$$
$$\updownarrow \text{ hypobromous acid}$$
$$H^+ + OBr^-$$

Fluorine and chlorine are by far the most reactive halogens. Fluorine reacts with all of the elements, even some inert gases, usually with much vigor. Chlorine combines directly, often vigorously, with all the elements except oxygen, nitrogen, carbon, and the inert gases. Bromine reacts with many metallic elements and some nonmetallic elements. Iodine is the least reactive halogen.

Prior to 1962 all evidence indicated that the inert gases were unreactive and unable to yield stable compounds. However, during 1962 it was discovered that elemental fluorine will react readily with some of the inert gases to yield stable compounds. To a member of the halogen family goes the distinction of indicating to man that some inert gases are chemically reactive.

If various amounts of two different halogens are mixed, several very active interhalogen compounds are produced. All of these are polar molecules in which the more electronegative element has the more negative character. For instance, in iodine bromide, IBr, the covalent bond is distinctly polar, the bromine kernel having the shared electrons closer to it. Some of the interhalogens are IF_5, ICl_3, IBr, BrF, BrCl, and ClF.

12.4 OXIDES AND OXY-ACIDS

a. *Hypochlorous acid*, HOCl, is a weak acid that can exist only in aqueous solutions. Its conjugate base, hypochlorite ion, OCl^-, is formed by adding chlorine to a solution of sodium hydroxide.

$$Cl_2 + 2OH^- \leftrightarrows Cl^- + \underset{\substack{\text{hypochlorite} \\ \text{ion}}}{OCl^-} + HOH$$

The solution produced is a good bleaching and sterilizing agent. If it is acidified, the concentration of undissociated hypochlorous acid is relatively high. Hypochlorite ion is a fairly strong base and an active oxidizing agent. It is, in fact, the strongest oxidizing agent among the oxy-halogen anions.

If chlorine is added to water, some hypochlorous acid is formed.

$$Cl_2 + 2HOH \leftrightarrows HOCl + OH_3^+ + Cl^-$$

An aqueous solution of hypochlorous acid is produced when chlorine(I) oxide, Cl—OCl, is added to cool water.

$$Cl_2O + HOH \leftrightarrows 2HOCl$$

Chlorine(I) oxide may be prepared by passing chlorine over mercury(II) oxide.

$$2Cl_2 + HgO \rightarrow HgCl_2 + Cl_2O$$

b. *Chlorous acid*, HOClO, is an unstable weak acid that can exist only in aqueous solution, if at all. Its conjugate base, chlorite ion, ClO_2^-, is formed by adding chlorine dioxide to a solution of sodium peroxide. The net reaction is

$$2ClO_2 + OH^- + O_2H^- \leftrightarrows 2ClO_2^- + O_2 + HOH$$

Sodium chlorite, $Na^+ClO_2^-$, is a very good bleaching agent and an active oxidizing agent.

Chlorine dioxide, ClO_2, is formed if concentrated sulfuric acid is carefully added to solid potassium chlorate, $K^+ClO_3^-$. The reactions presumably are

$$ClO_3^- + H^+ \leftrightarrows (HClO_3)$$
chloric acid
(unstable)

$$(2HClO_3) \rightarrow 2ClO_2 + \tfrac{1}{2}O_2 + HOH$$

Chlorine dioxide is also made by treating solid sodium chlorite with chlorine.

$$Na^+ClO_2^- + \tfrac{1}{2}Cl_2 \rightarrow Na^+Cl^- + ClO_2 \uparrow$$

Although chlorine dioxide (yellow-brown) is thermally unstable, it is a useful bleaching agent when diluted with air. (Partial pressure of the oxide in such a mixture is usually less than 40 mm.)

c. *Chloric acid*, $HOClO_2$, is unstable, but salts containing its conjugate base are known. Potassium chlorate, $K^+ClO_3^-$, the most common salt of chloric acid, is prepared by adding an excess of chlorine to a hot concentrated aqueous solution of potassium hydroxide. The net reaction is

$$3Cl_2 + 6OH^- \xrightarrow[\substack{aqueous\\solution}]{hot} ClO_3^- + 5Cl^- + 3HOH$$
chlorate
ion

Chlorate ions are also produced during the electrolysis (p. 503) of a solution of potassium chloride in which the electrodes are inert and the anodic and cathodic solutions are mixed by continual stirring. The net reaction is

$$Cl^- + 3HOH \xrightarrow[\text{``homogeneous''}]{electrolysis} ClO_3^- + 3H_2 \uparrow$$

Prolonged electrolysis of such a solution yields perchlorate ion, ClO_4^-.

Although potassium chlorate is more expensive than sodium chlorate, it is more commonly used because it is less deliquescent and therefore easier to handle. If potassium chlorate is carefully heated in the absence of a catalyst, it decomposes to yield potassium perchlorate and potassium chloride.

$$4(K^+ClO_3^-) \xrightarrow[\substack{pyrolysis\\(no\ catalyst)}]{careful} 3(K^+ClO_4^-) + K^+Cl^-$$
potassium
perchlorate

The pyrolysis of potassium chlorate to yield oxygen and potassium chloride has previously been mentioned on page 68.

Potassium chlorate is an active oxidizing agent and it often reacts explosively with substances easily oxidized, such as carbon, sulfur, phosphorus, and many organic compounds. It is used in fireworks and in the heads of safety matches.

d. *Anhydrous perchloric acid*, $HOClO_3$, the most stable oxy-acid of chlorine, is prepared by carefully distilling, under reduced pressure, a mixture of potassium perchlorate and 98 per cent sulfuric acid. Perchloric acid is usually sold as a 70 per cent aqueous solution. The pure acid freezes at $-112°C$ and boils at $19°C$ under 11 mm pressure without decomposition. The so-called monohydrate of perchloric acid is a crystalline solid (melting point 50°C) which apparently is oxonium perchlorate, $OH_3^+ClO_4^-$, because it is isomorphous with $NH_4^+ClO_4^-$. Although perchloric acid is one of the strongest Brönsted acids, its conjugate base (ClO_4^-) is, in acidic solutions, a weaker oxidizing agent than chlorate ion. Warm aqueous solutions of perchloric acid may react violently with substances that are easily oxidized.

Cautious dehydration of perchloric acid by diphosphorus pentoxide yields dichlorine heptoxide. This colorless liquid has a normal boiling point of 80°C. Although it is the most stable oxide of chlorine, it readily explodes when heated or struck.

$$2HOClO_3 + P_2O_5 \rightarrow \underset{\substack{\text{dichlorine} \\ \text{heptoxide}}}{Cl_2O_7} + 2HOPO_2$$

e. *Hypobromous acid*, $HOBr$, may be prepared by adding bromine to an aqueous suspension of precipitated mercury(II) oxide.

$$2Br_2 + 2HgO + HOH \rightarrow 2HOBr + HgBr_2 \cdot HgO \downarrow$$

The hypobromous acid, a straw-yellow liquid, is isolated from this reaction mixture by distillation under reduced pressure at 40°C. This acid is an active oxidizing agent but is less active than hypochlorous acid.

If bromine is added to a cool aqueous solution of sodium hydroxide, an appreciable concentration of hypobromite ions, OBr^-, is obtained.

$$Br_2 + 2OH^- \overset{cool}{\leftrightarrows} Br^- + OBr^- + HOH$$

f. *Bromic acid*, $HOBrO_2$, can exist apparently only in aqueous solutions. Its potassium salt, potassium bromate, $K^+BrO_3^-$, can be isolated from a solution obtained by adding bromine to a hot concentrated aqueous solution of potassium hydroxide.

$$3Br_2 + 6OH^- \leftrightarrows BrO_3^- + 5Br^- + 3HOH$$

Potassium bromate readily crystallizes when the solution is cooled because it is much less soluble than potassium bromide. Bromate ion is a weaker oxidizing agent than chlorate ion (oxidation of bromine by chlorate ion is nearly complete).

$$Br_2 + 2ClO_3^- \rightarrow 2BrO_3^- + Cl_2$$

However, bromate ion can oxidize iodine to iodate ion.

$$I_2 + 2BrO_3^- \rightarrow 2IO_3^- + Br_2$$

g. A dilute aqueous solution of *hypoiodous acid* (very weak), HOI, can be made by shaking a suspension of finely divided iodine and precipitated mercury(II) oxide.

$$2I_2 + 2HgO + HOH \rightarrow 2HOI + HgI_2 \cdot HgO \downarrow$$

Hypoiodite ion, OI^-, is obtained by adding iodine to a cool aqueous solution of an alkali metal hydroxide:

$$I_2 + 2OH^- \rightarrow OI^- + I^- + HOH$$

If this solution is heated, iodate ion, IO_3^-, is formed.

$$3OI^- \xrightarrow[\text{aqueous solution}]{\Delta} IO_3^- + 2I^-$$

h. *Iodic acid*, $HOIO_2$, may be prepared by adding iodine to concentrated nitric acid.

$$3I_2 + 10HONO_2 \rightarrow 6HOIO_2 + 10NO + 2HOH$$

The iodic acid, a white solid, precipitates in this reaction mixture. It melts at 110°C and is very soluble in water. Its most common salts, sodium iodate, $Na^+IO_3^-$, and potassium iodate, $K^+IO_3^-$, are much less soluble than many sodium and potassium salts of other common oxy-acids.

i. *Periodic acid*, in contrast with perchloric acid, has a rather unusual structure. The normal formula of the acid is $(HO)_5IO$, in which six oxygen kernels form an octahedral arrangement around the iodine kernel. The large size of the iodine kernel apparently permits a ligancy of 6 for iodine(VII), so that periodate ion, IO_6^{5-}, has six oxide ions complexed (coordinated) with one iodine(VII) ion.

Another form of periodic acid, which has the formula, $HOIO_3$, can exist only in the absence of water.

$$HOIO_3 + 2HOH \leftrightharpoons (HO)_5IO$$

Sodium periodate, $Na^+IO_4^-$ (sparingly soluble), is a salt of the acid, $HOIO_3$. It exists in crude Chile saltpeter (sodium nitrate). An aqueous solution of $Na^+IO_4^-$ yields on evaporation the salt, $Na_2(HO)_3IO_3$, which is a salt of the acid, $(HO)_5IO$.

Periodic acid is an active oxidizing agent. It can convert manganese(II) ion to permanganate ion.

Gentle heating of periodic acid yields diiodine pentoxide, a white solid.

$$2(HO)_5IO \rightarrow \quad I_2O_5 \quad + 5HOH + O_2 \uparrow$$
$$\text{diiodine}$$
$$\text{pentoxide}$$

12.5   TESTS FOR HALIDE IONS

There are several methods for the identification of chloride, bromide, and iodide ions in aqueous solution. In this section we shall describe a few of the common tests.

Silver fluoride is fairly soluble in water, but the other silver halides are only very slightly soluble. Silver chloride is white, silver bromide is cream-colored, and silver iodide is yellow. Silver chloride is quite soluble in 6 M aqueous ammonia because of the formation of silver ammonia complex ions.

$$AgCl + 2NH_3 \leftrightharpoons Ag(NH_3)_2^+ + Cl^-$$

Silver bromide is only slightly soluble in 6 M aqueous ammonia, but is soluble in the concentrated reagent. Although silver iodide is only slightly soluble in concentrated aqueous ammonia, it dissolves readily in aqueous solutions of sodium iodide to yield the complex ion, AgI_2^-. All the silver halides dissolve in sodium thiosulfate solution because of the formation of the silver thiosulfate complex ion, $Ag(S_2O_3)_2^{3-}$.

Iodide and bromide ions can be detected even if together because iodide ion is the better reducing agent. Iron(III) ions in acidic solutions oxidize iodide ions to iodine, but they do not oxidize bromide ions. If carbon tetrachloride (a dense, colorless liquid immiscible in water) is added to the solution, the elemental iodine dissolves in the lower layer yielding a purple solution.

$$2Fe^{3+} + 2I^- \rightarrow 2Fe^{++} + I_2$$

After extraction of the iodine by the carbon tetrachloride, the solution is acidified and an excess of 0.1 M potassium permanganate and carbon tetrachloride are added. If bromide ions are present, the lower liquid layer gains an orange-yellow color due to elemental bromine.

$$2MnO_4^- + 16H^+ + 10Br^- \rightarrow 5Br_2 + 2Mn^{++} + 8H_2O$$

12.6 SOME HALOGEN COMPOUNDS

The sodium and potassium salts of the halogens are used widely as water-soluble sources of the halide ions.   The fluorides are much less soluble than the other halides.

a. *Sodium chloride* is the most abundant chlorine compound. The amount of sodium chloride as the mineral halite in underground deposits and as dissolved salt in sea water seems boundless.   It is used directly in the commercial production of sodium, chlorine, hydrogen chloride, sodium hydroxide, and sodium carbonate and hydrogen carbonate by the Solvay process; it is also used as a seasoning agent in foods and in "melting" ice and snow.   It has hundreds of different uses, often as a chemical reagent.

b. *Calcium chloride*, $CaCl_2$, is the by-product of the Solvay process—the major process for the production of sodium carbonate.   The initial step in the process is the pyrolysis of limestone, $CaCO_3$, to yield calcium oxide, CaO, and carbon dioxide. $CaCO_3 + \Delta \rightarrow CaO + CO_2$.   The carbon dioxide is added (step 2) to aqueous ammonia to form an aqueous solution of ammonium hydrogen carbonate, $(NH_4)HCO_3$.   To this solution is added sodium chloride (step 3), whereupon sodium hydrogen carbonate, $NaHCO_3$, precipitates.   This solid is heated to convert it to sodium carbonate.

$$2NaHCO_3 \rightarrow Na_2CO_3 + CO_2 + H_2O$$

The ammonia used in step 2 of the process is recovered by heating the ammonium chloride from step 3 with the calcium oxide from step 1.   The calcium chloride is the by-product.

$$CaO + 2NH_4Cl \rightarrow CaCl_2 + 2NH_3 + H_2O$$

c. *Calcium hypochlorite*, $Ca(OCl)_2$ and $CaOCl_2$, are the two active ingredients in bleaching powder.   These compounds are produced by passing chlorine over dry calcium oxide.   The effective agent in bleaching powder is the chlorine; about 35 per cent is available.   Water hydrolyzes $CaOCl_2$ to yield chlorine and calcium hydroxide.   Calcium hypochlorite yields chlorine in acidic solutions.

d. *Sulfur monochloride*, S_2Cl_2, is a liquid having a disagreeable odor.   It fumes in moist air because it hydrolyzes to yield hydrogen chloride, sulfur, sulfur dioxide, and a mixture of oxy-acids of sulfur. It is a very good solvent for sulfur.   It reacts with ethene, C_2H_4, to produce a volatile liquid, mustard gas, $(ClC_2H_4)_2S$, an extremely dangerous vesicant.

e. *Sulfur hexafluoride*, SF_6, is a colorless, relatively stable gas (p. 195).

f. *Phosgene*, Cl_2CO, is the acyl chloride of carbonic acid. It is a poisonous gas that hydrolyzes readily to yield carbon dioxide and hydrogen chloride. It is made by treating carbon monoxide with chlorine.

g. *Carbon tetrachloride*, CCl_4, and trichloroethene, HC_2Cl_3, are excellent solvents for fats and oils; hence they are used in dry cleaning and in the degreasing of metals. Carbon tetrachloride is used in certain types of fire extinguishers.

h. *Silicon tetrachloride*, $SiCl_4$, and titanium tetrachloride, $TiCl_4$, are used with ammonia in the formation of smoke screens. These polyhalides are readily hydrolyzed in moist air to yield a mixture of finely divided solid particles.

$$SiCl_4 + 2H_2O \rightarrow SiO_2 + 4HCl$$

i. *Xenon difluoride* and *tetrafluoride, krypton tetrafluoride,* and *radon fluoride:* When heated in a nickel vessel at 400°C for an hour, one part of gaseous Xe and five parts of gaseous F_2 readily react to yield a colorless solid. Xenon tetrafluoride, XeF_4, is stable at room temperature, has a melting point of above 95°C, and sublimes easily at room temperature. Xenon difluoride, XeF_2, is prepared by a photochemical reaction. It is a stable colorless solid at room temperature and it sublimes readily. Krypton tetrafluoride, KrF_4, can be made by subjecting a mixture of krypton and fluorine to an electric discharge at 85–86°K. The colorless solid sublimes at $-40°$–$-30°$C. At present the composition of radon fluoride is indefinite.

Several organic halides are mentioned in Chapter 27.

Problems

1. In which system is gaseous chlorine the most soluble: water at 30°, at 20°, or at 10°? (See p. 373.)

2. In which solution is gaseous chlorine the most soluble: water at 25°, 0.1 M hydrochloric acid at 25°, or 0.1 M sodium hydroxide at 25°?

3. A solution is suspected of containing chloride ions and iodide ions. How would you determine either the presence or absence of each ion?

4. Assume that in the Solvay process the over-all conversion of sodium chloride to sodium carbonate is complete. (a) What is the theoretical yield, in tons, of sodium carbonate if the starting material is 2340 tons of sodium chloride? (b) How much calcium chloride is obtained as a by-product?

5. What is the *minimum* amount, in kilograms, of bromine necessary to produce 131.6 kg of ethylene bromide?

6. A dilute solution of bromine in water has a reddish-brown color. If 0.1 M sodium hydroxide is added to the solution, the coloration disappears. Suggest an explanation.

7. Suggest probable electronic formulations for IF_5, $HOBr$, SF_6, Cl_2CO, Cl_2O_7, ClO_3^-, Cl_2O, and $HOClO$.

8. The careful pyrolysis of potassium chlorate yields potassium perchlorate. In this reaction what is oxidized and what is reduced?

9. Suggest a reason for the fact that hypochlorite ion is a better oxidizing agent than perchlorate ion, although sulfite ion is a poorer oxidizing agent than sulfate ion, and phosphate ion is a better oxidizing agent than hypophosphite ion.

10. If sodium chlorite is added to pure water, is the solution acidic, basic, or neutral?

11. When added to hot concentrated potassium hydroxide solution, bromine yields bromate and bromide ions. What is oxidized and what reduced?

12. A clear solution contains silver ions and nitrate ions. To this is added a 0.2 M solution of potassium iodide, whereupon a precipitate appears. If the addition of the potassium iodide solution is continued, the precipitate disappears. (a) What is the precipitate? (b) What is its color? (c) Why does it dissolve eventually? (d) What might be done to the solution that contains the dissolved precipitate to cause the precipitate to reappear?

13. How would you collect gaseous chlorine in the laboratory?

14. If you wished to detect chlorine in drinking water or to determine whether the water were chlorinated, what tests might you perform?

13

THE NITROGEN FAMILY

13.1 OCCURRENCE AND PRODUCTION OF NITROGEN

The atmosphere is 75 per cent nitrogen, by weight. Some samples of natural gas contain considerable amounts of nitrogen. One of the major natural inorganic sources of combined nitrogen is the sodium nitrate of Chile. Ammonia is obtained by heating coal in by-product coke ovens. Plant and animal proteins are abundant sources of combined organic nitrogen. The natural nitrogen cycle is shown in Fig. 13.1.

The major commercial production of nitrogen uses the fractional distillation of liquid air. The so-called atmospheric nitrogen obtained in this way contains small amounts of the inert gases.

Nitrogen can be prepared in the laboratory by slowly adding a solution of sodium nitrite to a hot solution of ammonium chloride. The water is easily separated from the nitrogen.

$$\text{Na}^+\text{NO}_2^- + \text{NH}_4^+\text{Cl}^- \rightarrow \text{Na}^+\text{Cl}^- + \text{NH}_4^+\text{NO}_2^-$$

$$\downarrow \Delta$$

$$\text{N}_2 + 2\text{H}_2\text{O}$$

Gaseous nitrogen is colorless, odorless, tasteless, and less soluble in water than is oxygen. Although nitrogen molecules are very stable and rather inert, nitrogen atoms combine readily with many elements. The nitrogen atoms in the diatomic nitrogen molecule are held together very firmly. Hence high temperatures and catalysts are often needed either to activate and distort (deform) the molecules or to dissociate them to yield nitrogen atoms.

Since elemental nitrogen is relatively unreactive under ordinary conditions, it is customary to "fix" the nitrogen in more reactive substances. The major industrial nitrogen fixation process is the production of ammonia from the elements (see Haber process, p. 457).

The major natural fixation process occurs in the root nodules of legumes. The major chemical properties of ammonia are mentioned on pages 250, 542.

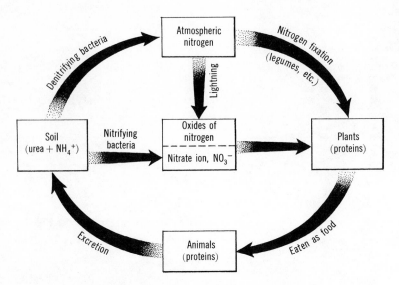

FIGURE 13.1   The natural nitrogen cycle.

13.2   OXIDES OF NITROGEN

Each of the five positive oxidation states of nitrogen is represented in the several oxides of nitrogen. The three negative oxidation states are represented in compounds such as ammonia, $NH_3(-3)$; hydrazine, $N_2H_4(-2)$; hydroxylamine, $NH_2OH(-1)$. In Table 13.1 the common oxides of nitrogen are identified.

TABLE 13.1   Oxides of nitrogen

Name	Formula	Oxidation State of Nitrogen	Physical State at Room Temperature
Dinitrogen monoxide	N_2O	$+1$	colorless gas
Nitrogen monoxide	NO	$+2$	colorless gas
Dinitrogen trioxide	N_2O_3	$+3$	gas; blue liq., $-21°$
Nitrogen dioxide	NO_2	$+4$	reddish-brown gas
Dinitrogen tetroxide	N_2O_4	$+4$	gas; yellow liq., $-10°$
Dinitrogen pentoxide	N_2O_5	$+5$	white solid

a. *Dinitrogen monoxide*, N_2O (also called nitrous oxide), is prepared by carefully heating ammonium nitrate. If the heating is too vigorous, an explosive decomposition may occur.

$$NH_4^+NO_3^- + \Delta \rightarrow N_2O + 2H_2O$$

Dinitrogen monoxide has been used as an anesthetic during minor surgery and in dentistry. Since the gas often produces a sense of exhilaration, it has been called "laughing gas." Because the gas dissociates readily when heated to yield oxygen, it supports combustion almost as well as does oxygen.

b. *Nitrogen monoxide*, NO (also called nitric oxide), is prepared in the laboratory by adding dilute nitric acid to copper. The net equation is

$$3Cu + 8H^+ + 2NO_3^- \rightarrow 3Cu^{++} + 2NO + 4H_2O$$

At the high temperatures of the electric arc, nitrogen and oxygen unite to produce nitrogen monoxide.

$$N_2 + O_2 + 43.2 \text{ kcal} \leftrightarrows 2NO$$

The process is impractical because even at 3000°C the equilibrium mixture contains only 5 per cent of oxide.

Nitrogen monoxide is oxidized by atmospheric oxygen to yield nitrogen dioxide. The electronic formulation of the radical nitrogen monoxide has been indicated earlier (p. 184).

c. *Nitrogen dioxide*, NO_2, is obtained, mixed with oxygen, by the pyrolysis of a "heavy" metal nitrate (p. 258). It is also produced by the reaction of copper with concentrated nitric acid. The net equation is

$$Cu + 4H^+ + 2NO_3^- \rightarrow Cu^{++} + 2NO_2 + 2H_2O$$

As mentioned above, oxidation of nitrogen monoxide yields the dioxide.

If nitrogen dioxide is cooled to $-10°C$ at 1 atm, a yellow liquid is obtained. The liquid consists of dinitrogen tetroxide molecules, N_2O_4, apparently produced by the exothermic dimerization of NO_2 molecules.

$$2NO_2(g) \leftrightarrows N_2O_4(g) + 14.6 \text{ kcal}$$

Since nitrogen dioxide is partially dimerized at room temperature, NO_2 and N_2O_4 exist together at this temperature. The gaseous mixture dissolves in water to yield nitric acid and nitrogen monoxide.

$$3NO_2 + H_2O \leftrightarrows 2HNO_3 + NO$$

We mentioned earlier (p. 184) that nitrogen dioxide is a radical and is paramagnetic. Its dimer, N_2O_4, is neither a radical nor paramagnetic because all of its electrons are paired.

If a solution made by adding sulfuric acid to sodium nitrite is heated gently, a dark red mixture of nitrogen monoxide and dioxide is obtained.

$$H^+ + NO_2^- \leftrightharpoons HNO_2$$
$$2HNO_2 + \Delta \rightarrow NO + NO_2 + H_2O$$

If the gaseous mixture is cooled to $-21°C$, a blue liquid, dinitrogen trioxide, N_2O_3, is obtained. This oxide dissociates appreciably at temperatures above $-10°C$ to yield the oxides from which it is formed.

$$NO + NO_2 \leftrightharpoons N_2O_3 + \Delta$$

If either N_2O_3 or a mixture of NO and NO_2 is added to cool water, nitrous acid, HONO, is obtained. This acid is weak and unstable. Its conjugate base, ONO^-, is called nitrite ion.

d. *Dinitrogen pentoxide*, N_2O_5, is prepared by the dehydration of pure nitric acid by diphosphorus pentoxide.

$$2HNO_3 + P_2O_5 \rightarrow 2HPO_3 + N_2O_5$$

Because dinitrogen pentoxide dissolves in water to yield nitric acid, it is called the anhydride of nitric acid.

13.3   OXY-ACIDS OF NITROGEN

a. *Nitrous acid*, HNO_2 (p. 538), exists only in aqueous solutions. If a solution of sodium nitrite, $Na^+NO_2^-$, is acidified, nitrous acid is obtained. This solution must be kept cool to inhibit decomposition of the acid. Sodium nitrite may be made by heating sodium nitrate with lead. The net equation is

$$\underset{\substack{\text{nitrate} \\ \text{ion}}}{NO_3^-} + Pb + \Delta \rightarrow \underset{\substack{\text{nitrite} \\ \text{ion}}}{NO_2^-} + PbO$$

If a freshly prepared solution of iron(II) sulfate is added to an acidic solution containing nitrite ion, the solution attains a dark brown coloration due to the complex ion, $Fe(NO)^{++}$.

b. *Nitric acid* (aqua fortis), HNO_3, may be prepared by treating either sodium or potassium nitrates with sulfuric acid (p. 273). In the Ostwald process, ammonia is oxidized by oxygen to yield nitrogen monoxide, which in turn is oxidized to nitrogen dioxide. The nitrogen dioxide is dissolved in water to yield nitric acid and NO, which is recycled in the process. Most of the nitric acid produced today is made by the Ostwald process.

The behavior of nitric acid as a strong monoprotic acid is described elsewhere (p. 538). Ordinary concentrated nitric acid is a 68 to 70 per cent aqueous solution that boils at 120°C. Pure nitric acid is a colorless liquid (bp, 86°C). Fuming nitric acid is made by dissolving nitrogen dioxide in concentrated nitric acid.

Concentrated nitric acid is a good oxidizing agent. It oxidizes chloride ions to chlorine and chlorine dioxide; charcoal to carbon dioxide; and iodine to iodic acid. A mixture of concentrated nitric and hydrochloric acids (1:3) is called *aqua regia* (p. 276). Dilute nitric acid oxidizes sulfide ions to elemental sulfur (p. 276); concentrated nitric acid oxidizes them to sulfate ion, SO_4^{--}.

Many metals reduce nitric acid, but since the nitrate ion is reduced more readily than loosely bound protons, *no* hydrogen is produced. Concentrated nitric acid is often reduced by the less active metals, such as copper, to NO_2, whereas the dilute acid is reduced to NO (p. 295). Depending on the conditions, metallic zinc reduces dilute nitric acid either to NH_4^+, N_2, or N_2O.

Nitric acid is used in the production of explosives such as nitroglycerin (p. 695), TNT (p. 695), picric acid and its salts (p. 540), and guncotton (p. 703).

Nitrate ion, NO_3^-, is a very common and important anion. Since nitrate salts are generally soluble in water, they are used commonly in the laboratory as sources of cations. The brown-ring test is a classic test for nitrate ions. It has definite limitations because ClO_3^-, I^-, Br^-, and NO_2^- ions interfere and the test is poor in highly colored solutions. The solution is acidified with dilute sulfuric acid and a few drops of freshly prepared 1 M iron(II) sulfate added. With the test tube held in a slanting position, about 1 ml of concentrated H_2SO_4 is poured carefully down the inner wall of the tube. At the junction of the two liquid layers a brown ring appears. The coloration is due to the complex ion, $Fe(NO)^{++}$. Another test for nitrate ion is based on the fact that elemental aluminum reduces nitrate ion to ammonia in a strongly basic solution.

$$8Al + 3NO_3^- + 5OH^- + 18H_2O \leftrightharpoons 3NH_3 + 8Al(OH)_4^-$$

13.4 OCCURRENCE AND PRODUCTION OF PHOSPHORUS

Because it reacts so readily with oxygen, phosphorus is found in nature only in combination with other elements. The major inorganic sources of phosphorus are phosphorite, $Ca_3(PO_4)_2$, and apatite, $3Ca_3(PO_4)_2 \cdot CaF_2$. The inorganic portion of the skeletons of animals is mainly calcium phosphate, $Ca_3(PO_4)_2$. Organic phosphates in plants and animals play important roles in cellular growth and metabolism.

Elemental phosphorus is produced commercially by heating calcium phosphate with sand and coke at high temperatures, usually in an electric furnace.

$$2Ca_3(PO_4)_2 + 6SiO_2 + 10C \rightarrow P_4 \uparrow + 6CaSiO_3 + 10CO$$

The phosphorus vapor can be condensed to yield a soft white solid that slowly turns yellow when exposed to light. The molecules in the vapor at 300° are tetratomic, P_4, but at 1200° more than 50 per cent are diatomic, P_2.

There are at least three allotropic forms of phosphorus. The "white" form is waxy and soluble in many organic solvents. The red form is crystalline and only sparingly soluble in most organic solvents. The red form is produced by heating the white form in the absence of oxygen, a transformation that is exothermic. The red form vaporizes to yield a vapor identical to that of the white form. If either the red or white form is subjected to extreme pressures, a black phosphorus is obtained.

Although white phosphorus ignites readily and burns vigorously in air at room temperature, the red form burns only if heated to 240°. In an open vessel, the combustion product is diphosphorus pentoxide, P_2O_5. This white solid dimerizes to form P_4O_{10}. If the supply of oxygen is limited, diphosphorus trioxide, P_2O_3 (actually, P_4O_6), is produced.

13.5 OXY-ACIDS OF PHOSPHORUS

a. Diphosphorus pentoxide reacts vigorously (exothermic) with excess water to yield *orthophosphoric acid*, H_3PO_4, a weak triprotic acid (p. 542). With limited water, metaphosphoric acid, HPO_3, is obtained.

$$P_2O_5 + 3H_2O \leftrightarrows 2H_3PO_4 + \Delta$$
$$P_2O_5 + H_2O \leftrightarrows 2HPO_3$$

If orthophosphoric acid is heated to 250° for several hours, pyrophosphoric acid is obtained.

$$2H_3PO_4 + \Delta \rightarrow H_4P_2O_7 + H_2O$$

Possible electronic formulations of the oxy-acids of phosphorus are shown in Fig. 13.2.

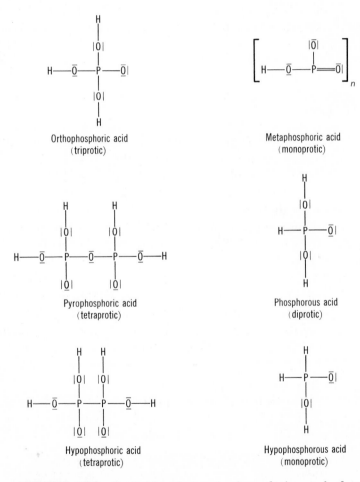

Orthophosphoric acid
(triprotic)

Metaphosphoric acid
(monoprotic)

Pyrophosphoric acid
(tetraprotic)

Phosphorous acid
(diprotic)

Hypophosphoric acid
(tetraprotic)

Hypophosphorous acid
(monoprotic)

FIGURE 13.2 Probable electronic formulations of the oxy-acids of phosphorus. Note that the formula of metaphosphoric acid is the monomer's representation, or the empirical formula.

b. *Phosphorous acid*, H_3PO_3, is prepared best by hydrolysis of phosphorus trichloride, PCl_3. The reaction mixture is evaporated until all of the by-product hydrogen chloride is vaporized. The acid is a white deliquescent solid.

$$PCl_3 + 3H_2O \rightarrow H_3PO_3 + 3HCl$$

Phosphorous acid is a good reducing agent and is a weak diprotic acid.

c. *Hypophosphorous acid*, H_3PO_2, is made by acidifying a solution that contains hypophosphite ion (p. 250). The acid and its conjugate base are strong reducing agents. The acid is weak and monoprotic.

13.6   ARSENIC

The most common allotrope of arsenic is a gray brittle crystalline solid that burns in air, if heated to about 200°, to yield arsenic(III) oxide, As_2O_3. Arsenic sublimes readily at 450° to yield a poisonous yellow vapor. At 650° the vapor molecules are tetratomic, As_4; at 1700° they are diatomic.

The most important natural sources of arsenic are the sulfides mentioned on page 270. The Marsh test for combined arsenic is described on page 251.

Arsenic(III) oxide (below 1500°, As_4O_6) exists in three forms, one amorphous and two crystalline. The crystalline form, stable at ordinary temperatures, sublimes at 130°–150°. The oxide is a fair reducing agent, being oxidized by hydrogen peroxide, chlorine, and nitric acid. Although it is only slightly soluble in water to yield arsenous acid, H_3AsO_3, it dissolves readily in basic solutions to yield the arsenite ions, $H_2AsO_3^-$ and $HAsO_3^{--}$.

Arsenic(V) oxide is a white deliquescent solid that decomposes on melting to yield arsenic(III) oxide and oxygen. It is made by oxidizing arsenic(III) oxide by nitric acid.

$$As_2O_3 + 2HNO_3 \rightarrow As_2O_5 + N_2O_3 + H_2O$$

Arsenic(V) oxide dissolves readily in water to yield the weak triprotic arsenic acid, H_3AsO_4.

The hydrolyses of the arsenic(III) and (V) halides, similar to those of phosphorus, are noted on page 577.

13.7 ANTIMONY

Antimony is a white metallic solid of brilliant luster. Molten antimony expands slightly during solidification. It burns slowly in oxygen. Some of the alloys of antimony are listed on page A-2.

The main natural source of antimony is stibnite, Sb_2S_3. In the presence of iron, the sulfide is converted to elemental antimony.

$$Sb_2S_3 + 3Fe \rightarrow 2Sb + 3FeS$$

Antimony trichloride, $SbCl_3$, is very soluble in water, but it tends to hydrolyze to yield a slightly soluble white oxychloride, $SbOCl$. The net equation is

$$SbCl_3 + H_2O \leftrightarrows SbOCl \downarrow + 2H^+ + 2Cl^-$$

Hydrolysis is prevented by acidifying the solution.

If hydroxyl ions are added to a solution of antimony trichloride, the slightly soluble antimony(III) hydroxide precipitates. This hydroxide is amphoteric (p. 576).

There are three oxides of antimony, Sb_2O_3, Sb_2O_4, and Sb_2O_5. The antimony(III) oxide is obtained by burning antimony in air. The antimony(V) oxide is made by oxidizing antimony with nitric acid. All the oxides are acidic, and the (III) oxide is slightly basic.

Antimony sulfide is mentioned on page 275.

13.8 BISMUTH

Bismuth (mp, 270°) has a brilliant metallic luster and a reddish-white color. As in the case of antimony, the molten metal expands slightly during solidification. It burns at bright red heat to yield bismuth(III) oxide, Bi_2O_3.

Bismuth hydroxide, $Bi(OH)_3$, is only slightly soluble in water but is soluble in acidic solutions. It is not amphoteric.

Bismuth chloride, $BiCl_3$, is soluble in water, but it hydrolyzes to yield a sparingly soluble oxychloride, $BiOCl$.

If bismuth(III) oxide is fused with potassium hydroxide, a brown solid, potassium bismuthate, $K^+BiO_3^-$, is obtained. This is a good oxidizing agent; it is able to oxidize manganese(II) ion to permanganate ion, MnO_4^-. It hydrolyzes to yield bismuth(V) oxide.

Bismuth sulfide is mentioned on page 275.

Problems

1. Write a probable electronic formula to represent the dinitrogen pentoxide molecule.

2. Considering the behavior of the oxides of nitrogen when they are added to water, which can be classed as Lewis acids?

3. The dimeric form, P_4O_{10}, of diphosphorus pentoxide is the predominant form in the solid state. Classify the reaction that occurs when the monomer P_2O_5 dimerizes. That is, is it acid-base or oxidation-reduction? Suggest an electronic formula for P_4O_{10}.

4. Write the equation to represent the oxidation of arsenic(III) oxide to dihydrogen arsenate ion, $H_2AsO_4^-$, by chlorine.

5. A clear solution is made by dissolving antimony trichloride in 0.1 M hydrochloric acid. A dilute sodium hydroxide solution is added dropwise and slowly to the solution until it is distinctly basic. The final solution is clear. What phenomena would be observed visually during the addition of the basic solution? (See p. 576.)

6. Explain why, according to Le Châtelier's principle, extensive hydrolysis of antimony trichloride is prevented in an acidic aqueous solution. (See p. 457.)

7. How many moles of electrons must be donated by 4.4 moles of hypophosphorous acid if the acid is oxidized to orthophosphoric acid?

8. How many tons of calcium phosphate will be needed to yield 15 tons of solid elemental phosphorus by using the commercial process? Assume the percentage theoretical yield is 92 per cent.

9. An aqueous solution contains nitrite ions and is suspected of containing nitrate ions. What test would you use to detect the nitrate ions?

10. Write the series of balanced equations representing the reactions of the Ostwald process.

11. Write the balanced equation for the reaction between water and dinitrogen pentoxide. Is this reaction acid-base or oxidation-reduction?

12. Considering the oxides listed in Table 13.1, which are paramagnetic?

13. What is the theoretical yield, in tons, of ammonia obtained by treating properly 1200 tons of nitrogen and 240 tons of hydrogen? (See Haber process, p. 457.)

14. Interpret the color change that is observed as a dark mixture of NO and NO_2 is cooled to yield the blue liquid, N_2O_3.

15. If bismuth(III) oxide is fused with potassium hydroxide, solid $K^+BiO_3^-$ is obtained. During this reaction, what is oxidized and what is reduced?

16. Write the formulas for sodium pyrophosphate, potassium metaphosphate, rubidium hypophosphite, sodium dihydrogen arsenite, calcium orthophosphate, and magnesium pyrophosphate.

14

THE GASEOUS STATE

14.1 A PERSPECTIVE

To view the gaseous state in its correct perspective, let us consider a simple "case history" of a sample of water. A small ice cube was dropped onto the floor of a warm kitchen. It was left undisturbed and after a short time a very shallow pool of water appeared where the cube had melted. Eventually this water evaporated and disappeared into the air. Since the kitchen window was open, some of the water escaped through the window.

A logical interpretation or explanation of this case history is based on a fundamental assumption: Water is composed of tiny particles called molecules. Therefore, both the ice cube and the pool of water were composed of molecules. Since the ice cube had a definite, rigid shape, the molecules in it were apparently held or packed together in a rather orderly fashion.

304

These molecules remained in this compact arrangement while the cube was at a relatively low temperature in the refrigerator, but when the cube was in the room at a higher temperature it "melted." When the cube melted, its molecules must have moved in order to form the shallow pool of liquid; because the cube was colder than the room, heat flowed from the surroundings to the cube. The molecules in the cube absorbed this heat, and their motion (kinetic energy) was more apparent. Because the shape of the pool of water was quite indefinite, the molecules must have been arranged more randomly in the pool than in the ice cube. Eventually each molecule in the liquid water must have broken away from its neighbors because the pool of water completely disappeared. The only place to which the molecules could have gone was the air (gas) in the room, and they must have moved from the surface of the liquid to enter the air. Since the molecules were in motion as they left the surface of the liquid, they must have absorbed energy from the surroundings. The very tiny molecules of water were in motion as they left the liquid, so it seems reasonable to assume that they kept moving once they were in the air. Therefore the molecules must have randomly moved (diffused) throughout the air in the room because some of them moved into the outdoor air. The molecules were invisible because of their tiny size.

If taken out of the context of physics and chemistry, the explanations of the above case history would probably appear quite imaginative and fantastic but they are embraced in the monumental kinetic-molecular theory of matter. This theory elaborates two fundamental concepts: the discontinuity of matter and the concept of matter in motion.

14.2 PROPERTIES OF GASES

Certain common properties indicate general characteristics of *all* ordinary gases. Of course, we must keep in mind that a gas is matter in a specific physical state.

a. Gases are easily and highly compressible. This implies that matter in the gaseous state is not so compact as in the liquid and solid states because liquids and solids are not easily compressible.

b. Gases are indefinitely expansible. This implies that matter in the gaseous state must be in motion—kinetic energy—because a gas will occupy the entire interior volume of any vessel in which it is confined. We should note that the atmosphere (gaseous mixture) which surrounds our planet is not indefinitely expansible because our atmosphere has some semblance of a boundary. The gravitational attraction exerted on the atmospheric gases by our planet decreases as the distance from our planet increases, until finally the amount of gas becomes infinitesimally small. With respect to the molecules in the atmosphere, the density of molecular population decreases as the distance from the earth increases. In a sense, the atmospheric gases "settle." However, by examining ordinary volumes of gases, it is not possible to demonstrate the settling of gases.

c. Gases exert pressure (a force) on the interior walls of those vessels in which they are confined; in other words, gases exert a pressure on all boundaries with which they are in contact.

d. Gases diffuse, or disperse, into each other so completely that all ordinary mixtures of gases are homogeneous.   If a gas dissolves in a liquid, the gas mixes with the liquid to produce a homogeneous mixture (this implies that matter in the gaseous state is in motion). The types of molecular motion are depicted in Fig. 14.1.

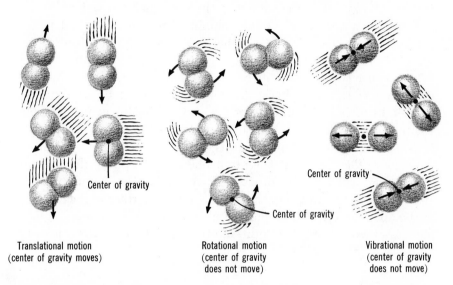

Translational motion
(center of gravity moves)

Rotational motion
(center of gravity
does not move)

Vibrational motion
(center of gravity
does not move)

FIGURE 14.1 Types of molecular motion. The diagrams depict diatomic molecules, and in the case of vibrational motion the atomic nuclei oscillate about an "imaginary" center of gravity.

14.3 MEASUREMENT OF GASEOUS PRESSURE

It would seem reasonable to expect that the pressure, or force, exerted by a gas would depend, at least in part, on the amount of gas.   Therefore, in order to make a definitive statement concerning a given amount of gas, we must identify the pressure of the gas.

The measurement of the pressure exerted by the atmosphere (atmospheric pressure) is the standard for the determination of gaseous pressures.   Atmospheric pressure is measured by a barometer.   There are two types of barometers in common use: the mercurial (mercury) barometer and the aneroid barometer.   The mercury barometer was invented by Evangelista Torricelli (Italian), and for this reason is often called a *Torricellian barometer*.   This rather simple device is an extremely significant instrument because it is used as the standard reference for the indication of ordinary gaseous pressure.

With respect to the procedure used in making an accurate mercury barometer, we might say that it is easier said than done. A clean glass tube about 85 to 90 cm long is sealed at one end. The tube is filled with pure mercury and then inverted in a well of mercury in such a way that no air enters the tube. When this is done, mercury flows out of the tube into the well until the weight (force) per unit area (pressure) of the column of mercury is equal to the pressure exerted by the atmosphere upon the free surface of the mercury outside the tube. Most of the mercury remains in the tube because the pressure of the atmosphere supports the column of mercury. The atmospheric pressure is measured by determining the height of the column of mercury. If the height is, for example, 755 mm, the atmospheric pressure is noted as 755 mm of mercury, or 75.5 cm of mercury. This height is equal to approximately 29 in. of mercury. The fact that the atmosphere can support this column of mercury will be more obvious if we realize that approximately 15 lb of air are resting on each square inch of surface of the mercury in the open well. This amount of air occupies an imaginary columnar vessel whose base is 1 sq in. in area and whose height is at least 50 miles. (See Fig. 14.2.)

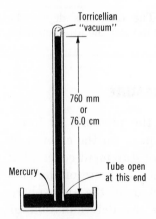

Torricellian "vacuum"

760 mm
or
76.0 cm

Mercury

Tube open at this end

FIGURE 14.2 Mercurial barometer whose prototype was first suggested by Torricelli. The open dish of mercury is exposed, in this case, to an atmospheric pressure of 760 mm.

At any given location, the pressure of the atmosphere varies considerably because of changes in the weather (temperature, humidity, and wind). Atmospheric pressure decreases with increasing altitude because the number of molecules in the air decreases as the distance from the earth increases. However, at sea level the variation in atmospheric pressure is relatively small (usually between

740 and 780 mm of mercury); the approximate mean value is 760 mm or 76 cm of Hg. This variation necessitates some standard reference pressure. The arbitrarily chosen standard pressure is 760 mm of Hg or 76 cm of Hg or 1 atm. This standard pressure is equivalent to approximately 14.7 lb/sq in.

14.4   BOYLE'S LAW

In 1660 Robert Boyle (British) measured the volumes occupied by a fixed amount of air under various pressures. (Since air is matter, the amount of air is the mass of the air, *not* its volume.) Boyle's data were reproducible, and so he formulated a quantitative relationship between pressure and volume of a given mass of air at constant temperature. Boyle's law states: For a given amount (mass) of gas at constant temperature, the volume of the gas is inversely proportional to the pressure exerted by the gas. Also, for a given mass of gas at constant temperature, the product of the volume times the pressure is constant.

These statements may be symbolized as follows:

(For a given mass of gas at constant temperature)

$$\underset{\text{(pressure)}}{P} \quad \times \quad \underset{\text{(volume)}}{V} \quad = k \text{ (a constant)}$$

If the pressure or the volume of a given mass of gas is changed at constant temperature, the product of the pressure times the volume under the new conditions is the same as under the original conditions because the product of $P \times V$ is constant. Therefore, if the original pressure is tripled, the new volume is one-third the original volume. (See Fig. 14.3.)

A certain mass of gas occupies a volume of 150 ml at a pressure of 700 mm of mercury and a temperature of 20°C. What is its volume at 1050 mm of mercury and 293°K?

Since 20°C is the same temperature as 293°K (because $293 - 273 = 20$), the temperature remains constant.

Original volume = 150 ml   Final volume = ?
Original pressure = 700 mm   Final pressure = 1050 mm
           of Hg   of Hg

The pressure is increased by the factor (ratio) 1050/700. Therefore the volume must be decreased by the factor (ratio) 700/1050. The arithmetical expression is:

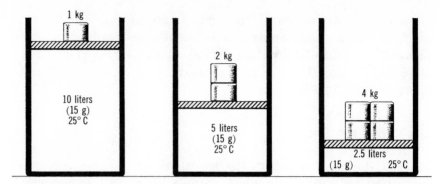

FIGURE 14.3 Effect of an increase in pressure on a given amount of gas, here 15 g at constant temperature.   (Boyle's law.)

Final volume = original volume × pressure-change factor

or

$$\text{Final volume} = 150 \times \frac{700}{1050} = 100 \text{ ml}$$

14.5 CHARLES' LAW AND GAY-LUSSAC'S LAW

About 1787 Jacques Charles (French) discovered a quantitative relationship between the volume of a gas and its temperature.   His experiments indicated that if a gas at constant pressure is heated from 0°C to 1°C, the volume occupied by the gas is increased by 1/273 of its original volume.   Also, if a gas at constant pressure is cooled from 0°C to −1°C, the volume of the gas is decreased by 1/273 of its original volume.   If we cool 273 ml of gas from 0°C to −273°C, with constant pressure, the volume of this gas should decrease by 273/273 of its volume at 0°C, and the gas should then have no volume at all.   Obviously matter cannot disappear when it is cooled; the only logical conclusion is that no gas can exist at −273°C.   This is a recognized fact.

Since matter is in motion in the gaseous state, and since the amount of kinetic energy that matter has depends on its temperature, it would seem reasonable that the behavior of gases depends on their temperatures expressed in degrees Kelvin (°K) or in degrees absolute (°A).   Only then can the volume and pressure of a gas be directly proportional to its temperature.

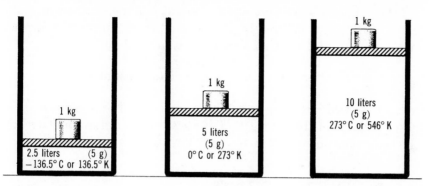

FIGURE 14.4   Effect of an increase in temperature on a given amount of gas at constant pressure.   (Charles' law.)

Charles' law states: At constant pressure, the volume of a given mass of gas is directly proportional to its absolute temperature. Or: At constant pressure, if the absolute temperature of a given mass of gas is changed by a certain factor, the volume of the gas is also changed by the same factor.   (See Fig. 14.4.)   These statements may be symbolized as follows:

(For a given mass of gas at constant pressure)

$$\frac{V}{T} = k \text{ (a constant)}$$

These statements indicate that for a given mass of gas at constant pressure, the value of V/T remains the same no matter how the volume and absolute temperature may be changed.

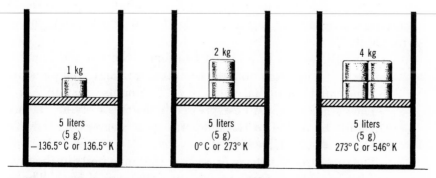

FIGURE 14.5   Effect of an increase in temperature on a given amount of gas at constant volume.   (Gay-Lussac's law.)

Gay-Lussac's law states: At constant volume, the pressure of a given mass of gas is directly proportional to the absolute temperature (see Fig. 14.5). Therefore at constant volume

$$P = kT \quad \text{or} \quad \frac{P}{T} = k \text{ (a constant)}$$

These two laws can be combined to state: For a given mass of gas, the value of the ratio PV/T is always constant, no matter how the conditions may change (see p. 330).

14.6 STANDARD CONDITIONS

Since the volume of a given amount of gas changes with pressure and with temperature, it is obvious that the volume of a gas has a definite meaning only if the pressure and temperature are specified. In the interest of uniformity, a standard reference set of conditions of temperature and pressure has been chosen. The standard conditions (SC) are: for temperature, 0°C (273°K) (273°A); for pressure, 760 mm of Hg (76 cm of Hg) (1 atmosphere). Often these standard conditions are noted as STP (standard temperature and pressure).

If the volume of a gas is known under conditions different from standard conditions, the gaseous volume may be "corrected" to SC (STP) by using the combined gas laws. In this way the volume that the gas would occupy if it were at SC can be calculated.

14.7 ARITHMETICAL PROBLEMS

1. A gas is confined in a heavy-walled container at 20°C and under a pressure of 570 mm of mercury. To what temperature, in degrees centigrade, must the gas be heated to increase its pressure to 1.5 atm?

Since the gas is in a closed container, the volume remains constant. Therefore only the pressure and temperature change, but the original value of P/T remains constant.

The value of T must be expressed in degrees Kelvin. Hence 273 must be added to the temperature in degrees centigrade: $273 + 20 = 293°K$.

The pressure must be expressed in the same units in the final and initial states. One atmosphere is 760 mm of Hg. Therefore 1.5 atm is equivalent to $1.5 \times 760 = 1140$ mm of Hg.

The temperature is increased by the same factor as the pressure, 1140/570.   Therefore:

$$\text{Final temperature in }°K = 293°K \times \frac{1140}{570} = 586°K$$

initial   pressure-
temperature   change
factor

Since the temperature in degrees centigrade is requested, the Kelvin temperature must be decreased by 273°.   Hence, 586 − 273 = 313°C is the final temperature.

2. Four hundred milliliters of a gas is confined at 30°C and 91.2 cm of mercury.   What is the volume of this amount of gas at SC (STP)?

Initial temperature is 303°K (273 + 30).   Standard conditions are 273°K and 76 cm of Hg.

Since the temperature decreases, the volume at SC will be less than the initial volume.   Because the pressure decreases, the volume at SC will be greater than the initial volume.   The actual volume at SC depends on which factor is the more prominent.   The temperature is decreased by the factor 273/303, and so the volume is decreased by the same factor. The pressure is decreased by the factor 76/91.2, and so the volume is increased by the factor 91.2/76.

To calculate the volume at SC:

$$\text{Volume at SC} = 400 \text{ ml} \times \frac{91.2}{76} \times \frac{273}{303} = 432 \text{ ml}$$

final   initial   pressure-   temperature-
volume   volume   change   change
factor   factor

14.8   DALTON'S LAW (PARTIAL PRESSURES)

In 1807 John Dalton (British) published a significant generalization about the pressures exerted by the individual gases in a mixture of gases.   His law states: In a mixture of gases, the pressure exerted by each gas is equal to the pressure it would exert if it were alone in a volume equal to that of the mixture and at the same temperature as that of the mixture.   This individual pressure is called the *partial pressure of the gas;* the sum of the partial pressures of the component gases is the total pressure of the gaseous mixture.

An inference from Dalton's law is that if two or more gases are mixed at constant pressure and temperature, their volumes are additive. This must be true because Dalton's law states that if two or more gases are mixed at constant volume and temperature, their pressures are additive.

The major components (average percentage by volume) of dry air are nitrogen (78.1 per cent), oxygen (20.9 per cent), argon (0.93 per cent), and carbon dioxide (0.03 per cent). (The percentages do not total 100 per cent because very small quantities of other gases are present.) Therefore 78.1 per cent of the total pressure of the dry air is the pressure exerted by the nitrogen (partial pressure of nitrogen), and the partial pressure of the oxygen is 20.9 per cent of the total pressure of the sample of air. In a 1000 ml sample of dry air under a pressure of 1 atm, the partial pressure of the nitrogen is 0.781 atm; of the oxygen, 0.209 atm; of the argon, 0.0093 atm; and of carbon dioxide, 0.0003 atm.

To determine the pressure which a gas collected over water would exert if it were alone in the volume measured, the vapor pressure of water must be subtracted from the total gaseous pressure. The pressure then obtained is the pressure of the "dry" gas. Of course, the temperature of the liquid water and of the gas must be determined. The value of the vapor pressure of water at ordinary temperatures can be found in Table A.1 (p. A-1). The collection of a gas over water is depicted in Fig. 14.6.

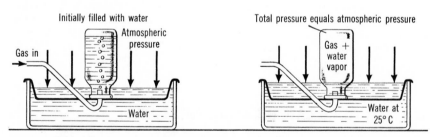

Vapor pressure of water at 25° C = 23.8 mm
Pressure of pure (dry) collected gas = (atmospheric pressure) −23.8 mm
Partial pressure of dry gas + partial pressure of water vapor = atmospheric pressure = total pressure of confined gas

FIGURE 14.6 Collection of a gas over water. The total pressure of the gaseous phase over the water is equal to the pressure exerted by the collected gas plus the pressure exerted by the water vapor. By applying Dalton's law, the pressure of the collected gas is easily determined.

14.9   GRAHAM'S LAW (RELATIVE RATES OF DIFFUSION)

Gases diffuse into one another because the molecules of the gases are in constant motion, and the rate of diffusion depends on the velocity of the molecules. Since molecules are minute particles of matter in motion, they have kinetic energy. These facts form the foundation of Graham's law.

In 1829 Thomas Graham (Scottish) recognized a quantitative relationship between the rates of diffusion and the densities of gases. He noted that the rates of diffusion of gases are inversely proportional to the square roots of their densities.

This generalization may be expressed mathematically as follows:

$$\frac{\text{rate of diffusion of gas } A}{\text{rate of diffusion of gas } B} = \sqrt{\frac{\text{density of gas } B}{\text{density of gas } A}}$$

Therefore, if gas A is 16 times as dense as gas B, gas B will diffuse 4 times as rapidly as gas A.

The derivation of Graham's law is based on the assumption that if two gases exist at the same temperature, all molecules in the two gases have the same average kinetic energy because, residing under the same temperature, they have the same degree of molecular motion.

Let us assume that gas A contains one kind of molecule whose symbol is A and that gas B contains another kind of molecule whose symbol is B. Then, if gas A is at the same temperature as gas B,

$$K.E._{(A)} = K.E._{(B)}$$

or

$$\tfrac{1}{2}m_A V_A^2 = \tfrac{1}{2}m_B V_B^2$$

where m_A = mass of molecule A
m_B = mass of molecule B
V_A = average velocity of molecule A
V_B = average velocity of molecule B

Multiplying both sides by 2:

$$m_A V_A^2 = m_B V_B^2$$

Collecting terms:

$$\frac{m_A}{m_B} = \frac{V_B^2}{V_A^2}$$

Taking the square root of each side:

$$\sqrt{\frac{m_A}{m_B}} = \frac{V_B}{V_A}$$

Since m_A is directly related to the mass of gas A and m_B to the mass of gas B, then the density of gas A is directly related to m_A and the density of gas B is directly related to m_B. Then

$$\sqrt{\frac{d_A}{d_B}} = \frac{V_B}{V_A}$$

Now if we assume that the rate of diffusion of a gas is directly proportional to the average velocity of its molecules, then

$$\sqrt{\frac{d_A}{d_B}} = \frac{r_B}{r_A}$$

where r_B/r_A is the ratio of the rates of diffusion of gas B and gas A.

At the same temperature, the rates of diffusion (average velocities) of the molecules of two gases are inversely proportional to the square roots of their masses. The molecular weight of the hydrogen molecule is approximately 2, and of the oxygen molecule, nearly 32. Since the approximate ratio of the masses is 1/16 (hydrogen to oxygen), and the square root of the inverse ratio is 4/1, hydrogen molecules diffuse approximately 4 times as rapidly as oxygen molecules (see Fig. 14.7).

When contrasting the molecules of two different gases at the same temperature, we see that the molecules having the smaller mass will diffuse (move through space) more rapidly than those having the larger mass. Of all the recognized molecules, the hydrogen molecule has the smallest mass, and so in the gaseous state (when it is contrasted with other molecules at the same temperature) it has the greatest velocity. At 0°C the average velocity of a hydrogen molecule is approximately 1.14 miles (1840 meters) per second.

The actual time required for a given amount of a gas to diffuse completely into another gas depends on the number of molecules present per unit volume in the other gas. The molecules of the diffusing gas continually collide with the molecules in the other gas. These elastic collisions increase the time required for complete mixing of the gases. Therefore the greater the number of molecules

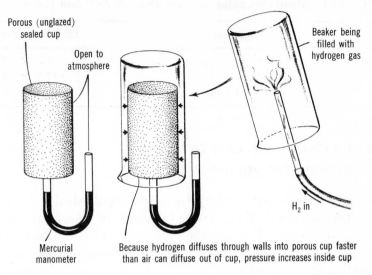

Porous (unglazed) sealed cup

Open to atmosphere

Beaker being filled with hydrogen gas

H_2 in

Mercurial manometer

Because hydrogen diffuses through walls into porous cup faster than air can diffuse out of cup, pressure increases inside cup

FIGURE 14.7 Experiment illustrating that the diffusion of hydrogen is more rapid than the diffusion of air. Since the molecules in gaseous hydrogen are much less massive than those in air, the hydrogen molecules move much more rapidly. (Graham's law.)

in a gas, the longer the time required for another gas to diffuse completely into it.

It is interesting to imagine the continuous, random motion of molecules in an ordinary gas, especially in regard to the probable distance (the mean free path) a given molecule travels between successive collisions with other molecules. The mean free path of the molecules in a given gas depends on the diameters (related to volumes) of the molecules, the mass of the molecules (related to speed), the number of molecules per unit volume (related to pressure), and the temperature (related to kinetic energy). If nitrogen molecules are at 0°C under a pressure of only 1×10^{-5} mm (1.32×10^{-8} atm), a probable value of the mean free path of the molecules is 450 cm. However, if the gaseous nitrogen is at 25°C under 1 atm of pressure, the mean free path is only 6.50×10^{-6} cm, or 650 A. Under these conditions there are approximately 9.0×10^{28} collisions per cm³ per second. The mean free path of an oxygen molecule at STP is about 1000 times the apparent diameter of an oxygen molecule.

TABLE 14.1   Mean free paths in some gases at 25°C and 1 atm

Gas	Mean Free Path	Collisions/cm³ sec
O_2	7.14×10^{-6} cm (714 A)	7.5×10^{28}
H_2	12.3×10^{-6} (1230)	17.7×10^{28}
He	19.0×10^{-6} (1900)	8.1×10^{28}

14.10   GAY-LUSSAC'S LAW OF COMBINING VOLUMES

Early in the nineteenth century Gay-Lussac published a significant generalization about the relative volumes of gases involved in chemical reactions.   Perhaps the importance of Gay-Lussac's concept may be emphasized best by noting that Avogadro used it as the foundation of his hypothesis.

Gay-Lussac's law of combining volumes states: Whenever two or more gases are involved in a chemical reaction, the ratios of the volumes of these gases may be expressed as the ratios of small integral numbers, provided the volumes are measured at the same temperature and pressure.   (See Fig. 14.8.)

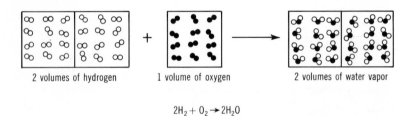

2 volumes of hydrogen   1 volume of oxygen   2 volumes of water vapor

$$2H_2 + O_2 \rightarrow 2H_2O$$

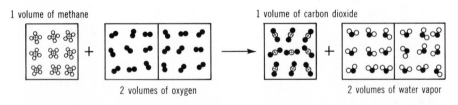

1 volume of methane   1 volume of carbon dioxide

2 volumes of oxygen   2 volumes of water vapor

$$CH_4 + 2O_2 \rightarrow CO_2 + 2H_2O$$

FIGURE 14.8   In each reaction all gases are at the same temperature and pressure, and the ratio of the volumes of the gases may be expressed by integral numbers.   (Gay-Lussac's law of combining volumes.)

Gay-Lussac based his law of combining volumes on experimental observations. Let us also base our understanding of this law on experimental facts. If all gases involved are measured at the same temperature and pressure, it is found that whenever one unit volume of hydrogen reacts completely with one unit volume of chlorine, two unit volumes of hydrogen chloride are produced.

$$H_2 + Cl_2 \rightarrow 2HCl$$

The combustion of ethane (C_2H_6) is a chemical reaction involving gases. We may assume that the conditions are such that all gases are measured at the same temperature and pressure.

$$2C_2H_6 + 7O_2 \rightarrow 4CO_2 + 6HOH$$

ethane   oxygen   carbon   steam
                           dioxide

The simplest integral ratios of the volumes are

$$C_2H_6 : O_2 : CO_2 : HOH$$
$$2 \ : 7 : \ 4 \ : \ 6$$

How many liters of oxygen are necessary to burn completely 100 l of ethane? How many liters of carbon dioxide and of steam are produced? (Assume all reactants and products are measured at the same temperature and pressure.)

Since the ratio of ethane to oxygen is 2:7, 3.5 times as many volumes of oxygen as of ethane are necessary. If 100 l of ethane are combusted, 350 l of oxygen are necessary.

Since the ratio of ethane to carbon dioxide is 2:4, the volume of carbon dioxide produced is twice the volume of ethane combusted. Therefore 200 l of carbon dioxide are produced.

The ratio of ethane to steam is 2:6, or 1:3. Therefore 300 l of steam are produced.

14.11 AVOGADRO'S HYPOTHESIS

In 1811 Amedeo Avogadro postulated a reasoned idea about the relative numbers of molecules in equal volumes of gases under identical conditions of temperature and pressure. Although we will use Avogadro's hypothesis as an exact generalization, it is an approximate law in the same sense as the other gas laws are.

Using the valid assumption that the molecules of two different gases at the same temperature have the same average kinetic energy, let us think about two different gases confined under identical pressures in separate containers of equal volume at the same temperature. We know that the molecules in the two containers exert equal pressures, that the average kinetic energy of the molecules in each container is the same as in the other, and that the molecules occupy equal volumes. Therefore it seems reasonable to assume that the two containers contain equal numbers of molecules. Enlarging this assumption, we conclude that under the same pressure and temperature equal volumes of all gases contain the same number of molecules, or in other words: under the same pressure and temperature, equal numbers of molecules of different gases occupy equal volumes.

Avogadro's hypothesis is a valuable concept, but if its significance is not immediately apparent and its validity seems questionable, one should remember that after Avogadro suggested his hypothesis in 1811 a period of at least 50 years elapsed before its significance and validity were recognized by the majority of the chemists. At an important scientific meeting held in 1860, one of Avogadro's students, Stanislao Cannizzaro, convinced a group of eminent scientists that his teacher's concept was sound and extremely useful. Soon after this meeting, Avogadro's idea "caught on." This revolutionized most of the prevalent ideas of the formulations of even the simplest molecules.

14.12 MOLAR WEIGHTS OF GASEOUS SUBSTANCES (MOLAR VOLUME)

A molar weight could not be assigned to the oxygen molecule until the number of atoms in one molecule was known. The determination of the number of atoms in an oxygen molecule involved logical reasoning based on experimental observations and on Dalton's atomic theory, Gay-Lussac's law of combining volumes, and Avogadro's hypothesis. It should be clear that agreement as to the exact nature of the oxygen molecule had to await acceptance of the validity of Avogadro's hypothesis.

The production of steam (gaseous water) from its elements is accomplished by initiating a reaction between hydrogen and oxygen. By applying Gay-Lussac's law of combining volumes, we find

$$\text{oxygen} \quad + \quad \text{hydrogen} \quad \rightarrow \text{gaseous water}$$
$$\text{(1 unit volume)} \quad \text{(2 unit volumes)} \quad \text{(2 unit volumes)}$$

Then according to Avogadro's hypothesis:

$$\text{oxygen} \; + \; \text{hydrogen} \rightarrow \text{gaseous water}$$

(1 molecule)   (2 molecules)   (2 molecules)

Applying Dalton's atomic theory (atoms are not split during ordinary chemical changes), two molecules of gaseous water must collectively contain at least two atoms of oxygen. Therefore one molecule of oxygen must contain at least two atoms of oxygen. Quantitative experimentation indicates that a molecule of oxygen yields only two discrete material particles, each having the chemical properties of the element oxygen. Therefore we may assume that a molecule of oxygen contains not more than two atoms of oxygen. Since the upper limit is two atoms of oxygen per molecule, and the lower limit is two, the oxygen molecule is considered diatomic. Since the assigned atomic weight of oxygen is approximately 16 amu, the assigned molar weight of oxygen is 32 g.

If the molar weight of a gaseous substance is to be determined by comparing the mass of a known volume to the mass of a known volume of oxygen, the volumes of the gases must be measured under identical conditions of temperature and pressure. It is customary to "correct" all volumes to the values they would have if the gases were measured at standard conditions (STP).

Under standard conditions (0°C and 760 mm of Hg), 1.43 g of oxygen occupies a volume of 1 l, and 32 g (1 mole) would occupy approximately 22.4 l (32 g/1.43 g × 1). Therefore the molar volume of oxygen is 22.4 l at SC. By applying Avogadro's hypothesis, we note that 22.4 l is the *molar volume* of any gas at standard conditions. The mass of 22.4 l of any gas at SC is the mass of one mole of the gas. Here we should recall that the molar weight of a gas expressed in grams is the mass of one mole of the gas.

One mole of any gaseous substance is 6.02×10^{23} molecules. At standard conditions 22.4 l of a gas contains 6.02×10^{23} molecules.

Below are two problems in which the molar weight of a gas is a factor.

1. The density of a gas at SC (STP) is 1.40 g/l. What is the molar weight of the gas?

   Since 1 liter has a mass of 1.40 g, 22.4 l has a mass of 31.4 g, or a mass of one mole. The molar weight is 31.4 g.

2. What is the volume of 2 g of methane, CH_4, at 2 atm and 0°C?

   The molar weight of methane is 16 g; hence 16 g (one mole) occupies 22.4 l at SC. Then 2 g occupies 2/16 of 22.4 l at SC or 2.8 l. The 2.8 l of methane at SC would occupy a different volume at 2 atm and 0°C. Since the temperature at the new condition is the same as at SC, only the pressure change affects the volume. Since the pressure is doubled, the volume is halved. Therefore the 2 g of methane that occupies 2.8 l at SC will occupy only 1.4 l at 2 atm and 0°C.

14.13 THE KINETIC-MOLECULAR THEORY

The group of concepts which appears to explain satisfactorily the behavior of gases is called the kinetic-molecular theory. The main postulates of this theory and some of their interpretations are noted below. We shall assume that they apply to ordinary gases at ordinary pressures and temperatures.

All gases consist of molecules. The actual volume of the molecules themselves is very small contrasted with the entire space occupied by a gas at ordinary pressures. All molecules of a specific pure gas have about the same size.

In all gases the molecules are constantly, rapidly, and randomly moving through space. The molecules continually collide with each other and with all confining boundaries. Collisions are perfectly elastic.

At any given temperature the molecules in a gas have the same average kinetic energy. This energy is dependent only on the absolute temperature.

Boyle's law, Charles' law, and Dalton's law, as usually employed in elementary treatments, are descriptions of general gaseous behavior. These suggest that the individuality of the molecules within a gas has little significance with respect to the volume occupied by the molecules, the pressure they exert, and their kinetic energy (temperature). The gas laws pertain to the volume occupied by the gas, but not to the total volume of the molecules themselves. The average kinetic energy of the molecules in a gas is dependent solely on their temperature, and this energy is independent of the kind of molecules in the gas. Since the pressure exerted by a gas is dependent only on the number of molecules per unit volume (concentration or density of molecular population) and on the temperature of the molecules, the pressure of a gas is independent of the kinds of molecules in it.

Gases diffuse into each other because the molecules are in

constant, random motion; within the gas there is ample empty space for more molecules. In an ordinary mixture of gases, the random motion of the molecules results in uniform composition throughout the system. (See p. 306.)

The pressure exerted by a given amount of gas at constant temperature is inversely proportional to the volume occupied by the gas (Boyle's law) because the pressure is due to bombardment of the confining boundaries by the molecules. At a given temperature, the pressure exerted by a gas is proportional to the number of molecules per unit volume, or the density of the molecular population (concentration). If the volume of a given mass of gas at constant temperature is doubled, the same number of molecules occupies a volume twice the original volume. Therefore the density of the molecular population is halved. Because of this the number of molecular bombardments per unit time as well as the pressure exerted by the gas are also halved. If the volume of a given mass of gas at constant temperature is decreased to one-half the original volume, the same number of molecules occupies a volume one-half the original. Because the density of molecular population is then twice the original density, the pressure is twice the original pressure.

No gas can exist at zero degrees of absolute temperature (0°A or 0°K) because in the absence of heat there is essentially no molecular motion. Since the molecules in a gas are in motion, they must have kinetic energy. The kinetic-molecular theory assumes that molecular motion and heat are identical.

Considering the unity of heat and molecular-kinetic energy, if the pressure exerted by a gas is directly proportional to the kinetic energy of the molecules, the pressure must also be directly proportional to the absolute temperature.

14.14 LIQUEFACTION OF GASES

All known gases can be liquefied provided they are under appropriate conditions of pressure and temperature. The molecules in such liquids are held to their neighbors by intermolecular attractive (cohesive) forces which apparently compensate for the kinetic energy of the molecules. In order to liquefy a gas, conditions must be arranged so that the intermolecular attractive forces counterbalance the kinetic energy of the molecules. The most favorable conditions for the liquefaction of a gas are high pressures (increased significance of cohesive forces) and low temperatures (decreased significance of kinetic energy).

Since the kinetic energy of the molecules in a gas is directly proportional to the absolute temperature, it seems reasonable to expect that the higher the temperature of a gas, the more difficult it will be for the cohesive forces to counterbalance the kinetic energy of the molecules. Because the inherent strength of the inter-molecular attractive forces depends in part on the structure of the molecules, and because different gases contain different molecules, we should expect that the inherent strength of these cohesive forces would differ in different gases. In any event, there must be for every known gas a temperature at which the kinetic energy of the molecules is so great that it is impossible for the cohesive forces to overcome or counterbalance it, although the molecules are as close together as the intermolecular repulsive forces will permit. For every known gas there is a temperature above which it is impossible to liquefy the gas, no matter how great the pressure. This tempera-ture is called the *critical temperature*. The minimum pressure necessary to liquefy a gas at its critical temperature is its *critical pressure*. At its critical temperature a substance exhibits a con-tinuity of state: both its liquid and gaseous states merge, and the concentration of the liquid state is the same as the concentration of the gaseous state.

Table 14.2 lists the critical temperatures and pressures of some familiar substances. We usually think of oxygen as a gas, but it can also be a liquid. The critical temperature of oxygen ($-118°C$) is that temperature above which it is impossible to liquefy oxygen or above which liquid oxygen cannot exist. The normal boiling point of oxygen ($-183°C$) is the highest temperature at which oxygen may be liquefied if the pressure on the gaseous oxygen is 1 atmosphere.

The information in Table 14.2 yields a significant generalization. If two different substances have approximately the same molar weight, and if the inherent strengths of the cohesive forces between the molecules in the two substances are nearly identical, the two will have approximately the same critical temperature. If the critical temperatures of the substances differ, it is because the inherent strengths of the intermolecular attractive forces differ. For example, nitrogen and carbon monoxide have approximately the same molar weight. The critical temperature of nitrogen is slightly lower than that of carbon monoxide. Therefore the in-

TABLE 14.2   Critical temperatures and pressures

Substance	Molar Weight	Critical Temperature, °C	Critical Pressure, Atm	Normal Boiling Point, °C
Helium	4.003	−268	2.7	−269
Hydrogen	2.016	−240	14	−253
Nitrogen	28.016	−147	33	−196
Carbon monoxide	28.01	−140	35	−192
Oxygen	32.0	−118	50	−183
Argon	39.944	−117.5	52	−186
Carbon dioxide	44.01	+31	73	−78
Hydrogen chloride	36.465	+51	81	−85
Hydrogen sulfide	34.082	+100	89	−60
Chlorine	70.914	+146	94	−35
Sulfur dioxide	64.066	+157	78	−10
Water	18.016	+374	217	+100

herent strength of the intermolecular attractive forces must be slightly weaker in nitrogen than in carbon monoxide.

Another useful generalization is: If the molecular masses of two different substances are significantly different, and if the inherent strengths of the intermolecular attractive forces in the two substances are approximately identical, the substance with the larger molar weight will have the higher critical temperature. Of course, if the substance having the larger molar weight has the lower critical temperature, then its intermolecular attractive forces are much weaker. If the substance having the smaller molar weight has the higher critical temperature, then its intermolecular attractive forces are much stronger.

14.15   STORAGE OF GASES

Excluding water from consideration for the moment, we shall discuss the storage at room temperature of each substance listed in Table 14.2. At room temperature (15°–40°C) and under a pressure of 1 atmosphere, all of the tabulated substances (except water) are gaseous. If we assume that these substances are to be transported and stored at temperatures between 15°C and 40°C, we see that hydrogen sulfide, chlorine, and sulfur dioxide may be stored as liquids in closed containers. With care, hydrogen chloride and carbon dioxide might be stored as liquids in closed containers, but the temperature of the carbon dioxide must not be above 31°C if it is to remain a liquid. The storage containers are heavy-walled steel tanks (closed cylinders) because the gaseous state above the liquid exerts a high pressure. Argon, oxygen, carbon monoxide, nitrogen, hydrogen, and helium cannot exist in the liquid state at temperatures as high as 15°C. Therefore, if any one of these is stored at temperatures between 15°C and 40°C in a closed container, it is in the gaseous state. If these substances are to be transported in the liquid state, they must be contained in open (or at least vented) vessels. In this case the pressure over the liquid is atmospheric pressure. The temperature of each liquid under these conditions is approximately its normal boiling point. Therefore if liquid oxygen is stored in a large Thermos flask or a Dewar flask, the temperature of the liquid is about −183°C. The liquid oxygen slowly evaporates, but the rate of loss by evaporation is decreased by insulating the liquid, as well as possible, from the warmer surroundings by use of a near-vacuum in the walls of the vessel.

It might be interesting to comment briefly on the handling of a small (closed) tank of oxygen and to note the differences when handling a small tank of chlorine. Let us assume that we have a "full," or recently purchased, tank of each gas, and that on each tank there is a valve and a gauge used to measure the pressure exerted by the gas inside the tank. After taking appropriate precautions, the valves are opened and about one-third of the contents of each tank is allowed to rush out rapidly. Then the valves are closed quickly and the gauges watched. The gauge on the oxygen tank indicates that the gaseous pressure inside the tank is slightly less than two-thirds the pressure of the "full" tank. However, the gaseous pressure inside the tank increases slowly, and finally, after the gaseous pressure is about two-thirds of the original pressure in the "full" tank, no further increase is observed. This final gaseous pressure is about two-thirds of the original because about one-third of the oxygen was removed. When the valve on the tank was opened, the rapid expansion of the oxygen cooled the gas in the tank, so that the gaseous pressure is momentarily lower than at the final higher temperature. Although the volume of the oxygen in the tank remains constant, the temperature of the gas gradually increases to that of the surroundings. Hence the gaseous pressure increases slightly soon after the valve is closed.

At the time the valve is closed on the opened tank of chlorine, the gauge indicates a gaseous pressure slightly less than that of the "full" tank. However, the pressure of the gas inside the tank increases slowly until it is the same as that before any of the gas was removed. The reason for this is that the tank contains liquid and gaseous chlorine, and if gaseous chlorine is removed, molecules leave the liquid to replace those molecules that left the opened tank. So long as there is liquid chlorine in the tank and the temperature of tank and contents remains constant, the gaseous pressure inside the tank is constant. Actually the pressure of the gaseous chlorine in the tank is the vapor pressure of liquid chlorine at the temperature in question. Because there is no liquid oxygen in the tank of oxygen, any gas removed is not replaced, and the pressure therefore drops steadily as gas is removed. The gaseous pressure in the tank of chlorine does not drop until all the liquid chlorine is gone. However, since the total mass of the tank and contents does decrease as chlorine is removed, this mass decrease is an indication of the amount of chlorine removed.

Each value for the critical pressure listed in Table 14.2 is actually the vapor pressure of the substance in its liquid state at its critical temperature. We shall discuss the concept of vapor pressure in the next chapter.

The normal boiling point of each substance listed in Table 14.2 is the temperature at which the liquid state has a vapor pressure equal to 1 atm. Since the critical pressure is related in part to the kinetic energy of the molecules, it is not surprising that at very low temperatures the critical pressures are much lower than at the higher temperatures.

If a substance exists in its gaseous state below its critical temperature, it is considered a vapor. If a substance exists as a gas above its critical temperature, it is called a gas. Therefore gaseous water at temperatures below 374°C is water vapor, whereas oxygen at any temperature above −118°C is a gas. Oxygen gas at any temperature below −118°C is oxygen vapor.

14.16 THE IDEAL GAS AND DEVIATIONS
FROM IDEALITY

Actually the gas laws are descriptions of the behavior of a hypothetical gas in which each molecule behaves as a completely independent particle unaffected by the presence of other molecules. Since this imaginary gas was conceived to fit exactly all the gas laws, it is called the *ideal gas*. No known gas portrays exactly the ideal behavior of this gas. The ideal gas is an arbitrary standard to which the behavior of a known gas is related. (See Fig. 14.9.)

If the behavior of a known gas is quite different from that of the ideal gas, it is said to deviate from ideality. When known gases are compressed at relatively high pressures, the volumes they occupy are slightly greater than the volumes predicted by the gas laws. As the amount of empty space between the molecules diminishes, the ease of compression decreases. This deviation from ideality is due to the actual volume of the molecules. The concept of molecular volume is related intimately to the concept of intermolecular repulsive forces, which are significant factors at small intermolecular distances. In the case of an individual molecule, the effective "sphere of influence" of these repulsive forces may be considered its molecular volume. We should recall that in the ideal gas there are no intermolecular repulsive forces.

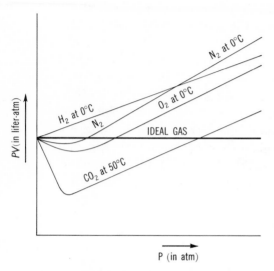

FIGURE 14.9 The product $P \times V$ is plotted versus P for one mole of gas at the temperature specified. Note that hydrogen exhibits positive deviations from ideality at all pressures at 0°C, whereas nitrogen and oxygen show a negative deviation at low pressures and a positive deviation at higher pressures.

When known gases are examined at low temperatures, the volumes occupied by the gases are usually slightly less than those predicted by the gas laws. Intermolecular attractive forces apparently tend to pull the molecules closer together than is predicted. These forces are more apparent at low temperatures at which the molecules have low kinetic energy. There are no intermolecular attractive forces in the ideal gas.

The intermolecular repulsive forces in a known gas cause a deviation from ideality opposite to that caused by the intermolecular attractive forces. Under certain conditions these opposing factors balance. Then the deviations from ideality may be very small. At high temperatures and low pressures, many gases behave ideally insofar as can be determined by experimentation.

The structures and electrical characteristics of known molecules play an important role in our interpretation of intermolecular attractive and repulsive forces. These forces appear to be electrostatic in character, and their relative strengths may be recognized by investigating the deviation, from ideality, of a known gas. The intermolecular forces in real gases are often called *van der Waals forces*.

Generally if an ordinary gas under relatively high pressure and at room temperature is allowed to expand, the gas cools and, if possible, gathers heat from the surroundings. The absorption of heat during the free expansion (effusion) of a gas is called the *Joule-Thomson effect*. The extent of the temperature decrease is characteristic of the gas in question (its initial and final pressure and its initial temperature). As a general rule, free expansion results in cooling the gas if the gas exhibits negative deviation from ideality; it results in warming the gas if the gas shows a positive deviation. At temperatures near 0°C rapid free expansion of gaseous hydrogen is accompanied by an increase in temperature, but on expansion at temperatures below −100°C the gas decreases in temperature. Since there are no intermolecular attractive forces in the ideal gas, expansion of the ideal gas does not cause cooling.

The free expansion of nitrogen at 25°C and 200 atm to a pressure of 1 atm causes the temperature of the gas to drop to −6°C, a decrease of 31°C. Successive expansions in a cyclic process can cool the gas to its liquefaction temperature.

Compression of a gas causes an increase in temperature of the gas because each molecule on the average has received more kinetic energy by the action of the compressor. There can be no heating of the gas unless work is done on the gas, and conversely, there can be no cooling of the gas unless it loses internal kinetic energy. If the gas does work, it comes from the kinetic energy of the molecules; hence the temperature of the gas decreases.

We conclude, therefore, that if work is done on the gas, the temperature of the gas increases. If work is done by the gas, the temperature of the gas decreases. The free expansion of an ordinary gas involves work done by the molecules to overcome intermolecular attractive forces.

14.17 THE EQUATION OF STATE FOR THE IDEAL GAS

The previous sections of this chapter have emphasized the concept that the four variables volume (V), pressure (P), temperature (T), and the number of moles (n) must be considered collectively whenever we interrelate the various conditions under which a gaseous state may exist. An equation of state for the ideal gas is derived by collecting, in one expression, the pertinent variables. We should recall that the volume factor is the volume occupied by the molecules in the gaseous phase, and that it has nothing to do with the actual volume of the molecules themselves. It is therefore the measure of empty space within the confining vessel.

$$V = k \frac{1}{p} \text{ (at constant } T \text{ and } n) \qquad \text{Boyle's law}$$

$$V = k_1 T \text{ (at constant } P \text{ and } n) \qquad \text{Charles' law}$$
$$V = k_2 n \text{ (at constant } T \text{ and } P) \qquad \text{Gay-Lussac's law}$$

where k, k_1, and k_2 are proportionality constants, which when combined yield the universal gas constant, R.

Combination of the three equations yields the equation of state

$$V = \frac{R(T)(n)}{(P)} \qquad \text{or} \qquad PV = nRT$$

The value of R as determined if $P = 1$ atm, $V = 22.4$ l, $n = 1$, and $T = 273°K$ is 0.0821 l-atm/°K mole. This value of the gas constant R can be used in the equation of state only if n is the number of moles, P is in atm, V is in liters, and T is in °K. If the volume is expressed in cm³, instead of in liters, $R = 82.1$ cm³-atm/°K mole.

Since R involves the dimensions of work (energy), the gas constant has the dimensions of energy/deg mole. Therefore we can evaluate R as 8.31×10^7 erg/deg mole; or if joules, 8.31 joules/deg mole. But since 4.18 joules is 1 calorie, $R = 1.99$ cal/deg mole.

Although there are other more sophisticated derivations of the perfect-gas expression, the one presented here is adequate for our current needs. It is well to recall that the units of pressure and volume dictate the numerical value of the constant R.

14.18   THE VAN DER WAALS EQUATION

In 1873 van der Waals (Dutch) suggested a semiempirical relation to express the behavior of ordinary gases in terms of the equation of state by inserting in the equation suitable correction factors for the variables, pressure and volume. This was the first attempt to correct the original molecular model of the gaseous state so that it might fit more nearly the perfect-gas expression.

We have mentioned previously that the volume of the molecules in a gas may, under specific conditions, cause deviations from ideal behavior. In an attempt to correct for this, van der Waals inserted in the equation of state a factor b (proportional to the actual volume of the molecules) that is subtracted from the volume occupied by the gas. Although the value of b is constant for a given gas, it is different for different gases. Insertion of this factor yields the expression

$$P(V - b) = nRT$$

Since the intermolecular attractive forces decrease the velocity of the molecules in an ordinary gas at a specific temperature, the actual pressure exerted on the confining walls is less than that expected for the ideal gas. The lower the velocity of the molecules, the fewer the number of collisions per unit time. Therefore the pressure factor in the equation of state is increased by a term a/V^2, where a, a constant for each gas, is related to the magnitude of the intermolecular attractive forces.

A suitable but abridged expression of the van der Waals equation, if V is the volume of one mole, is

$$\left(P + \frac{a}{V^2}\right)(V - b) = RT$$

This relation is presented only to provide some evidence that attempts are made to discover the nature and magnitude of the factors that contribute to a deviation from ideal gas behavior. It is not intended that the student understand thoroughly either the genesis or the quantitative utility of the equation.

14.19   THE BOLTZMANN PRINCIPLE

One of the most useful and fundamental principles applicable to all systems at equilibrium is the Boltzmann expression

$$N = Ape^{-\epsilon/kT}$$

where N is the number of molecules present in a state such that the energy per molecule is ϵ; A is a proportionality constant; p expresses the number of different paths by which the energy can be attained; k is the Boltzmann constant, R/N (the gas constant per molecule), and T is the temperature in °K.

The evaluation of Boltzmann's constant is

$$\frac{R}{N} = \frac{8.31 \times 10^7 \text{ erg/deg mole}}{6.02 \times 10^{23} \text{ molecules/mole}} = 1.38 \times 10^{-16} \text{ erg/deg molecule}$$

The Boltzmann principle, conceived by Ludwig Boltzmann (German), yields information about the way that molecules in the earth's atmosphere are distributed within the earth's gravitational field. Let us apply this principle to derive the barometric formula.

For the factor ϵ in the expression we shall substitute mgh, where m is the mass of the molecule, g the gravitational constant, and h the height above a level at which the energy is said to be zero. Since the term p is one (unity), the Boltzmann relation becomes

$$N = Ae^{-mgh/kT}$$

To formulate a more useful equation, let us substitute pressure, P, for N because pressure is proportional to the number of molecules. Also, $m/k \times N/N = M/R$, where M is the molecular weight of the molecules. And further, A is changed to P_0 (if $h = 0$, $P = P_0$). The resultant expression becomes the barometric formula

$$P = P_0 e^{-Mgh/RT}$$

Examination of this expression yields the conclusions that (1) pressure decreases with height, approaching but not reaching zero; (2) the greater the molecular weight of the gas, the greater the rate of decrease in pressure; and (3) the higher the temperature, the lower the rate of decrease in pressure.

The barometric formula (a Boltzmann principle) can be used to evaluate the distribution of colloids (p. 392) in an ultracentrifuge. However, the value of g is much larger than that in the earth's gravitational field. The distribution of ions in an electrical field, in electrolytic solutions (p. 501), for instance, can be determined by using the Boltzmann distribution principle.

If the expression seems formidable, you should try to see the qualitative aspects only. The exponential nature of the relation is the most significant characteristic because this implies the logarithmic nature of the principle.

The kinetic energy of a given molecule at a constant temperature may vary over a period of time because of encounters (elastic collisions) with other molecules to which and from which energy can be transferred. The average kinetic energy of all the molecules and the total kinetic energy are nonetheless dependent only on the temperature, in °K, of the gas. At a given instant, however, some molecules have more kinetic energy than the average, some may have less than the average, but most, of course, will have an energy near the average.

James Clerk Maxwell (Scottish) in 1860 suggested an equation by which the distribution of kinetic energy among the molecules in a given gas at a specific temperature can be derived from the Boltzmann expression. One of the initial steps in the derivation of the Maxwell-Boltzmann distribution expression is the substitution of $\frac{1}{2}mv^2$ (kinetic energy) for the factor ϵ in the Boltzmann relation (p. 332). Hence the fraction of the total number of molecules that lie in the range of velocities between v and $v + dv$ depends exponentially on the kinetic energy of the molecules with this velocity. This leads to the expression

Fraction of total number of molecules $= Ae^{-1/2mv^2/kT}$

Since this energy distribution expression has an exponential form, the probability that molecules will have high speeds decreases rapidly with increasing temperatures. In other words, there is with increasing temperatures a continuous decrease in the number of molecules having high speeds. (The term *speed*, rather than *velocity*, is used because in Maxwell's three-dimensional treatment only the magnitude of the molecular velocities is considered, and not the direction.)

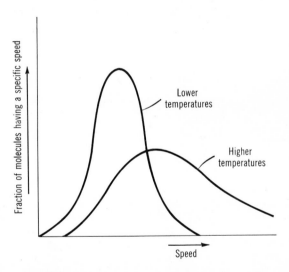

FIGURE 14.10 The distribution of molecular speeds in a gas at two different temperatures. This distribution is very similar to that of the molecular-kinetic energies.

A typical graphic depiction of the distribution of the molecules having specific speeds in a gas at two different temperatures is given in Fig. 14.10. Each point on each curve indicates the fraction of the total number of molecules that have a specific speed. These curves can also be considered as illustrating the distribution of energy in a gas in that the speeds of the molecules are intimately related to their kinetic energies.

Figure 14.10 indicates that if the molecules are at low temperatures, their energies and speeds tend to be distributed within a relatively narrow range. However, the distribution of speeds and energies is much broader at higher temperatures. The curve that depicts the probable distribution at the higher temperature tends to flatten out (broaden) at the high-speed end.

14.20   ENTROPY

Let us consider two closed vessels X and Y of identical capacity and shape and connected by a large pipe that has a closed valve (Fig. 14.11). Vessel X contains a specific number of molecules of

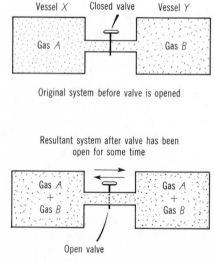

Original system before valve is opened

Resultant system after valve has been open for some time

Open valve

FIGURE 14.11 Diagrams showing the result of spontaneous mixing (attainment of maximum randomness) of two pure inert gases A and B. The entropy of the resultant system is greater than that of the original system because there has been an increase in randomness, and the probability that the resultant system can exist is greater than for the original system.

pure inert gas A; vessel Y contains an identical number of molecules of inert gas B. The temperature of each gas is kept constant exactly at 25°C; hence the gaseous pressure in X is equal to that in Y.

When the valve in the pipe is opened, molecules of gas A

immediately diffuse into vessel Y, and molecules of gas B move into vessel X. Complete mixing of the two gases is the final result; that is, a state of equilibrium (a steady state) is attained in which the rate of diffusion of gases into X from Y is identical to the rate at which molecules leave X to enter Y. The spontaneous mixing process therefore yields a system in which both X and Y contain identical numbers of A and B molecules.

During the mixing process, heat is neither absorbed nor evolved by the system. The process does not occur because of the attainment of a lower energy state. Although complete mixing occurs without enlisting any outside agency, energy must be expended to put all of the A molecules back in X and all of the B molecules back in Y. We can compare the mixing process to a ball rolling downhill, whereas the return to the original unmixed state can be compared to pushing the ball back uphill.

If we are to interpret the behavior of gases A and B in the model system, we must realize that the gases are distributed randomly in the final mixed state. There is much less order in the final state than in the initial state, where each vessel contained only pure gas. We should also realize that if gas A is in contact with gas B, the probability that mixing will occur is much greater than the probability that the components of the mixture will separate by themselves to yield pure A and pure B. We necessarily conclude that the random, or mixed, state has the greater probability of existence.

The comments in the previous paragraph should help us to accept the axiom: if a system goes from one state to another without a change in energy, it always goes to the state that has the greater degree of randomness and the higher probability of existence.

The term *entropy*, S, is used to identify the degree of randomness and the probability of existence of a system. Therefore we say that the entropy of the system increased during the mixing of the gases A and B in the system we have described. There are many natural processes that occur spontaneously and irreversibly, such as the flow of heat from a warmer body to a cooler body. In all of these processes, the entropy of the system increases.

The entropy of a gas increases as its volume increases because an increase in volume yields more space for the molecules, and therefore a greater probability.

Let us return momentarily to the model in which we had gas A mixing spontaneously with gas B, and vice versa. We recall that a state of equilibrium is eventually reached in which the degree of randomness in X is equal to that in Y. As the randomness remains constant after equilibrium has been attained, the entropy remains constant. It is an important fact that the change in entropy is zero in any system in equilibrium.

If we think about the concept of entropy as a means of assessing the degree of disorder in a system, we should conclude, because of the unity of heat and molecular motion, that the entropy of a pure crystalline solid is a minimum at 0°K.

The entropy, S, of a substance in a specific state is proportiona to the logarithm of the probability of finding the substance in that state. The relationship is logarithmic because the entropies are additive and subtractive. Since Boltzmann suggested that entropy is a measure of the probability that a specific system is found in a specific energy state (p. 332), we might expect to find the Boltzmann constant in the expression

$$S = k \ln W$$

where k is the Boltzmann constant, and W the probability. Because $k = R/N$, the entropy of one mole ($N = 1$) of molecules of a substance in a specific state is

$$S = R \ln W$$

But to change $\ln W$ from natural logs to $\log_{10} W$, we must multiply by 2.303. Therefore $S = 2.303R \log W$.

Since R is the gas constant (cal/deg mole), S is the molar entropy in cal/deg mole and W is the probability. A simplified viewpoint is that W can be measured by the number of ways to reach the state in question.

If a heat reservoir (a sample of ordinary matter) at constant temperature and pressure absorbs an amount of heat, Q, its entropy increases by an amount equal to Q/T (T in °K), whether or not the process is reversible. The entropy change is usually symbolized by ΔS. In fact, the classic definition of entropy is identified by the equation, $\Delta S = Q/T$ (for processes at constant T and P), which states that the specific entropy change is equal to the heat absorbed divided by the temperature at which the heat is absorbed. In Chapter 15 we shall consider entropy changes during certain transformations of state.

The fact that the energy of an isolated system is constant led Rudolf Clausius (German) to make his classic comment: "The energy of the universe is constant, the entropy of the universe tends always toward a maximum." Sir Arthur Eddington (English) has suggested the concept that entropy is "time's arrow."

Since the idea of entropy is so important, we shall mention it again in subsequent chapters.

14.21 THE PLASMA STATE

All ordinary fluids (gases and liquids) consist of molecules in constant motion. The fluid states of covalent compounds consist primarily of uncharged molecules, whereas those of ionic compounds consist of charged molecules (ions). Solids consist either of uncharged or charged molecules. The three ordinary states of matter are well known, so let us now consider a fourth, lesser-known state called the *plasma state*.

A plasma, according to the physicist, is a fluid neutral collection of electrons and positive ions. The term *plasma* was suggested in 1920 by Irving Langmuir (American) to identify the portion of a gaseous electrical discharge that (1) consists of identical numbers of electrons and positive ions that preserve charge neutrality; (2) is passive, at least in relation to the mechanism of the discharge; (3) molds itself to any probes or electrodes that are introduced into the phase; (4) occupies the entire enclosure that confines it. Plasma in the above context has nothing to do with mammalian blood.

The actual state of a plasma cannot be determined by optical spectroscopy (p. 102). Since the positive ions and the electrons in a plasma are in constant motion, the particles are continually accelerated and decelerated. Therefore the "free-free" collisions emit radiation in the radiofrequency portion of the electromagnetic spectrum (p. 69). The nature of a plasma is investigated most readily by means of the radiofrequency radiation that it emits.

The outer edge of the earth's atmosphere, the ionosphere, is a plasma state. The plasma character of this portion of the earth's gaseous envelope is the result of ionizations induced by ultraviolet radiation from the sun. All plasmas are produced by the ionization of atoms, either thermally, photolytically, or electrically.

The frequencies used in long-wave radio communication are lower than the plasma frequency of the naturally occurring ionosphere. Hence long-wave radio waves bounce off the natural plasma state, and thus are not so readily lost because of the curvature of the earth. Microwaves of sufficiently high frequency exceed the critical plasma frequency of the ionosphere, thereby penetrating the earth's plasma blanket. If the density of this plasma were increased by artificial means (addition of positive ions and electrons), ordinary microwaves might be unable to get through into outer space, and communications with objects beyond the ionosphere would thereby be greatly inhibited.

Radio telescopes, such as the one at Jodrell Bank in Manchester, England, are employed to detect emissions from naturally occurring plasma states in the far-away stars. The radio-frequency noise from such plasmas, as well as from plasmas created in the laboratory (the Princeton stellarator, for example), are incompletely understood. Usually there are two major types of radiation received, one a relatively steady emission, the other great bursts of noise. Since the sun is one of our best natural nearby plasmas, a study of its plasma state is of considerable current interest.

The control, through magnetic fields, of the plasmas involved in extremely high temperature nuclear fusion reactions (p. 658) is an extremely important factor in the design and manipulation of these fusion reactions. The plasma in nuclear fusion engines must be controlled properly if a practical device is to be forthcoming.

A plasma pinch engine is proposed as an efficient type of propulsion device for travel in interstellar space. The plasma (ionized nitrogen) is manipulated by a magnetic field toward a nozzle where it is ejected at velocities up to 100,000 miles per hour. The proposed engine is relatively small and it is exceptionally efficient.

Problems

1. A gas is expanded at constant temperature from a volume of 100 ml to 0.350 l. How much greater was the original pressure than the final pressure?

2. Two vessels L and M have identical capacities and each is at 10°C. L contains 2 g of gaseous Q at 1.2 atm, and M contains 4 g of gaseous argon at 2.4 atm. What is the mass of 3 moles of Q?

3. A certain heavy-walled vessel has a capacity of 5 l. It is in an oil bath at 136.5°C. Into this vessel is put 4 g of gaseous oxygen and an equal amount of gaseous helium. What is the total pressure, in atm, in the vessel?

4. A gas is expanded, at constant temperature, from a volume of 430 ml to a volume of 1.98 l, where its final pressure is 100 mm of Hg. What was the original pressure, in centimeters of Hg, of the gas?

5. How many grams of gas at 1 atm and 273°C must occupy 3 l of volume if, under these conditions, the density of the gas is 4.48 g/l?

6. How many grams of gaseous oxygen at 380 mm of Hg and 273°K contain the same number of molecules as 200 ml of nitrogen at 0.5 atm and 0°C?

7. What is the mass of 1.25 moles of a gas if its density is 1.5 g/l at 273°K and 380 mm of Hg?

8. Ten grams of gaseous argon occupies a vessel whose capacity is 2.80 l. The pressure of the gas is 76 cm of Hg. What is the temperature, in °C, of the argon?

9. A vessel that has a capacity of 56 l is occupied by gaseous oxygen at a pressure of 4 atm and at a temperature of 273°C. How many grams of oxygen are in the vessel?

10. Vessel A has a capacity of 450 ml and contains 1.0 g of pure gas X under a pressure of 380 mm of Hg and at a temperature of 25°C. Another vessel, Z, has a capacity of 0.45 l and it is occupied by 500 mg of pure gas M under a pressure of 1 atm and at a temperature of 298°K. (a) Which vessel contains the larger number of gaseous molecules? (b) Which vessel contains the larger amount of matter? (c) What is the molar weight of X? (d) How many moles of M at STP occupy the same volume as 50 g of oxygen at STP?

11. At what temperature, in °C, does 1 l of nitrogen gas weigh 1 g, if the pressure is 1 atm?

12. Two hundred milligrams of a gas occupies 200 ml at 136.5°C and 1 atm. What is the mass of 1 mole of the gas at 0.5 atm and 0°C?

13. What is the mass, in grams, of 4.3 l of gaseous CO at 40°C and 500 mm of Hg?

14. What would be the volume, in milliliters, of 0.2 mole of CH_4 (gaseous) at 273°C and 0.2 atm?

15. One-third of a gaseous mixture that contains only gases X, Y, and Z is gas X; one-half is gas Y; and the remainder is gas Z. The total pressure is 1.8 atm. What is the partial pressure of each gas, expressed in centimeters of Hg?

16. A student collected 300 ml of helium over water at 30°C. The total pressure of helium and water vapor was 1 atm. (a) How many grams of "dry" helium were collected? (b) What volume, in milliliters, would this amount of helium occupy at STP? (c) What was the partial pressure of the helium in the mixture? (d) How many grams of water were in the gaseous phase?

17. Vessel B contains 4.4 g of gaseous CO_2 at 273°K and 0.5 atm. Vessel C contains gaseous CO whose density is 1.4 g/l. The number of molecules in vessel C is identical to the number in vessel B. What is the capacity of vessel C?

18. A hypothetical chemical equation that represents a reaction involving gases is:

$$2X_3Z_5 + 8Q_2 \rightarrow 3X_2Q_2 + 5Z_2Q_2$$

(All gases mentioned in this problem are measured at the same temperature and pressure.) (a) What is the maximum volume, in milliliters, of X_2Q_2 that could be obtained from a reaction initiated by mixing 28 ml of X_3Z_5 and 104 ml of Q_2? (b) How many cubic feet of Q_2 are needed to react completely with 27 cu ft of X_3Z_5? (c) If 56 ml of X_3Z_5 reacts as completely as possible with the molecules in 208 ml of Q_2 in a closed vessel, the product mixture will contain what gases? How many milliliters of each gas are present?

19. How many liters of H_2S at 22°C and 1.2 atm can be obtained by treating correctly 0.85 kg of FeS with excess aqueous hydrogen chloride?

20. Twenty liters of nitrogen and 4 l of oxygen both at 2 atm are forced into a volume of 5 l. What is the partial pressure of each gas in the mixture?

21. Four grams of argon is confined in a heavy-walled tank at 100°C under considerable pressure. To what temperature, in °C, must the gas be cooled to decrease the pressure to one-half the original pressure?

22. What would be the molar volume of oxygen at STP if the molecular weight assigned to oxygen were 48 instead of the current value?

23. A heavy-walled vessel at sea level has a capacity of 8 l and has a cover that can withstand considerable pressure. Into the "empty" vessel is placed 30.8 g of solid CO_2, and the cover is clamped immediately on the vessel. If the vessel is heated to 273°C to vaporize all of the CO_2, what is the approximate gaseous pressure, in atm, in the vessel?

24. At 0°C and 2 atm, the density of a gas is 2.5 g/l. (a) What is the density of the gas at standard conditions? (b) What is the mass of 2.5 moles of the gas?

25. Considering hydrogen chloride and hydrogen sulfide as liquids, in which liquid are the intermolecular attractive forces the weaker?

26. Considering carbon dioxide and carbon monoxide as liquids, in which liquid are the intermolecular attractive forces the stronger?

27. What is the highest temperature at which gaseous SO_2 can be liquefied if the pressure on the gas is 1 atm?

28. Why can liquid chlorine exist at room temperature and liquid nitrogen cannot?

29. What is the highest temperature at which nitrogen and argon can exist together as liquids?

30. Why is the critical pressure of hydrogen so much less than that of oxygen?

31. Can liquid oxygen exist at $-100°C$?

32. Can gaseous argon be liquefied at $-116°C$?

33. When a gas liquefies, does its entropy increase, decrease, or remain constant?

15

THE LIQUID

15.1 A PERSPECTIVE

All liquids consist of molecules in constant motion, although the molecular motion is more restricted than it is in ordinary gases. The intermolecular forces are very significant in ordinary liquids because the molecules are so close together. A molecule within a liquid is never an independent particle because its physical behavior is closely related to that of its neighbors to whom it is strongly attracted and from whom it is strongly repelled. A balance of the attractive forces and the repulsive forces exists in the liquid state to yield a fluid that has some semblance of unity. The fluidity of liquids is evidence of molecular motion.

If a liquid partially fills a closed vessel, molecules of the substance in question actually occupy the entire interior of the vessel. Part of the interior is occupied by the liquid phase of the substance, the remainder by

AND SOLID STATES

the vapor phase. Because of continual molecular motion, molecules are constantly leaving the liquid to enter the vapor phase, and they are continually leaving the vapor phase to enter the liquid phase. The vapor of a liquid is gaseous, of course; hence it exerts a pressure on all confining boundaries just as does any gas.

The liquid state of a substance has an entropy greater than the solid state at any given temperature, and the gaseous state of a substance has an entropy greater than the liquid state at any given temperature. Any phase change that yields a more random state is a transition that results in an increase in entropy. The tendency for solids to melt and for liquids to vaporize is in the direction of an increase in entropy—to the formation of more probable states, to more disorder.

Nearly all pure liquids solidify if they are cooled sufficiently. The removal of heat from a liquid decreases the kinetic energy, thus allowing the inter-

343

molecular forces to increase their influence. We should recall, however, that the molecules continue to vibrate about fixed positions as long as the temperature is above 0°K. In fact, many molecules at the surfaces of certain molecular solids have enough energy to escape from the solid and enter the gaseous state. If this process absorbs most of the heat gained from the surroundings, as in the case of solid carbon dioxide ("dry ice"), the solid vaporizes completely without melting.

It is reasonable to expect that if a solid is heated, a temperature would eventually be reached at which the kinetic energy of the molecules is sufficient to overcome at least partially the intermolecular attractive forces to the extent that the solid liquefies.

The above remarks indicate the close relationship between the liquid and solid states and their kinship to the gaseous state. These relationships are interpreted most readily by using the kinetic-molecular theory.

15.2 EVAPORATION OF LIQUIDS

The molecules of a liquid, at any given temperature, have a specific average kinetic energy that is dependent on the absolute temperature of the liquid. Since there always are some molecules at the surface with energies greater than the average energy, molecules continually leave the surface and enter the gaseous phase. The transformation of a liquid into its vapor is called *vaporization* or *evaporation*. During vaporization the average kinetic energy of the molecules in the liquid steadily decreases. Unless heat is supplied from the surroundings, the liquid cools. This fact substantiates our concept of the equivalence of heat and molecular energy.

The cooling of a liquid, especially during rapid vaporization, is used in certain types of refrigeration and cooling devices. The human body uses the evaporation of water to regulate body temperature.

At any given temperature, the amount of heat needed to change one gram of a liquid to one gram of its vapor is called the *heat of vaporization* of the liquid (expressed in calories per gram). The heat of vaporization of a liquid usually decreases as the temperature increases. It is zero at the critical temperature.

15.3 VAPOR PRESSURE OF LIQUIDS

To understand the concept of the vapor pressure of a liquid, let us examine a simple system. If a liquid is poured into a vessel until it is partly full and the vessel then covered tightly, we should rightly predict that neither liquid nor vapor would leave the closed vessel. We cannot state correctly, however, that no liquid will evaporate, and we should not say that vaporization ceases simply because the vessel is closed. As soon as the liquid is placed in the closed vessel, molecules begin to enter the "empty space" above the liquid. While the number of molecules in the vapor state steadily increases, more and more of these molecules collide with the liquid surface and many are trapped there by the intermolecular forces in the liquid. A condition is reached eventually in which molecules are returning to the liquid as fast as others are leaving. Two phenomena are in balance; vaporization and condensation are occurring at equal rates. *Condensation* is the term used to identify the liquefaction of vapor.

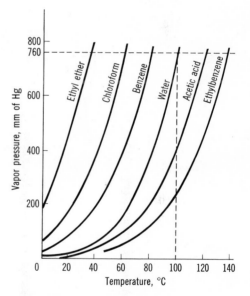

FIGURE 15.1 The effects of temperature on the vapor pressure of a liquid. The temperature at which the liquid's vapor pressure is 760 mm is the standard boiling point of that liquid.

Such a state of affairs is usually called a *system in equilibrium*: a system in which two opposing processes are taking place at equal rates.   Systems in equilibrium are dynamic.   The two reversible processes occur continuously.   In the example just described, vaporization and condensation never cease because the molecules are in continuous motion.   Because this equilibrium system involves two simple physical changes, it is a physical equilibrium.   We shall eventually discuss many examples of chemical equilibria in which the reversible processes are chemical changes.

Returning to our simple system, we note that at any given temperature the number of vapor molecules remains constant; that is, a constant pressure is exerted by the vapor. The pressure exerted by the vapor over the liquid is called the *vapor pressure* of the liquid. The vapor pressure of a liquid, at any given temperature, is the pressure of the vapor in equilibrium with the liquid at that temperature.

If the temperature of a liquid is increased, the molecules gain energy and a larger percentage of them have enough energy to escape from their neighbors at the surface. As the temperature increases, the vapor pressure increases so long as the liquid phase exists. At the critical temperature of certain substances, the vapor pressure is very high. The vapor pressure of water at its critical temperature is 217 atm. This is also its critical pressure because the vapor pressure of a substance at its critical temperature is its critical pressure. See Fig. 15.1 for the effect of temperature on the vapor pressures of a few liquids. Two different methods of determining approximate vapor pressures of certain liquids are shown in Figs. 15.2 and 15.3.

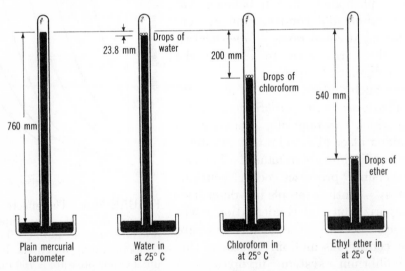

FIGURE 15.2 Determination of the vapor pressure of a liquid by placing a few drops of the liquid in a mercurial barometer (height of mercury before adding the liquid minus the height after the addition of the liquid gives the value of the vapor pressure). Vapor pressure of liquid cannot be measured in this way if it is greater than the atmospheric pressure.

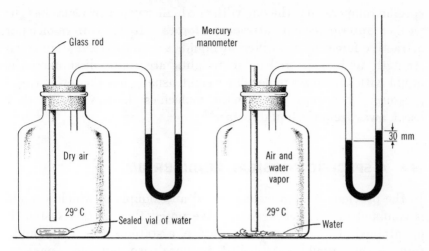

FIGURE 15.3   Determination of the vapor pressure of water by using a mercury manometer.   Pressure of dry air in the vessel is atmospheric pressure; the increase in pressure after breaking the vial is due to the pressure exerted by the water vapor.   (Dalton's law of partial pressure.)

Table 15.1 lists the vapor pressures of a few common liquids at various temperatures.   The values may give us a clue to the relative magnitude of the intermolecular attractive forces in the liquids. If two liquids having similar molecular weights are compared at a

TABLE 15.1   Approximate vapor pressures (in mm of Hg)

Temper- ature °C	Ethyl Ether (74)*	Carbon Bisulfide (76)	Acetone (58)	Water (18)	Acetic Acid (60)
0	185	127	—	4.6	—
10	292	198	116	9.2	—
20	442	298	185	17.5	12
30	647	433	283	31.8	21
40	920	617	422	55.3	35
50	1276	859	613	92.5	57
60	1730	1170	860	149	89
80	3000	2052	1611	355	202
100	4864	3359	2789	760	417
120	7494	5244	4568	1489	806

* Individual molecular weights are in parentheses.

specific temperature, the one with the higher vapor pressure has the weaker intermolecular attractive forces. If the intermolecular attractive forces in two different liquids are of approximately equal strength and their molecular weights are quite dissimilar, the liquid with the larger molecular weight usually has the lower vapor pressure. The more massive the molecules the less readily they break away from the liquid surface.

15.4   A SPECIFIC PHYSICAL EQUILIBRIUM

In the previous section we suggested an example in which a liquid is confined in a closed system. We noted that, if this system is maintained at a constant temperature, a state of dynamic equilibrium is eventually established because two opposing physical processes (vaporization and condensation) are taking place at equal rates.

Since vaporization is an endothermic process and condensation an exothermic process, we might represent these two reversible physical processes in a symbolic manner, similar to the way in which we express chemical processes.

For vaporization of water:

$$HOH + \Delta \rightarrow HOH$$
$$\text{(liq)} \qquad\qquad \text{(vapor)}$$

For condensation of water:

$$HOH \rightarrow HOH + \Delta$$
$$\text{(vapor)} \qquad \text{(liq)}$$

If these two processes occur at the same temperature, as they do in a state of equilibrium, we can combine them in a single representation.

$$HOH + \Delta \leftrightarrows HOH$$
$$\text{(liq)} \qquad\qquad \text{(vapor)}$$

The arrow pointing right indicates the direction of the vaporization process; the arrow pointing left, the condensation process. This type of symbolic representation is commonly used for all reversible physical and chemical processes (p. 73). It implies that the system can, under the appropriate conditions, reach a state of equilibrium.

Now let us consider a simple system at 25°C in which liquid

water is in equilibrium with water vapor. At this temperature the pressure exerted by the water vapor is 23.6 mm of Hg. We disturb the equilibrium by raising the temperature of the system to 30°C and we keep the system at this higher temperature for a period of time, say one hour. If we examine the system, we now find that the vapor pressure is 31.5 mm of Hg. We also notice that so long as the temperature is kept at 30°C, the vapor pressure remains constant. A new state of equilibrium has been established at 30°C, and at this temperature there is more water vapor present in the system. We can correctly infer that as the temperature was increased from 25°C to 30°C, the vaporization process was momentarily favored and the original equilibrium position shifted or displaced in the direction of the production of water vapor.

The addition of heat upset or put a stress on the original equilibrium. The vaporization process (absorption of heat) was favored during the attempt made by the system to dissipate the added heat and hence to overcome or reduce the stress placed on the original equilibrium.

Now let us cool the system from 30°C to the original 25°C, and then keep it at 25°C for a period of time. We notice that the original state of equilibrium has been reproduced because the vapor pressure is 23.6 mm.

By decreasing the temperature of the system from 30°C to 25°C, the condensation process was momentarily favored and the equilibrium position shifted or displaced in the direction of the production of liquid water. The removal of heat (cooling) upset or put a strain on the equilibrium and the condensation process (evolution of heat) was favored during the attempt made by he system to increase its temperature and thereby overcome or reduce the stress placed on the equilibrium.

Since all equilibria have common characteristics, we may make an extremely important generalization. Originally suggested by Henri Louis Le Châtelier, it is so significant we shall refer to it many times throughout the remainder of the text. Le Châtelier's principle states: Whenever a system in equilibrium is upset by a change in any factor or constituent that determines the position of the equilibrium, the system always responds with a tendency to offset, overcome, or reduce the effect of the change. Or, in other words: Whenever a stress is placed on a system in which two opposing processes are occurring at equal rates, that process is favored which reduces or tends to counteract the stress, and the equilibrium position is shifted or displaced in the direction of the favored process.

15.5 BOILING POINT OF A LIQUID

Vaporization is a surface phenomenon. However, if certain liquids are heated, a temperature is eventually reached at which bubbles of the vapor of the liquid form within it. These bubbles rise to the surface and there they burst as the vapor escapes into the gaseous phase above the liquid. This type of bubbling is called ebullition, or boiling. The vapor bubbles can form and increase in volume only if the vapor pressure of the liquid is equal to or perhaps slightly greater than the external pressure upon the surface of the liquid. The *boiling point of a liquid* is the temperature at which the vapor pressure of the liquid is equal to or slightly greater than the external pressure on the surface of that liquid. Therefore the boiling point of a liquid varies with the external pressure on its surface. If the pressure on the surface is increased, the liquid must be heated to a higher temperature to increase its vapor pressure so that bubbles of vapor can form within the liquid; hence the boiling point is increased. If the external pressure on the surface is decreased, it will be easier to boil the liquid because the required vapor pressure is less, and a lower temperature will be sufficient to induce the formation of vapor bubbles.

If a bubble of vapor within a liquid is close to the surface, the vapor pressure inside the bubble is approximately equal to the pressure exerted on the surface by the gaseous phase. However, if a given volume of liquid is relatively deep, say three inches or more, it is more difficult for a bubble of vapor to form deep within the liquid because the vapor pressure in the bubble must be equal to the pressure on the surface of the liquid plus the pressure exerted by the weight of the liquid above the bubble. Since a liquid is often heated at its lowest extremity (bottom of the vessel), the boiling process is not always smooth if bubbles must form deep below the surface. Of course, some bubbles eventually form, and as they rise to the surface they burst with considerable vigor because their internal pressure is greater than the pressure of the gaseous phase above the surface. This rather violent bursting of these vapor bubbles may cause considerable agitation of the liquid. This phenomenon is often called bumping. Bumping may be diminished by any means which provide nuclei that assist the formation of vapor bubbles deep within the liquid. Liquids usually boil more smoothly in containers which have relatively rough interior surfaces. Before boiling a liquid in ordinary glass apparatus, it is wise to add some agent to enhance smooth ebullition. Inert porous materials such as chips of unglazed pottery, fine particles of pumice or bits of dry, porous wood are often used. They are fairly effective either because air is slowly expelled from them upon heating or because they provide an irregular surface on which bubbles of vapor can form.

If a liquid is boiling erratically (bumping) and several small particles of an inert solid are added, or if the vessel is agitated, extremely vigorous ebullition will occur instantaneously—often so violently that some of the liquid may be literally forced from the mouth of the vessel by the escaping vapor bubbles. This behavior of a bumping liquid can lead to disastrous results, especially with corrosive and flammable liquids.

If a liquid is heated in a vessel open to the atmosphere, the boiling point depends on the atmospheric pressure. On the summits of high mountains, a liquid boils at a temperature lower than that at sea level. Whenever water is boiling in an open vessel at high elevations, it is not so hot as water boiling at sea level. Thus the cooking of food in open containers becomes a more time-consuming process at high elevations than at lower ones. However, if a pressure cooker is used, the external pressure on the surface of the water may be increased (usually 1.7 to 2 atm) by partially confining the water vapor so that the liquid boils at a higher temperature. This increases the temperature of the food being cooked, thereby markedly decreasing the cooking time required.

If the external pressure on the surface of a liquid is appropriately controlled, a stable liquid can be boiled at any temperature between its freezing point and its critical temperature.

From Table 15.1 we can see that water will boil at 10°C if the external pressure on its surface is 9.2 mm. To accomplish this, the water is placed in a closed vessel from which the air is pumped until the pressure of the gaseous phase is 9.2 mm. The pumping process must be continuous because the pressure of the gaseous phase must be maintained at 9.2 mm during rapid vaporization of the liquid. Acetic acid will boil at 30°C if the external pressure on the liquid surface is approximately 21 mm of Hg.

The boiling points of many substances are listed in textbooks and in handbooks. Unless specified otherwise, these boiling points are the normal or standard boiling points. The normal or standard boiling point of a liquid is the temperature at which the vapor pressure of the liquid is 760 mm of Hg, or 1 atm. Table 15.2 lists the

TABLE 15.2   Normal boiling points, in °C

Substance	Boiling Point
Bromine (159.83)*	58.8
Carbon bisulfide (76.12)	46.3
Mercury (200.61)	356.9
Tin(IV) chloride (260.53)	114.1
Glycerine (92.06)	290
Benzene (78.05)	80.08
Carbon tetrachloride (153.83)	77
Chloroform (119.38)	61.3
Chlorobenzene (112.5)	132
Phenol (94.05)	182
Methyl iodide (142)	42.5
Methanol (32)	64.7
Ethylene glycol (62.05)	198
Ethyl ether (74.08)	34.5
Heptane (100)	98
1-Hexanol (102)	156.4
Acetic acid (60)	118
Acetamide (59)	222
Ethanol (46)	78.5
Water (18)	100

* Molecular weights are in parentheses.

normal boiling points of a few common liquids. The normal boiling points of liquids of comparable molecular weights are useful indications of the relative strengths of the intermolecular attractive forces within those liquids. The higher the normal boiling point, the stronger the attractive forces between the molecules; the lower the normal boiling point, the weaker the forces.

If a liquid is boiled and its vapor then condensed by cooling, the over-all process is called *distillation*. This process is often used to purify a liquid or to separate it from a mixture. (See Fig. 15.4.)

Certain liquids decompose at relatively low temperatures—

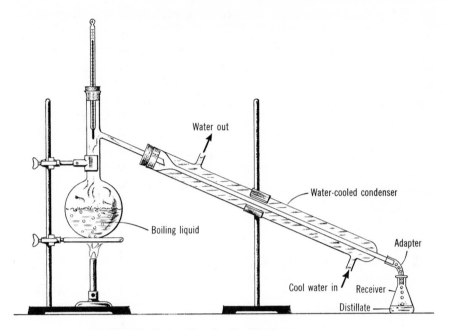

FIGURE 15.4 Simple distillation apparatus.

often temperatures at which their vapor pressures are well below 760 mm. Therefore such liquids decompose if they are boiled or distilled under atmospheric pressure (in open vessels). Usually the boiling or distillation may be effected without decomposition if the liquid is heated under greatly reduced pressures. These distillations are called reduced-pressure or "vacuum" distillations.

The heat that must be continually added to a boiling liquid is absorbed by the molecules in the liquid so that they can escape. The molecules need this energy to overcome the intermolecular attractive forces. During boiling all of the added heat is absorbed by the molecules. Hence the temperature of the liquid surface and the vapor just above the liquid remains constant so long as the external pressure remains constant.

The heat of vaporization of a liquid remains constant at the boiling point. Since it is easy to maintain a constant temperature at the boiling point, the heat of vaporization of a liquid is often determined at its normal boiling point. The heat of vaporization of water is 540 cal/g, but most molecular substances have a smaller heat of vaporization at their normal boiling points. Because in liquid water there are relatively strong intermolecular attractive forces, hydrogen-bonding, we expect a high heat of vaporization of water.

Earlier in this chapter we mentioned that at any given temperature the entropy of a liquid is less than that of its vapor. Let us now calculate the entropy change involved in the reversible conversion of 1 mole of water at 100°C to vapor at 100°C and 1 atm. By definition, the entropy change $\Delta S = Q/T$, where Q is the amount (in cal) of heat absorbed, and T is the temperature in °K at which the reversible phase change occurs. Since the heat of vaporization of water at 100°C is 540 cal/gram, 9720 cal of heat is absorbed during the production of 1 mole of water vapor at 100°C.

$$\Delta S = \frac{9720 \text{ cal}}{373°} = 26 \text{ cal/deg mole}$$

This means that during this specific reversible phase change at constant temperature there is an increase in entropy of 26 calories per degree per mole. Also, it can be said that the increase in entropy is 26 entropy units (eu) in the specific process here described.

15.6 SOLIDIFICATION (FREEZING) OF A LIQUID

The close relationship between the liquid and solid states is just as intimate as the one between the liquid and gaseous states, and the significance of heat and kinetic energy remains paramount.

When heat is removed from a molecular liquid, the molecules move less and less rapidly because their kinetic energy is being decreased. As more and more heat is removed from most liquids, the influence of the intermolecular attractive and repulsive forces becomes stronger and stronger. The molecules are eventually forced to arrange themselves in the orderly, geometric pattern of a solid. Whenever a true solid is formed by cooling a liquid, the process is called *freezing* or *crystallization*, and the liquid is said to be frozen. The term *crystallization* indicates that the solid has a crystalline structure and that the visible particles of the solid are crystals.

With most common liquids, the freezing temperature is well above absolute zero (0°K), and since the molecules in the molecular solid have kinetic energy, we should readily accept the fact that these molecules exhibit a limited but definite degree of motion.

Because the molecules in a crystalline, molecular solid are in relatively fixed positions in space, the motion of each molecule is a vibration (oscillation) about a fixed position. The orderly, geometric arrangement of these vibrating molecules forms a crystal lattice. This crystal lattice is gradually built during the solidification (crystallization) process, and eventually a visible, solid particle having a definite spatial structure is formed. The crystal has smooth surfaces and sharp edges which compose the boundaries.

Certain liquids do not solidify to produce rigid, geometric particles (crystals). When these liquids are cooled to lower and lower temperatures, they gradually become more and more brittle and somewhat rigid, but they do not assume a distinct shape or structure; that is, they have no definite morphology. For this reason they are called amorphous substances. These amorphous solids do not form at a definite temperature.

15.7 FREEZING POINT AND MELTING POINT

When most molecular solids begin to solidify, the temperature of the liquid and solid phases remains constant until all of the liquid has solidified. After solidification is complete, further cooling decreases the temperature of the solid.

When a crystalline solid commences to melt, or fuse, the temperature remains constant until all of the solid has melted. After fusion is complete, further heating increases the temperature of the liquid.

For a specific substance under a specific pressure (usually 1 atm), the freezing point of its liquid state and the melting point of its solid state is the temperature at which both states exist together in equilibrium. This temperature is a characteristic physical constant of the substance. It is the temperature at which the vapor pressure of the solid state of the substance is identical to the vapor pressure of its liquid state. For pure water this temperature is 0°C by definition. Melting points of solid substances are used widely as a partial means of identification, especially for organic compounds.

At the normal melting point of a solid, the heat of fusion of the solid is the amount of heat required to change one gram of the solid to one gram of the liquid at that temperature. At any specific temperature and pressure, the heat of fusion of a solid substance is equal to the heat of solidification of its liquid state. At 0°C and 1 atm, the heat of fusion of ice is 79 cal. This value is much higher than that of most molecular solids because strong intermolecular attractive forces exist in solid water.

The melting point of a molecular solid is usually an indication of the relative strength of the intermolecular attractive forces. Considering substances of comparable molecular weight, those with the lower melting points have the weaker intermolecular attractive forces; those with the higher melting points, the stronger forces.

15.8 VAPOR PRESSURE OF A SOLID

The vapor pressure of a molecular solid may be measured by essentially the same method as is used for a liquid. The vapor pressures of such solids usually increase with an increase in temperature. Certain solids have relatively large vapor pressures at room temperatures. Most of us know that dry ice (solid carbon dioxide) vaporizes rapidly and that crystals of some moth repellents disappear rather quickly in open containers. If a pure solid has a perceptible odor, the odor is that of the vapor of the solid. This may be demonstrated by removing the cover of a bottle containing solid iodine. If the bottle has been in a warm room for some time, purple vapor will issue from the bottle and the odor of iodine will be apparent.

The vapor pressure and melting points of some volatile solids are listed in Table 15.3.

TABLE 15.3 Some volatile solids

Substance	Vapor Pressure at Melting Point, in Mm Hg	Melting Point, in °C
Carbon dioxide	3900	−57
Hexachloroethane	780	186
Phosphorus pentachloride	760	166
Camphor	370	179
Iodine	90	114
Naphthalene	7	80
Water	4.6	0
Bromine	0.44	−7

The fact that some solids vaporize appreciably at temperatures below their melting points may be demonstrated by solid iodine. Vaporization of a solid without melting is called *sublimation*. If a solid has a relatively high vapor pressure at ordinary temperatures, it is often possible by sublimation to separate it from solids that have much lower vapor pressures.

15.9   THE CRYSTALLINE SOLID

The visible structural character of a crystal is undoubtedly a manifestation of the spatial arrangement of the tiny particles within the crystal. The mere fact that matter arranges itself in different crystalline forms or shapes is a distinct indication that matter is discontinuous and composed of discrete particles. The electron microscope and x-ray studies of the structure of crystals substantiate our idea of the atomic concept of matter.

Since the crystals of different substances often exhibit markedly different structural character, the appearance of the crystals of a substance is often a clue as to its possible identity. Well-formed crystals of sodium chloride are either tiny cubes or tiny octahedrons. If a white solid is composed of long, needle-like crystals, we know the substance is not sodium chloride. Certain minerals exist in nature in remarkably distinct crystalline forms. Geologists and mineralogists can identify certain minerals immediately because of their unique crystalline structures. The formal study of crystal structure is called crystallography, a science which requires a sound knowledge of solid geometry and a strong sense of spatial perception.

Different substances occasionally form crystals of identical structure. These substances are isomorphic and the phenomenon is called *isomorphism*. For example, calcium carbonate (as calcite), $CaCO_3$, and magnesite, $MgCO_3$, form the same type of hexagonal crystals. These two substances are isomorphic forms of matter and each substance is said to be isomorphous.

In certain cases a specific solid substance may exist in two different crystalline forms—the individual units of matter which compose the substance may be arranged in two or more different three-dimensional, geometric patterns. This phenomenon is called *polymorphism*. Under certain conditions calcium carbonate, $CaCO_3$, forms hexagonal crystals of calcite; under different conditions it forms orthorhombic crystals of aragonite. The calcite form is stable at ordinary temperatures, but if calcite is heated under pressure, crystals of aragonite are formed. At ordinary temperatures and pressures, aragonite changes very slowly to calcite.

Certain elemental solid substances, such as carbon, sulfur, and phosphorus, exhibit polymorphism. This phenomenon is usually called allotropy; hence carbon, sulfur, and phosphorus exist in more than one allotropic form. Diamond crystals (hard, transparent) and graphite crystals (soft, black, opaque) are the two different crystalline forms of carbon. At room temperature sulfur forms rhombic crystals, but rhombic sulfur, when heated slightly above 96°C, is transformed to monoclinic sulfur (needle-shaped crystals). This change is easily reversible. If "white" phosphorus is heated in the absence of air, this allotropic form of phosphorus is changed to "red" phosphorus. If the two allotropic forms are subjected to extreme pressures, a black allotropic form is produced. Red phosphorus will sublime, and when its vapor is condensed, the white allotropic form is obtained.

The disruption of the orderly arrangement in the crystalline state during melting is shown in Fig. 15.5.

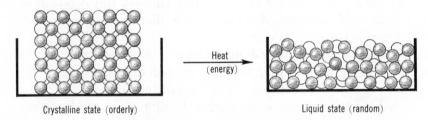

Crystalline state (orderly)   Liquid state (random)

Heat (energy)

FIGURE 15.5 Orderly arrangement of the molecular particles in the solid, crystalline state is destroyed during fusion (melting) of the solid. The greater mobility of the particles in the liquid state allows the molecules to flow over the entire bottom of the container. The entropy of the liquid is greater than that of the solid.

15.10 CRYSTAL LATTICE DEFECTS

The actual composition of certain solids is not always that implied by the conventional molar formula of the substance; that is, in the crystal lattices of many solids there are vacancies which yield what are called *lattice defects*. Also, there are crystals whose defects result from either misplaced or displaced atoms or ions (that is, entities being where they shouldn't be). The number of vacant lattice sites has a marked effect on the composition of the solid. If the number of vacancies varies during the production of different samples of the compound, any application of the law of constant proportions (p. 23) is invalid.

The solid that exhibits an actual molar ratio of constituents that is different from the expected molar ratio is said to be *nonstoichiometric*. Actually there are many compounds that show nonstoichiometric proportions; hence they are called nonstoichiometric compounds. Two specific examples are copper(I) sulfide, $Cu_{1.7}S$, and copper(I) telluride, $Cu_{1.65}Te$. The stoichiometric formulas are Cu_2S and Cu_2Te. In these nonstoichiometric compounds (as in several metal oxides, sulfides, selenides, and tellurides), there seems to be a tendency toward a deficiency of the metallic element. This tendency is probably due to the fact that the cation, being smaller than the anion, is the more likely to be lost.

Lattice defects often occur because of physical constraints during the formation of the crystal. Inclusion in the lattice of either foreign solid particles or of solution (mother liquor) from which the crystals are separated leads to crystal defects.

The lattice defects in ionic crystals are electrically active because they serve as either electron donors or electron acceptors. An anion vacancy can act as a donor, a cation vacancy as an acceptor. Because of this defect structure, certain solid compounds exhibit electrical conductivity as electrons move from electron-rich sites to electron-poor sites (p. 363).

The actual composition of a specific crystal is affected by its environment during its formation. The partial pressure (escaping tendencies) of foreign entities and of constituents of the crystal may markedly alter the composition and construction of the lattice.

An external phase in equilibrium with the crystal can effect a specific lattice composition. An investigation of an equilibrium between solid lead sulfide and a gaseous phase containing hydrogen sulfide, H_2S, has yielded typical equilibria that describe a system for PbS.

$$PbS \leftrightarrows Pb_{(ext)} + S_{(ext)}$$

$$S_{(ext)} \leftrightarrows S_s + V_{Pb}^- + e^+$$

$$Pb_{(ext)} \leftrightarrows Pb_{Pb} + V_s^+ + e^-$$

$$PbS \leftrightarrows V_{Pb}^- + V_s^+$$

The subscripts (ext) refer to the external phase; the subscripts Pb and s represent lead and sulfur sites in the lattice. V_{Pb}^- is a vacancy on a Pb site, V_s^+ a vacancy on a S site; Pb_{Pb} is a lead atom on a normal Pb site; S_s is a sulfur atom on a normal S site; e^+ is a hole in the lattice (a missing valence electron); e^- is a conduction electron (an electron in excess of the valence electrons).

At very high "sulfur" (S) pressures;

$$\text{concentration of } V_{Pb}^- = \text{concentration of } e^+ \text{ (holes)}$$

(Concn of vacancies on normal Pb sites)　　　　(Concn of lattice holes)

Under these conditions the concentrations of V_s^+ and of e^- (vacancies on normal S sites and conduction electrons) are less than the concentrations of vacancies on normal Pb sites and of lattice holes. The lattice is then a p-type lattice that has more holes than conduction electrons.

At very low "sulfur" pressures, the concentrations of vacancies on normal sulfur sites and of conduction electrons are greater than those of V_{Pb}^- and e^+. The lattice then is an n-type lattice that has more conduction electrons than holes. That is, the concentration of V_s^+ and e^- is greater than the concentration of V_{Pb}^- and e^+.

Solids that have defect structures have the ability to fluoresce. In other words, if such solids are exposed to radiation (either electromagnetic or electron beam), the crystals absorb the radiation and then emit part of the energy as visible light of a frequency characteristic of the specific type of defect structure in question. If the emission step is relatively rapid, the over-all phenomenon (absorption and emission) is called *fluorescence*. However, if the emission consumes an appreciable period of time, the effect is called *phosphorescence*. Defect solids, such as zinc sulfide, ZnS, that show phosphorescence (p. 86) are called *phosphors*. Such materials are used widely in cathode-ray and television tubes.

A silver bromide crystal lattice within a gelatin emulsion on a photographic film is altered if exposed to light. Presumably the combined sulfur in the gelatin interacts physically with the silver bromide lattice, thereby altering the lattice. The resultant lattice defects seem to increase the susceptibility of the silver ions toward reduction to metallic silver. Exposed silver bromide is reduced more readily than unexposed AgBr.

In the next section we shall describe the general character of solids known as semiconductors. These materials are industrially important defect solids.

Certain kinds of defect crystals, such as imperfect rubies (Al_2O_3), that have specific types of impurities trapped in their lattices act as the essential parts of some types of lasers and masers. One or more valence electrons of the impurities are excited by some external energy source, and subsequent events yield essentially monochromatic radiant energy. The visible electromagnetic radiation emitted by lasers is the most nearly monochromatic coherent visible light known. A maser involves microwaves (longer wave length than infrared), whereas a laser involves visible light. In fact, the word *laser* is formed from the words *l*ight *a*mplification by *s*timulated *e*mission of *r*adiation.

15.11 SEMICONDUCTORS

Most people have heard of transistors now that these devices are used so widely in radios. Transistors are defect solids that have peculiar electrical properties in that they are semiconductors. That is, they allow an electric current to pass in only one direction (rectification) (p. 363), a rather unusual effect. Many semiconductors are solid solutions (alloys) of germanium and silicon.

The electrical conductance of semiconductors seems to be due to lattice holes and conduction electrons (p. 362). A conduction electron is an electron in excess of the normal number of valence electrons at a specific site. A lattice hole is considered an absence of a valence electron at a specific site. The extent of conductance of a semiconductor is closely related to the number of holes and to the number of conductance electrons.

The solid solutions made by dissolving chemical impurities in a semiconductor are, in many respects, analogous to aqueous solutions that contain ions. The conduction electrons and holes in an "impure" semiconductor are analogous to the oxonium (OH_3^+) and hydroxide (OH^-) ions in an aqueous solution (p. 210).

We have mentioned previously (p. 533) that for water at 25°C the product of the concentrations (in moles/l) of the OH_3^+ and OH^- is approximately 1×10^{-14}. If the ionic concentrations are expressed in numbers of ions per cm^3, the ion-product constant of water at 25°C is about $4 \times 10^{27} cm^{-6}$.

The simplified representation of the autoionization (p. 210), or autoprotolysis, of water is

$$HOH \leftrightharpoons H^+ + OH^-$$

The autoionization of the silicon lattice is represented by

$$\text{Si lattice} \leftrightharpoons e^- + e^+$$

where e^- represents a conduction electron, and e^+ signifies a lattice hole. The product of $(e^- \times e^+)$ is constant at a specific temperature just as is the product of $(H^+ \times OH^-)$. For the silicon lattice at 25°C, the product of $e^- \times e^+$ is about 1×10^{20} cm^{-6}. It is evident that elemental silicon is an ionized solid, just as water is an ionized liquid. The autoionizations of water, silicon, and germanium are functions of temperature: the higher the temperature, the greater the extent of ionization.

An impurity that when added to either silicon or germanium produces an excess of conduction electrons over holes is called a donor entity. It is, in a sense, comparable to a base that when added to water increases the OH^- ion concentration. Since phosphorus acts as a donor in silicon, $P \leftrightharpoons P^+ + e^-$, it is analogous to a base. Boron, however, acts as an acceptor in silicon, $B \leftrightharpoons B^- + e^+$. Therefore boron's action is similar to an acid. It is apparent that addition of phosphorus yields an increase in conduction electrons, whereas addition of boron causes an increase in lattice holes.

The conduction electron and lattice hole mobilities in semiconductors are generally much greater than the mobilities of ions in aqueous solutions. However, the mobilities of ions such as P^+ in semiconductors are less than ionic mobilities in aqueous solutions.

A semiconductor, actually a defect crystal, is usually constructed by adding controlled amounts (a few parts per million) of impurity to exceptionally pure crystals of either silicon or germanium. A transistor, for instance, may be made by treating one surface of a disc of germanium with a gaseous boron compound to allow a few boron atoms to replace germanium atoms in the lattice. The opposite surface is treated similarly with a compound of arsenic. Each boron atom of the boron side of the disc has three valence electrons instead of the four of each germanium atom it has displaced. On the arsenic side of the disc, each arsenic atom has five valence electrons instead of the four of the germanium atom. Consequently, the boron atoms create an electron deficiency (lattice holes) on the boron side, whereas the arsenic atoms yield an electron superfluity (conductance electrons) on the arsenic side. The positive charges of the atomic kernels balance the tendency for conduction electrons to fill the lattice holes, thereby yielding an equilibrium state. An electric current (a flow of electrons) is permitted in the direction from the arsenic (electron-rich) side to the boron (electron-poor) side; this acts to fill lattice holes. An electron flow is resisted in the opposite direction because such a flow would be from an electron-poor site to an electron-rich site.

Although transistors are useful because of their small size and tiny power requirements, they have limitations, the most serious being the limitation on the amount of power they can handle.

One type of solar battery consists of thin discs of silicon contaminated at the surfaces with tiny amounts of arsenic and boron. Electron-rich sites are adjacent to electron-poor sites, so that an equilibrium of electron flow is established. If these discs are exposed to light, the conduction electrons and the holes are upset, and a small electron flow occurs between the sites. This current can be used to do work. For example, solar batteries are used in satellites and by the Bell System in certain rural telephone lines.

PROBLEMS

1. In which liquid—carbon bisulfide or acetone—are the intermolecular attractive forces weaker?

2. In which liquid—methyl iodide or heptane—are the intermolecular attractive forces stronger?

3. What is the boiling point of carbon bisulfide if the external pressure on the liquid surface is 4.42 atm?

4. If the external (gaseous) pressure on the surface of a sample of acetone is 61.3 cm of Hg, at what temperature would the liquid boil?

5. The directions in a laboratory manual suggest that, if a student is purifying carbon bisulfide by distillation, the "pure" compound is to be collected as distillate when the vapor leaving the distillation flask is at a temperature between 46.0° and 47.0°C. How would you modify these directions if you were conducting a laboratory class in Golden, Colorado, where a usual atmospheric pressure is 617 mm?

6. Considering the fact that a specific pure liquid has countless possible boiling points, what is the major factor on which the boiling point of the liquid depends?

7. A pure sample of water is boiling vigorously. What correct, positive statement can be made about the vapor pressure of the water?

8. What is the maximum temperature at which pure chloroform vapor under a pressure of 1 atm will condense to yield liquid chloroform?

9. How many calories of heat are expended in vaporizing, at 100°C, 45 g of pure water?

10. How many kilocalories of heat are evolved, at 100°C, during the liquefaction of 45 g of pure water vapor?

11. What is the increase in entropy, in entropy units, during the production of 9 g of water vapor at 100°C and 1 atm from 9 g of liquid water at 100°C?

12. Is the equilibrium vapor pressure of water measured at 25°C at sea level greater than, less than, or the same as that measured at 25°C at an elevation of 1 mile?

13. How would you convince a housewife that although her wet laundry has frozen on the clothes line during the morning of a cold, windy winter day, she may expect the clothes to be dry by dusk even though the outdoor temperature never rises above 30°F?

14. At 20°C, why does ethyl ether have a higher vapor pressure than acetone, even though the individual ether molecules are more massive than the individual acetone molecules?

15. What would probably be the most convenient way to purify a small sample of solid camphor that is contaminated by marble chips, iron filings, and table salt?

16. By using only the data given in Table 15.1, determine an approximate value for the standard boiling point of acetone.

17. Describe a simple apparatus that might be used to measure the vapor pressures of solid camphor at room temperature.

18. What mass of water could be heated from 5°C to 35°C by the heat evolved during the freezing, at 0°C, of 1000 g of water?

19. Substance X (mol wt 60) has a normal boiling point of -195°C, whereas substance Y (mol wt 62) has a normal boiling point of -175°C. (a) In which liquid—X or Y—are the intermolecular attractive forces the stronger?   (b) Can liquid Y exist at -174°C?   (c) Which liquid has the greater vapor pressure at -180°C?   (d) Which of these temperatures— -196°C, -205°C, -194°C, or -170°C—seems the most probable critical temperature of X?

20. Bottle A contains 425 ml of atmospheric air, and bottle B contains 792 ml of the same kind of air.   Into bottle A is poured 25 ml of pure ethanol, the normal boiling point of which is 78°C.   Into bottle B is put 250 ml of pure bromobenzene, the normal boiling point of which is 156°C.   The bottles are stoppered tightly and kept at 25°C.   In which bottle does the vapor of the liquid exert the greater pressure?

21. The standard boiling point of chloroform is determined correctly at different locations. The first is at sea level in New York City, the second on the summit of Pike's Peak, Colorado. Is the temperature reading obtained on Pike's Peak higher than, lower than, or the same as that determined in New York City?

22. The covalent compounds Tom, Dick, and Harry have nearly identical molar weights and their molecules have similar volumes. Although all 3 substances are at 22°C, the normal boiling point of Harry, they are in separate vessels at sea level. Tom is in vessel T, Dick in D, and Harry in H. In vessel D the equilibrium vapor pressure of Dick is 100 cm of Hg. Tom, in T, is boiling vigorously, and has been for some time, and the gaseous pressure on the surface of Tom is 500 mm of Hg. (a) In which substance, Tom, Dick, or Harry, are the intermolecular attractive forces the strongest? (b) In which compound are the intermolecular attractive forces the weakest? (c) Predict which compound has the highest critical temperature. (d) Which compound has the lowest vapor pressure at 293°K? (e) Which vessels, if any, are either definitely open or vented to the atmosphere?

23. Three ordinary tightly stoppered glass bottles A, B, and C, each having exactly 150 ml capacity, have been sitting together undisturbed for 24 hours on the same laboratory bench at 20°C. At the time the bottles were partially filled, each was "empty" and dry, and each was stoppered *immediately* after the liquid was added. The barometric pressure in the laboratory at the time of filling was 760 mm of Hg, and the temperature of the liquids and of the laboratory was 20°C.

Bottle A contains 60 ml of liquid acetone, C_3H_6O, whose vapor pressure at 20°C is 185 mm of Hg. Bottle B contains 75 ml of liquid carbon bisulfide, CS_2, whose vapor pressure at 20°C is 298 mm of Hg. Bottle C contains 50 ml of liquid benzene, C_6H_6, whose vapor pressure at 20°C is 80 mm of Hg. (a) What volume, in milliliters, inside bottle A is occupied by acetone molecules? (b) What is the partial pressure, in centimeters of Hg, of the CS_2 vapor in bottle B? (c) In which bottle are the molecules in the gaseous phase apparently moving through space with the greatest velocity? (d) In which bottle does the gaseous phase have the greatest density of molecular population? (e) In which liquid are the intermolecular attractive forces the weakest? (f) Which liquid probably has the highest freezing point? (g) What is the approximate total gaseous pressure, in mm of Hg, on the surface of the liquid in bottle C? (h) Which bottle has the largest amount of matter, *other than air*, in the gaseous state? (i) How many milligrams of CS_2 is in the gaseous state in bottle B? (j) Which liquid probably has the lowest normal boiling point?

16

SOLUTIONS

16.1 A PERSPECTIVE

A solution is usually defined as an apparently homogeneous mixture whose composition may be varied within certain limits. Because it is matter, a solution is either liquid, solid, or gaseous. Cane sugar dissolved in water is a liquid solution, brass is a solid solution, and air is a gaseous solution.

A true solution constitutes what is called a homogeneous phase. The term *phase* is used when certain systems are differentiated by physical states. If a system consists of two or more phases, each phase is a specific physical state of matter. For example, let us think about a glass bottle partially filled with sand and sea water. The liquid phase is the sea water, a liquid solution; the gaseous phase is the air in the bottle, a gaseous solution. The sand is the solid phase, but since it is probably heterogeneous, it is not a true solution.

366

The glass bottle is a brittle noncrystalline solution.

Nearly every chemical reaction performed in the laboratory occurs in a solution, usually either liquid or gaseous. Since liquid solutions are handled more conveniently than gaseous solutions, liquid systems are more common in the instructional laboratory. Gaseous solutions are used frequently in the chemical industry since they are so adaptable in continuous processes.

Liquid and gaseous solutions are propitious media for chemical reactions because the reactant molecules are much more mobile than those in a solid. Also, the dispersion of the individual reactant molecules enhances the probability of contact and any subsequent reaction. The molecules of a solid reactant have little opportunity to interact with those of another substance since they are so intimately associated with molecules of their own kind.

Liquid solutions are frequently classified relative to

367

the electrical character of their solute molecules (the solute is the dissolved material).   A mixture of molten sodium chloride (Na^+Cl^-) and potassium nitrate ($K^+NO_3^-$) is a liquid solution that consists of mobile charged molecules (ions).   Such a system is a good electrical conductor.   In fact, any solution of an ionic compound can conduct an electric current, apparently because of the presence of mobile ions.   The electric conductance shown by a solution that contains ions is called *electrolytic conductance* (p. 501), and such a solution is said to be an *electrolytic solution*.   The solute in an electrolytic solution is usually called an *electrolyte;* hence all ionic compounds are electrolytes.   Since ionic compounds are often called salts, all salts are electrolytes.   Ionic compounds yield solutions that are often called electrolytes.

Since water is such a common solvent (dispersion medium), it is customary to classify water-soluble covalent substances according to their behavior when added to water.

Some covalent compounds dissolve in water to yield solutions that contain no more ions than does pure water.   These compounds are classed as *nonelectrolytes.*

Other covalent compounds, those whose uncharged molecules dissolve readily in water, interact chemically with water molecules to yield solutions that contain many more ions than does pure water.   These   compounds   are   classed   as   *pseudoelectrolytes.*   Covalent compounds that contain loosely bound protons (p. 215) usually act as pseudoelectrolytes (acids) when they are added to water.

If two gases X and Y at identical pressure and temperature are placed in contact with each other (p. 306), the gases mix to yield a gaseous solution.   As we mentioned earlier (p. 335), any system such as gas X with gas Y adopts that state which has the greater randomness (disorder), the greater probability of existence. The trend is in the direction of an increase in entropy.

Let us consider two different liquids A and B which have identical vapor pressures at 25°C and whose molecules have nearly identical masses.   If pure A is added to pure B, the liquids mix completely to yield a true solution.   Since the escaping tendency of A molecules is identical to that of B molecules, the mixing process is just what we should expect if we recall the previous discussion of entropy (p. 335).   When liquid A is added to liquid B, the tendency to establish a more random state of molecular distribution is the driving force, just as if gas X had mixed spontaneously with gas Y.

Therefore the tendency for substances to mix and thereby yield solutions is not unexpected.

This brief introduction will be elaborated later, but it should help you to realize that the concept of entropy directs us to accept the inherent tendency for substances to mix and thereby form solutions.

16.2　TERMINOLOGY

Some of the terms used in the qualitative description of solutions may seem rather arbitrary. Since they are conventional, it will be well if we know them and learn to use them properly. In thinking of the terms, you may assume that most of the solutions that you encounter will be liquid solutions.

a. The *solvent* is usually considered to be the medium in which the *solute* is dissolved. In most of the aqueous solutions described in later chapters, the solvent, water, is more abundant than the solute. If two substances are completely miscible, it is impossible in some solutions to identify the solvent and the solute. For instance, if 50 ml of water is added to 50 ml of ethanol to yield a clear solution, it is impossible to use clearly the terms *solute* and *solvent*.

b. A *dilute solution* is a system that contains a small amount of solute in a large amount of solvent. Sea water is a dilute solution.

c. A *concentrated solution* is a system that contains a relatively large amount of solute dissolved in a solvent. Molasses is a concentrated solution of cane sugar in water.

d. A *saturated solution* is a system in which the dissolved solute can exist in equilibrium with the undissolved solute. If the solute is a solid and the solvent a liquid, the saturated solution may contain undissolved solid in continual contact with the solution. In this system the rate of dissolving of the solid is equal to the rate of its precipitation (crystallization). If the solute and solvent are liquid, the saturated solution is a system in which the solute forms a separate liquid phase, either on top of, on the bottom of, or suspended in the solution. If the solute is a gas and the solvent is a liquid, the pressure of the solute on the surface of the solution is equal to the partial pressure of the solute gas in the solution. In a saturated solution the tendency of the solute either to enter or to dissolve in the solvent is equal to its tendency to leave the solvent.

e. An *unsaturated solution*, at a given temperature and pressure, contains less dissolved solute than the saturated solution of that solute under the same conditions. In an unsaturated solution the tendency of the solute to enter the solvent is greater than its tendency to leave the solvent.

f. A *supersaturated solution*, at a given temperature and pressure, contains more dissolved solute than the saturated solution of that solute under the same conditions. A supersaturated solution is not a system in equilibrium. If solid solute is added to it, solute crystallizes immediately and eventually equilibrium is attained (a saturated solution is produced). In a supersaturated solution the tendency for the solute to enter the solvent is less than its tendency to leave the solvent.

If sodium acetate trihydrate, $Na^+C_2H_3O_2^- \cdot 3HOH$, is heated carefully in a clean, dust-free vessel, the solid liquefies at 58°C. The liquid system produced is an aqueous solution of sodium acetate, in which the loosely bound water in the crystalline hydrate serves as the solvent. If this solution is cooled carefully, a supersaturated solution is obtained. If a small crystal of sodium acetate or a particle of dust is added to this supersaturated solution, solid immediately crystallizes from the solution. Since heat was used to dissolve the solid, heat is evolved during its crystallization.

An ordinary carbonated beverage, when tightly bottled, is a supersaturated solution of carbon dioxide in the aqueous beverage. If the bottle is shaken after it is opened, bubbles of carbon dioxide readily escape from the solution.

g. The *solubility* of a pure substance in a given solvent is its concentration in a saturated solution at a specified temperature. The solubility of a solute, when expressed as its concentration in a saturated solution, is independent of the amount of solvent used because the concentration of solute is expressed in terms of the amount of solute either in a unit volume of solution or in a unit mass of solvent.

The solubilities (in water) of many substances are listed in the common chemical handbooks (*Handbook of Chemistry and Physics* and *Lange's Handbook*). The figures are usually given as the number of grams of substance (as solute) per 100 g or 100 cc of water.

The actual amount of a substance that can be dissolved in a given solvent depends on the amount of solvent used: the more solvent used, the more solute that can be dissolved.

The common classifications—soluble, insoluble, or slightly soluble—are relative, and the term *insoluble* must not be taken literally.

It is often stated that silver chloride is insoluble in water; yet at 10°C, 0.0009 g of this compound dissolves in 100 g of water. It is better to use the term *slightly soluble* instead of the term *insoluble*.

16.3   CONCENTRATION OF SOLUTIONS

The various common ways of expressing concentration of solutions are:

    a. *Mass of solute per unit mass of solvent*—usually expressed as the number of grams of solute per 100 g of solvent to designate the concentration of the saturated solution at a given temperature.

    b. *Weight percentage of solute in the solution.* For instance, a 10 per cent solution of glucose contains 10 g of glucose in 90 g of water, or 10 g in 100 g of solution, thus identifying the amount of solute in a specific amount of solvent.

    c. *Molarity.* The molarity of a solution is the number of moles of solute per liter (or millimoles per milliliter) of solution; the symbol for molarity is M. For example, a 0.5 M aqueous solution of glucose, $C_6H_{12}O_6$, is one-half molar; its molarity is 0.5. Each liter contains 0.5 mole (90 g) of glucose; each milliliter contains 0.5 millimole (90 mg) of glucose. This 0.5 M solution may be prepared by adding 0.5 of a mole (90 g) of glucose to an amount of water that will give a total volume of one liter.

    An advantage of the concept of molarity for solutions of nonelectrolytes is that equal volumes of two different solutions with the same molarity contain an equal number of molecules of solute. A disadvantage of the concept of molarity is that the molarity changes with temperature.

    d. *Molality* (weight molarity). The molality of a solution is the number of moles of solute in 1000 g of solvent, or the number of millimoles of solute per gram of solvent. For example, a 0.5 molal aqueous solution of glucose may be prepared by adding 0.5 of a mole of glucose to 1000 g of water.

    Two advantages of the concept of molality are that the mass of solvent is identified and that the molality of the solution does not vary with the temperature. A disadvantage is that masses are measured with more difficulty than are volumes.

    e. *Formality.* The formality of a solution is the number of gram-formulas of solute per liter of solution; the symbol for formality is F. For example, a 0.5 F (one-half formal) aqueous solution of sodium chloride may be prepared by dissolving 0.5 of a gram-formula (58.5 g/2, or 29.25 g) of Na^+Cl^- in sufficient water to make one liter of solution. This solution contains 0.5 mole of Na^+ and 0.5 mole of Cl^-, since the crystal lattice disintegrates when the solid dissolves in water. Molarity and formality are often considered synonymous. As in the case of molarity, the formality of a solution varies with the temperature. Mole and gram-formula are synonymous.

f. *Mole fraction.* The mole fraction of a solute in a solution is the number of moles of solute divided by the total number of moles in the system (solute and solvent). The mole fraction of the solute is readily calculated from the molality (weight molarity) of the solution. For example, in a 0.5 molal aqueous solution of glucose, the 1000 g of water contains 1000/18, or 55.5, moles. The mole fraction of glucose is 0.5/(0.5 + 55.5) = 0.00892. The mole fraction of water is 55.5/56.0 = 0.991. The sum of the mole fractions of all the molecular entities in a solution is equal to unity (1). Mole fractions do not change with temperature.

g. *Normality.* The normality of a solution is the number of gram-equivalent weights (gram-equivalents) of solute per liter of solution, or the number of milligram-equivalents of solute per milliliter of solution. The gram-equivalent weight of a solute often depends on the chemical reaction in which the solute is a participant. The application of the concept of normality can be readily applied to problems of the type found in section 22.18 (p. 554).

16.4 SOLUBILITY OF A SUBSTANCE

Any gas at ordinary pressures can mix or dissolve completely in any other gas. In other words, any ordinary gas can serve as a solvent for any other gas because there is ample room between the molecules and because the intermolecular attractive forces are relatively weak.

A gas, at ordinary pressures, will dissolve in a liquid if the molecules of the gas are attracted strongly to solvent molecules or if the gas reacts chemically with the solvent to yield soluble products. Gaseous ammonia is very soluble in water mainly because of strong hydrogen-bonding between ammonia and water molecules. There is some chemical interaction between ammonia and water molecules to yield ions. A proton-transfer reaction occurs.

$$NH_3 + HOH \leftrightarrows NH_4^+ + OH^-$$

Many ionic compounds are reasonably soluble in certain polar liquids; they are usually only slightly soluble in nonpolar liquids. This is expected because the nonpolar molecules are unable to attract the ions of the ionic compound as readily as can polar molecules. The crystal lattice of the ionic compound must disintegrate if it is to dissolve. If the polar solvent molecules can attract the ions about as strongly as they are attracted to each other, the ionic compound will dissolve. In the next chapter we shall amplify this concept by using water as the solvent.

Most pure metals and covalent solids are poor solvents unless they are molten. Many solid alloys, such as brass, are simple solid solutions (p. 180). Copper, silver, and gold are miscible with each other. The members of the alkali metal family are mutually miscible. Mercury dissolves many metals to yield alloys called *amalgams*. Nickel, palladium, and platinum are fairly good solvents for gaseous hydrogen.

16.5 EFFECT OF TEMPERATURE
ON SOLUBILITY

When a pure solute is added to a good solvent, there is a high tendency for the solute entities to escape from the solute. But as more and more solute dissolves in the solvent, the tendency of the solute entities to escape from the solution and return to the solute phase gradually increases. Eventually a situation is reached in which the escaping tendency from solution to solute phase is equal to the escaping tendency from solute phase to solution: a state in equilibrium or a saturated solution is produced. Since the vapor pressures of molecular solids and liquids are measures of their escaping tendencies, the vapor pressure of the dissolved solute in a saturated solution is theoretically equal to that of the undissolved solute. In a supersaturated solution the escaping tendency of the dissolved solute is greater than that of the pure solute.

To determine the effect of temperature on the solubility of a substance in a given solvent, let us consider a saturated solution because we can then use Le Châtelier's principle to interpret the effect of temperature. If the temperature of a saturated solution (a system in equilibrium) is increased, the process that absorbs heat is favored. If the process by which solute enters solution is favored (more solute dissolves), we know that the dissolving of solute is an endothermic process. In this case, therefore, the solubility of the solute increases with a rise in temperature. If, however, the temperature of the saturated solution is increased and solute precipitates (comes out of solution), we know that the separation of solute from solution is endothermic. Consequently, the dissolving of solute is exothermic and the solubility decreases with a rise in temperature.

Using the concept of escaping tendencies, we expect that an increase in temperature would increase the escaping tendency in the phase in which the strongest intermolecular attractive forces exist, because the individual entities in this phase need more energy to escape from each other. Since intermolecular attractive forces in gases are weaker than those in liquids, the solubility of a gas either in a liquid or a solid decreases with a rise in temperature. Since the forces in solids are stronger than those in liquids, the solubility of a solid in a liquid usually increases with a rise in temperature, whereas the solubility of a liquid in a solid usually decreases with a rise in temperature. Since the intermolecular attractive forces are similar in all nonpolar liquids, it is impossible to predict correctly the effect of temperature on the solubility of nonpolar liquids in each other. The effect of temperature on the solubilities of some ionic compounds is shown in Fig. 16.1.

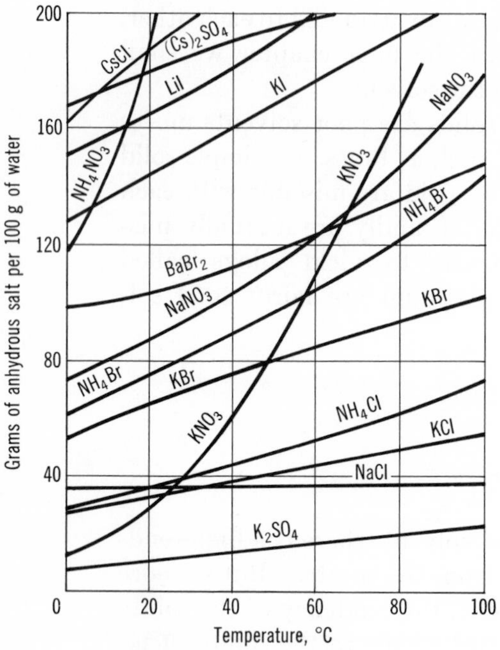

FIGURE 16.1 Effect of temperature on the solubility, in water, of a group of common ionic compounds.

16.6 EFFECT OF PRESSURE ON SOLUBILITY

The effect of pressure on solubility is slight in most liquid–solid systems but is pronounced in solutions of a gas in a liquid. By applying Le Châtelier's principle, we see that an increase in pressure on a saturated solution of a gas in a liquid favors the dissolving of gas because the volume of the system is decreased as gas dissolves in the liquid. The concentration of the gaseous phase increases as the pressure increases; hence the escaping tendency of the gas increases.

In 1803 William Henry (British) suggested a relationship between the pressure of a gas and its solubility in a liquid. A simplified statement of Henry's generalization is: The solubility (in terms of mass dissolved) of a gas in a liquid, at constant temperature, is directly proportional to the pressure of the gas. If there is a mixture of gases, the solubility of each gas is directly proportional to its partial pressure.

16.7 RAOULT'S LAW

In 1881 François Raoult (French) proposed an extremely significant generalization: The vapor pressure of each volatile substance in a solution is directly proportional to the mole fraction of the substance. This is an approximate generalization because it is true only for ideal solutions, just as Boyle's and Charles' laws are true only for the ideal gas. (An ideal solution is a system in which attractive forces between all entities in the solution are identical.) Because in a dilute solution, which is more nearly ideal, the mole

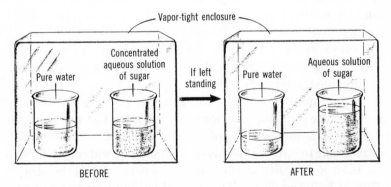

FIGURE 16.2 Diagram of an experiment showing that water will evaporate in a pure state much more rapidly than in an aqueous solution of sugar, and that in the sugar solution the rate of condensation exceeds that of evaporation. Since the two systems attempt to attain identical vapor pressures, water is transferred from the vessel of pure water to the sugar solution.

fraction of the solute is nearly proportional to the molality of that solution, Raoult's law is often stated: The lowering of the vapor pressure of the solvent in a solution is directly proportional to the molality of that solution. This law holds fairly well for certain solutions whose molalities are 0.1 molal or less, but it is seldom accurate for solutions with molalities of 1 molal or greater.

In nearly ideal solutions any decrease in the vapor pressure of the solvent depends on the number of solute and solvent entities present; it does not depend on the character of these entities. The solute has the property of lowering the vapor pressure of the solvent, but since this property depends on the number of solute entities, it is a rather unusual one. A property that depends on the number of entities is called a *colligative property*, or an *extensive property*. (See Fig. 16.2.)

16.8 BOILING POINTS OF SOLUTIONS OF NONELECTROLYTES

If a solution consists of a nonvolatile solute dissolved in a liquid solvent, the boiling point of the solution, under a given external pressure, is higher than the boiling point of the pure solvent at the same pressure. The elevation of the boiling point is directly proportional to the molal concentration of the solute. The proportionality factor, or the molal (weight molar) boiling point elevation constant, of water is approximately 0.52°C. [Some other approximate molal boiling point elevation constants are: ethanol, C_2H_5OH, 1.19°C; ethyl ether, $(C_2H_5)_2O$, 2.11°C; benzene, C_6H_6, 2.65°C.] The effect of a nonelectrolyte on the vapor pressure of water is graphically illustrated in Fig. 16.3.

If we assume that we may disregard the character of the solute entities in dilute aqueous solutions, we can say: The normal boiling point of water is increased approximately 0.52°C for each mole of nonvolatile solute entities dissolved in 1000 g of water. For water: $\Delta T_{bp} = 0.52 \times$ molality of the solution, where ΔT_{bp} is the observed elevation in boiling point. The normal boiling point of benzene is increased 2.65°C for each mole of solute entities dissolved in 1000 g of benzene.

Let us consider a typical problem. Eighteen grams of glucose, $C_6H_{12}O_6$, is dissolved in 250 g of pure water. What is the boiling point of this solution at 1 atm? The molecular weight of glucose is 180, so 18 g of glucose is 18/180, or 0.1 mole of glucose. Since 0.1 mole is in 250 g of water, this is a 0.4 molal solution (1000 g/250 g × 0.1). If the solution were 1 molal, the boiling point of the solution would be 100.52°C; for a 0.4 molal solution, the boiling point would be (0.52 × 0.4) + 100°C, or 100.21°C.

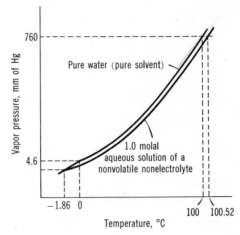

FIGURE 16.3 Effect of a nonvolatile solute in decreasing the vapor pressure of water. When the vapor pressure of water is decreased, the boiling point is increased and the freezing point is lowered.

16.9 FREEZING POINTS OF SOLUTIONS OF NONELECTROLYTES

The use of antifreeze in the cooling systems of motor vehicles is a practical application of the knowledge that the freezing point of a liquid is decreased by the presence of solute entities. Some of the more common liquid "antifreezes" are: ethanol, C_2H_5OH; methanol, CH_3OH; ethylene glycol, $C_2H_4(OH)_2$; glycerol, $C_3H_5(OH)_3$. When these liquids are dissolved in water, they lower its vapor pressure; the freezing points of the solutions are less than 0°C. The use of sodium chloride to "melt" ice on sidewalks, streets, and highways is another practical application of lowering freezing points.

With dilute aqueous solutions, for each mole of solute entities in 1000 g of water, the freezing point of water is depressed (lowered) 1.86°C. This freezing point depression is proportional to the molality of the solution. The proportionality factor, or molal freezing point depression constant, of water is approximately 1.86°C. For water: $\Delta T_{fp} = 1.86 \times$ molality of the solution, where ΔT_{fp} is the observed depression in freezing point. Some other approximate freezing point depression constants are: benzene, 5.1°C; acetic acid, CH_3COOH, 3.9°C; phenol, C_6H_5OH, 7.27°C; camphor, 40°C.

Let us consider a typical problem.   To 100 g of water is added 17.1 g of sucrose, $C_{12}H_{22}O_{11}$.   What is the freezing point of the solution?   The molecular weight of sucrose is 342; hence 17.1 g of sucrose is 0.05 of a mole.   Since this 0.05 mole is in 100 g of water, the solution is 0.5 molal.   If the solution were 1 molal, the freezing point would be −1.86°C.   For this 0.5 molal solution the freezing point is −0.93°C.

16.10   DETERMINATION OF APPROXIMATE
MOLAR WEIGHTS

We know that one mole of a water-soluble nonelectrolyte in 1000 g of water depresses the freezing point of water to −1.86°C.   Therefore we can calculate the mass of one mole (molar weight) of a water-soluble nonelectrolyte, if, for a given solution, we know the mass of solute, the mass of water, and the freezing point of the solution.   This method may be extended to other solvents whose freezing point depression constants are known, but it is applicable only to dilute solutions.   The freezing point depression method is easier to perform than the boiling point elevation method because in the latter a constant pressure must be carefully maintained on the surface of the solution.   With the boiling point method, the molar weight of the solute nonelectrolyte can be calculated from experimental data which indicate the mass of solute in 1000 g of solvent and the extent to which the boiling point of the pure solvent is elevated.

Let us use two sample problems to illustrate these methods.

1. Two grams of a nonelectrolyte is dissolved in 50 g of water. The boiling point of the solution is 100.15°C at 1 atm.   What is the approximate molar weight of the solute?

   If 1000 g of water were used, the mass of solute would be 2 g/50 g $\times$ 1000 g = 40 g of solute/1000 g of water.

   In this example a boiling point elevation of 0.15°C is caused by 0.15/0.52 = 0.29 mole of solute, since a 0.52° elevation is caused by 1 mole.

   If 40 g is 0.29 mole, then the mass of one mole is 40/0.29 = 140 g.   The approximate molar weight of the solute is 140 g.

2. Fifteen grams of a nonelectrolyte is dissolved in 250 g of pure acetic acid. The freezing point of the solution is 14.4°C. (The freezing point of pure acetic acid is 16.6°C.) What is the molar weight of the nonelectrolyte?

The mass of solute if 1000 g of acetic acid were used is 15/250 × 1000 g = 60 g/1000 g of acetic acid.

In this case the freezing point depression of 2.2°C (16.6 − 14.4) is caused by (2.2/3.9) or 0.56 mole of solute.

If 60 g is 0.56 mole, the mass of one mole is (60/0.56) or 108 g. The approximate molar weight of the nonelectrolyte is 108 g.

16.11   EFFECT OF ELECTROLYTES ON THE FREEZING AND BOILING POINTS OF WATER

An ionic compound consists of at least two different ions. When it is dissolved in water, the solution contains the different ions that compose the ionic crystal. When many ionic compounds are added to water, chemical interactions occur between water and certain ions. For the moment, however, let us consider the behavior of two ionic compounds whose ions, in dilute solutions, do not chemically interact with water. If 1 mole of sodium chloride, Na^+Cl^-, is dissolved in 1000 g of water, the solution is theoretically 1.0 molal in sodium ion, Na^+, and 1.0 molal in chloride ion, Cl^-. Since there are 2 moles of particles in 1000 g of water, the theoretical freezing point of the solution is (2) (−1.86°C) = −3.72°C. The actual freezing point of a 1 molal aqueous solution of sodium chloride is not quite so low as −3.72°C. If 1 mole of calcium chloride, $Ca^{++}(Cl^-)_2$, is dissolved in 1000 g of water, the solution is 1.0 molal in calcium ion, Ca^{++}, and 2.0 molal in chloride ion. Since there are 3 moles of particles in 1000 g of water, the theoretical freezing point of the solution is (3) (−1.86°C) = −5.58°C, but the actual freezing point of this solution is not so low. One-molal solutions of these ionic compounds are not ideal solutions, but 0.1-molal solutions are more nearly ideal, and 0.01-molal solutions are still more nearly ideal. These facts indicate that, for aqueous solutions of an electrolyte, the more dilute the solution the more nearly ideal it is.

The boiling points of aqueous solutions of electrolytes are lower than those calculated from theory, but as in the case of freezing points, the more dilute the solution the more nearly do the boiling points agree with the expected values (as calculated for nonelectrolytes).

Let us briefly identify the two theories—one old and one more modern—originally proposed to interpret this behavior of solutions of electrolytes.

16.12 THE ARRHENIUS THEORY

In 1887 Svante Arrhenius (Swedish) published a paper concerning the ionic dissociation of certain substances. He suggested that certain substances ionize (dissociate to yield ions) when they are added to water and that the degree of ionization increases upon dilution of the solutions. He implied that these substances consist of uncharged particles and that the solute substances dissociate in water, with the result that ions are formed. Today we know that the ionic compounds (true electrolytes) are ionic in their solid state and that the ionic crystal lattice simply disintegrates in water. Arrhenius' concept, however, is an admirable interpretation of the behavior of pseudoelectrolytes.

At the time Arrhenius proposed his theory, the electron had not been identified. His concept that charged particles existed in aqueous solutions was considered by many scientists extremely questionable. Nearly two decades passed before all chemists accepted Arrhenius' notion. Although Arrhenius' theory of ionic dissociation is not completely valid, it is one of the prominent landmarks in the development of chemistry and undoubtedly led to our present concept of solutions of electrolytes.

16.13 THE DEBYE-HÜCKEL THEORY

In 1923 Peter Debye (Dutch) and E. Hückel (German) developed a theory to interpret such facts as this: a 0.1 m solution (aqueous) of potassium bromide, K^+Br^- (0.1 molal in K^+ and 0.1 molal in Br^-), freezes at $-0.345°C$, instead of at the theoretical value (based on complete dissociation) of $-0.372°C$. Debye and Hückel suggested that this deviation is due to the fact that the effective concentrations of K^+ and Br^- are not 0.1 molal. They proposed the concept that strong interionic attractions decrease the concentrations of the individual ions. Debye and Hückel also noted that these interionic attractive forces decrease as the density of the ionic population (concentration of the solution) decreases. The influence of the interionic forces is less in very dilute solutions than in more concentrated solutions because in the very dilute solutions the ions are much farther apart. The electrical properties of the solvent are important in regard to ionic interactions (p. 404).

16.14 FRACTIONAL DISTILLATION OF MIXTURES OF LIQUIDS

Space does not permit a detailed discussion of the distillation of liquid mixtures, but the fractional distillation of solutions of two or more liquids is very common in the research laboratory and in the chemical and petroleum industries. If two or more liquids have reasonably different boiling points (reasonably different vapor pressures) and if they do not chemically interact or form a constant-boiling mixture, it is usually possible to separate them by fractional distillation because one liquid vaporizes more readily than the other(s). Using a suitable fractionating column, the vapor of the lower boiling liquid is allowed to pass through the column, but the vapor of the higher boiling liquid(s) is condensed as much as possible. Vapor leaves from the top of the fractionating column. This vapor is condensed to yield an initial distillate, mainly of the lower-boiling liquid.

The fractional distillation of liquid air is an extremely important industrial process because most of the nitrogen, oxygen, and inert gases used in industry are obtained from the atmosphere. The fractional distillation of millions of gallons of crude petroleum and mixtures of liquid hydrocarbons occurs daily in the petroleum industry.

16.15 CONSTANT-BOILING (AZEOTROPIC) MIXTURES

There are some binary liquid systems (solutions) from which it is impossible to separate completely the constituents of the mixture by distillation.

The normal boiling point of pure ethanol (grain alcohol) is 78.5°C. If a 95 per cent aqueous solution of ethanol is distilled, the distillate has the same composition as the original mixture.

Such a mixture is called a *constant-boiling mixture* or an *azeotrope*. The ethanol produced by fermentation of certain carbohydrates (starch and sucrose) in aqueous solutions is separated from the "mash" by fractional distillation, but the distillate is approximately 95 per cent ethanol and 5 per cent water.

Nitric acid, $HONO_2$, and water form a constant-boiling mixture (68 per cent nitric acid) that boils at 120°C (1 atm). If a solution that is 80 per cent nitric acid and 20 per cent water is distilled, the initial vapor is richer in nitric acid than was the original solution. On continued distillation, the residue becomes progressively less rich in nitric acid until 68 per cent of the residue is nitric acid. The residue then boils at 120°C at 1 atm and the distillate is 68 per cent aqueous nitric acid.

A 20.22 per cent aqueous solution of hydrogen chloride (hydrochloric acid) is a constant-boiling mixture (bp, 108.6°C at 1 atm; density, 1.10 g/ml).

16.16   SOLVENT EXTRACTION

There are several methods other than ordinary fractional distillation (p. 381) used to separate the components of ordinary solutions. Among these are extraction, ion exchange, chromatography, and molecular distillation.

We mentioned earlier (p. 368) that similar substances are more likely to mix spontaneously than are dissimilar substances. Many polar liquids, for instance, are only slightly soluble in most nonpolar liquids, whereas most nonpolar liquids are completely miscible in each other. When diethyl ether, a relatively nonpolar liquid, is added to water at room temperature, only about 7.5 parts of the ether dissolve in 100 parts of water, and about 1.5 parts of water dissolve in 100 parts of ether. If a solute is added to a mixture of ether and water, it dissolves in each liquid to the extent that it is soluble in each. A relatively nonpolar solute dissolves preferentially in the ether, and a more polar solute is more soluble in the water, provided its molecules can hydrogen-bond with water molecules. A mathematical relation that expresses the distribution relationship is the Nernst distribution principle. Assume that the solute is S, one solvent is A, the other solvent is B, and that all are at a specific temperature.

$$K_d = \frac{\text{concn of } S \text{ in } A}{\text{concn of } S \text{ in } B} = \frac{\text{g of } S/\text{volume of } A}{\text{g of } S/\text{volume of } B} = \frac{\text{solubility of } S \text{ in } A}{\text{solubility of } S \text{ in } B}$$

The term K_d, the distribution constant or ratio, is a proportionality constant that has no dimensions (units).

A relation that allows the determination of the extent of extraction is

$$M_{st(n)} = M_{st} \left[\frac{K_d V_{sol}}{K_d V_{sol} + V_{sv}} \right]^n$$

where $M_{st(n)}$ is the mass of solute remaining after the nth extraction, M_{st} the mass of dissolved solute, V_{sol} the volume (ml) of the solution, K_d the distribution ratio, V_{sv} the volume (ml) of extraction solvent, and n the number of extractions.

Let us consider solid benzoic acid as a typical solute that is a little less polar than water, but a little more polar than diethyl ether. The solid is quite soluble in ether, but much less soluble in water. Most of the benzoic acid in 100 ml of an aqueous solution of the substance can be extracted from the solution by using diethyl ether. Successive additions of 25 ml of ether are more effective means of extraction than is a single extraction by 100 ml of ether. This is a consequence of the distribution principle illustrated by the above equation. After the extraction, the volatile ether can be easily evaporated from the ether extract to yield the pure solid benzoic acid.

16.17 ION-EXCHANGE SEPARATIONS

A specific solute may distribute itself between a liquid and a solid phase just as well as between two liquid phases. If the solute in solution is ionic, it may distribute either its cations or its anions (sometimes both) in certain solids that are called *ion exchangers.* A cation exchanger absorbs cations from a solution (H^+ are replaced in the exchange), an anion exchanger absorbs anions (OH^- are replaced in the exchange). The total process is called an *ion-exchange separation.*

A typical cation exchanger is a huge organic molecule (a polymeric resin) that has many sulfonic acid groups, SO_3H, called exchange sites, in the molecule. If the resin, $(RSO_3H)_x$, is put in water, the firmly attached sulfonic acid groups tend to ionize protolytically.

$$RSO_3H + HOH \leftrightarrows RSO_3^- + OH_3^+$$

The proton (H^+) is free to wander in the water and in the ion-exchanger resin. Because of this mobility, other cations, Na^+ for example, can replace H^+ in the resin, and thereby be extracted from a solution.

$$RSO_3^-H^+ + Na^+ \leftrightharpoons RSO_3^-Na^+ + H^+$$

Dipositive and tripositive ions can be extracted from a solution by an exchanger that picks up cations. The extent of extraction of a specific cation depends on the type of cation exchanger, the size of the cation, and the charge of the cation. By arranging propitious conditions, it is possible to separate individually from an aqueous solution the alkali metal ions and the cations of the $4f$ and $5f$ elements, even though the members of these families are chemically very similar. The use of ion exchangers is the best means of separating many types of cations from their closest relatives.

The use of anion-exchange resins is comparable to that of cation-exchange resins. The exchange sites in the anion exchangers may be organic derivatives of ammonium ion, R_4N^+, where each R is a large organic group that is closely associated with an anion, An^-. Therefore the sites are $R_4N^+An^-$. The mobile ion in these resins is the anion, An^-, just as the proton, H^+, is the mobile ion in the cation exchangers. The An^- in the resin can be replaced by other different anions, just as the H^+ is replaced by different cations in the cation exchangers. If the anion is OH^- in the resin, it might be replaced by chloride ion, Cl^-, from an aqueous solution.

$$R_4N^+OH^- + Cl^- \leftrightharpoons R_4N^+Cl^- + OH^-$$

It is evident that if a system had both a cation and an anion exchanger, passage of sea water through the system would yield nearly pure water. There are devices on the market, called de-ionizers, that by ion exchange convert ordinary tap water to a product as good as, if not better than, ordinary distilled water. The use of zeolites in the softening of hard water is described elsewhere (p. 610).

16.18 CHROMATOGRAPHY

A practical method for the separation of organic solids is a technique known as *chromatography*. In the classic procedure the solids (dissolved in some liquid solvent) are selectively absorbed on some finely divided material (usually a solid) that presents a large surface. Solids such as powdered sugar, starch, and alumina have been used extensively as adsorbents.

Usually the liquid mixture is forced through a vertical tube that contains the adsorbent. This mixture is followed by the extraction solvent, which preferentially extracts each solute to "develop" the chromatogram. The least strongly adsorbed material is washed through the column faster than the more strongly adsorbed components. A good chromatogram consists of different bands in the column, each of which in turn consists of some nearly pure component of the original mixture. If the components are colored, the bands have the corresponding colors. If the components fluoresce under ultraviolet light, they can be detected with ultraviolet light.

Chromatography can be applied to the separation of certain organic nonelectrolytes by using a technique called *salting-out chromatography*. In this method the water-soluble nonelectrolytes are separated from each other by elution with aqueous salt solutions (the *eluents*) through columns of ion-exchange resins. Closely related compounds such as methanol, ethanol, and 1-propanol (p. 689) can be separated by this method. If plain water is used as the eluent (extraction medium), separation is unclear. However, if a salt (electrolyte) is present in the eluent, the presence of the salt decreases the solubility of the solute (nonelectrolyte) in the aqueous phase, thereby allowing a more practical distribution between the resin and the aqueous phase.

Paper chromatography is a technique in which a sheet of filter paper is used in place of the usual column of solid material. Commonly an edge or corner of the paper is spotted with a mixture of the solutes, and then the paper is hung in an atmosphere of some volatile solvent mixture so that the different solutes seep either up or down the paper at different rates. Appreciable separations can be achieved by changing the orientation of the paper. The paper chromatographic technique is an extremely useful method for the separation of the components of complex mixtures of either biological products or extracts of plants. The separation of the amino acids (p. 707) in a mixture is particularly neat by this method.

Gas chromatography is a novel technique that applies gas–solid equilibria in the detection of the components of a gaseous mixture. The mixture of gases, or vapors, is passed through a column packed with some granular adsorbent. The specific gases are adsorbed and desorbed on and from the surface of the adsorbent at different rates, depending mainly on their structure and molar weight. The carrier gas in the stream of gases is regulated so that the rate of passage of the gases can be controlled. Helium is a common carrier. The detection along the column of the presence of the various fractions is effected by using miniature thermal conductivity cells, called thermistors. These may be calibrated so that readings of the recording unit yield direct information about concentrations.

16.19 MOLECULAR DISTILLATION

A recent development in the field of devices for the separation of materials from solutions is the use of a microfactor. This apparatus is a high-vacuum molecular distillation device that is very useful for mixtures of materials whose molecular weights are within the range of 250 to 1200. The molecular distillation is actually an evaporation from a very thin film above which there is an extremely low gaseous pressure. No ebullition occurs. The microfactor consists of moving steel bands that act both as evaporators and condensers. The device is based on the concept of least mixing. That is, each fraction of material separated from the mixture joins similar material instead of diluting richer distillate. One distinctly favorable asset of the microfactor is the elimination of high temperatures at condensers, pumps, and pipelines.

16.20 SOLVATION

Although many solids and liquids have limited solubilities in most solvents, they may exhibit considerable solubility in a few specific liquids. For instance, potassium iodide is only slightly soluble in all liquid hydrocarbons, whereas it is very soluble in water. Carbon tetrachloride is very soluble in all liquid hydrocarbons, but it is only slightly soluble in water. Substances that have similar intermolecular attractive forces are more likely to be miscible than those that have dissimilar intermolecular attractive forces. If solvent molecules are attracted to each other more strongly than to solute molecules, any tendency toward miscibility is greatly inhibited. This seems to be the case with water (solvent) and carbon tetrachloride (solute). If the solute molecules are attracted to each other more strongly than to the solvent molecules, solubility is likely to be slight. This seems to be the case with potassium iodide (solute) and the liquid hydrocarbons (solvents).

If the intermolecular attractive forces in a given solute are relatively strong, as, for instance, those in most ionic compounds and in highly associated liquids and solids (p. 187), work must be done to overcome the attractive forces. Part of the necessary energy in many apparently spontaneous solutions (mixings) of these kinds of solutes is supplied by physical interactions (electrostatic) between solvent and solute molecules. If the interaction is strong enough to be recognized, the process is called *solvation*, and the solute molecules are said to be *solvated*.

Solvation plays a major role during the dissolving of many substances in liquid solvents. The reason for water's ability to dissolve so many different types of substances is that water molecules are able to solvate many kinds of molecules, thereby attracting them away from the molecular aggregate, the solute (see Chap. 17).

Among the solvents that exhibit marked solvation ability, the best seem to be water, liquid ammonia, methanol, and ethanol. These are polar molecules that have strong tendencies to hydrogen-bond with solute molecules. Ionic compounds are more soluble in solvents such as these than in any other types. In the next chapter we shall describe the solvation of molecules by water, a process called hydration. If the solvent is ammonia, the process is called ammonation; if it is methanol, the process is methanolation; if it is ethanol, the process is ethanolation. The solvation of certain ions is so strong that ionic compounds crystallized from a solvent retain molecules of that solvent. Some examples are given below.

Ammonation of $Cu^{++}SO_4^{--}$ yields

$$Cu^{++}SO_4^{--} \cdot 4NH_3$$
copper(II) sulfate-4-ammonia

or depicted otherwise,

$$[Cu(NH_3)_4]^{++}SO_4^{--}$$
tetramminecopper(II) sulfate

Hydration of $Cu^{++}SO_4^{--}$ yields

$$Cu^{++}SO_4^{--} \cdot 5H_2O$$
copper(II) sulfate-5-water

or depicted otherwise,

$$[Cu(OH_2)_4]^{++}SO_4^{--}(H_2O)$$

tetraquocopper(II) sulfate-1-water

Ethanolation of $Ca^{++}(Cl^-)_2$ yields

$$Ca^{++}(Cl^-)_2 \cdot 2C_2H_5OH$$

calcium chloride-2-ethanol

16.21 ENTROPY AND SOLUTIONS

Our earlier discussion of entropy (p. 334) led to the conclusion that in systems of constant energy the equilibrium position is that of largest entropy. Another conclusion is: In systems of constant entropy the equilibrium position is that of lowest energy.

We have presented earlier (p. 336) an expression, which was treated only qualitatively, for the entropy of a system as it is related to the probability of the existence of a specific state of the system. This expression can be used to consider the molecular interpretations of the entropy of mixing in yielding an ideal-type solution (p. 376). Provided the number of possible arrangements of the molecules that constitute the unmixed and mixed states can be determined, the entropy of mixing can be obtained by using the relation

$$S = k \ln W \quad \text{or} \quad S = k\, 2.303 \log W$$

where k is Boltzmann's constant (p. 332), $\ln W$ is the natural log of W (W is the probability), and $\log W$ is log to the base 10 of W.

If N_A molecules (Avogadro's number) of A and N_B molecules of B are placed in a lattice arrangement to yield one mole of solution $A + B$, there is a specific number of different arrangements of the two kinds of molecules. This huge number indicates a high probability. Since the total number of ways that N objects can be arranged in N lattice sites is $N!$, it is possible to state an expression for W, the probability:

$$W = \frac{N!}{N_A! N_B!}$$

Solutions that behave as predicted by Raoult's law (p. 375) are considered ideal solutions. An ideal solution is different from an ideal gas solution because there must be molecular interactions to yield a liquid. However, if all components in a liquid solution are attracted equally to each other, the solution's behavior warrants the term *ideal solution*. Substances of very similar molecular structure are more likely to mix spontaneously than are those of dissimilar structure because the intermolecular forces are similar. This observation prompts the comment that like dissolves like.

During the theoretical formation of an ideal liquid solution, no volume change occurs and heat is neither absorbed nor evolved. With this fact in mind, we can consider the energetics of mixing by using the thermodynamic relation (p. 390) for systems at constant pressure and temperature.

$$\Delta F = \Delta H - T \, \Delta S$$

In this equation ΔF is the change in free energy (F), ΔH is the change in enthalpy (H), T is in °K, and ΔS is the change in entropy. The expression is one way to define ΔF, or free-energy change, which is a measure of the reversible useful work, in excess of that of expansion, that can be harnessed from a constant-pressure process. ΔH is a measure of the heat absorbed during the process at constant pressure and temperature if the only work is that done against the confining pressure. For processes in most liquids and solids where volume changes are negligible, the *enthalpy* is a measure of the internal energy of the system.

The concept of free-energy change in a constant pressure and temperature process is important because ΔF is a measure of the tendency for the process to proceed spontaneously. If ΔF is 0, the system is in equilibrium (two processes have equal tendencies to proceed). If ΔF is negative $(-)$, the process tends to proceed spontaneously. However, if ΔF is positive $(+)$, the process tends to go spontaneously in the opposite direction, and work must be done to alter its direction. The larger the negative value of ΔF, the greater the tendency for the process to occur spontaneously.

The value of ΔH is positive $(+)$ for all endothermic processes at constant pressure and temperature. That is, during endothermic reactions the internal energy of the system increases, provided pressure and temperature are constant. The value of ΔH is negative $(-)$ for all exothermic processes at constant pressure and temperature because the internal energy of the system decreases.

During the spontaneous mixing of pure liquid A with pure liquid B to yield an ideal solution $A + B$, no heat is absorbed. Hence $\Delta H = 0$ in the expression $\Delta F = \Delta H - T \, \Delta S$. Since the $\Delta H_{mixing} = 0$,

$$\Delta F_{mixing} = - T \, \Delta S_{mixing} \qquad \text{or} \qquad \Delta S_{mixing} = \frac{-\Delta F_{mixing}}{T}$$

This relation reveals that the tendency shown for spontaneous mixing of two components of an ideal solution is the entropy factor; neither the free-energy nor the enthalpy factor is relevant.

Table 16.1 lists the free-energy changes and entropy changes during the formation of one mole of an ideal binary solution. Many pairs of liquids yield such simple, practically ideal solutions. Some of these are: benzene (C_6H_6)—toluene (C_7H_8), carbon tetrachloride (CCl_4)—silicon tetrachloride ($SiCl_4$), and hexane (C_6H_{14})—heptane (C_7H_{16}).

TABLE 16.1 **Formation of 1 mole of an ideal binary solution and the free-energy and entropy changes at 25°C**
$$A + B \rightarrow \text{solution } (A + B)$$

Mole Fractions of A	of B	ΔS of Mixing (cal/deg mole)	ΔF of Mixing (cal/mole)
1.0	0.0	0.0	0
0.8	0.2	0.995	-297
0.6	0.4	1.337	-399
0.5	0.5	1.378	-411
0.4	0.6	1.337	-399
0.2	0.8	0.995	-297
0.0	1.0	0.0	$-\ 0$

Table 16.1 reveals that the maximum value of ΔS is attained when equimolar amounts of A and B are present, or when mixing is complete. The minimum value of ΔF is reached when mixing is complete. Therefore the decrease in free energy (decrease in reversible useful work) is maximum for the process of complete mixing, whereas the increase in entropy (increase in randomness) is maximum for complete mixing.

Let us now reconsider the thermodynamic relation for processes at constant pressure and temperature ($\Delta F = \Delta H - T\,\Delta S$).

We should recall that if dissolution (mixing) is to be spontaneous, ΔF must be negative. It will be helpful to consider what conditions either do or must prevail to yield a free-energy decrease ($-\Delta F$). (Recall that T is always positive.)

a. If $\Delta H = 0$, ΔS must be positive (entropy must increase).

b. If ΔH is positive (dissolution is endothermic), ΔS must be positive.

c. If ΔH is negative (dissolution is exothermic), ΔS may be negative.

d. If $\Delta S = 0$, ΔH must be negative (exothermic dissolution).

e. If ΔS is negative, ΔH must be negative.

f. If ΔS is positive, ΔH may be positive.

If chloroform ($CHCl_3$) is added to acetone (CH_3COCH_3), mixing is spontaneous (ΔF is negative) and a nonideal solution is obtained. Since heat is evolved during mixing, ΔH is negative. Because there is definite interaction (hydrogen-bonding) between the chloroform and acetone molecules, the entropy increase (ΔS) is less than for a more nearly ideal solution. Therefore the decrease in free energy ($-\Delta F$) is greater than that during the formation of an ideal solution.

16.22 OSMOSIS AND OSMOTIC PRESSURE

If dried beans, raisins, dried peas, or red blood cells are placed in pure water, they will swell owing to the passage of water through their outer cell walls. Inside the cell walls are certain solutes, but they cannot permeate the walls. The cell wall is thus a *semipermeable membrane* because water can permeate it, but solute molecules cannot. Water enters the cells in an effort to establish a state of equilibrium—a state in which the vapor pressure of the water inside the cell would be equal to the vapor pressure of pure water. Under ordinary conditions, equilibrium cannot be attained because the cell walls are unable to withstand the hydrostatic pressure that must be reached if equilibrium is to be attained.

The passage of water molecules from pure water through a semipermeable membrane into an aqueous solution is called *osmosis,* a process which occurs when two aqueous solutions of different concentrations are separated by a membrane that permits the passage only of water molecules. The direction of the passage of water is always from the more dilute to the more concentrated solution because the system attempts to attain an equilibrium in which the aqueous vapor pressures of the two solutions are identical. (See Fig. 16.4.)

Osmotic pressure is that pressure which must be applied to maintain the equilibrium flow when a membrane separates two solutions of different concentration. The osmotic pressure of a solution is a colligative property, since it depends on the molality of the solution. If two solutions having the same molality are separated by a semipermeable membrane, there is no osmosis and no osmotic pressure. Such solutions are *isotonic*.

A common laboratory-made semipermeable membrane is prepared by precipitating copper(II) ferrocyanide, $Cu_2Fe(CN)_6$, within the pores of an unglazed porcelain vessel. Since this membrane is mechanically supported, it can withstand pressures at least as high as 250 atm.

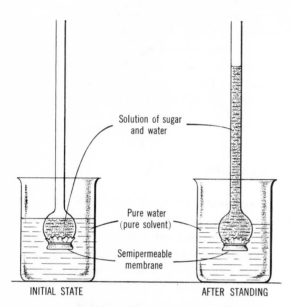

FIGURE 16.4 Diagram of an experiment illustrating the phenomenon of osmosis. The osmotic pressure is that pressure necessary to maintain equilibrium conditions.

16.23 COLLOIDAL SYSTEMS (SUSPENSIONS)

True solutions appear to be completely homogeneous in all known respects. If the solution is unsaturated, the solute under ordinary conditions can be neither precipitated nor settled. In true solutions most of the solute particles are so tiny and far apart that the physical properties of the solution are essentially independent of the character of the solute entities. In this respect a true solution is similar to a gas.

Certain systems that appear to the unaided eye to be clear (optically homogeneous) are systems in which extremely tiny particles are actually suspended in the solvent. If a beam of light is passed through such a solution, the path of the beam is clearly visible because light either is refracted by or reflected from the tiny particles. This phenomenon is the *Tyndall effect*. A solution which exhibits the Tyndall effect is not a true solution because the path of a beam of light is invisible in a true solution (see Fig. 16.5).

About a century ago Thomas Graham (British) named these particles *colloids*. Since colloids are larger than most molecules, we might consider them either as very large molecules or as aggregates of many molecules. The solutions in which these colloids are

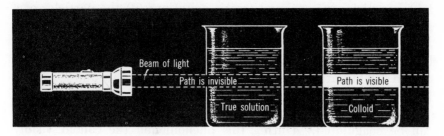

FIGURE 16.5 The Tyndall effect.

suspended are called *colloidal systems*.   All colloidal systems consist of two different phases: the colloidal particles constitute the discontinuous phase; the medium in which the colloid is suspended is the continuous phase.

The relative size of a colloid may be roughly demonstrated by means other than the Tyndall effect.   It is possible to select a membrane through which ordinary tiny molecules can diffuse but through which colloids cannot.   Cellophane and collodion (a cellulose nitrate) are commonly used as membranes.   If an aqueous solution of gelatin and cane sugar is placed in a cellophane bag and the bag submerged in running water, the sugar passes through the membrane into the water, leaving behind the gelatin.   This phenomenon is called *dialysis*.   It is commonly used to remove electrolytes and amino acids from certain solutions of proteins.   Most proteins are colloids; hence they are either relatively huge molecules or aggregates of larger-than-ordinary molecules.   Some proteins have molecular weights over 1,000,000; many have molecular weights in the neighborhood of 68,000.

By using a *Bredig arc*, a colloidal system of gold and water may be produced.   An electric arc is passed (under water) between a gold electrode and a platinum electrode.   The arc rips extremely tiny (colloidal size) particles from the gold.   The colloidal system produced usually has a beautiful color and is clear to the unaided eye.   Over a century ago Michael Faraday prepared such a gold colloid, and today it remains apparently unchanged.   Colloidal gold can also be prepared by adding a very weak reducing agent to a dilute solution of gold chloride.

Under ordinary conditions, colloidal particles are uniformly distributed in the continuous phase of the colloidal system.   There appear to be three main reasons for this behavior: (1) the *Brownian movement* of the molecules in the continuous phase keeps the colloidal particles in continual erratic agitation; (2) the particles of a given colloid have identical electrical charges (either all positive or all negative); (3) most colloidal particles are surrounded by a molecular film of some agent that seems to prevent coagulation of the colloid. This latter phenomenon is called *peptization* and the agent is the peptizing agent.

The dispersed discontinuous phase of some colloidal systems can be coagulated. During this phenomenon the colloid visibly precipitates (settles out). Colloidal hydrous iron(III) oxide (a red colloid) can be coagulated by adding an electrolyte that supplies ions to upset the charge identity of the colloidal particles. If the colloid is negatively charged, an electrolyte that supplies an ion with a strong positive charge is added to the colloidal system. If the colloid is positively charged, an electrolyte supplying a strongly negative ion is chosen. A negative colloid will usually coagulate a positive colloid.

In this section we have mentioned only colloidal systems in which the colloid is practically invisible to the unaided eye. If we should consider all those systems in which the discontinuous phase is visible to the naked eye, we would find many examples but a discussion of these is more physical than chemical. We must keep in mind, however, that since the suspended "solute" in a colloidal system is a separate phase, Henry's and Raoult's laws concerning the behavior of true solutions do not apply to colloidal systems.

PROBLEMS

1. How many grams of K^+Cl^- are needed to prepare 235 ml of a 0.5 F solution?

2. How many grams of $NH_4^+NO_3^-$ are used in the preparation of 130 ml of 0.35 M $NH_4^+NO_3^-$?

3. If 45 ml of water is added to 140 ml of 0.25 M Na^+Cl^-, what is the molarity of the more dilute solution?

4. If 100 ml of water is evaporated from 1000 ml of a 0.12 M solution of sodium chloride, what is the molarity of the more concentrated solution?

5. What volume of water, in milliliters, must be added to 55 ml of 1.5 M ammonium nitrate to decrease the molarity to 0.2 M?

6. What volume of water, in milliliters, must be vaporized in 444 ml of 0.4 M Na^+Cl^- if a 0.88 F solution is desired?

7. Three grams of a nonelectrolyte is added to 15 g of water to yield a solution that freezes at $-0.93°C$. What is the molar weight of the solute?

8. A solution that contains 5.0 g of a nonelectrolyte in 75 g of water boils at $100.26°C$ at 1 atm. What is the molar weight of the solute?

9. An aqueous solution of glycerol, $C_3H_8O_3$, is 77 per cent glycerol (by weight); its density is 1.20 g/ml. Calculate (a) its molarity; (b) its molality; (c) the mole fraction of glycerol in solution; (d) the freezing point of the solution; (e) the boiling point of the solution at 1 atm.

10. Fifteen grams of an organic compound is dissolved in 500 g of benzene. The freezing point of the solution is $0.51°C$ below that of pure benzene. What is the molecular weight of the compound?

11. The solubility of oxygen at 1 atm in water at $18°C$ is 45 mg per liter. How many grams of oxygen at 5 atm dissolve in 200 ml of water at $18°C$?

12. The freezing point of a 0.01 M aqueous solution of covalent compound X is $-0.035°C$, whereas the freezing point of a 0.01 M aqueous solution of covalent compound Y is $-0.0185°C$. Interpret these data.

13. A solution at $25°C$ contains 50 g of potassium bromide in 100 g of water. Is the solution saturated or unsaturated? (See Fig. 16.1.)

14. Approximately how many grams of sodium nitrate are dissolved per 100 g of water in a saturated aqueous solution at $30°C$?

15. What would be observed if a nearly saturated aqueous solution of sodium nitrate were added to a saturated aqueous solution of sodium chloride?

16. What would be observed if a nearly saturated solution of sodium nitrate at $50°C$ were added to a saturated solution of potassium chloride at $50°C$?

17. What would be observed if a nearly saturated solution of potassium nitrate at $40°C$ were added to an unsaturated solution of sodium iodide at $40°C$?

18. At what temperature is the solubility of barium bromide identical to that of sodium nitrate?

19. At $40°C$, which is the more concentrated solution—a saturated solution of sodium chloride or a saturated solution of ammonium chloride?

20. At 20°C, which is the more dilute solution—a saturated solution of potassium nitrate or a saturated solution of potassium chloride?

21. At 30°C, which is the more dilute—a saturated solution of potassium nitrate or a saturated solution of potassium chloride?

22. What is the minimum amount of anhydrous solute, in grams, which should be added to 200 g of water to prepare a saturated solution of potassium iodide at 40°C?

23. What is the minimum amount, in grams, of anhydrous sodium nitrate needed per gram of water to prepare a saturated solution at 10°C?

24. If 260 g of a saturated solution of potassium iodide at 40°C is cooled to 20°C, how many grams of potassium iodide (measured as anhydrous) crystallizes from the solution?

25. What is the mole fraction of solute and of solvent in a saturated aqueous solution of potassium iodide at 40°C?

26. What is the molality of a saturated aqueous solution of potassium iodide at 40°C?

27. Calculate the molarity of the aqueous solution of hydrogen chloride that is called a constant-boiling mixture (azeotrope) on page 382.

28. Solution A is made by dissolving 50 g of sucrose, $C_{12}H_{22}O_{11}$, in 300 g of water. Solution B is made by dissolving 25 g of glucose, $C_6H_{12}O_6$, in 300 g of water. Which solution has the lower osmotic pressure?

29. The standard boiling point of heptane (a saturated hydrocarbon) is 98.5°C, whereas that of decane (also a saturated hydrocarbon) is 174°C. Describe briefly how you would separate the heptane from a 50-50 mixture of the two liquids.

30. Why do dried raisins swell only slightly when in a concentrated aqueous solution of sucrose, whereas they swell appreciably when added to pure water?

31. What is the decrease in free energy $(-\Delta F)$ during the formation of one mole of an ideal binary solution $(A + B)$ in which the mole fraction of A is 0.3?

32. If compound X is added to liquid Y, the mixing process is endothermic and spontaneous to yield a solution $(X + Y)$. (a) During the mixing was there a decrease or an increase in entropy? (b) Is solution $(X + Y)$ an ideal solution?

33. The solubility of caffeine in solvent X at 25°C is twice that in solvent Y at 25°C. What is the distribution constant, K_d, for caffeine in this relationship?

17

17.1 A PERSPECTIVE

Water is the most abundant liquid compound known to man. It is therefore not surprising that it is man's most abundant and most useful solvent. Of course, water is unable to dissolve all compounds, and it is well that it is not, but its solvent abilities are more versatile than those of any other known liquid. Water's solvent ability seems to stem from its molecular structure, and especially from its polar character. Hence we shall stress this aspect when we describe water's physical behavior.

In this chapter we shall discuss briefly some of the physical aspects of aqueous solutions. The chemical aspects of aqueous solutions and water's role therein are discussed elsewhere throughout this text. Before we proceed very far, we should pause to recall that, in a sense, pure water is an aqueous solution because it

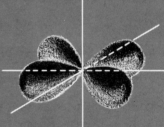

OF AQUEOUS SOLUTIONS

contains oxonium (OH_3^+) ions and hydroxide (OH^-) ions whose concentrations vary with temperature. Because of this fact we cannot avoid a brief discussion of pure water.

17.2 PHYSICAL PROPERTIES OF WATER

The polar character of the water molecule (p. 185) and its tendency to hydrogen-bond seem to be the basis of a logical interpretation of the unusual physical properties of water and ice. All of the physical constants of water have much higher values than do the corresponding constants of most covalent compounds of comparable and even much larger molar weight. This fact is evident if we contrast water with the other covalent compounds that contain hydrogen (p. 189). The extensive hydrogen-bonding between water molecules seems to be the major reason for water's unusual values for its physical constants.

The heats of vaporization and fusion of water and the specific heat of water are, when contrasted with many substances, unusually high. These facts seem to be logically interpreted by assuming that during the absorption of heat by water much energy is expended in disrupting (or overcoming) the intermolecular hydrogen-bonding. (See Fig. 17.1.)

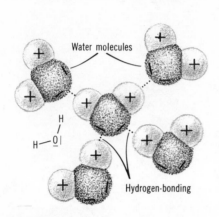

The influence of temperature on the density of water is unusual. If water at room temperature is gradually cooled, its density increases progressively until the temperature reaches 3.98°C; at this temperature the density is 1 g/ml. During further cooling, however, the density gradually decreases until at

FIGURE 17.1 Polar character of water molecules, and the association of water molecules due to hydrogen-bonding, a type of dipole-dipole interaction.

0°C it is approximately 0.92 g/ml. Water has its maximum density (1 g/ml) at 3.98°C. At this temperature the water molecules are oriented, under the influence of hydrogen-bonding, so that the associated molecular aggregate is most compact (most dense). When water at 3.98°C is heated, the kinetic energy of the molecules increases. Consequently, the molecular aggregation becomes less compact as the orientation of the molecules becomes more random. When water at 3.98°C is gradually cooled, the molecules lose kinetic energy and the influence of the intermolecular attractive and repulsive forces increases progressively. These forces induce a reorientation of the molecular aggregate, and a less compact or more "open" molecular association is formed. During the formation of ice, the intermolecular forces—especially the repulsive ones—are extremely significant, since the molecules seem to "elbow" their way into their "assigned" positions. The hexagonal pattern of snowflakes is a manifestation of the underlying "open" hexagonal pattern set up by the water molecules as they orient themselves in the solid state.

17.3   ORDINARY WATER AND DEUTERIUM OXIDE

Since there are two physically different stable hydrogen atoms (protium and deuterium) and three physically different stable oxygen atoms (oxygen-16, oxygen-17, and oxygen-18), there are several physically different water molecules. Actually present in ordinary (natural) water are: $H^{16}OH$, $H^{17}OH$, $H^{18}OH$, $H^{16}OD$, $D^{17}OD$, $D^{18}OD$, $H^{16}OD$, $H^{17}OD$, and $H^{18}OD$.   [The unstable isotope of protium and deuterium, tritium (T), or hydrogen-3, is present in trace amounts in nature.]   Since the ratio of protium to deuterium in ordinary hydrogen and the compounds of hydrogen is about 5000:1, and since 99.81 per cent of natural oxygen is oxygen-16, the most abundant molecule in ordinary water is $H^{16}OH$ (approximate molecular weight of 18 amu).

In the interest of simplicity, we shall assume that in ordinary water protium oxide, $H^{16}OH$, is by far the most abundant molecule, and deuterium oxide, $H^{16}OD$, is the next most abundant. Deuterium oxide is often called "heavy" water because its approximate mass is 20 amu; protium oxide ("light" water) has an approximate mass of 18 amu.   Because of this difference in mass, deuterium oxide has physical properties somewhat different from ordinary water. In Table 17.1 certain common physical constants of natural water are contrasted with those of deuterium oxide.

TABLE 17.1   Physical constants of ordinary water and of deuterium oxide

	Ordinary Water	Deuterium Oxide
Normal boiling point	100.000°C	101.42°C
Melting point	0.000°C	3.82°C
Density (g/ml at 20°C)	0.9982	1.105
Temperature of maximum density	3.98°C	11.6°C
Heat of fusion (cal/mole)	1436	1520
Heat of vaporization (cal/mole)	9710	9970

Protium oxide and deuterium oxide are almost identical chemically, but their chemical reaction rates, under identical conditions, differ.   Fairly pure deuterium oxide is obtained by the continued electrolysis (p. 504) of an ordinary water solution of an ionic hydroxide because at the cathode protium gas, H_2, is produced more rapidly than deuterium gas, D_2. During the prolonged electrolysis the solution at the cathode becomes richer in D_2O.

Since protium atoms are, from a chemical viewpoint, practically identical to deuterium atoms, it is often possible to prepare compounds in which deuterium atoms replace ordinary hydrogen atoms. "Heavy" sodium hydroxide, Na^+OD^-, can be prepared by adding metallic sodium to deuterium oxide; gaseous deuterium is the by-product.

$$2Na + 2DOD \rightarrow 2(Na^+OD^-) + D_2 \uparrow$$

The chemist usually identifies natural (ordinary) water by using the symbol H_2O (or HOH). In this section we have used the conventional symbol, D_2O, to identify deuterium oxide. Hence it is reasonable to suggest that the symbol H_2O implies protium oxide. Since natural water is about 99.9 per cent protium oxide, it will be customary in certain sections of this book to assume that the symbol HOH identifies the covalent molecule in which each H represents a proton attached, by means of a shared pair of electrons, to a oxygen kernel.

17.4 SOLUBILITY OF NONELECTROLYTES IN WATER

If a nonelectrolyte (covalent compound) (p. 368) dissolves readily in water in the absence of any appreciable chemical reaction, the molecules of the covalent compound are attracted to water molecules about as strongly as water molecules are attracted to each other. The molecules of the dissolved substance are, in a sense, able to "break into" the tightly knit association of water molecules. Associated liquids and solids (those with extensive hydrogen-bonding) are generally quite miscible with water.

If the molecules of a nonelectrolyte have little tendency to form hydrogen bonds, the nonelectrolyte is only slightly soluble in water. Compounds such as ethyl ether, benzene, and the hydrocarbons in gasoline, kerosene, and lubricating oils are unable to "break into" the association of water molecules. Hence they do not dissolve readily in water.

It is unnecessary for us to discuss in detail the complex relationships between the structure of a nonelectrolyte and its solubility in water. We should note, however, that the presence of a hydroxyl group, O—H, in the structure of the nonelectrolyte usually greatly enhances its solubility in water. For instance, methane, CH_4, is only slightly soluble in water, whereas methanol, CH_3OH, is completely miscible with water. Hexane, C_6H_{14}, is very slightly soluble in water; yet sorbitol, $C_6H_8(OH)_6$, is quite soluble. (See p. 690.)

Many covalent substances that are very soluble in water are said to be hygroscopic because they absorb water from atmospheric air. Methanol, CH_3OH, ethanol, CH_3CH_2OH, and glycerine, $C_3H_5(OH)_3$, are hygroscopic. All are completely miscible with water. Cane sugar, $C_{12}H_{22}O_{11}$, often "cakes" in humid weather because of its hygroscopic nature. Many water-soluble ionic compounds are hygroscopic.

17.5 SOLUBILITY OF PSEUDOELECTROLYTES IN WATER

Pseudoelectrolytes, as we mentioned earlier (p. 368), are covalent compounds (uncharged molecules) that interact chemically with water to yield ions (charged molecules). Most of these pseudoelectrolytes have been classified already as either acids or bases (pp. 213–528). Since the interactions between water and pseudoelectrolytes are chemical as well as physical, we shall not review them here. Suffice it to say that many covalent compounds dissolve in water partly because they react chemically with water to yield water-soluble products.

17.6 WATER—A SOLVENT FOR ELECTROLYTES

Water is an exceptionally good solvent for many ionic compounds (salts) mainly because water molecules associate rather strongly with most ions, just as they do with certain polar molecules. These associations are called ion-dipole interactions, the water molecules and ions being attracted to each other by electrostatic forces.

Whenever an ionic compound dissolves in water, the initial phenomenon is the disintegration of the orderly arrangement of the ions in the crystalline solid. The solid association of ions dissociates, or collapses; the ions separate from each other and diffuse randomly within the solution. The strong tendency of water molecules to associate with ions is a major factor in the dissociation of the ionic crystal lattice.

Since the separation of oppositely charged particles requires the expenditure of energy, you may wonder why the crystalline structure of an ionic compound disintegrates so easily in water at temperatures far below the melting (fusion) point of the ionic compound. Let us now consider this problem.

According to Coulomb's law, the force between two electric charges x and y is inversely proportional to the square of the distance between them. If we have the electric charges as ions in a medium of uniform properties, the proportionality constant is called the dielectric constant of the medium. The expression for Coulomb's law then becomes

$$\text{force} = \frac{(x)\,(y)}{Dr^2}$$

where x and y are the charged particles, D the dielectric constant of the medium in which the particles are dispersed, and r the distance between the particles. Inspection of the expression reveals that the larger the value for the dielectric, the smaller the force between the charges. Therefore, if we consider electrical effects alone, it will be easier to separate ions in a liquid with a high dielectric constant than in a liquid with a low dielectric constant.

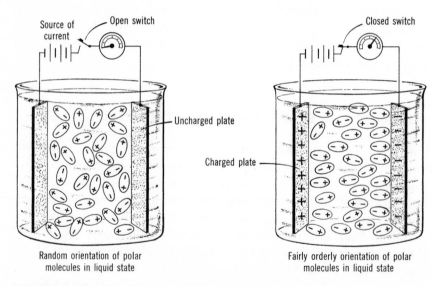

Random orientation of polar molecules in liquid state

Fairly orderly orientation of polar molecules in liquid state

FIGURE 17.2 Orientation of polar molecules between two charged plates (an electrostatic field). Since this effect partially neutralizes the applied field, the liquid is said to have a dielectric constant greater than 1. With water between the plates, one volt of potential energy between the plates will charge the plates to the same extent as will 80 volts with a vacuum between the plates (each at 20°C). Hence water is said to have a dielectric constant of approximately 80 at 20°C.

The dielectric constant of a liquid is a measure of the tendency of the molecules in the liquid to orient themselves between the plates of a condenser (see Fig. 17.2). In the case of most liquids, the greater the polarity of the molecules and the larger the charge separation within the individual molecules, the higher the dielectric constant of the liquid. Since the orientation of the molecules between the plates of the condenser is opposed by the ordinary motion of the molecules, the dielectric constant is dependent on the temperature. The higher the temperature and the more thermal the agitation, the lower the dielectric constant.

The dielectric constant of water at 18°C is approximately 80, which means that the separation of two oppositely charged ions in water is about 80 times easier than in a vacuum. Gasoline, a mixture of hydrocarbons, has a dielectric constant of about 2.1; that of ethanol is about 20.

It seems that a high dielectric constant is a necessary attribute of a good solvent for ionic compounds, but it is by no means the only one. This is evident when we consider the case of liquid hydrogen cyanide, HCN. Although the dielectric constant of HCN is higher than that of water, HCN is a poor solvent for ionic compounds. Apparently the reason for water's distinct ability as a solvent for ionic compounds is its ability to interact physically with ions, to attract and hold the ions by relatively strong electrostatic forces. The physical interactions occur between ions and the polar water molecules, and unless these interactions exist between ions and solvent molecules, few ions will dissolve in the solvent.

The ion-dipole interactions between water molecules and ions is called hydration of the ions; the ions are said to be *hydrated* (see Fig. 17.3). The negative "pole" of the water dipole attracts the positive ions, and the positive "pole" attracts the negative ions. The water molecules that surround the ions tend to enhance the separation of oppositely charged ions by shielding them from each other, thereby inhibiting their reas-

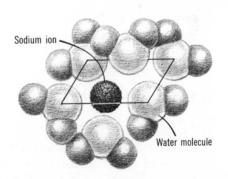

Sodium ion

Water molecule

FIGURE 17.3 Possible three-dimensional arrangement of six water molecules around a sodium ion, forming a hydrated sodium ion.

sociation to form the ionic crystals. If insufficient water is used in dissolving some ionic compounds, so many water molecules are "tied up" in the hydrated ions that there are insufficient unlocalized water molecules to serve as a fluid medium in which the ions can be kept far enough apart to prevent formation of a hydrated ionic crystal. (See Fig. 17.4.)

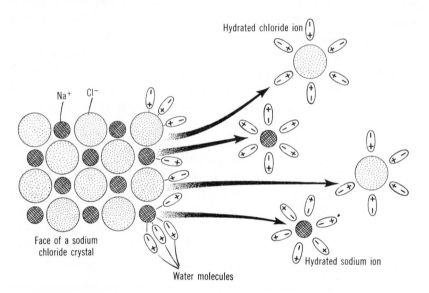

FIGURE 17.4 Dissolution of a crystal of sodium chloride in water. Strong hydration forces exerted on the ions by the water molecules overcome the interionic forces in the crystal lattice.

17.7 IONIC HYDRATES

Some ions are hydrated so strongly that they retain at least part of their water of hydration even after the ionic compound has crystallized from the aqueous solution. If an ionic solid contains water of hydration, it is called a *hydrate*. The ionic compound without water of hydration is said to be *anhydrous*.

For example, anhydrous magnesium sulfate, $Mg^{++}SO_4^{--}$, is quite soluble in water. This compound can crystallize from an aqueous solution to yield a solid of definite composition. Since there are seven moles of water of hydration per mole of magnesium ion in this solid, it is called a *heptahydrate*. Its conventional formula is $MgSO_4 \cdot 7H_2O$. It is possible, under certain conditions, to obtain magnesium sulfate monohydrate, $MgSO_4 \cdot H_2O$. Evidently some ionic compounds have two or more different hydrate compositions.

If anhydrous copper(II) sulfate, $Cu^{++}SO_4^{--}$, a white solid, is dissolved in water at room temperature, a blue solution is obtained. The hydrated copper(II) ions impart a blue color to the solution, whereas hydrated sulfate ions do not impart a color to an aqueous solution. An aqueous solution of copper(II) sulfate yields a blue crystalline solid, copper(II) sulfate pentahydrate, $CuSO_4 \cdot 5H_2O$ (blue vitriol). Copper(II) sulfate monohydrate, $CuSO_4 \cdot H_2O$, is a white solid; the water of hydration is apparently attached to the sulfate ion by hydrogen bonding.

In Table 17.2 are listed a few common anhydrous compounds and some of their hydrates obtained from aqueous solutions.

TABLE 17.2   Common compounds and their hydrates

Anhydrous Compound	Hydrate
Aluminum chloride, $AlCl_3$ (white)	$AlCl_3 \cdot 6H_2O$ (white)
Aluminum sulfate, $Al_2(SO_4)_3$ (white)	$Al_2(SO_4)_3 \cdot 18H_2O$ (white)
Gold(III) chloride, $AuCl_3$ (red)	$AuCl_3 \cdot 2H_2O$ (orange)
Barium hydroxide, $Ba(OH)_2$ (white)	$Ba(OH)_2 \cdot 8H_2O$ (white)
Barium perchlorate, $Ba(ClO_4)_2$ (white)	$Ba(ClO_4) \cdot 3H_2O$ (white)
Chromium(III) chloride, $CrCl_3$ (pink)	$CrCl_3 \cdot 6H_2O$ (violet or green)
Chromium(III) sulfate, $Cr_2(SO_4)_3$ (rose)	$Cr_2(SO_4)_3 \cdot 5H_2O$ (green)
	$Cr_2(SO_4)_3 \cdot 15H_2O$ (violet)
Cobalt(II) chloride, $CoCl_2$ (blue)	$CoCl_2 \cdot 6H_2O$ (red)
Copper(II) chloride, $CuCl_2$ (brown-yellow)	$CuCl_2 \cdot 2H_2O$ (green)
Iron(III) chloride, $FeCl_3$ (black)	$FeCl_3 \cdot 6H_2O$ (red-yellow)
Iron(III) fluoride, FeF_3 (green)	$FeF_3 \cdot 4.5H_2O$ (yellow)
Iron(II) bromide, $FeBr_2$ (green)	$FeBr_2 \cdot 6H_2O$ (red)
Lithium phosphate, Li_3PO_4 (white)	$Li_3PO_4 \cdot 12H_2O$ (white)
Magnesium bromide, $MgBr_2$ (white)	$MgBr_2 \cdot 6H_2O$ (white)
Nickel(II) bromide, $NiBr_2$ (yellow)	$NiBr_2 \cdot 3H_2O$ (green)
Sodium sulfate, Na_2SO_4 (white)	$Na_2SO_4 \cdot 10H_2O$ (white)

Regarding the nomenclature of hydrates, it has been suggested that the term *hydrate* be omitted in the names. By following this suggestion, the name of $MgSO_4 \cdot 7H_2O$ is magnesium sulfate-7-water, and that of $CuSO_4 \cdot 5H_2O$, copper(II) sulfate-5-water.

Because in a subsequent chapter we shall discuss complex ions (p. 579), we shall comment only very briefly here about complex ions that consist, in part, of water molecules.   A certain type of complex ion is produced whenever a positive ion interacts physically with basic entities to yield relatively stable complexes.   The ionic hydrates mentioned in this section are compounds in which the positive ions are surrounded by water molecules which undoubtedly create some sort of complex ion.   Such a complex ion is called an aquo-complex ion, and a typical example is $[Mg(OH_2)_4]^{++}$, which is called tetraquomagnesium ion.

If copper(II) sulfate-5-water is written as $[Cu(OH_2)_4]^{++}$ $SO_4^{--}(H_2O)$, a logical name for the hydrate is tetraquocopper(II) sulfate-1-water.   If $FeCl_3 \cdot 6H_2O$ is written as $[Fe(OH_2)_6]^{3+}(Cl^-)_3$, a pertinent name is hexaquoiron(III) chloride.

17.8   WATER VAPOR PRESSURE OF IONIC HYDRATES

An ionic hydrate is, in a sense, an aqueous crystalline solid composed of ions and water molecules.   In most such solids the water molecules exhibit, at ordinary temperatures, definite escaping tendencies.   Hence these solid hydrates have measurable vapor pressures.   To escape from the hydrate, the water molecules must have sufficient energy to overcome the hydration forces.   If the temperature of an ionic hydrate is increased, the water vapor pressure of the hydrate usually increases.   By simply heating (110°–130°C) some hydrated salts, all the water of hydration can be expelled, leaving the anhydrous salt.   (Some salts decompose on heating; when some others are heated, the water of hydration interacts chemically with the ions.)

If water of hydration escapes from a given ionic hydrate, its composition is changed, resulting in either a hydrate containing less water of hydration or the anhydrous salt.   The water vapor pressure of an ionic hydrate, at a given temperature, is the water vapor pressure of a heterogeneous system in equilibrium involving the hydrate and its initial decomposition product.

A typical equilibrium system in which a trihydrate is the initial decomposition product of a pentahydrate is

$$\Delta + CuSO_4 \cdot 5H_2O(s) \leftrightharpoons CuSO_4 \cdot 3H_2O(s) + 2H_2O(g)$$

As long as the pentahydrate and trihydrate are together at 50°C in a closed vessel, the partial pressure of water vapor is 47 mm.   (This system is a typical heterogeneous equilibrium whose behavior may be predicted by using Le Châtelier's principle.)   At 25°C the water vapor pressure of this hydrate pair is 7.8 mm.

Another typical hydrate system is:

$$\Delta + CuSO_4 \cdot 3H_2O(s) \leftrightarrows CuSO_4 \cdot H_2O(s) + 2H_2O(g)$$

As long as trihydrate and monohydrate are together at 50°C in a closed vessel, the partial pressure of water vapor is 30 mm.   At 25°C the water vapor pressure of this hydrate pair is 4.7 mm.

Another heterogeneous system is

$$\Delta + CuSO_4 \cdot H_2O(s) \leftrightarrows CuSO_4(s) + H_2O(g)$$

As long as monohydrate is present at 50°C in a closed vessel, the partial pressure of water vapor is 4.5 mm; at 25°C this pressure is 0.5 mm.

An ionic hydrate usually absorbs water from the air only if the water vapor pressure of the system composed of that hydrate and its next higher hydration product is less than the partial pressure of water vapor in the air in contact with it.   An anhydrous salt absorbs water from the air if the water vapor pressure of the system composed of the anhydrous salt and its immediate hydration product is less than the partial pressure of the water vapor in the air to which the anhydrous salt is exposed.   An ionic hydrate will lose water to the air if the water vapor pressure of the system composed of that hydrate and its initial decomposition product is greater than the partial pressure of water vapor in the air.   This phenomenon is called *efflorescence*.   If a hydrate loses water to the air, it is efflorescent.

Let us assume that the partial pressure of water vapor is 10 mm in the indoor air of a laboratory.   What is the fate of certain hydrates as they are exposed to this air?

1. If $CuSO_4 \cdot 5H_2O$ is heated to 50°C, it effloresces because its water vapor pressure is much greater than 10 mm.
2. If $CuSO_4 \cdot 3H_2O$ is heated to 50°C, it effloresces.
3. If $CuSO_4 \cdot H_2O$ is heated to 50°C, it does not effloresce.
4. If anhydrous $CuSO_4$ is heated to 50°C, it slowly absorbs water from the air.

At 25°C in this laboratory, the anhydrous salt, the monohydrate, and the trihydrate will all absorb water from the indoor air.

Usually the water vapor pressure of a hydrate increases with an increase in temperature, just as would be expected.   Hence many hydrates can be dehydrated by heating them to expel their water of hydration. If $CaCl_2 \cdot 6H_2O$ is heated to 200°, most of the water of hydration can be expelled to yield essentially anhydrous $CaCl_2$. Barium chloride-2-water, $BaCl_2 \cdot 2H_2O$, loses its water of hydration readily at 160°. Some hydrates do not yield the anhydrous compound when heated because they decompose—usually the water of hydration reacts chemically with at least one of the ions. For example, iron(III) chloride-6-water, $FeCl_3 \cdot 6H_2O$, decomposes on heating to yield mainly iron(III) oxide and hydrogen chloride.

Many anhydrous salts and some hydrates that consist of ions having strong tendencies to hydrate absorb water from moist air. Some, such as calcium chloride and sodium hydroxide, may pick up so much atmospheric water that the solid eventually dissolves in the absorbed water. Such salts are deliquescent; they undergo deliquescence. If a salt picks up atmospheric water but does not absorb enough to yield a solution, the salt is hygroscopic. Among the readily water-soluble ionic compounds, the most soluble tend to be deliquescent, and the less soluble tend to be hygroscopic.

Deliquescent substances are often used as drying agents (desiccants) because of their ability to absorb water. Some salts, usually anhydrous, that are commonly used as desiccants are calcium chloride, magnesium sulfate, potassium carbonate, sodium sulfate, calcium sulfate, and magnesium perchlorate, $Mg(ClO_4)_2$.

17.9 HYDRATION OF IONS

It is difficult to determine exactly the number of water molecules attached to a given cation (positive ion) in an aqueous solution. In many cases it seems that six water molecules per cation may be likely (see Fig. 17.3). The number of molecules of water of hydration retained by a given cation in an ionic crystal is often used as presumptive evidence of the ability of that cation to be hydrated.

The evidence indicates that the size and charge of the ion are the most prominent factors. We shall use the term *charge density* when we contrast different ions as to their size and charge. If two different ions have the same charge but different sizes, the smaller ion has the greater charge density. If two different ions are of similar size but are different in magnitude of charge, the ion with the greater charge has the greater charge density.

Among the alkali metal ions, those of lithium seem to have the strongest tendency to hydrate. This seems reasonable since the lithium ion is the smallest alkali metal ion and thus it has the largest charge density. Potassium ions seem to have a much weaker tendency to hydrate than do calcium ions. This can be interpreted easily since the calcium ion is favored by its doubly positive charge and its size, which is smaller than that of the potassium ion. As might be expected, calcium ions hydrate more readily than barium ions.

17.10   SOLUBILITY OF IONIC COMPOUNDS IN WATER

In regard to the disintegration of the crystal lattice of an ionic compound during its dissolving in water, certain major factors must be identified. The factors related to the crystal are the repulsive forces that enhance the separation of the ions and the attractive forces that deter or resist their separation. The factors related to the solvent water are mainly the attractive forces (hydration-bonding) exerted on the ions by the water molecules. The stability of the crystal lattice depends, of course, on the character of the interionic forces. The relative sizes and charge densities of the ions in the crystal are related intimately to the interionic forces and to the tendencies that the ions have to be attracted to water molecules.

It seems reasonable to assume that, if an ionic compound is fairly soluble in water, the interionic repulsive forces between ions of like charge and the hydration bonding forces between the ions and water molecules overbalance the interionic attractive forces in the crystal lattice.

If an ionic compound is only slightly soluble in water, the interionic attractive forces apparently overbalance the repulsive forces and the hydration forces. It seems that the stability of the crystal lattice greatly influences the solubility of an ionic compound in water. Generally the greater the stability of the crystal, the less soluble the compound. The less stable the ionic lattice, the more soluble the compound.

The distance that separates ions of identical charge influences the stability of the crystal. Usually if ions of like charge reside close together, strong repulsive forces tend to decrease the stability of the crystal, and its solubility in water is increased. In ionic hydroxides, however, the polar hydroxyl ions, although of like charge, tend to be attracted to each other because of hydrogen-bonding. The closer together these ions are, the greater the interionic attraction. Although barium hydroxide is much less soluble than any alkali metal hydroxide, it is at least a thousand times more soluble than beryllium hydroxide. Because the barium ions are larger than the beryllium ions, they separate the hydroxyl ions more effectively. This prevents such extensive hydrogen-bonding as in beryllium hydroxide. As might be expected, cesium hydroxide is more soluble than lithium hydroxide.

The interionic attractive forces are strongest between ions that have relatively high charge densities. Among the alkali metal ions, lithium ion has the highest charge density. Fluoride ion, among the halide ions, has the highest charge density. Compounds of lithium are generally much less soluble than the corresponding compounds

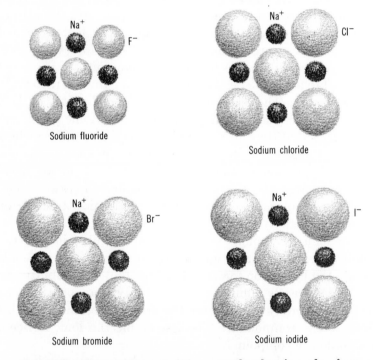

FIGURE 17.5 Sodium halide crystals showing the face-centered cubic arrangement. Iodide ions in sodium iodide are closer together than are fluoride ions in sodium fluoride; therefore iodide ions in sodium iodide are repelled by each other more strongly than are fluoride ions in sodium fluoride. Sodium fluoride therefore has the more stable lattice and is less soluble than sodium iodide.

of cesium because of lithium ion's higher charge density. Many iodides are more soluble than the corresponding fluorides. Lithium fluoride is much less soluble than cesium iodide.

Although ions having relatively high charge densities may tend to increase crystal stability, they are generally more readily hydrated than ions of lower charge density. This greater ease of hydration may at times offset the effect of increased crystal stability, thereby increasing solubility.

In contrasting the solubilities of the various alkali metal halides, it is evident that generally the most soluble compounds are those in which the size of the alkali metal ion differs most widely from that of the halide ion (see Fig. 17.5).

Nearly all ionic nitrates, many ionic sulfates, most ammonium salts, and nearly all ionic acetates are soluble in water. The nitrate ion, NO_3^-, the sulfate ion, SO_4^{--}, the ammonium ion, NH_4^+, and the acetate ion, CH_3COO^-, have relatively low charge densities and have strong tendencies to hydrogen-bond with water molecules.

17.11　GENERAL SOLUBILITIES OF COMMON SALTS

In this section are brief notations about the general water-solubility characteristics of some salts of the common cations Na^+, K^+, Rb^+, Cs^+, NH_4^+, Ag^+, Mg^{++}, Ca^{++}, Sr^{++}, Ba^{++}, Al^{3+}, Cr^{3+}, Fe^{3+}, Mn^{++}, Fe^{++}, Co^{++}, Ni^{++}, Cu^{++}, Zn^{++}, Cd^{++}, Sn^{++}, Hg_2^{++}, Mg^{++}, Pb^{++}.

The generally readily soluble ionic compounds are:

All acetates—they contain acetate ion, CH_3COO^-.

All nitrates—they contain nitrate ion, NO_3^-.

All chlorides, bromides, and iodides except those of silver, mercury(I), and lead. Lead chloride and lead bromide are three to five times more soluble in hot water than at 20°.

All sulfates except those of barium, strontium, and lead.

All alkali metal hydroxides and barium hydroxide. Calcium and strontium hydroxides are somewhat soluble.

All common salts of sodium, potassium, and ammonium.

All alkali metal carbonates, $(M^+)_2CO_3^{--}$, hydrogen carbonates, $M^+HCO_3^-$, phosphates, $(M^+)_3PO_4^{3-}$, hydrogen phosphates, $(M^+)_2HPO_4^{--}$ and $M^+H_2PO_4^-$, and sulfides, $(M^+)_2S^{--}$.

All alkaline-earth metal hydrogen carbonates, $M^{++}(HCO_3^-)_2$.

The generally very slightly soluble salts are:

All metal hydroxides except those of the alkali metals barium, and
ammonium.
All inorganic carbonates and phosphates except those of the alkali
metals and ammonium.
All sulfides except those of the alkali metals and ammonium.
Silver, lead, and mercury(I) chlorides; lead bromide; lead iodide;
and barium, strontium, and lead sulfates.

17.12 PRECIPITATION

The term *precipitation*, as used in chemistry, usually identifies the
process during which a finely divided solid appears in a solution and
gradually settles to the bottom of the vessel.

If 5 ml of 0.001 M silver nitrate, $Ag^+NO_3^-$, is added to 5 ml of
0.001 M sodium chloride, Na^+Cl^-, a precipitate of silver chloride
appears.   We might ask why this precipitate appears in this specific
solution.   The simplest answer is that the precipitate appears in the
solution because insufficient solvent is present to keep the silver
chloride in solution.

Since silver chloride is a very slightly soluble compound, we
expect it to precipitate in solutions of ordinary concentrations.
Because sodium chloride is soluble in water, we might not expect it
to precipitate in a solution.   We must remember, however, that the
conditions for precipitation are only relative to the solubility of the
material that precipitates.   If a clear concentrated solution of
sodium nitrate, $Na^+NO_3^-$, is added to a concentrated solution of
potassium chloride, K^+Cl^-, a precipitate of sodium chloride appears.
The undissolved sodium chloride appears simply because of insufficient water to keep it in solution.

We must keep in mind that the precipitation of an ordinary
compound in aqueous solution is never complete in that some of the
compound remains dissolved in the solvent.   That is, if the coagulated precipitate of silver chloride is separated by filtration from the
suspension, the filtrate contains silver and chloride ions.

17.13 THE SOLUBILITY-PRODUCT CONCEPT

If a 0.1 M solution of silver nitrate, $Ag^+NO_3^-$, is added to a 0.1 M
solution of sodium chloride, a white precipitate (undissolved silver

chloride) appears in the solution.   The sodium and nitrate ions are "spectator" ions.   The net reaction is

$$Ag^+ + Cl^- \leftrightarrows AgCl(s) \downarrow$$

Since the precipitation of silver chloride is reversible, the undissolved silver chloride is in a dynamic equilibrium with the silver and chloride ions in solution.   This system is a saturated solution of silver chloride: silver and chloride ions (in pairs) continually leave the surface of the undissolved solid at the same rate that silver and chloride ions (in pairs) leave the solvent phase and attach themselves to the surface of the undissolved solid.   The rate of dissolution of the solid is equal to the rate of deposition of the solid.

Let us set up the following expression to represent the equilibrium in this saturated solution:

$$K = \frac{[Ag^+][Cl^-]}{[AgCl]}$$

The amount of solid silver chloride per milliliter of solid phase remains practically constant in the saturated solution; hence the factor [AgCl] is combined with the equilibrium constant.

$$K \times [AgCl] = [Ag^+][Cl^-] = K_{sp} \text{ of } AgCl$$

Since the concentration either of silver ions or of chloride ions in a saturated solution of silver chloride (in pure water) is a quantitative measure of the solubility of silver chloride, this modified equilibrium constant, K_{sp}, is called the solubility-product (the ion-product) constant.   The value of this constant is unchanged, at a given temperature, over all ordinary ranges of ionic concentrations.

Before we can determine the magnitude of the solubility-product constant of silver chloride, we must know its solubility. The solubility of silver chloride at 20°C is 1.8×10^{-3} g/l, but we must convert this value to moles/liter because the concentrations of the ions in the expression for the K_{sp} are in moles/1.   The molar weight of AgCl is approximately 143 g; hence:

$$\frac{1.8 \times 10^{-3} \text{ g/l}}{1.43 \times 10^2 \text{ g/mole}} = 1.3 \times 10^{-5} \text{ moles AgCl/l}$$

Since AgCl is completely dissociated in dilute solutions, the silver ion concentration, $[Ag^+]$, is equal to the chloride ion concentration: $[Ag^+] = [Cl^-] = 1.3 \times 10^{-5}$ moles/l.   Then

$$[Ag^+] \times [Cl^-] = K_{sp} \text{ of AgCl}$$
$$(1.3 \times 10^{-5}) \times (1.3 \times 10^{-5}) = 1.7 \times 10^{-10} \text{ (moles}^2/l^2)$$

The various phenomena that may occur in a saturated solution of silver chloride or any other slightly soluble solid may be predicted qualitatively by applying Le Châtelier's principle. The predictions are verified quantitatively by using the solubility-product concept. Let us now consider a few qualitative aspects of a specific system.

If sodium chloride is added to a saturated solution of silver chloride, the chloride ion concentration in the solution is increased, and since the equilibrium is upset, chloride ions (each accompanied by a silver ion) leave the solution and attach themselves to the undissolved solute, thereby increasing the amount of solid silver chloride. If silver nitrate is added to a saturated solution of silver chloride, the amount of undissolved silver chloride increases because silver ions (each accompanied by a chloride ion) leave the solution and attach themselves to the solid phase in an attempt to relieve the stress placed on the equilibrium by the addition of the silver ions. These two phenomena, each producing the same result, are typical examples of the common ion effect. They lead us to an evident conclusion: the solubility of silver chloride in solutions having either relatively high chloride ion concentrations or relatively high silver ion concentrations is less than its solubility in pure water.

Let us now calculate the solubility of silver chloride in a 0.05 M solution of sodium chloride. In this solution the solubility of silver chloride must be based on the silver ion concentration of the solution because only a small portion of the total chloride ion concentration represents dissolved silver chloride (concentration of Cl^- due to dissolved Na^+Cl^- is 0.05 M). Let us assume

$$x = \text{solubility of AgCl in moles/l}$$

Since each molecule of AgCl yields one silver ion and one chloride ion,

concentration of Ag^+ (due to dissolved AgCl) = $[Ag^+] = x$
total concentration of Cl^- (in solution) = $[Cl^-] = (x + 0.05)$

Since the solubility of AgCl is determined in a saturated solution of AgCl,

$$[Ag^+][Cl^-] = 1.7 \times 10^{-10} = K_{sp} \text{ of AgCl}$$
$$(x)(x + 0.05) = 1.7 \times 10^{-10}$$

We know that the value of x must be less than $1.3 \times 10^{-5} M$ (concentration of Ag^+ if AgCl is dissolved in pure water). Since x

is much less than 0.05, let us disregard x in the term $(x + 0.05)$. Then

$$(0.05)(x) = 1.7 \times 10^{-10}$$
$$x = 3.5 \times 10^{-9} = [Ag^+] = \text{solubility of AgCl (moles/l)}$$

Since the solubility of silver chloride in pure water is 1.3×10^{-5} moles/l, the presence of a 0.05 M concentration of chloride ion decreases the solubility approximately 4000-fold.

The solubility-product concept offers reasonably valid quantitative evaluations of phenomena only when the ionic concentrations in the solution are 0.1 M or less.   The effective concentrations of the uncombined ions are very different from their actual concentrations if the ionic concentrations are much above 0.1 M.   We again encounter the problem of interionic forces (Debye-Hückel concept) (see p. 380).

Silver chloride is more soluble in concentrated hydrochloric acid (high concentration of OH_3^+ and Cl^-) than in pure water because in solutions with extremely high chloride ion concentrations the silver ions (and probably the AgCl molecules) combine (act as Lewis acids) with chloride ions to form the silver chloride complex ion, $AgCl_2^-$. Since this complex ion rather effectively "ties up" silver ions, the position of the equilibrium in the saturated solution is shifted in the direction of the dissolution of silver chloride.   Although this effect appears to be contrary to Le Châtelier's principle, it definitely is not. The formation of the silver chloride complex ion sets up a second equilibrium system and the application of Le Châtelier's principle offers a valid interpretation of these two coexistent equilibria.

$$AgCl(s) \leftrightarrows \ Ag^+ \ + \ Cl^- \text{ (the saturated solution)}$$
$$+$$
$$2Cl^-$$
$$\Updownarrow$$
$$AgCl_2^-$$

Below are listed a few comments pertinent to the solubility-product concept.

a. The solubility-product concept applies only to saturated solutions of solid electrolytes and pseudoelectrolytes that are very slightly soluble in water.

b. If in a given solution the product of the concentrations of the ions derived from a slightly soluble solid is less than the solubility product constant, K_{sp}, of that solid, the solution is unsaturated with respect to the solid, and all of the solid is dissolved (no precipitate)

c. Although two oppositely charged ions may be able, under ordinary conditions, to combine in a solution to yield a precipitate, this undissolved solid will not appear if the product of the concentrations of these ions is less than the K_{sp} of the solid. A precipitate forms only if the product of the constituent ions exceeds the K_{sp} of the slightly soluble solid.

d. The published value of the solubility-product constant of a substance is based on the concentrations of the simple, uncombined (hydrated but unhydrolyzed) ions derived from the solid. If one or more different ions derived from the solid are hydrolyzed by water, a dilute solution of the solid contains actually fewer simple ions than would be expected if the effect of hydrolysis were ignored. In the interest of simplicity, elementary treatments of the solubility-product concept often neglect these hydrolysis effects. (Solubility-product constant values are given in Table A-4, p. A-5.)

PROBLEMS

1. For each of the following pairs, predict which compound is the more soluble in water at room temperatures.

(a) CH_3OH, C_2H_4 (e) $(C_2H_5)_2O$, C_4H_{10}

(b) C_2H_5I, C_2H_5OH (f) CH_3CONH_2, CH_3COOCH_3

(c) $(CH_2)_3(OH)_2$, $C_5H_{11}OH$ (g) H_2S, NH_3

(d) CH_3COOH, CH_3COOCH_3

2. Predict which compound has the higher standard boiling point.

(a) C_3H_7OH, C_3H_5Cl (d) CH_3OH, C_2H_4

(b) C_3H_7COOH, $C_3H_7COOCH_3$ (e) C_2H_5I, C_2H_5OH

(c) $C_2H_5CONH_2$, $C_3H_7COOCH_3$

3. Which liquid would you expect to have the smaller specific heat: methyl iodide, CH_3I, or methanol, CH_3OH?

4. How many grams of water are present per mole of manganese(II) sulfate-5-water?

5. A handbook states that the melting point of anhydrous lithium nitrate is 261°C and of lithium nitrate-3-water, 29.9°C. Interpret these facts.

6. State two plausible reasons why you would expect sodium chloride to be much more soluble in water than in hexane, C_6H_{14}.

7. A bottle contains a blue solid, and the label simply bears the name "cobalt(II) chloride." The solid dissolves readily in water to yield a pink solution.   If the solution is concentrated by evaporation of water at room temperature, pink crystals can be separated from the solution.   Gentle heating of the pink solid yields a blue solid.   The blue solid dissolves in water to yield a pink solution.   Briefly interpret these phenomena.

8. Four and one-tenth grams of a hydrate of manganese(II) sulfate, $MnSO_4$, is heated gently to constant weight.   The residue weighs 3.02 g.   (a) What is the formula of the hydrate?   (b) What is the systematic name of the hydrate?   (c) What is the percentage of water of hydration?   (d) What is the molarity of the sulfate ion in a solution prepared by adding 50.0 g of the hydrate to enough water to yield 212 ml of solution?

9. Strontium iodide-6-water is so soluble in water that 456 g of the salt dissolves in 100 g of water at 0°C.   However, 754 g of calcium iodide-6-water also dissolves in 100 g of water at 0°C.   (a) Would you expect barium iodide-6-water to be more soluble than strontium iodide-6-water?   (b) Suggest a plausible reason why the alkali metal iodides are less soluble in water at 0°C than are the alkaline-earth metal iodides mentioned here.

10. Which would you expect to be more deliquescent: cesium hydroxide, sodium hydroxide, or barium hydroxide?

11. Ethanol (grain alcohol), C_2H_5OH, picks up water from ordinary atmospheric air.   Why is it better to say it is hygroscopic rather than to say it is deliquescent?

12. Devise a simple apparatus to determine approximately the water vapor pressure of copper(II) sulfate-1-water at 50°C.

13. For each of the following pairs, predict which ionic compound is more soluble in water at 25°C.
(a) cesium chloride, cesium iodide
(b) rubidium chloride, sodium chloride
(c) lithium hydroxide, rubidium hydroxide
(d) strontium hydroxide, barium hydroxide
(e) cesium carbonate, sodium carbonate
(f) sodium fluoride, sodium iodide
(g) rubidium carbonate, strontium carbonate
(h) calcium nitrate, calcium sulfate
(i) ammonium iodide, lithium fluoride
(j) sodium sulfate, cesium sulfate

14. A student was given a bottle that had not been opened since it was received from the chemical supply house.   On the bottle was a label that identified correctly the name and formula of the solid compound inside. The student dissolved 9.40 g of the solid in enough water to yield 500 ml of a neutral solution X. The only entities in X, other than water and its ions, were lithium ions and iodide ions. The concentration of lithium ions was 0.1 M, identical to that of the iodide ions. What formula and name appeared on the label of the bottle in question?

15. A pure dark-brown binary solid dissolves in water to yield a yellow acidic solution A. A pure yellow solid dissolves in water to yield a solution identical in all respects to solution A. Suggest an explanation.

16. The solubility of calcium carbonate in water at room temperature is 8.3×10^{-4} g per 100 ml of solution. Calculate the solubility-product constant of this compound.

17. The solubility-product constant of barium sulfate is 1.5×10^{-9}. Calculate the solubility of the compound in terms of grams of solute per 100 ml of solution.

18. Which compound is more soluble in water at room temperature: zinc hydroxide or calcium fluoride? (See p. A-5.)

19. Which compound is least soluble in water at room temperature: silver iodide, copper(II) carbonate, or barium sulfate? (See p. A-5.)

20. How many moles of silver bromide will dissolve in 5 l of 0.1 M potassium bromide solution? (See p. 416.)

21. The concentration of barium ion in a solution is 0.01 M. (a) Calculate the minimum concentration of sulfate ion, in moles per liter, necessary to start precipitation of barium sulfate at room temperature. (b) How many moles of barium ion are present in 300 ml of a saturated solution of barium sulfate at room temperature?

22. One liter of a solution contains chloride ions (0.01 M) and bromide ions (0.01 M). Tiny crystals of solid silver nitrate are slowly stirred into the solution. Which precipitates initially, $AgCl$ or $AgBr$?

23. What is observed if solid sodium chloride is added to the clear supernatant liquid of a saturated solution of lead chloride?

24. An aqueous solution has suspended in it a small amount of yellow undissolved cadmium sulfide. The solution is acidic. Gaseous nitrogen is bubbled slowly into the solution, and eventually all of the undissolved solid disappears. Suggest a logical interpretation. (See p. 249.)

25. Why is lead chloride less soluble in a 0.1 M aqueous solution of sodium chloride than in pure water?

18

PHYSICAL ASPECTS

18.1 A PERSPECTIVE

In Chapter 4 we mentioned the fact that a specific chemical equation simply identifies the participants (reactants and products) of the chemical reaction. If our knowledge of a reaction is confined solely to the equation that represents it, we really know little about the reaction. We may think of the participants only as specific kinds of matter, but in most reactions heat is either a reactant or a product. Occasionally light is a participant. Since the chemical equation itself indicates neither the rate nor the yield of the reaction, a useful description of a given reaction may require many words to accompany the equation. Long hours of careful experimentation may be necessary to determine the proper conditions under which the reaction is economically feasible.

In this chapter we shall discuss some of the impor-

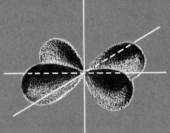

OF CHEMICAL REACTIONS

tant factors that affect the rates and yields of chemical reactions. We shall also introduce the concept of the activated state, and we shall consider the reasons why chemical reactions occur and the roles played by free energy, enthalpy, and entropy.

18.2 Reaction Rate

The velocity of a chemical reaction is often called the *reaction rate*. To formulate a suitable definition of this term, let us assume that the reaction involves at least two reactants and two products. The velocity or reaction rate is then defined as the number of moles of one of the reactants, per unit of volume occupied by the reactant system, which react or disappear per unit of time. Another definition is: The reaction rate is the number of moles of one of the products, per unit of volume of the product system, which are produced or appear per unit of time. It should be noted that the concept of volume is an important factor in these definitions. In molecular reactions the density of the molecular population (number of molecules per unit of volume) is extremely significant.

18.3 EFFECT OF THE CHARACTER OF REACTANTS ON REACTION RATES

The effect of the character of the reactants on the rate of a reaction can be demonstrated easily by simply burning some combustible materials. Dry wood, for instance, burns much more rapidly than either wet or freshly cut wood. Wood shavings and excelsior burn more rapidly than large sticks of wood. Powdered magnesium burns rapidly in air, whereas a piece of magnesium ribbon burns slowly. The particle size of solid materials usually has a marked effect on reaction rate.

The inherent chemical character of the reactants may affect the rate of a reaction. Powdered magnesium burns rapidly in air, but powdered copper, instead of burning, is slowly converted to oxide. When magnesium ribbon burns in air, the products are magnesium oxide and magnesium nitride. Although at least 75 per cent of the air is nitrogen, the oxygen converts most of the magnesium to the oxide.

18.4 EFFECT OF TEMPERATURE ON REACTION RATES

Heat (thermal energy) plays an exceedingly important role in the regulation of the rates of many chemical reactions. In the laboratory it is common practice to accelerate some slow reactions by using heat. In many homogeneous reaction systems, an increase in temperature of 10°C may cause the reaction rate to be doubled or even tripled. Reaction rates may often be greatly decreased by lowering the temperature of the system. In this respect the preservation of food by refrigeration is one of the most universal applications of temperature control to decrease the rate of chemical changes.

If the temperature of a reaction system is increased, the reactants gain energy. If these reactants are gaseous molecules, their rate of motion is obviously increased, so that there are more molecular collisions per unit of time. Since two different reactant molecules must either collide or come close together to interact chemically, the greater the number of collisions, the greater the velocity of the reaction. However, if the temperature of a gaseous system is increased 10°C, the average kinetic energy of the molecules is never doubled; hence the total number of molecular collisions is not doubled. Yet we know that often the reaction rate is doubled. To interpret the effect of temperature on a homogeneous gaseous reaction system, it is conventional to assume that only relatively few molecular collisions result in the formation of reaction product.

18.5   ENERGY OF ACTIVATION AND THE ACTIVATED STATE (COMPLEX)

It has been suggested that if two molecules are to interact chemically, they must be in an activated state. If two different molecules have obtained sufficient energy to be in this activated complex, then a collision of these molecules would presumably result in a chemical transformation. Only an effective molecular collision, or a collision of activated molecules, results in the formation of product.

For a given reaction system, the minimum energy which molecules must have to be in the activated state is called the *energy of activation*, or the *activation energy*. In many reaction systems at room temperature, the value of this activation energy is much greater than the average energy of the molecules. In certain cases some molecules do have energies greater than the average kinetic energy, and it is quite probable that many of these molecules have an energy equal to the activation energy. If a reaction rate is measurable, at room temperature, we can assume that a certain number of molecules have the requisite activation energy because effective collisions are occurring. Now let us suppose that the temperature of such a reaction system is increased. Then more molecules obtain sufficient energy to be activated; there is an increased number of effective collisions per unit of time; the reaction rate increases. What happens if the temperature is decreased? Fewer molecules are able to reach the activated state; there is a decreased number of effective collisions; the reaction rate decreases. In a sense, the velocity of a molecular chemical reaction is an indication of the number of molecules that become activated per unit of time.

The combustion of wood, coal, or paper in air does not commence until the materials are heated, or kindled. Since these combustions are exothermic reactions, they continue, after the kindling temperature is reached, without further absorption of energy from the surroundings. The initial heating or kindling supplies energy to activate a certain number of molecules, and these react with oxygen. One of the reaction products is heat, and some of this energy is absorbed by a certain number of unreacted molecules. Some of these molecules become activated, and then they exothermally react with oxygen. This process is repeated over and over until combustion occurs. During the actual combustion, the evolved heat continually activates unreacted molecules. To maintain the optimum rate of combustion, the combustible material

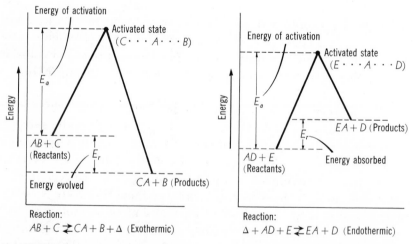

FIGURE 18.1 Relationships between the reactant and product systems and the activated state, for exothermic and endothermic reactions.

should be arranged so that adequate heat exchange is possible between the burning material and the unburned material, because the rate of activation is a limiting factor. The supply of oxygen to the activated molecules is the other limiting factor.

The general idea of the activated state is shown in Fig. 18.1.

18.6 SPONTANEOUS COMBUSTION

The spontaneous combustion of some materials in contact with air is a familiar phenomenon during which an exothermic reaction proceeds at a progressively increasing rate until the number of molecules being activated per unit of time is sufficient to cause the material to burst into flames. In such a system, the heat initially evolved during the interactions of a very few molecules is absorbed by unactivated molecules, so that they become activated. When they react, more heat is evolved. This process is continually repeated until combustion occurs. This phenomenon is a sort of thermal chain reaction.

A striking example of spontaneous combustion may be demonstrated by placing a fairly dry piece of white phosphorus, at room temperature, in contact with air.

Spontaneous combustion may not occur if, during the initial successive reactions, most of the evolved heat is dissipated to the surroundings, rather than to molecules of the combustible substance. In such a circumstance, relatively few molecules are activated per unit of time, and this rate of activation does not increase progressively.

18.7 EFFECT OF CONCENTRATION
ON REACTION RATES

We know that materials such as wood, paper, and coal burn much more rapidly if the supply of air is increased by fanning the flames. If a wad of steel wool is heated in the flame of a Bunsen burner, the oxidation (by oxygen) of the iron proceeds rather slowly. However, if the glowing wad of steel wool is placed in pure gaseous oxygen, the iron is very rapidly oxidized. In a sample of pure oxygen, the number of oxygen molecules per unit volume is much greater than in air (20 per cent oxygen); the increased rate of reaction is due to the larger number of oxygen molecules per unit volume.

If the temperature and volume of a reaction system remain constant and if pure reactants are involved, the velocity of a simple reaction is primarily dependent on the concentration of the reactants. Within a given phase (gas, liquid, or solid) the concentration of a substance is the amount of the substance in a unit of volume of that phase.   Concentration is usually expressed either in moles per liter or in millimoles per milliliter.   This pattern is useful, in the case of covalent compounds, because a given number of moles contains a definite number of molecules.

18.8   THE LAW OF MASS ACTION

In 1865 Cato Guldberg and Peter Waage (Norwegian) suggested a relationship between the driving force of a reaction and the masses of the reactants.   Their Law of Mass Action is: At constant temperature, the driving force of a reaction is directly proportional to the product of the masses of the reactants each raised to some definite power.   They also stated that if the reaction volume is changed, the effect of the mass is inversely proportional to the volume.   For simple one-step reactions their original ideas can often be expanded to imply the effect of the concentration of a reactant on the reaction rate.

Let us now illustrate an idealized application of the mass action generalization by using the reaction of hydrogen with iodine vapor. Although this is reversible, we shall for the moment focus our attention on the reaction during which hydrogen iodide is produced.

$$H_2(g) + I_2(g) \rightarrow 2HI(g)$$

At a given temperature, all molecules have equal opportunity to be activated.   Hence the rate of this reaction is dependent on the number of collisions per second between hydrogen molecules and iodine molecules.   Since the number of effective collisions per second increases directly with the total number of collisions per second, it is possible to increase the rate of reaction by increasing the total number of collisions per second.   Therefore the rate of reaction may be increased by increasing the number of hydrogen molecules and/or by increasing the number of iodine molecules.   If the number of hydrogen molecules is doubled, the reaction rate is doubled because then there are twice as many chances for an iodine molecule to encounter a hydrogen molecule.   If both the number of hydrogen molecules and the number of iodine molecules are doubled, there are four times as many chances for collisions.   The number of molecular collisions in the reaction system may be increased either by adding more molecules or by decreasing the volume of the reaction system. In each case the number of molecules per unit of volume is increased.

Since the reaction rate depends on the number of molecules per unit of volume, we need some way to identify or represent the density of the molecular population of each reacting substance. This is accomplished by using the concept of concentration, in which the concentration of a substance expresses the number of moles of the substance per unit of volume, usually in moles/liter.

Not all collisions of hydrogen and iodine molecules are effective, so the rate of reaction is not equal to the product of the concentration of hydrogen times the concentration of iodine. Instead it is proportional to the product of these concentrations. The algebraic expression of the rate equation for the reaction, $H_2 + I_2 \rightarrow 2HI$, at a given temperature is

$$r = k[H_2][I_2]$$

where r is the rate of reaction; $[H_2]$ the concentration of hydrogen in moles/l; $[I_2]$ the concentration of iodine in moles/l. (The use of brackets around the symbol of a reactant is a conventional means of representing "concentration of" that entity.)

The symbol k represents a proportionality factor. Its value usually remains constant for a given reaction at constant temperature. This proportionality constant is called the rate constant of the reaction, but its value varies directly with the temperature. The value of the rate constant is an indication of the degree of activation of the reactants.

The rates of some reactions and the expressions of their rate equations cannot be determined so readily as that for the combination of hydrogen and iodine to yield hydrogen iodide. It is frequently necessary to investigate the behavior of the reaction under different conditions in order to find the correct rate equation, a process called *chemical kinetics*.

Let us consider two examples, the first being the oxidation of hydrogen iodide by hydrogen peroxide,

$$H_2O_2 + 2HI \rightarrow 2H_2O + I_2$$

which has a rate equation quite different from the one that might be expected. The experimentally verified rate equation is

$$r = k[H_2O_2][HI]$$

According to the idealized mass action concept, we might expect the rate to be proportional to the product of the concentration of H_2O_2 times the square of the concentration of HI: $r = k[H_2O_2][HI][HI]$.

The air oxidation of iron(II) ion has the equation

$$4Fe^{++} + O_2 + 4H^+ \rightarrow 4Fe^{3+} + 2HOH$$

The mass action concept might lead us to expect that the rate of disappearance of Fe^{++} increases with increasing concentration of active H^+. Actually the rate decreases with increasing concentration of a source of H^+.

The mass action concept seems to hold for many simple one-step reactions in which the reactants directly yield the products. If a reaction proceeds in two or more steps from reactant system to product system, the mass action concept rarely applies.

An appreciable number of chemical reactions have rates that, at a specific temperature and volume, are proportional to the concentrations of either one, two, or perhaps three reactants. In each rate expression of such a reaction, the concentration of one or more reactants is raised to some small integral power. Let us consider the substances A, B, and C as possible reactants in chemical reactions. The chemical reactions that fit the category we have just mentioned can be classified in terms of what is called an *order*. These types, or classes, of reactions will now be considered in turn.

A reaction is first-order if the rate expression has only one concentration term, such as

$$rate = k[A]$$
(a first-order reaction)

A reaction is second-order if the rate expression has two concentration terms, such as

$$rate = k[A]^2 \quad or \quad rate = k[A][B]$$
(a second-order reaction)

A reaction is third-order if the rate expression has three concentration terms, such as

$$rate = k[A]^3 \quad or \quad rate = k[A]^2[B] \quad or \quad rate = k[A][B][C]$$
(a third-order reaction)

Many reactions do not have such simple rate expressions because they have nonintegral powers such as $rate = k[A]^{1/2}$ or $rate = k[A]^{2/3}$. Others have more elaborate and complex algebraic relations.

The units of the rate constants (k) for first-order reactions are units of the reciprocal of time (sec^{-1} or min^{-1}) independent of the concentration units. Second-order rate constants, however, have units such as liters per mole second or $(moles/l)^{-1}sec^{-1}$.

18.9   DEVIATIONS FROM THE LAW OF MASS ACTION

The quantitative generalization concerning reaction rates is only an approximate law. Thus its character is similar to the generalizations of Boyle and Charles. In a specific reaction at constant temperature, if the concentrations of the reacting entities are relatively large, the rate constant, k, may vary with the concentrations of the reactants. If the molecular population is dense, physical interactions between the reactants apparently inhibit free and random collisions. In a sense, the Law of Mass Action is a theoretical expression involving the following assumptions: The reacting entities exert neither repulsive nor attractive forces on each other; the reacting entities are infinitely small; the reacting entities move randomly so that collisions occur simply by chance and the reactants lead directly to the products.

In the case of gaseous reactions at high pressures, and for reactions in concentrated solutions, the rate equation as derived by using the Law of Mass Action is an inadequate expression. For gaseous reaction systems at low pressures, and for very dilute solutions, especially of nonelectrolytes, the mass action equation for the reaction rate is often compatible with experimental data. In other words, the rate constant is essentially constant at a constant temperature.

In certain one-step reaction systems for which the Law of Mass Action predicts an erroneous rate equation, it is possible to derive a correct one by assigning an activity or corrected concentration to each reacting entity. The activity of a reactant is obtained by multiplying the actual concentration of the reactant by an activity coefficient. This activity coefficient is a sort of correction factor, but since it often changes with the concentration of the reactants and with the temperature, it must be determined experimentally.

A simplified statement of the revised Law of Mass Action is: The rate of a chemical reaction is proportional to the arithmetical product of the activities (effective concentrations) of one or more entities; the value of the activity of each entity that appears in the rate equation is raised to a power usually deduced from an investigation of the kinetics of the reaction.

18.10 THE ARRHENIUS CONCEPT

We have mentioned earlier (p. 429) that the rate constant of a reaction varies with the temperature. In 1889 Arrhenius observed that the rate constant increases exponentially with the temperature. In other words, a plot of log k versus $1/T$ yields a linear relationship.

If it is assumed that the activated state (complex) has an energy (E_a) greater than the reactants, the number of molecules in the activated complex compared to the total number of reactant molecules is derived by using the Boltzmann distribution law (p. 332).

$$\frac{\text{Number of activated-complex molecules}}{\text{Total number of reactant molecules}} = e^{-E_a/RT}$$

or

$$\text{Fraction of molecules in activated complex} = e^{-E_a/RT}$$

Since the Arrhenius concept states that the rate of a reaction is proportional to the number (or concentration) of molecules in the activated complex, we can use A as a proportionality constant and derive a Boltzmann expression (p. 332) for the rate constant.

$$k = Ae^{-E_a/RT}$$

This relation indicates the distribution, in a given system, of the molecules that have an energy equal to E_a, the energy of activation (energy needed to yield the activated complex).

Inspection of the logarithmic form of the Boltzmann relation reveals the reason why a plot of log k vs $1/T$ is linear.

$$\log k = -\frac{E_a}{2.303R}\frac{1}{T} + \frac{A}{2.303}$$

18.11 EFFECT OF CATALYSTS ON REACTION RATES

There are many instances in which it is possible to increase the rate of a chemical reaction without increasing either the temperature or the concentration of the reacting substances. Such reactions are accelerated by material entities called *catalysts*. During some of these reactions the catalyst appears to be essentially unchanged. In most cases a relatively small quantity of catalyst greatly increases the rate of the reaction.

A catalyst is often called a *catalytic agent*.   The phenomenon of its action is termed *catalysis*.   During most, if not all, catalyses, the catalyst undergoes some degree of chemical and/or physical change. A catalyst never initiates (starts) a reaction, but instead it simply accelerates a reaction already in progress.

For a given reaction system at a given temperature, the rate of the catalyzed reaction is greater than the rate of the uncatalyzed reaction.   Since the rate of a chemical reaction depends primarily on the number of reacting entities in the activated state, per unit of time, it seems logical to conclude that the catalyst lowers the activation energy of the reactants.   In the presence of the catalyst, the molecules need to absorb less energy to get to the activated state.   Hence more molecules are able to be in the activated state in the presence of the catalyst than without it.   Catalytic effect is shown in Fig. 18.2.

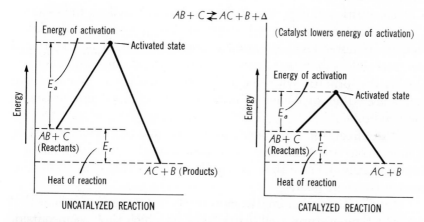

FIGURE 18.2   Effect of a catalyst in lowering the energy of activation in a catalyzed reaction.

When a covalent entity undergoes a chemical change, one or more covalent bonds are usually "broken."   Certain atomic kernels must be separated from each other.   Since the covalent entity is held together by covalent bonds or intramolecular forces, it is necessary to overcome these forces if structural changes are to occur. Since a catalyst increases the rate at which these structural changes occur, it seems likely that the catalyst assists in overcoming the intramolecular forces.   In many molecular reactions the catalyst interacts with a covalent entity so that certain covalent bonds are either weakened or broken by a deformation of the molecule. In certain reactions the catalyst reacts with some entity to produce an unstable intermediate.

18.12 HOMOGENEOUS CATALYSIS

A homogeneous catalysis is a system in which the catalyst is in the same phase as the reacting substances. In gaseous phase reactions the catalyst is a gas; in liquid phase reactions it is dissolved in the reaction medium.

During many homogeneous catalyses, the catalyst appears to interact with at least one of the reacting entities to form an intermediate. A rapid dissociation or interaction of this intermediate yields the reaction product and the catalyst. Since the catalyst reappears as product is formed, it can assist in the formation of many product entities. This role of the catalyst is based on the assumption that the formation and eventual disappearance of the intermediate requires less activation energy than would be required if the reacting substances were directly transformed to product. During the formation of the reaction intermediate, certain covalent bonds are either weakened or broken as the catalyst interacts with the reactants.

The effects of some acids and bases on the rates of certain homogeneous reactions are quite pronounced. In many cases it appears fairly definite that the catalyst's main role is in weakening certain covalent bonds.

In all plant and animal organisms there are many reactions that occur at temperatures well below those at which they occur outside the living organism. Many of these reactions are catalyzed by organic substances called enzymes. Most, if not all, enzymes are proteins that contain or are attached to a unique molecular grouping responsible for the catalytic character. Proteins are large molecular aggregates constructed with amino acids in living organisms. All amino acids contain the elements carbon, hydrogen, oxygen, and nitrogen; a few also contain sulfur. There is much evidence that some vitamins combine with some proteins to form enzymes.

The *in vivo* (in a living organism) oxidation of glucose, $C_6H_{12}O_6$, to carbon dioxide and water occurs in several different steps or reactions. Each is apparently catalyzed by an enzyme. In the absence of an enzyme, the *in vitro* (in a glass vessel) oxidation of glucose occurs only at relatively high temperatures.   The enzymatic oxidation of glucose can occur fairly rapidly at 37°C (the temperature of the human body), but in the uncatalyzed oxidation, the glucose must be heated well above 37°C to supply the necessary energy of activation.

There are many different enzyme systems in the human body. These enzyme catalysts play a vital role in the metabolism of food from which we gain energy.   The conversion of starch (a very large molecule) to maltose, $C_{12}H_{22}O_{11}$, is catalyzed by ptyalin, an enzyme in saliva.   In the stomach, an enzyme, pepsin, catalyzes the primary reaction in the over-all digestion of proteins.

18.13   HETEROGENEOUS CATALYSIS

In heterogeneous catalysis the catalyst and the reacting substances exist in separate phases.   Since this type of catalysis appears to occur at the point of contact of the two phases, the catalytic agent is often called a contact catalyst.   The reactants appear to be adsorbed on the surface of the catalyst, whereby the density of the molecular population increases greatly, causing an increase in reaction rate.   In certain molecular reactions, adsorption of the reactants at the catalytic surface seems to deform the molecules, thereby weakening certain covalent bonds.

The contact process for the commercial production of sulfur trioxide, SO_3, is a catalysis in which the reactants, sulfur dioxide and oxygen (an excess of air), are passed over a contact catalyst (either vanadium pentoxide, V_2O_5, or finely divided platinum) at a temperature between 400° and 500°C ($2SO_2 + O_2 \leftrightarrows 2SO_3$).   If platinum is the catalyst, the sulfur dioxide must be carefully purified because certain impurities, especially compounds of arsenic, adsorb strongly on the catalytic surface.   This greatly decreases the efficacy of the catalyst.   This type of inactivation of a contact catalyst is often called poisoning of the catalyst.   The industrial application is illustrated in Fig. 11.3, page 272.

The laboratory preparation of elemental oxygen by the pyrolysis of potassium chlorate, $K^+ClO_3^-$, is a familiar example of heterogeneous catalysis.

$$2[K^+ClO_3^-] + \Delta \rightarrow 2[K^+Cl^-] + 3O_2$$

The catalyst used in this thermal decomposition is manganese dioxide, MnO_2.   It appears that an interaction between the catalyst and the chlorate ions, ClO_3^-, weakens certain covalent bonds. At the melting point of potassium chlorate (357°C), the pyrolysis is impractical without a catalyst because the rate of production of oxygen is very slow. At 357°C in the presence of manganese dioxide, the rate of pyrolysis is greatly increased.

The behavior of platinum as a contact catalyst may be easily demonstrated by hanging a small hot platinum gauze within the gaseous phase above a concentrated aqueous solution of ammonia. This gaseous phase contains a relatively high concentration of ammonia molecules and oxygen molecules (in the air). When the hot platinum is placed in the gaseous phase, it catalyzes the oxidation of ammonia by oxygen. Since this oxidation is exothermic and the reaction occurs on the surface of the platinum, the metal glows brightly so long as the correct proportions of reactants are present. The main reaction is

$$4NH_3 + 5O_2 \leftrightarrows 4NO + 6HOH + \Delta$$

nitrogen
monoxide

Many different substances are used as catalysts. It is interesting to note that a large number of these are either transition elements in their elemental state or compounds containing a transition element. The valence-electron configurations of the transition elements seem to be peculiarly adapted for catalytic activity.

18.14 INHIBITORS

Certain substances called *inhibitors* markedly decrease the rates of certain reactions. A detailed discussion of the actual behavior of an inhibitor is beyond the scope of this book, but in many cases an inhibitor seems to play an important role in retarding chain reactions by interacting with the chain propagators (see Sec. 18.15).

A few examples of the use of inhibitors may be noted. Sodium diacetate and calcium propionate are added to bread and rolls to retard molding. Acetanilide is added to 3 per cent (aqueous) hydrogen peroxide to inhibit its decomposition. Complex organic compounds are added to rubber to inhibit oxidation (by oxygen). Certain organic substances are added to fats and oils to inhibit oxidation and rancidity.

18.15 CHAIN REACTIONS

Under appropriate conditions, some gaseous phase reactions occur at an explosive rate; many of them are chain reactions. As an example of a typical chain reaction, let us discuss the reaction between gaseous hydrogen and gaseous chlorine, during which the dissociation of one molecule of chlorine initiates a series of subsequent reactions that produce hundreds of product molecules.

If hydrogen and chlorine are mixed in equimolar amounts at room temperature away from a source of blue light, no observable reaction occurs. However, if this gaseous mixture is heated to above 250°C, the chlorine and hydrogen react with explosive rapidity. The over-all reaction is

$$H_2 + Cl_2 \rightarrow 2HCl + \Delta$$

The proposed steps in this chain reaction are noted below. In the first step the chain initiators, activated chlorine atoms, are formed. These chlorine atoms result from the thermal dissociation (homolytic fission) of chlorine molecules.

(1) $|\overline{Cl}:\overline{Cl}| + \Delta \rightarrow 2|\overline{Cl}\cdot$ (endothermic)

(2) $|\overline{Cl}\cdot + H:H \rightarrow H:\overline{Cl}| + H\cdot$ (exothermic)

(3) $H\cdot + |\overline{Cl}:\overline{Cl}| \rightarrow H—\overline{Cl}| + |\overline{Cl}\cdot$ (exothermic)

Since the activation energy of reaction 2 is relatively low, it occurs more readily than the reaction between two chlorine atoms to form a chlorine molecule. The activation energy of reaction 3 is less than that of reaction 2; thus collisions of hydrogen atoms with chlorine molecules are very effective. Reaction 1 is the chain initiation process; reactions 2 and 3 are the chain propagation processes. The chain of events indicated by reactions 2 and 3 continues at a progressively faster and faster rate until an explosive rate is reached.

There is experimental evidence to substantiate the idea that one chlorine atom can initiate the production of hundreds of hydrogen chloride molecules. If metallic sodium is added to a mixture of hydrogen and chlorine, chlorine atoms are produced by the reaction.

$$Na\cdot + |\overline{Cl}:\overline{Cl}| \rightarrow Na^+ + |\overline{Cl}|^- + |\overline{Cl}\cdot$$

M. Polanyi found that each sodium atom initiates a chain reaction formation of approximately 100,000 hydrogen chloride molecules.

There are many known chain reactions and much experimentation is in progress. The combustion of hydrocarbon fuels in common internal combustion engines may produce the phenomenon known as "knocking." This is an explosive combustion, a sort of chain reaction. Tetraethyl lead, $Pb(C_2H_5)_4$, inhibits knocking by decreasing the effectiveness of the chain propagators, thereby decreasing the rate of combustion of the hydrocarbons.

18.16 DETONATION

If a thermal reaction, usually a decomposition of either a solid or a liquid, proceeds at a faster and faster rate until a shock wave moves at maximum speed in the substance, the reaction occurs so rapidly that it appears to be instantaneous. This phenomenon is usually called a *detonation*. It is extremely difficult to determine the actual rate and mechanism of such a rapid process because the shock wave may move through the substance at velocities as high as 20,000 ft/sec, and there are pronounced changes of pressure and temperature.

Prior to the detonation of a substance, each successive exothermic process increases the temperature of the remaining mass. Hence more and more of the substance is activated and eventually detonation occurs. Detonation will occur only if sufficient material is tightly packed or piled so that too much heat is not dissipated to the surroundings. Under a specific set of conditions there appears to be a minimum quantity of material, the critical mass, necessary for detonation. The size of this critical mass depends on the material in question, the rate of thermal decomposition, and the amount of heat evolved during the decomposition. (The critical mass of nitrogen triiodide, for example, is less than 1 g, whereas the critical mass of certain military explosives may be as high as 300 to 400 g.)

Since the detonation of ammonium nitrate has received much attention, let us describe briefly the thermal decomposition of this substance. Spontaneous heating of ammonium nitrate occurs if the mass is sufficiently large. If its temperature reaches approximately 450°C, detonation occurs. Detonation will also occur if a large mass of ammonium nitrate is heated under conditions such that the temperature of the solid reaches 450°C.

Ammonium nitrate melts at 170°C. At this temperature it commences to decompose as follows:

$$NH_4^+NO_3^- \rightarrow 2HOH + \underset{\substack{\text{dinitrogen} \\ \text{monoxide}}}{N_2O} + \Delta$$

This process is exothermic (13.21 kcal/mole) at 170°C.

At 270°C the thermal dissociation-sublimation of ammonium nitrate occurs:

$$\Delta + NH_4^+NO_3^- \leftrightarrows NH_3 + HNO_3$$

This process is endothermic (38 kcal/mole) at 270°C.

If a small sample of ammonium nitrate is heated at atmospheric pressure, the temperature of the solid cannot exceed 300°C since the endothermic dissociation absorbs the added heat. If ventilation is adequate, large amounts of the solid may be heated without danger of detonation. But if the solid mass is so large and dense that the ammonia and nitric acid cannot escape readily, the pressure rises. If the temperature of the solid eventually reaches 450°C, detonation occurs.

On April 16, 1947, in Texas City, Texas, two tremendous detonations of FGAN (Fertilizer Grade Ammonium Nitrate) occurred. The FGAN (solid particles coated with wax and packed in paper sacks) was being loaded into two freighters when fire broke out in one of them. Ventilation was poor in the hold of the freighter and the sacks were compactly piled. The temperature of the 2000 tons of FGAN progressively increased; ultimately detonation occurred. About 16 hours later a second detonation of 1000 tons of FGAN occurred. During the Texas City disaster 576 persons were killed, at least 3000 persons were injured, and 100 million dollars worth of property was destroyed or damaged.

The detonation of a large mass of ammonium nitrate may be produced by a shock wave initiated by a percussion. This apparently occurred on September 21, 1921, at the Oppau (Germany) plant of the Badische Anilin und Soda Fabrik when charges of dynamite were used to break up a huge stockpile of 2:1 ammonium nitrate–ammonium sulfate. The terrific detonation leveled buildings in the immediate vicinity, 430 lives were lost, and the air concussion wave caused considerable damage in Frankfort, 50 miles away.

With proper precautions, detonation of ammonium nitrate can be prevented. There is a considerable evidence that a large quantity can be heated without subsequent detonation, if it is well ventilated. In 1949 at Independence, Kansas, a fire destroyed 1000 tons of FGAN, but detonation did not occur.

18.17 HEAT OF REACTION

In Section 16.21 we implied that the enthalpy change (ΔH) during a chemical reaction at constant pressure is the heat of reaction if no work is done other than that against the atmosphere. The value of the enthalpy change (ΔH) is negative (enthalpy decreases) for an exothermic reaction, whereas ΔH is positive (enthalpy increases) for an endothermic reaction. For a system at constant pressure and volume, a change in enthalpy is closely related to what is called a change in internal energy of the system. Hence during an exothermic reaction at constant pressure and volume, the internal energy change is measured by the change in ΔH, a decrease in ΔH being a decrease in the internal energy.

For example, the reaction between gaseous hydrogen and iodine is endothermic (ΔH is positive), 6.2 kcal of heat being absorbed per mole of hydrogen iodide produced. The molar enthalpy change is therefore +6.2 kcal/mole. This change is noted in the ordinary chemical equation, qualitatively in (I) and quantitatively in (II) and (III). The notation shown in (III) is the one usually used.

$$\text{(I)} \quad \tfrac{1}{2}H_2 + \tfrac{1}{2}I_2 + \Delta \to HI$$
$$\text{(II)} \quad \tfrac{1}{2}H_2 + \tfrac{1}{2}I_2 + 6.2 \text{ kcal} \to HI$$
$$\text{(III)} \quad \tfrac{1}{2}H_2 + \tfrac{1}{2}I_2 \to HI \qquad \Delta H = +6.2 \text{ kcal}$$

The reaction which is the reverse of the one written above is exothermic (ΔH is negative), 6.2 kcal of heat being evolved per mole of HI dissociating. The molar enthalpy change is −6.2 kcal/mole.

$$HI \to \tfrac{1}{2}H_2 + \tfrac{1}{2}I_2 \qquad \Delta H = -6.2 \text{ kcal}$$

Since the heat of reaction usually depends on the physical states of the reaction participants, the physical state of each participant is identified by a suitable subscript. If the substances are in their standard states, the temperature is 25°C and the pressure is 1 atm.

The combustion of elemental hydrogen in the presence of ordinary oxygen to yield liquid water is an exothermic reaction.

$$H_2(g) + \tfrac{1}{2}O_2(g) \rightarrow H_2O(liq) \qquad \Delta H = -68.4 \text{ kcal}$$

For the reverse reaction,

$$H_2O(liq) \rightarrow H_2(g) + \tfrac{1}{2}O_2(g) \qquad \Delta H = +68.4 \text{ kcal}$$

The enthalpy change for a specific chemical reaction is related most directly to the change in strengths and numbers of bonds as the reactants are converted to products.

18.18   MEASUREMENT OF HEATS OF REACTION

The procedure used in the experimental determination of heats of reaction is called *calorimetry*. Some heats of reaction cannot be measured readily in a calorimeter. In these cases the heats of reaction are calculated from calorimetric data obtained during the measurement of the heats of related reactions.

One of the easiest types of reactions which can be studied calorimetrically is that in which elemental oxygen is one of the reactants. These reactions are called *combustions* or *oxidations*. The heats of combustion of many elements and hundreds of compounds have been measured calorimetrically. The calorific or caloric value of a fuel is measured in a calorimeter by determining the amount of heat evolved during the complete combustion (oxidation) of a known amount of the fuel. This is the theoretical heat of combustion. The amount of energy actually obtained from a given amount of fuel in a boiler or engine is usually much less than the theoretical calorific value. The efficiency of the boiler or engine is usually dependent on its design; the most efficient get the largest percentage of the theoretical calorific value of the fuel. The calorific value of simple organic foodstuffs, such as cane sugar, is determined by combusting (oxidizing) the substances in a calorimeter. The calorific value of such a foodstuff is also its theoretical heat of combustion.

A brief description of the measurement of the heat of combustion of a substance will serve as an illustration of calorimetry. The actual character of the calorimeter varies with the requirements of the reaction to be studied, but the basic principle of calorimetry is fairly simple.

A known amount of the substance is placed in a strong-walled vessel, or "bomb," and an excess of gaseous oxygen is admitted. This "bomb" containing the reactants has a known specific heat, or heat capacity. It is placed in a larger container of known heat capacity. The bomb is then covered with a known amount of water. The whole system, the calorimeter, is housed in a well-insulated enclosure, and the temperature of the system is then measured as precisely as possible.

The reaction is initiated by producing an electrical spark inside the bomb. Combustion occurs, and the heat evolved increases the temperature of the bomb, the water around it and the container which holds the water. After the calorimeter has come to thermal equilibrium, the rise in temperature is measured. Because the heat capacity (calories of heat absorbed per degree rise in temperature) of the calorimeter is known, the total number of calories of heat evolved during the combustion (heat of reaction) may be calculated.

18.19   HEAT OF FORMATION

The *heat of formation* of a compound (ΔH_f) is defined as the heat of reaction (change in enthalpy, ΔH) during the production of 1 mole of the compound from its elements in their standard states ($25°C$ and 1 atm). The most common allotrope of an element is chosen as the standard state (for carbon, graphite; for oxygen, O_2; for sulfur, rhombic sulfur).

In Section 18.17 we stated that the heat of reaction during the exothermic formation of 1 mole of liquid water from its elements is 68.4 kcal. Hence the heat of formation (ΔH_f) for 1 mole of liquid water is -68.4 kcal. The heat of formation of hydrogen iodide (p. 440) is $+6.2$ kcal.

For carbon dioxide,

$$C(graphite) + O_2(g) \rightarrow CO_2(g) \qquad \Delta H = -94.05 \text{ kcal}$$

Therefore the heat of formation of CO_2 is -94.05 kcal.

For nitrogen monoxide,

$$\tfrac{1}{2}N_2 + \tfrac{1}{2}O_2 \rightarrow NO \qquad \Delta H = +21.60 \text{ kcal}$$

Hence ΔH_f of NO is $+21.60$ kcal.

Compounds such as NO which have positive heats of formation ($+\Delta H_f$) are called endothermic compounds because they have larger internal energies per mole than do the elements from which they are produced. Compounds such as CO_2 which have negative heats of formation are called exothermic compounds. Of course, these compounds have smaller internal energies per mole than do their constituent elements in their standard states.

The standard heats of formations of a few common compounds are listed in Table 18.1.

TABLE 18.1   Some standard heats of formation

Compound	ΔH_f (kcal/mole)
Carbon dioxide, $CO_2(g)$	-94.05
Carbon monoxide, $CO(g)$	-26.42
Carbon bisulfide, $CS_2(liq)$	$+21.0$
Hydrogen fluoride, $HF(g)$	-64.2
Hydrogen bromide, $HBr(g)$	-8.65
Hydrogen iodide, $HI(g)$	$+6.20$
Methane, $CH_4(g)$	-17.90
Ethane, $C_2H_6(g)$	-20.24
Ethene, $C_2H_4(g)$	$+12.50$
Ethyne, $C_2H_2(g)$	$+54.19$
Sodium fluoride, $Na^+F^-(s)$	-136.0
Sodium iodide, $Na^+I^-(s)$	-68.84
Lithium hydroxide, $Li^+OH^-(s)$	-116.5
Rubidium hydroxide, $Rb^+OH^-(s)$	-98.9
Water, $H_2O(liq)$	-68.4
Water, $H_2O(g)$	-57.82
Water, $H_2O(s)$	-66.83

18.20   ADDITIVITY OF THERMOCHEMICAL EQUATIONS

In certain reactions whose heats of reaction cannot be easily determined experimentally, it is possible to calculate the heats of reaction from known experimental data.   The fundamental principle involved was suggested by G. H. Hess (Russian) in 1840.   Hess's law is: The heat evolved or absorbed during a chemical change at constant pressure is always the same, whether the transformation occurs in one or in several steps.   That is, there is a constant relationship between the total energy content of a specific reactant system and that of a specific product system.   The method by which the product system is attained from the reactant system is incidental.

Hess's law suggests that thermochemical equations can be

treated as ordinary algebraic equations. That is, they may be added, subtracted, multiplied by constant factors, and divided by constant factors. It is possible to calculate some heats of reaction by using suitable combinations of related equations, the equations being treated algebraically.

If the heat of formation of each reactant and product in a given reaction is known, the heat of reaction may be calculated by subtracting the sum of the heats of formation of the reactants from that of the products.

Let us now consider an application of Hess's law. It is almost impossible to measure accurately the heat of reaction when carbon reacts with oxygen to yield carbon monoxide.

$$C(graphite) + \tfrac{1}{2}O_2(g) \rightarrow CO(g) \tag{18.1}$$

However, the heats of reaction for the combustion of carbon to carbon dioxide and for the combustion of carbon monoxide to carbon dioxide can be determined calorimetrically.

$$C(graphite) + O_2(g) \rightarrow CO_2(g) \qquad -94.05 \text{ kcal} \tag{18.2}$$
$$CO(g) + \tfrac{1}{2}O_2(g) \rightarrow CO_2(g) \qquad -67.63 \text{ kcal} \tag{18.3}$$

(Assume the arrows may be read as equality signs. The notations for heat are ΔH values.)

To calculate the heat of reaction of Eq. 18.1, we must manipulate Eqs. 18.2 and 18.3 algebraically. If Eqs. 18.2 and 18.3 are left unchanged, neither addition nor subtraction will yield Eq. 18.1. However, if Eq. 18.3 is reversed, we have

$$CO_2(g) \rightarrow CO(g) + \tfrac{1}{2}O_2(g) \qquad +67.63 \text{ kcal} \tag{18.4}$$

Now if Eq. 18.4 is added to Eq. 18.2 and identical terms on opposite sides of the arrow canceled,

$C(graphite) + O_2(g) \rightarrow CO_2(g)$	-94.05 kcal	(18.2)
$CO_2(g) \rightarrow CO(g) + \tfrac{1}{2}O_2(g)$	$+67.63$ kcal	(18.4)
$C(graphite) + \tfrac{1}{2}O_2 \rightarrow CO(g)$	-26.42 kcal	

The sum is the thermochemical equation, Eq. 18.1.

When doing problems of this type, it is helpful to manipulate the equations so as to get the superfluous, identical substances on opposite sides of the equations in order that they may be canceled when the equations are added.

The heat of combustion of glucose (dextrose) can be determined in a bomb calorimeter. The thermochemical equation is

$$C_6H_{12}O_6(s) + 6O_2 \rightarrow 6CO_2 + 6HOH \qquad \Delta H = -671 \text{ kcal}$$

The amount of heat evolved during the combustion (oxidation) of any amount of glucose can be calculated because the equation indicates that during the complete combustion of one mole (180.16 g) of glucose, 671,000 cal of heat is evolved. For any fraction of a mole of glucose combusted, the same fraction is obtained of the heat of combustion.

Whenever we eat glucose, the ultimate fate of this substance is its transformation or metabolism by means of several steps (reactions) to carbon dioxide and water. Biochemical studies have indicated that the over-all conversion in this metabolism is the same as during the combustion of glucose in the bomb calorimeter. Because the initial state of glucose and the final state of the products are the same in the animal body as in the calorimeter, the number of calories evolved during the metabolism of 180.16 g of glucose in our body is approximately 671 kcal. The validity of this statement has been confirmed experimentally.

The three classes of common foodstuffs are carbohydrates, fats, and proteins. Every carbohydrate contains the elements carbon, hydrogen, and oxygen. Glucose, $C_6H_{12}O_6$, and sucrose, $C_{12}H_{22}O_{11}$ (cane sugar, beet sugar), are simple carbohydrates; starch and cellulose are complex carbohydrates. Fats contain the same elements as do carbohydrates, but the ratio of carbon and hydrogen to oxygen is much greater in fats than in carbohydrates. Proteins contain primarily the elements carbon, hydrogen, oxygen, and nitrogen, but their composition and formulas are much more complex and variable than those of fats and carbohydrates.

The heats of combustion of carbohydrates and fats can be measured in the bomb calorimeter. In all cases the products are carbon dioxide and water. Proteins can also be combusted in the calorimeter; the products are carbon dioxide, water, and nitrogen. When common foodstuffs are combusted completely in the calorimeter, they yield the following average heats of combustion:

Carbohydrates	4.1 kcal/gram
Fats	9.45 kcal/gram
Proteins	5.65 kcal/gram

(These values are weighted averages because the amounts of the different carbohydrates, fats, and proteins vary in ordinary foods.)

In the human body fats and carbohydrates are converted to the same products (CO_2 and HOH) as in the calorimeter; they yield approximately the same amounts of heat (thermal energy) in the body as in the calorimeter. However, in the body the nitrogen in the proteins is not converted to elemental nitrogen, but instead the protein nitrogen either is retained in the body within compounds derived from the proteins or is excreted as combined nitrogen. Therefore the actual amount of heat obtained by the body per gram of protein is less than in the calorimetric combustion. The actual heat of conversion of protein during metabolism of previously absorbed protein is 4.35 kcal per gram.

The actual physiologic "fuel" values of the three common food constituents are less than the values of the average heats of combustion (the value for proteins being corrected to 4.35 kcal per gram) because there is some loss during digestion. Therefore the average values of heat per gram must be corrected for this loss. These approximate physiologic fuel values of the foodstuffs are:

Carbohydrates	4 kcal/gram
Fats	9 kcal/gram
Proteins	4 kcal/gram

(These fuel values are called the Atwater and Bryant factors.)

The approximate fuel value of a food may be calculated by means of the above factors if the amount of fat, protein, and carbohydrate in the food is known. An average composition of milk is 3.3 per cent of protein, 4.0 per cent of fat, and 5.0 per cent of carbohydrate. The approximate fuel value of 100 g of this milk would be:

From protein	(3.3×4)	$= 13$ kcal
From fat	(4.0×9)	$= 36$ kcal
From carbohydrate	(5.0×4)	$= 20$ kcal

or a total of 69 kcal per 100 g of milk.

18.21 ENTROPY AND FREE-ENERGY CHANGES

We have mentioned previously (p. 335) that, if the energy of a system is constant, any change is in the direction of an increase in entropy (ΔS is positive or $\Delta S > 0$). (Recall that entropy, S, is a measure of the randomness or of how energy is distributed in a given system.) We also noted that, if the entropy of a system is constant (as it is in most mechanical processes), any change is in the direction of a decrease in energy (at constant pressure and volume, a decrease in enthalpy, H). The general tendency for most changes is toward a state of equilibrium, and in most chemical reactions both energy and entropy change. The two major driving forces for chemical reactions, as well as for physical processes, are a decrease in enthalpy (ΔH is negative) and an increase in entropy (ΔS is positive).

If entropy increases ($+\Delta S$) and enthalpy decreases ($-\Delta H$) during a specific reaction, both driving forces favor the reaction in the direction in question. In this case the more probable state is the one having the lower energy. However, in other cases the more probable state is the one that has the higher energy. In the latter cases the reactions' tendency to go to the more probable state is opposed by a sort of energy barrier, the need to add energy to the system. Since the reaction will proceed in the direction of the larger change, the driving force is the difference between the increase in energy and the increase in randomness. This net driving force may be called the *free energy*. For systems at constant temperature and pressure, this is the Gibbs free energy, F (p. 389). But for systems at constant temperature and volume, it is the Helmholtz free energy, A. Therefore in the case of chemical reactions at constant temperature and pressure, we can use the thermodynamic relation mentioned previously (p. 389):

$$\Delta F = \Delta H - T \Delta S$$

Before this expression is reconsidered, it might be helpful to review the principles of free energy (p. 389). Since we know that ΔF must be negative if a process is to be spontaneous, we can see how different values of ΔH and ΔS affect the change in free energy (ΔF). It is well to keep in mind that a reaction will occur under the specified conditions if the free-energy change term, ΔF, is negative.

a. If ΔH and ΔS are both larger than zero, ΔF may be either positive or negative. The reaction may or may not be spontaneous because the enthalpy and entropy changes oppose each other. A positive ΔS enhances an endothermic reaction, especially if $T \Delta S$ has a value greater than that of ΔH.

b. If ΔH is positive and ΔS is negative, ΔF can only be positive. The reaction is not spontaneous, unfavored either by ΔS or by ΔH.

c. If ΔH is negative and ΔS is negative, ΔF may be either positive or negative. The enthalpy and entropy changes oppose each other. A negative ΔS hinders an exothermic reaction.

d. If ΔH is negative and ΔS is positive, ΔF can only be negative. Since both ΔH and ΔS are favorable, reaction is spontaneous.

Endothermic reactions (ΔH is positive) can be spontaneous (ΔF is negative) if ΔS is positive and $T \Delta S$ is larger than ΔH. If the products are in a more random state and if their energy is distributed more randomly than in the reactants, ΔS is positive.

A change from a solid reactant to a gaseous product occurs with an increase in entropy.

$$C(s) + H_2O(g) \rightarrow CO(g) + H_2(g) \qquad \Delta H = +31.4 \text{ kcal}$$

Although ΔH is positive, the reaction is spontaneous at high temperatures because $T \Delta S$ can exceed ΔH (ΔS is positive).

If all reaction participants are gaseous, the sign of ΔS may depend on the change in the number of molecules. The more product molecules, the greater the chance that ΔS is positive.

$$2NH_3 \rightarrow N_2 + 3H_2$$

In this reaction both ΔH and ΔS are positive, but a relatively high value of $+\Delta S$ is favorable.

In the decomposition of $K^+ClO_3^-$, a solid yields one gaseous product, O_2.

$$2[K^+ClO_3^-] \rightarrow 2[K^+Cl^-] + 3O_2 \qquad (\Delta H \text{ is positive})$$

Although ΔH is positive, ΔS is also positive. Therefore at high temperatures $T \Delta S$ can exceed ΔH to yield a negative ΔF. The randomness of the location of the O_2 molecules and of their energies is greater than that of the oxygen atoms in the ClO_3^-. Hence ΔS is positive for the reaction. In fact, since ΔS is positive for all dissociations, if the temperature is high enough, every dissociation (decomposition) is spontaneous because $T \Delta S$ can be greater than ΔH.

Although the sign of the enthalpy (energy) term may be a controlling factor at ordinary temperatures, the entropy term $T \Delta S$ may reverse this at high temperatures. At low temperatures, on the other hand, where $T \Delta S$ is small a reaction may proceed in the direction predicted by the energy change. At $0°K$ ($T \Delta S = 0$) the value of ΔF is equal to that of ΔH. Therefore at this temperature the energy change dictates the direction.

18.22   STANDARD FREE ENERGY

The meaning and determination of the heat of formation of a compound were discussed in Section 18.19. The heat of formation of a compound may be considered the standard enthalpy of formation of the compound. In this section we shall define the standard free energy of a substance.

The *standard free energy* (ΔF°) of a compound is the change in free energy (ΔF) during the formation of one mole of the substance at 25°C and 1 atm. This standard free energy of formation is often called the *molal free energy* of the compound. The standard free energy of the stable common form of an element is assigned a zero (0) value.

The standard free energy of a compound (at 25°C) can be calculated, if the standard heat of formation and the standard entropies are known, by using the expression

$$\Delta F^\circ = \Delta H_f - T \Delta S^\circ$$

Let us calculate the standard free energy of carbon dioxide. We know that ΔF° for CO_2 is the free-energy change for the reaction

$$C(s) + O_2(g) \rightarrow CO_2(g)$$

ΔH_f for $CO_2 = -94.05$ kcal/mole
$T = 298°K$
ΔS° for $CO_2 = S_{CO_2(g)} - S_{O_2(g)} - S_{C(s)}$
ΔS for $CO_2 = 51.06 - 49.0 - 1.36 = 0.7$ eu/mole CO_2

Substituting in $\Delta F^\circ = \Delta H_f - T \Delta S^\circ$,

$$\Delta F^\circ = -94,050 - (298)(0.7) = -94,260 \text{ cal} = -94.26 \text{ kcal}$$

Therefore -94.26 kcal/mole is the standard free energy of CO_2.

The standard entropy change (ΔS°) for a reaction is calculated by subtracting the standard entropies of the reactants from those of the products. This is similar to the calculation of ΔH of a reaction by using the heats of formation of the reactants and products (see p. 444).

Table 18.2 lists the standard free energies and standard entropies of a few common substances.

The standard free-energy change of a specific reaction at 25°C and 1 atm can be calculated if the ΔF° values of the reaction participants are known. For example, let us calculate the ΔF° for the reaction between ethyne, C_2H_2, and hydrogen to yield ethene, C_2H_4, at 25°C and 1 atm.

$$C_2H_2 + H_2 \rightarrow C_2H_4$$

$\Delta F^\circ = \Delta F^\circ_{C_2H_4} - \Delta F^\circ_{H_2} - \Delta F^\circ_{C_2H_2} = \Delta F^\circ$ for the reaction/mole C_2H_4
$\Delta F^\circ = (+16.28 \text{ kcal}) - 0 - (+50.00 \text{ kcal}) = -33.72$ kcal

TABLE 18.2 Standard free energies and entropies of formation (25°C and 1 atm)

Substance	$\Delta F°$, kcal/mole	$S°$, eu
$O_2(g)$	0.0	49.0
$H_2(g)$	0.0	31.2
$N_2(g)$	0.0	45.8
$H_2O(g)$	−54.64	45.11
$H_2O(liq)$	−56.56	16.9
$HCl(g)$	−22.77	44.62
$HBr(g)$	−12.72	47.44
$HI(g)$	−0.31	49.31
$NO(g)$	+20.72	50.34
$NH_3(g)$	−3.98	46.01
$CO(g)$	−32.81	47.30
$CO_2(g)$	−94.26	51.06
$C_2H_6(g)$	−7.86	54.85
$C_2H_4(g)$	+16.28	52.45
$C_2H_2(g)$	+50.00	48.00
$CH_4(g)$	−12.14	44.50
Na^+Cl^-	−91.79	17.30
Li^+OH^-	−106.1	12.0
CuO	−30.1	10.4

Problems

1. Assume a hypothetical reaction system: $A + B \rightarrow AB$. Also assume that the rate of reaction is r at 25°C and that A and B are present in identical concentration in a suitable medium. If the temperature remains constant, to what extent does r increase if the concentration of A is doubled and the concentration of B is tripled?

2. Two gases A and B are placed in a glass vessel X, and the rate of their chemical interaction at temperature T is determined. The interior walls of X are subsequently coated with a very thin layer of paraffin wax. The initial experiment is repeated with the same amounts of A and B at temperature T. The rate of chemical interaction is much different from that found in the initial experiment. Suggest a logical explanation.

3. Using moles/l as the concentration unit and minutes as the time unit, derive the units of the specific rate constant for a third-order reaction. (Recall that reaction rate is expressed in units of moles per liter per minute.)

4. The order of some simple reactions, such as first- and second-order reactions, may be determined graphically. If a plot of log concentration vs. time yields a straight line, the reaction is first-order. If a plot of the reciprocal of concentration (1/concn) vs. time yields a straight line, the reaction is second-order. With these facts in mind, determine the order of the reaction, some data of which appear below.

Time (min)	0	10	20	30	40
Concn (moles/l)	2.5	1.6	1.1	0.75	0.68

5. Recall the comments made in Problem 4 about the determination of reaction orders by constructing simple graphs. Use the data given below to determine the order of the reaction.

Time (min)	0	10	20	30	40
Concn (moles/l)	1.0	0.58	0.37	0.28	0.20

6. The reaction between nitrogen monoxide (NO) and oxygen to yield nitrogen dioxide is said to be first-order with respect to oxygen and second-order with respect to nitrogen monoxide. (a) What is the order of the over-all reaction? (b) What is the expression of the rate equation $(r = ?)$?

7. The data for a specific first-order reaction system are:

Time (min)	0	10	20	30
Concn (moles/l)	1.0	0.72	0.52	0.37

(The concentrations are of reactant remaining at time T.) Recall that the rate of the reaction between two time intervals is determined by dividing the concentration change by the time interval. With all of these facts in mind, determine the approximate specific rate constant for the reaction. (Notice that because only three differences in concentration are given, only three values of the specific rate constant can be calculated. Report the average value.)

8. The half-time, or half-life, of a chemical reaction is defined as the time necessary for the reaction to be half-completed. The expression for the half-life of a first-order reaction is

$$t_{1/2} = \frac{\ln 2}{k_1} = \frac{0.693}{k_1} \qquad k_1 = \text{rate constant}$$

(Note that the half-life of a first-order reaction is independent of concentration.) With these facts in mind, calculate the half-life of the reaction mentioned in Problem 7.

9. Recall that on page 432 we stated that a plot of the log of the rate constant (log k) versus the reciprocal of the Kelvin temperature (1/T) yields a straight line. The linear relationship is evident in the equation (p. 432) that relates the rate constant, the temperature, and the Arrhenius energy of activation, E_a. By recognizing this linearity ($y = mx + b$), suggest a means to determine the Arrhenius energy of activation for the reaction whose rate constants at different temperatures are listed below.

Temperature (°C)	0	10	20	00
Rate constant × 10^3	2.6	6.5	9.2	14.8

10. In the case of a specific reaction under given conditions of temperature and pressure, the enthalpy change is positive and the entropy change is negative. Under the given conditions, is the reaction spontaneous?

11. What concept is the basis for the comment that, if conditions are chosen properly, all decompositions of solids and liquids to yield gaseous products can be spontaneous?

12. Using the data listed in Table 18.1, calculate the values of ΔH (enthalpy change) of the following reactions.
   (a) $CH_4(g) + 2O_2(g) \rightarrow CO_2(g) + 2H_2O(liq)$
   (b) $2C_2H_2(g) + 5O_2(g) \rightarrow 4CO_2(g) + 2H_2O(liq)$
   (c) $C_2H_2(g) + H_2 \rightarrow C_2H_4(g)$
   (d) $C_2H_2(g) + 2H_2 \rightarrow C_2H_6(g)$
   (e) $CH_4(g) \rightarrow C + 2H_2(g)$

13. For the reaction, combustion of ethanol, C_2H_5OH, in oxygen to yield gaseous CO_2 and liquid water, $\Delta H = -327$ kcal/mole. The heat of combustion (in oxygen) of ethene, C_2H_4, is $\Delta H = -332$ kcal/mole. Calculate the value of ΔH for the reaction

$$C_2H_4 + H_2O \rightarrow C_2H_5OH$$

14. The heat of combustion of methanol, CH_3OH, is $\Delta H = -171$ kcal/mole. By using this and the value for the heat of combustion of methane found in Problem 12(a), calculate the value of ΔH for the reaction

$$2CH_4 + O_2 \rightarrow 2CH_3OH$$

15. How many kilocalories of heat are evolved during the combustion of 45.5 g of ethene? (See Prob. 13.)

16. During the complete combustion of some ethanol, 71.94 kilocalories of heat was evolved. How many grams of ethanol was burned?

17. The free-energy change (ΔF) of a given reaction system under specific conditions of temperature and pressure has a positive value. Does this mean that it is impossible to carry out this reaction?

18. Calculate the standard entropy change ($\Delta S°$) of the following reactions.
   (a) $CH_4 + 2O_2 \rightarrow CO_2 + 2H_2O$
   (b) $C_2H_4 + H_2 \rightarrow C_2H_6$
   (c) $2C + O_2 \rightarrow 2CO$
   (d) $N_2 + 3H_2 \rightarrow 2NH_3$
   (e) $2H_2 + O_2 \rightarrow 2H_2O$

19. Calculate the standard free-energy change ($\Delta F°$) of each reaction mentioned in Problem 18.   Assume reactions are at 25°C and 1 atm.

20. Calculate the "standard" enthalpy change ($\Delta H°$) of each reaction mentioned in Problem 18.   (Recall that temperature is 298°K.)

19

19.1 A PERSPECTIVE

The concept of equilibrium has been discussed several times previously in connection with equations for reversible reactions, vapor pressure of liquids and solids, saturated solutions, the solubility product concept, and the dissociation of acids. Hence you should readily recall that an equilibrium is a special state in which two opposing processes are occurring at equal rates.

As we reconsider the concept of the equilibrium vapor pressure of a liquid (p. 346), we remember that once the pressure of the vapor of a liquid has reached the equilibrium value at a specific temperature and volume, no further spontaneous change is favored over the other so long as the temperature is constant. In other words, once the equilibrium state is reached, the system never changes spontaneously from that position. The system can, of course, be changed from the equi-

454

EQUILIBRIUM

librium position, but energy must be expended to do so. Spontaneous changes always proceed in the direction toward an equilibrium, and never away from an equilibrium. If the liquid's vapor pressure is greater than the equilibrium value at a specific constant temperature, condensation is the process favored toward equilibrium. However, if the vapor pressure is less than the equilibrium value, evaporation is favored until equilibrium is attained.

There is for every specific nonequilibrium system a state of equilibrium toward which the system may proceed spontaneously, but away from which it can be altered only by expending some other system which then in turn proceeds toward another equilibrium.

An extremely important chemical observation is that a chemical reaction will proceed spontaneously in a specific direction only until a state of equilibrium is reached. Also we observe that any true equilibrium state may be approached from two opposite directions. In fact, the criterion of an equilibrium is that an identical state is reached from opposite directions. The production of gaseous hydrogen iodide from its elements is reversible.

$$H_2 + I_2 \leftrightarrows 2HI$$

If pure hydrogen and pure iodine are heated together in a closed vessel at 450°, HI is formed and eventually a specific percentage of the equilibrium mixture is HI. If pure HI is heated at 450° in a closed vessel, some of the HI decomposes to yield eventually an equilibrium state in which the percentage of HI is identical to that obtained when H_2 reacted with I_2.

We shall find that Le Châtelier's principle (p. 349) is a valuable tool in the qualitative interpretations of systems in equilibrium because the treatment of chemical equilibria is comparable to that of physical equilibria.

It is well to keep in mind that if a system is in a state of equilibrium, both the free-energy change (ΔF) and the entropy change (ΔS) are zero.

19.2 CHEMICAL EQUILIBRIUM

If a sample of mercury(II) oxide is gradually heated in a closed system, the products (mercury and oxygen) are in continual contact with any undecomposed mercury(II) oxide. As more and more oxide is decomposed, more and more product molecules appear in the gaseous phase above the solid oxide. While the concentration of oxygen and the amount of mercury gradually increases, the rate of the reaction between oxygen and mercury to produce the oxide gradually increases. Eventually the rate of formation of the oxide is equal to the rate of its decomposition. If the temperature is then kept constant, the system is in a state of equilibrium in which two opposing processes are occurring at equal rate, the partial pressure of the oxygen remains constant, and the amount of mercury(II) oxide and the amount of mercury remain constant.

The reaction system, $2HgO + \Delta \leftrightarrows 2Hg + O_2$, can attain a state of equilibrium only if the oxide, the mercury, and the oxygen are in continual contact. Although this reaction system is relatively simple, its behavior is similar to thousands of others in which the reactants are in continual contact with the products. These examples of chemical equilibria can be manipulated either to favor the formation of product or reactant entities; all experimentation is based on the principle of Le Châtelier.

Le Châtelier's principle states: Whenever any participating factor in a chemical equilibrium is changed, the system always tends to offset, counterbalance, or overcome the effect of the change. In other words, if a stress or strain is placed on the equilibrium, the reaction that tends to counterbalance the tension is favored and the composition of the equilibrium mixture is thereby altered in the direction of the favored reaction. With this in mind let us consider the equilibrium system, $2HgO + \Delta \leftrightarrows 2Hg + O_2$, say at temperature T_1.

Now let us increase the temperature of the system to T_2 and hold it there. An inspection of the equilibrium mixture reveals there is more mercury and oxygen, but less mercury(II) oxide than at T_1. This is expected since the increase in temperature upset the equilibrium by adding heat. The endothermic reaction is favored because it dissipates the added heat. *(SCATTERS IT)*

If we lower the temperature of the reaction system from T_2 to T_1, the equilibrium mixture has the same composition as the original mixture. A decrease in the temperature of the equilibrium tends to favor the exothermic reaction; hence at T_1 there is more oxide and less mercury and oxygen than at T_2.

If we decrease the volume of the equilibrium system at T_1, we increase the concentration of the oxygen and mercury vapor. This upsets the system and the favored reaction is the production of oxide from the elements. This reaction tends to offset the increase in concentration of the gaseous factors. The new equilibrium mixture contains less mercury and oxygen, but more oxide, than the original mixture.

19.3   THE HABER PROCESS

To consider in more detail the qualitative aspects of chemical equilibria, let us use as a model system the production of ammonia by the Haber process.

$$N_2 + 3H_2 \leftrightarrows 2NH_3 \qquad \Delta H = -24.1 \text{ kcal}$$

Because this reaction system involves gaseous substances, the reactants and product are in continual contact. Since the production of ammonia from its elements is reversible, the yield of ammonia depends on the composition of the system at the time equilibrium is attained. Under ordinary conditions the yield is very low. Applying Le Châtelier's principle, Fritz Haber (German), after approximately 16 years of patient research, succeeded in 1914 in manipulating the reaction conditions so that the production of ammonia from nitrogen and hydrogen is economically feasible. Since that time the process has been improved.

If a mixture of nitrogen and hydrogen in mole ratio 1:3 is kept at 500°C under a pressure of 200 atm until equilibrium is attained, 20 per cent of the equilibrium mixture is ammonia. If pure ammonia is kept at 500°C and the pressure of the gaseous system maintained at 200 atm until a steady state (equilibrium) is attained, it is found that 80 per cent of the ammonia has decomposed, or 20 per cent of the equilibrium mixture is ammonia. These experimental facts indicate that a specific chemical equilibrium may be approached from two directions, either by starting with the reactant system only or by starting with the product system only.

Since the yield of ammonia is only 20 per cent at 500°C and 200 atm, it is necessary to change conditions to favor the reaction during which ammonia is produced. According to Le Châtelier's principle, a decrease in the temperature of the system should favor the formation of ammonia because that process is exothermic. Unfortunately, however, if the temperature is much lower than 500°C, equilibrium is established so slowly that the process is not practical. According to Le Châtelier's principle, an increase in pressure should favor the formation of ammonia because by increasing the density of the molecular population the equilibrium is upset, favoring the process that causes a decrease in the molecular population. (Every time two molecules of ammonia are formed, four molecules—three of hydrogen and one of nitrogen—disappear.)

The fact that increasing the pressure and decreasing the temperature of the reaction system do yield equilibrium mixtures with a higher ammonia concentration is amply demonstrated by experiment. At 500°C and 200 atm, the equilibrium mixture is about 20 per cent NH_3; at 500°C and 800 atm, about 51 per cent; at 300°C and 300 atm, about 70 per cent; and at 300°C and 850 atm, about 90 per cent.

Although the yields of ammonia are high at 300°C if the pressure is high, the reaction system attains equilibrium too slowly. In normal practice the attainment of equilibrium is hastened by using a catalyst. This does not alter the position of the equilibrium; that is, the catalyst does not change the composition of the equilibrium mixture. A catalyst commonly used in the Haber process is a promoted iron catalyst, a mixture of iron and potassium aluminate, $K^+AlO_2^-$.

In typical industrial applications of the Haber process, a mixture of purified hydrogen and nitrogen (3:1) is passed slowly over the catalyst at temperatures between 450° and 600°C, and at pressures between 300 atm and 1000 atm. The actual yield of ammonia is much less than that expected in an equilibrium mixture under the conditions used because the practical rate at which the gases are passed over the hot catalyst does not allow sufficient time for establishment of equilibrium conditions. After the gaseous mixture has passed over the catalyst, the gases are cooled. Only the ammonia liquefies. The unreacted hydrogen and nitrogen, along with more H_2 and N_2, are again passed over the catalyst. This cycle is repeated, and since the entire process is continuous, it requires little attention.

19.4 QUANTITATIVE ASPECTS
OF CHEMICAL EQUILIBRIA

A quantitative prediction of a chemical system in equilibrium may be made by formulating an equilibrium equation. This equation is derived from the specific chemical equation that is used to represent the equilibrium system. Let us use a simple homogeneous system, such as

$$A + B \rightleftharpoons C + D$$

The concentrations, in moles per liter, of the reaction participants are inserted in the equilibrium expression. The concentrations on the right side of the chemical equation are placed in the numerator, and those of the substances on the left are put in the denominator. The symbol $[A]$ means concentration of A in moles/liter. (See Fig. 19.1.)

$$\frac{[C][D]}{[A][B]} = K$$

where K is the equilibrium constant.

This ratio of the concentrations of the reaction participants remains constant at a given temperature, but the value of the

K

equilibrium constant varies with the temperature. Ideally, at a given temperature the equilibrium constant never changes either as the concentrations of the reaction participants are varied or in the presence of a catalyst. Although a catalyst may increase the rates of the two reactions in the equilibrium system, it affects each reaction equally.

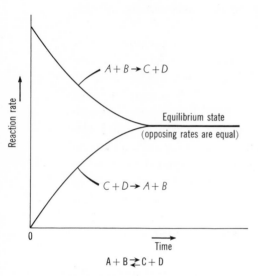

$A + B \rightarrow C + D$

Equilibrium state
(opposing rates are equal)

$C + D \rightarrow A + B$

0

Time

$A + B \rightleftharpoons C + D$

FIGURE 19.1 Graphic representation of the decrease in rate of the reaction $A + B \rightarrow C + D$ (upper curve) as reaction proceeds, and of the increase in rate of the reaction $C + D \rightarrow A + B$ (lower curve) as reaction proceeds. The rates of these two reactions eventually reach a common value at the time equilibrium is established.

Actually the activities, or effective concentrations, of the reacting substances should appear in the equilibrium expression. However, if the concentrations are so low (gaseous pressures small and solutions dilute) that physical interactions between the participants are insignificant, the activities and molal concentrations are nearly identical. The equilibrium expression is an ideal case, in a sense similar to the ideal gas laws.

It should be recognized that, if we reverse our original chemical equation (which is quite in order if we wish to do so), the equilibrium constant K_1 is the reciprocal of K.

$$C + D \rightleftharpoons A + B$$

$$\frac{[A][B]}{[C][D]} = K_1$$

The equilibrium equation for more complicated systems may involve exponential terms. In these the molar concentration of a reactant is raised to a power numerically equal to that of the coefficient of the substance as it appears in the chemical equation. For example,

$$2NO_2 \rightleftharpoons N_2O_4 + \Delta$$

$$\frac{[N_2O_4]}{[NO_2]^2} = K$$

The arithmetical expression for the equilibrium constant of the system, $N_2 + 3H_2 \rightleftharpoons 2NH_3$, indicates that at a given temperature there is an infinite number of possible combinations of individual concentrations of ammonia, of hydrogen, and of nitrogen.

The equilibrium constant of a specific reversible reaction is usually an indication of the extent to which the reactants form the products, or vice versa. If the equilibrium constant, K, is relatively large, in the equilibrium mixture the concentration of reactants is much less than the concentration of product(s) because in the expression for this equilibrium constant the numerator is much larger than the denominator. If the value of K_{equil} is much less than unity (1), then the reactants are predominant in the equilibrium mixture because in the expression for K_{equil} the numerator is much smaller than the denominator.

For certain simple reaction systems, the concept of mass action can be applied in the derivation of the ideal equilibrium expression. As a model system we may use the reversible formation of hydrogen iodide from its elements.

$$H_2 + I_2 \overset{(2)}{\underset{(1)}{\rightleftharpoons}} 2HI$$

The rate of reaction (1) is $r_1 = k_1[H_2][I_2]$, where k_1 is a specific rate constant. The rate of reaction (2) is $r_2 = k_2[HI]^2$, where k_2 is a specific rate constant. At equilibrium, $r_1 = r_2$ or $k_1[H_2][I_2] = k_2[HI]^2$.

At a given temperature the specific rate constants, k_1 and k_2, are constant, so they may be combined to yield the equilibrium constant K.

$$\frac{k_1}{k_2} = K = \frac{[HI]^2}{[H_2][I_2]}$$

For a reaction involving one or more gases at constant temperature, the partial pressure of a gaseous substance may be considered a measure of its concentration. In the system

$$N_2 + 3H_2 \rightleftharpoons 2NH_3$$

the partial pressures of the gases may be substituted for the concentrations.

$$K_p = \frac{p_{NH_3}^2}{p_{N_2} p_{H_2}^3}$$

where p_{NH_3} is the partial pressure of NH_3, etc., and where K_p is the equilibrium constant in terms of partial pressures.

If a heterogeneous reversible reaction involves one or more solid substances, the concentrations of the solid substances do not appear in the expression for the equilibrium constant. For example,

$$Ba^{++}SO_3^{--}(s) + \Delta \leftrightarrows Ba^{++}O^{--}(s) + SO_2(g)$$

barium sulfite

$$K = [SO_2] \quad \text{or} \quad K_p = p_{SO_2}$$

This equilibrium constant expression indicates that at a given temperature there is only one pressure at which gaseous sulfur dioxide can be in equilibrium with the two solids, barium oxide and barium sulfite. If this reaction system is in equilibrium, and if the pressure of the sulfur dioxide is increased (temperature constant), sulfur dioxide combines with barium oxide to form barium sulfite until the original pressure is restored. If the pressure of the sulfur dioxide is decreased (temperature constant), more barium sulfite decomposes and the original pressure, due to SO_2, is restored.

19.5 THE IDEAL LAW OF CHEMICAL EQUILIBRIUM

A general rule to be used in formulating the equilibrium expression for the ideal case is:

1. Raise the concentration of each participating substance (the partial pressure of each gaseous substance) to a power equal to the coefficient that precedes the symbol of the substance as it appears in the reaction equation.
2. Formulate a fraction such that the numerator is the product of the terms in (1) that involve substances on the right side of the reaction equation, and the denominator is the product of the terms in (2) that involve substances on the left side of the reaction equation.
3. Omit in the fraction any term that represents the concentration of a pure solid or liquid phase, especially the concentration of the solvent in a dilute solution.

The value of the fraction is constant, for the ideal case, at constant temperature. The equilibrium expression is useful only if gaseous participants are at low pressures, if solutions are dilute, and if each solid or liquid phase is an essentially pure substance.

19.6 SAMPLE PROBLEMS

1. Assume that the reaction system, $2HI \leftrightarrows H_2 + I_2$, is at equilibrium at 450°C. The concentration of hydrogen and of iodine

is $4.6 \times 10^{-3}\ M$, and of HI, $3.4 \times 10^{-2}\ M$. What is the value of the equilibrium constant, K?

The expression for K is $\dfrac{[H_2][I_2]}{[HI]^2} = K$

Then

$$\frac{(4.6 \times 10^{-3})(4.6 \times 10^{-3})}{(3.4 \times 10^{-2})^2} = \frac{21.2 \times 10^{-6}}{11.6 \times 10^{-4}} = 1.8 \times 10^{-2}$$

In a given reaction system at $450°$ the concentration of H_2 is $0.1\ M$, and of I_2, $1 \times 10^{-3}\ M$. What is the concentration of HI?

Substituting into the expression for K,

$$\frac{(1 \times 10^{-1})(1 \times 10^{-3})}{x^2} = 1.8 \times 10^{-2}$$

$$(1.8 \times 10^{-2})x^2 = 1 \times 10^{-4}$$
$$x^2 = 5.6 \times 10^{-3} = 56 \times 10^{-4}$$
$$x = 7.5 \times 10^{-2}\ M = 0.075\ M\ \text{(concn of HI)}$$

2. Pure acetic acid, CH_3COOH, is added to water to yield a solution whose OH_3^+ ion concentration is $1 \times 10^{-3}\ M$. What is the concentration of undissociated acetic acid in the solution?

The chemical equation is

$$CH_3COOH + HOH \leftrightharpoons OH_3^+ + CH_3COO^-$$

The equilibrium expression for dilute solutions (concentration of HOH is constant) is

$$K = \frac{[OH_3^+][CH_3COO^-]}{[CH_3COOH]} = 1.8 \times 10^{-5}\ \text{(at 25°C)}$$

Since $[CH_3COO^-] = [OH_3^+] = 1 \times 10^{-3}\ M$,

$$K = \frac{[1 \times 10^{-3}][1 \times 10^{-3}]}{[CH_3COOH]} = 1.8 \times 10^{-5}$$

$$[CH_3COOH] = \frac{1 \times 10^{-6}}{1.8 \times 10^{-5}} = \frac{10 \times 10^{-7}}{1.8 \times 10^{-5}}$$
$$= 5.5 \times 10^{-2} = 0.055\ M$$

19.7 IONIC EQUILIBRIA

There are so many examples of chemical equilibria involving ions in aqueous solution that it would be impossible in this book to mention all of them. Because nearly every ionic reaction that occurs in an aqueous solution is reversible, it generally resides in some specific equilibrium state. Most ionic reactions are never actually complete in aqueous solutions because an equilibrium state is reached prior to completion of the reaction. If an ionic reaction in an aqueous solution is incomplete, it is very likely that an equilibrium state has been reached, provided an adequate amount of each reactant is present.

Nearly all Brönsted acid-base reactions and many Lewis acid-base reactions are demonstrably reversible, especially in solutions. We have mentioned these previously in Chapter 9, and we shall discuss them further in Chapter 22. Every saturated solution of an ionic compound is an equilibrium state that involves interaction between ions. The autoionization of certain liquid solvents (p. 212) yields ionic equilibria in pure liquids.

Considering the general problem of the completeness of ionic reactions in solution, we should realize that it is simply a question of how to apply Le Châtelier's principle. Generally ionic reactions are shifted more nearly to completion by the formation of (1) a very slightly soluble precipitate; (2) a slightly soluble gas that may be expelled from the solution; (3) a fairly stable complex ion; (4) a slightly dissociated substance (weak electrolyte). The reversible reactions listed below are shifted more nearly to completion by one of these four factors.

(1) $Ba^{++}O_2^{--} + 2H^+ + SO_4^{--} \leftrightarrows H_2O_2 + Ba^{++}SO_4^{--} \downarrow$
$HgS_2^{--} + 2H^+ \leftrightarrows H_2S \uparrow + HgS \downarrow$

(2) $CdS + 2H^+ \leftrightarrows Cd^{++} + H_2S \uparrow$
$Cl^- + H_2SO_4 \leftrightarrows HSO_4^- + HCl \uparrow$

(3) $Zn(OH)_2 + 2OH^- \leftrightarrows Zn(OH)_4^{--}$
$Ag^+ + Cl^- + 2NH_3 \leftrightarrows Ag(NH_3)_2^+ + Cl^-$

(4) $OH_3^+ + OH^- \leftrightarrows 2HOH$
$OH_3^+ + CO_3^{--} \leftrightarrows HCO_3^- + OH_2$

In these equations the precipitates are identified by the downward arrows $\downarrow$, the gases by the upward arrows $\uparrow$, and the slightly dissociated substances by *italics;* the complex ions are products of the reactions of type (3).

19.8 THE COMMON-ION EFFECT

Let us consider a given system in equilibrium that consists, in part, of specific ionic participants. According to Le Châtelier's principle, either addition to or removal from the system of any one of these ions will cause a shift, or change, in the equilibrium position. In other words, addition of any mixture that has an ion in common with the equilibrium system will cause a change in the equilibrium position. The nature of this phenomenon, called the _common-ion effect_, will be understood more readily after we cite a few common examples.

In pure water and all aqueous solutions there exists an equilibrium system, the autoprotolysis of water (p. 210).

$$HOH + HOH \leftrightarrows OH_3^+ + OH^-$$

Addition to pure water either of a solution containing a higher concentration of OH^- than pure water or of a pure ionic hydroxide $[M^+OH^-$ or $M^{++}(OH^-)_2]$ yields a common-ion effect. Addition of the common ion, OH^-, causes an immediate decrease in the OH_3^+ ion concentration of the solvent water. Addition to water of extra OH_3^+ causes a decrease in the concentration of OH^-, another common-ion effect.

A saturated aqueous solution of sodium chloride at 25°C is an equilibrium system in which the concentration of chloride ion is about 6 M.

$$Na^+Cl^- \leftrightarrows Na^+ + Cl^-$$
undissolved in solution
solid

If concentrated hydrochloric acid (12 M) is added to the clear supernatant of the saturated solution of Na^+Cl^-, a precipitate of sodium chloride appears. Addition of the common ion Cl^- favors the formation of more undissolved solid, the reaction reading from right to left. If 10 M sodium hydroxide solution is added to a fresh portion of the supernatant solution of the saturated system, the common ion Na^+ causes the appearance of solid Na^+Cl^-.

If no chemical reactions occur when common ions are added to the equilibrium systems, the solubility of every slightly soluble solid can, by the addition of any common ion, be decreased, thereby causing precipitation to be more nearly complete. For example, barium sulfate is only slightly soluble in water. Therefore addition of either barium ions or sulfate ions to a saturated solution of barium sulfate will decrease the solubility and increase the extent of precipitation.

$$Ba^{++}SO_4^{--} \leftrightarrows Ba^{++} + SO_4^{--}$$
undissolved in solution

Acetic acid (CH_3COOH) is partially dissociated when it is added to water to yield a dilute solution. Therefore a dilute solution ($0.1\ M$) of acetic acid is a system in equilibrium.

$$CH_3COOH + HOH \leftrightharpoons OH_3^+ + CH_3COO^-$$

acetic acid   acetate ion

If OH_3^+ ions, in say $3\ M$ HCl, are added to a $0.1\ M$ solution of acetic acid, the common ion OH_3^+ upsets the equilibrium to favor the reaction reading from right to left. Hence dissociation of acetic acid molecules is suppressed by the common ion OH_3^+. Consequently, the acetate ion, CH_3COO^-, concentration is less after the addition of OH_3^+ than before. If solid sodium acetate, $Na^+CH_3COO^-$, is added to a $0.1\ M$ acetic acid solution, the dissociation of acetic acid is suppressed and the OH_3^+ ion concentration is much less than in the original solution.

19.9 FREE ENERGY AND EQUILIBRIA

Previously (p. 389) an expression was presented that relates changes in free energy, enthalpy, and entropy at constant temperature.

$$\Delta F = \Delta H - T\,\Delta S$$

We should also recall that $\Delta F = 0$ for a system in equilibrium, and that the net change in entropy in a system in equilibrium is zero, $\Delta S = 0$. The tendency for a system to proceed spontaneously toward equilibrium is indicated by the extent of the decrease in free energy ($-\Delta F$). The larger the negative value of ΔF, the greater the tendency toward equilibrium.

The equilibrium constant of the reaction for the formation of a compound from its elements at 25°C and 1 atm is related to the standard free energy (p. 449) by the expression:

$$\Delta F^\circ = -RT \ln K \qquad \text{or} \qquad \Delta F^\circ = -RT\ 2.303 \log_{10} K$$

In many reaction systems, it is much easier to determine the value of ΔF than that of K, the equilibrium constant, for the system. K can be calculated from ΔF° values by the relation

$$\log K = -\frac{\Delta F^\circ}{2.303RT}$$

This relationship is consistent with our prior comments about the equilibrium constant of a chemical reaction. A large positive value of K implies a large negative value of ΔF, both suggesting a strong tendency for the reaction to proceed to equilibrium. Values of K

and of $-\Delta F$ are thermodynamic factors; hence the nature of the path (route) and the rate of the reaction are not relevant. These latter factors are related solely to the initial and final states of the system.

Let us now use the free-energy equilibrium relationship to calculate the equilibrium constant K for the Haber process at 25°C.

$$N_2 + 3H_2 \leftrightarrows 2NH_3$$

$\Delta F°$ for the reaction is

$$\begin{array}{ccc} N_2 & + \quad 3H_2 & \rightarrow \quad 2NH_3 \\ \Delta F° = 0 & \Delta F° = 0 & \Delta F° = (2)\,(3940) \\ & & = -7880 \quad \text{cal} \end{array}$$

$$\log K = \frac{-\Delta F°}{2.303RT} = \frac{7880 \quad \text{cal}}{(2.303)(1.99)(298)} = 5.78$$

$$K = 6 \times 10^5 = \frac{(P_{NH_3})^2}{(P_{N_2})(P_{H_2})^3}$$

The large positive value of K means that the equilibrium position favors the production of ammonia.

19.10 A SUMMARY

a. A chemical equilibrium is a dynamic reaction system in which two opposing chemical reactions are occurring at equal rates. In this steady state the formation of a product entity is accompanied by the simultaneous formation of a reactant entity.

b. Under appropriate conditions, if all reactants are in continual contact with all products, every reversible chemical reaction eventually reaches a state of equilibrium. The composition of the equilibrium mixture is influenced by the original concentration of the reactants and the temperature of the reaction system. If the reacting substances are gaseous, the composition of the equilibrium mixture may be affected by the total pressure on the reaction system. The equilibrium state can be approached by starting with either the pure reactant system or the pure product system.

c. If one or more solid substances are involved in a reversible reaction at constant temperature, the particle size (amount of surface exposed) of the solid does not affect the composition of the equilibrium mixture, but the particle size does affect the rate at which equilibrium is attained. (The larger the surface of the solid, the greater the rate.)

d. In a specific reversible reaction at constant temperature, a catalyst never affects the composition of the equilibrium mixture. The catalyst cannot displace or shift a chemical equilibrium, but the catalyst does hasten the attainment of equilibrium.

e. A chemical equilibrium at constant temperature can usually be shifted or displaced by changing the concentration of any one of the participating chemical entities, whether reactant or product. If the concentration of a reactant entity is increased, the equilibrium is displaced to favor the reaction in which that reactant entity disappears. If the concentration of a reactant is decreased, the reaction is favored in which that reactant entity appears. If a product entity is removed, the equilibrium shifts to favor the formation of more product.

f. In a chemical equilibrium involving one or more gaseous substances, at constant temperature, if the total volume of reactants is different from the total volume of products, the equilibrium is displaced by a change in the total pressure on the reaction system. If the pressure on the system is increased, that reaction is favored which results in a decrease in volume (causes the disappearance of molecules). If the pressure is decreased, that reaction is favored which causes the appearance of molecules (increase in volume).

g. In a chemical equilibrium involving gaseous substances, at constant temperature, if the total volume of reactants is equal to the total volume of products, the equilibrium cannot be displaced by a change in the total pressure.

h. A chemical equilibrium can be displaced or shifted by changing the temperature of the system. If the temperature is increased, the reaction that absorbs heat (endothermic) is favored. If the temperature is decreased, the reaction that evolves heat (exothermic) is favored. An increase in temperature hastens the attainment of equilibrium.

i. Le Châtelier's principle can be applied to any system in equilibrium.

j. The equilibrium constant of a reversible reaction is constant at any given temperature. It is unaffected by changes in the concentrations of reactants and products; it is also unaffected by a catalyst. The equilibrium constant nearly always varies with the temperature of the reaction system.

k. An equilibrium is a state to which any spontaneous process proceeds. An equilibrium is never displaced, nor is the equilibrium position ever altered, spontaneously. The equilibrium constant of a specific reaction is related closely to the standard free-energy change. The larger the value of K, the greater the decrease in free energy.

  l. The change in free energy (ΔF) of a system in equilibrium is zero. At equilibrium each reaction involved has the same tendency to proceed as the other.

  m. The change in entropy (ΔS) of a system in equilibrium is zero. At equilibrium one of the reactions involved proceeds with an increase in entropy, while the other proceeds with an equal decrease in entropy. The net change is zero.

Problems

1. A chemical reaction system that involves only gaseous substances is in a state of equilibrium at 100°C. The chemical equation is

$$M_2X_2 + 4ZT + \Delta \leftrightarrows 2MXZ_2 + T_4$$

(a) The temperature of the system is changed to 65°C and then held constant. How does the composition of the "new" system differ from that of the original? (b) The volume of the original system is decreased to one-third of the original volume. How does this change affect the system? (c) A catalyst is added to the original system at 100°C. What effect does the catalyst probably have on the reactions? (d) What effect would be observed following the addition of ZT to the original system? (e) What effect would the addition of gaseous helium (at constant pressure) have on the original system? (f) If the pressure of the gaseous system were decreased, at constant temperature, what reaction would be favored? (g) Suggest the expression of the equation for the equilibrium constant of the reaction system.

2. Derive the equilibrium constant expression for the reversible dissociation of dinitrogen tetroxide to yield nitrogen dioxide. How is the equilibrium constant determined?

3. A gaseous phase reaction system is

$$CO_2 + H_2 + \Delta \leftrightarrows CO + H_2O$$

At 980°C the value of the equilibrium constant is 1.60. Which reaction in this system is favored at high temperatures?

4. A hypothetical reaction system is

$$A + B \leftrightarrows C + D$$

(a) When pure A and pure B are mixed initially, the concentration of each is 1.5 moles/l. After equilibrium is reached at 30°C, the concentration of D is 1.0 mole/l. What is the value, at 30°C, of the equilibrium constant? (b) What is the concentration of B in an equilibrium mixture at 30°C if the concentration (moles/l) of A is 0.7, of C 0.9, and of D 1.0? (c) What is the concentration of C in an equilibrium mixture at 30°C if the concentration of D is 0.75 M, of A 0.5 M, and of B 0.4 M?

5. If identical concentrations (molarities) of hydrogen and iodine are mixed and react at 25°C to yield hydrogen iodide, the reaction rate constant, k_1, is 808 times as large as k_2. What is the value of the equilibrium constant at 25°C?

6. Considering the reversible decomposition of hydrogen iodide at 25°C to yield hydrogen and iodine and using the information given in Problem 5, what is the equilibrium constant for this reaction system?

7. Sulfur dioxide reacts with oxygen to yield sulfur trioxide in the contact process for the production of sulfuric acid. (a) What is the expression for the equilibrium constant? (b) At a given temperature, is the production of sulfur trioxide increased or decreased by doubling the total pressure of the reaction system? (c) Can the percentage theoretical yield be increased, at a given temperature and pressure, by the use of a suitable contact catalyst?

8. A student is wondering whether a specific system is in equilibrium at a given temperature. How can he resolve his dilemma?

9. If binary compound X is heated progressively, its degree of dissociation (decomposition) progressively increases. Is the production of compound X from its elements an exothermic or an endothermic reaction?

10. Considering the gaseous reaction system in which hydrogen and iodine react reversibly to yield hydrogen iodide, how much is the production of HI favored by doubling the pressure on the system at constant temperature?

11. For the production of Y at 25°C in the system $X \leftrightarrows Y$, the value of the equilibrium constant is 0.52. A vessel initially has 1.0 mole of X and 0.02 mole of Y. What amounts of X and Y will be present after the system attains equilibrium at 25°C?

12. What is the oxonium ion concentration of a 0.1 M aqueous solution of acetic acid (monoprotic) whose $K_a = 1.8 \times 10^{-5}$? (Acetic acid is CH_3COOH.)

13. To a given solution of aqueous acetic acid, sodium acetate is added until the concentration of acetate ion, CH_3COO^-, is equal to that of the undissociated acetic acid. What is the oxonium ion concentration of the solution? (See Problem 12 for K_a.)

14. The oxonium ion concentration is 1.5×10^{-4} M in a 0.1 M solution of HA made by adding pure HA to pure water. What is the value of the equilibrium constant for the dissociation of HA in water?

15. The equilibrium constant for the thermal decomposition of calcium carbonate to yield carbon dioxide and calcium oxide at 1000°C is 800 mm. What mass of $CaCO_3$ is necessary to establish equilibrium conditions ($CaCO_3$, CaO, and CO_2 in equilibrium) in a 1.00 liter flask at 1000°C? ($CaCO_3$ and CaO are solids at 1000°C.)

16. If equal numbers of moles of reactants and products are involved, to what extent does the reaction of A with B to yield C and D occur under conditions such that $\Delta F = 0$? ($A + B \rightarrow C + D$.)

17. What is the value of $\Delta F°$ (kcal/mole) for the reaction $N_2O_4 \leftrightarrows 2NO_2$ at 25°C if the value of the equilibrium constant at that temperature is 0.143?

18. (a) Is the production of hydrazine, N_2H_4, from its elements in their standard states (1 atm and 25°C) favorable under these conditions? (ΔF_f for N_2H_4 is $+37.9$ kcal per mole.) (b) What is the equilibrium constant for this reaction at 25°C?

20

20.1 A PERSPECTIVE

This chapter is devoted to a more elaborate discussion of the concept of oxidation-reduction than that presented in Chapter 9. Since you have been introduced to the major aspects of redox reactions, it is not necessary to identify the major functional terms here.

We customarily identify the extent to which the one element is oxidized and the other is reduced by the number of electrons accepted or donated per atom. The *oxidation state* is identified by an oxidation number, and the oxidation numbers constitute a sort of oxidation-reduction scale. The standard reference point on this scale is zero (0), and this symbol is used to indicate the oxidation state of an element in its elemental state. At zero the element has neither accepted nor donated electrons. Positive integral numbers $+1$, $+2$, $+3$, etc., indicate the extent of oxidation of an

REDUCTION

element in reference to its elemental state. In other words, a positive oxidation number indicates the number of electrons donated per atom by an element during the transition from its elemental state to its oxidation state in the entity in question. Negative integral numbers, -1, -2, -3, etc., indicate the extent of reduction of an element in reference to its elemental state. In other words, a negative oxidation number indicates the number of electrons accepted per atom by an element during the transition from its elemental state to its state in the entity in question. If elemental sulfur accepts two electrons per atom during a chemical change, the oxidation number of the sulfur is -2 in the compound produced. Or if elemental sulfur donates four electrons per atom during a chemical change, the oxidation number of the sulfur is $+4$ in the compound produced. (See Fig. 20.1.)

Using conventional oxidation numbers to identify

oxidation states, it is often possible to determine whether oxidation or reduction of an element has occurred during a specific chemical reaction. If an element is oxidized, its oxidation number increases algebraically; if an element is reduced, its oxidation number decreases algebraically. The extent of increase in the oxidation number indicates the number of electrons donated; the extent of decrease in the oxidation number indicates the number of electrons accepted.

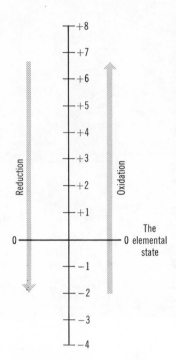

FIGURE 20.1 Oxidation number scale. Oxidation numbers identify oxidation states.

The assignment of oxidation numbers to certain representative elements is made according to specific conventions. This assignment is rather simple because these elements undergo a rather specific pattern of oxidation and reduction. However, it would be extremely difficult to develop a general scheme for the assignment of oxidation numbers to all elements. The one described in this chapter is very limited and must not be extended beyond its intended limits. In a sense the scheme is a means to an end because it is an elementary pedagogic device for understanding and illustrating the concepts of oxidation and reduction.

The scheme of oxidation number assignment may seem arbitrary in the case of covalent molecules, but it is useful and not illogical. The assignment is based on the fact that various elements apparently have differing electronegativities (p. 206). In assigning oxidation numbers to elements in covalent molecules, the more electronegative element is considered the electron acceptor, the less electronegative, the electron donor.

20.2 CONVENTIONS AND GENERALIZATIONS

The conventions used in the assignment of oxidation numbers are as follows:

a. The oxidation number of an element in its elemental state is zero (0).

b. The algebraic sum of the oxidation numbers of the atoms in a compound is zero (0).

c. In a monatomic ion the oxidation number of the element is equal to the charge on the ion.

d. In an ion which contains more than one atom, the algebraic sum of the oxidation numbers of the atoms is equal to the charge on the ion. Actually such ions are electrically charged covalent entities.

Certain conventional generalizations are used in the actual assignment of specific oxidation numbers. These will be extremely useful, but a few exceptions must be recognized.

e. Whenever an alkali metal element ($1a$) is a component of a compound, its oxidation number is $+1$.

f. Whenever an alkaline-earth metal element ($2a$) is a component of a compound, its oxidation number is $+2$.

g. Whenever the element fluorine is a component of a compound, its oxidation number is -1.

h. *Usually* when the element oxygen is a component of a compound, its oxidation number is -2. The exceptions are: the compound F_2O, in which oxygen has an oxidation number of $+2$; all simple peroxides in which all oxygen atoms are in the grouping O—O, in which oxygen has the oxidation number of -1; certain peroxy compounds in which some oxygen atoms have an oxidation number of -1 and some -2.

i. Whenever the element hydrogen is a component of a covalent compound, its oxidation number is $+1$. (Note that if a compound is gaseous or liquid at room temperature and 1 atm, it is a covalent compound; also, if hydrogen is combined with an electronegative element, a covalent compound results.)

j. Whenever a halogen is combined with an electropositive element within a binary compound, its oxidation number is -1.

k. Whenever the element sulfur is combined with an electropositive element within a binary compound, its oxidation number is -2.

l. If a molecule consists of two or more atoms of a given element, a "total-oxidation number" can be assigned. This does not necessarily imply oxidation states of individual atoms of the element in question.

20.3   EXAMPLES OF OXIDATION NUMBER ASSIGNMENTS

In potassium permanganate, $K^+MnO_4^-$,

> oxid. no. of K is $+1$
> oxid. no. of each O is -2
> total oxid. no. of O is $(-2)(4)$ or -8

Then

$$+1 + -8 + \text{oxid. no. of Mn} = 0$$
$$\underset{\text{for K}}{} \quad \underset{\text{for O}}{}$$

Therefore $+7$ is the oxidation number of manganese (Mn) in $K^+MnO_4^-$.

In sulfuric acid, H_2SO_4 (a liquid),

> total oxid. no. of H is $(+1)$, (2), or $+2$
> total oxid. no. of O is (-2), (4), or -8

Then

$$+2 + -8 + \text{oxid. no. of S} = 0$$
$$\underset{\text{for H}}{} \quad \underset{\text{for O}}{}$$

Therefore $+6$ is the oxidation number of sulfur (S) in H_2SO_4.

In sulfite ion, SO_3^{--},

> total oxid. no. of O is (-2), (3), or -6

Then

$$-6 + \text{oxid. no. of S} = -2$$

Therefore $+4$ is the oxidation number of S in SO_3^{--}.

In ammonium ion, NH_4^+,

> total oxid. no. of H is $(+1)$, (4), or $+4$

Then

$$+4 + \text{oxid. no. of N} = +1$$

Therefore -3 is the oxidation number of nitrogen (N) in NH_4^+.

In barium peroxide, $Ba^{++}O_2^{--}$,

> oxid. no. of Ba is $+2$

Then the total oxidation number of O is -2 and each oxygen atom has an oxidation number of -1.

20.4   HIGHEST AND LOWEST OXIDATION STATES

Table 20.1 lists the oxidation numbers of the highest and lowest oxidation states possible for some of the more common elements.

For each representative element, except fluorine and oxygen, the numerical notation of its highest oxidation state is equal to the number of its valence electrons, or the number of that family (periodic chart) in which the element resides.   For each element in

TABLE 20.1   Oxidation numbers

Elements	In Highest Oxidation State	In Lowest Oxidation State
All alkali metals (1a)	+1	0
All alkaline-earth metals (2a)	+2	0
All members of family 3a	+3	0 (for boron, −3)
Carbon, silicon, germanium	+4	−4
All members of family 5a	+5	−3
Sulfur, selenium, tellurium	+6	−2
All halogens (except fluorine)	+7	−1
Oxygen	+2	−2
Fluorine	0	−1
Hydrogen	+1	−1
Zinc, cadmium, mercury	+2	0
Chromium	+6	0
Manganese	+7	0
Tin, lead	+4	0
Iron, cobalt	+3 (commonly)	0
Nickel, copper	+2 (commonly)	0
Silver	+1	0
Ruthenium, osmium	+8	0

the halogen family, the oxygen family, and the nitrogen family, the numerical notation of its lowest oxidation state is equal to the difference between 8 and the element's number of valence electrons (see Fig. 20.2).

If an element is in its highest oxidation state, it can be reduced, but it cannot be oxidized.   If an element is in its lowest oxidation state, it can be oxidized, but it cannot be reduced.   Certain elements have several different states between their highest and lowest oxidation states.   Therefore it is not uncommon for an element to have many different kinds of compounds which are both oxidizing agents and reducing agents.

Decreasing electron-donor tendency →

Decreasing metallic character →

Increasing metallic character →

Increasing electron-donor tendency →

Decreasing electronegativity →

1a (always donate 1 electron)	2a (always donate 2 electrons)											3a	4a	5a	6a	7a	8a
1 **H**																1 **H**	2 **He**
3 **Li**	4 **Be**											5 **B**	6 **C**	7 **N**	8 **O**	9 **F**	10 **Ne**
11 **Na**	12 **Mg**	21 **Sc**	22 **Ti**	23 **V**	24 **Cr**	25 **Mn**	26 **Fe**	27 **Co**	28 **Ni**	29 **Cu**	30 **Zn**	13 **Al**	14 **Si**	15 **P**	16 **S**	17 **Cl**	18 **Ar**
19 **K**	20 **Ca**	39 **Y**	40 **Zr**	41 **Nb**	42 **Mo**	43 **Tc**	44 **Ru**	45 **Rh**	46 **Pd**	47 **Ag**	48 **Cd**	31 **Ga**	32 **Ge**	33 **As**	34 **Se**	35 **Br**	36 **Kr**
37 **Rb**	38 **Sr**	57-71 See La series	72 **Hf**	73 **Ta**	74 **W**	75 **Re**	76 **Os**	77 **Ir**	78 **Pt**	79 **Au**	80 **Hg**	49 **In**	50 **Sn**	51 **Sb**	52 **Te**	53 **I**	54 **Xe**
55 **Cs**	56 **Ba**	89-102 See Ac series										81 **Tl**	82 **Pb**	83 **Bi**	84 **Po**	85 **At**	86 **Rn**
87 **Fr**	88 **Ra**																

Best oxidizing agent

Next to best oxidizing agent

Elements to the left of this "stairway" nearly always act, in their elemental states, as electron donors

Electropositive elements ↕ Electronegative elements

Best reducing agents (electron donors)

Lanthanide series

57 **La**	58 **Ce**	59 **Pr**	60 **Nd**	61 **Pm**	62 **Sm**	63 **Eu**	64 **Gd**	65 **Tb**	66 **Dy**	67 **Ho**	68 **Er**	69 **Tm**	70 **Yb**	71 **Lu**

Actinide series

89 **Ac**	90 **Th**	91 **Pa**	92 **U**	93 **Np**	94 **Pu**	95 **Am**	96 **Cm**	97 **Bk**	98 **Cf**	99 **Es**	100 **Fm**	101 **Md**	102 **No**	103 **Lw**

FIGURE 20.2 Periodic chart with special reference to the electron affinity of the elements.

20.5   OXIDIZING AGENTS AND REDUCING AGENTS

An *oxidizing agent* is any chemical entity which causes another chemical entity to be oxidized. The oxidizing agent is the electron acceptor and is reduced thereby.

A *reducing agent* is any chemical entity which causes another chemical entity to be reduced. The reducing agent is the electron donor and is oxidized thereby.

The above definitions lead to the obvious conclusion that in all oxidation-reduction reactions, there is at least one oxidizing agent and one reducing agent.

If the oxidizing agent is an avid electron acceptor, it may cause even the least active electron donors to be oxidized. Also, an active or strong reducing agent may cause even the least active electron acceptors to be reduced. In other words, the actual behavior of a specific oxidizing agent depends on that agent's relative tendency to accept electrons and on the relative electron-donor ability of the entity with which the oxidizing agent is in contact. Therefore, whenever an entity is classified as a good or active oxidizing agent, it is implied that, relative to that entity, many different entities are good electron donors. The term *good oxidizing agent* is relative, to say the least. (See Tables 20.2 and 20.3.)

20.6   GENERALIZATIONS

Following are certain generalizations concerning oxidizing agents and reducing agents.

a. If an element is in its highest oxidation state in a chemical entity, that entity is a potential oxidizing agent or electron acceptor because the element's oxidation number may be decreased.

b. If an element is in its lowest oxidation state in a chemical entity, that entity is a potential reducing agent or electron donor because the element's oxidation number may be increased.

c. If a chemical entity contains an element whose oxidation state is between its highest and lowest oxidation states, that entity is a potential oxidizing agent and a potential reducing agent because the element's oxidation number may be either decreased or increased.

TABLE 20.2 Some commonly used oxidizing agents

Oxidizing Agent	Element and Usual Extent of Reduction	Reduction Product
Nitric acid, HNO_3		
concd aq soln	N ($+5$ to $+4$)	NO_2
dilute aq soln	N ($+5$ to $+2$)	NO
Permanganate ion, MnO_4^-		
in acidic solns	Mn ($+7$ to $+2$)	Mn^{++}
in nonacidic solns	Mn ($+7$ to $+4$)	MnO_2
All halogens	0 to -1	singly negative ion
Hydrogen peroxide, H_2O_2	O (-1 to -2)	HOH
Perchlorate ion, ClO_4^-	Cl ($+7$ to -1)	Cl^- (usually)
Chlorate ion, ClO_3^-	Cl ($+5$ to -1)	Cl^- (usually)
Hypochlorite ion, ClO^-	Cl ($+1$ to -1)	Cl^-
Bromate ion, BrO_3^-	Br ($+5$ to -1)	Br^- (usually)
Dichromate ion, $Cr_2O_7^{--}$	Cr ($+6$ to $+3$)	Cr^{3+}
Iron(III) ion, Fe^{3+}	Fe ($+3$ to $+2$)	Fe^{++}
Iron(III) cyanide complex ion, $Fe(CN)_6^{3-}$	Fe ($+3$ to $+2$)	$Fe(CN)_6^{4-}$
Sulfuric acid, H_2SO_4	S ($+6$ to $+4$)	SO_2
Oxygen, O_2	O (0 to -1 or -2)	O^{--} or O_2^- or H_2O
Sulfur, S	S (0 to -2)	S^{--}
Ozone, O_3	O (0 to -1 or -2)	same as for O_2
Proton, H^+, OH_3^+	H ($+1$ to 0)	H_2
Silver ion, Ag^+	Ag ($+1$ to 0)	Ag
Copper(II) ion, Cu^{++}	Cu ($+2$ to $+1$ or 0)	Cu^+ or $Cu°$
Manganese(IV) oxide, MnO_2	Mn ($+4$ to $+2$)	Mn^{++}

d. If a strongly electronegative element is in its highest oxidation state in a chemical entity, that entity is among the best oxidizing agents.

e. If a strongly electropositive element is in its lowest oxidation state in a chemical entity, that entity is among the best reducing agents.

20.7 ARITHMETICAL PROBLEMS

The following problems may serve as useful illustrations of the application of the oxidation and reduction concepts.

TABLE 20.3　Some commonly used reducing agents

Reducing Agent	Element and Usual Extent of Oxidation	Oxidation Product
Lithium, Li	0 to +1	Li^+
Sodium, Na	0 to +1	Na^+
Potassium, K	0 to +1	K^+
Magnesium, Mg	0 to +2	Mg^{++}
Calcium, Ca	0 to +2	Ca^{++}
Aluminum, Al	0 to +3	Al^{3+}
Iron, Fe	0 to +2 (usually)	Fe^{++}
Zinc, Zn	0 to +2	Zn^{++}
Tin, Sn	0 to +2 (usually)	Sn^{++}
Hydrogen, H_2	0 to +1	H^+ (bound)
Iron(II) ion, Fe^{++}	+2 to +3	Fe^{3+}
Tin(II) chloride, $SnCl_2$	Sn (+2 to +4)	Sn^{4+}
Sulfite ion, SO_3^{--}	S (+4 to +6)	SO_4^{--}
Nitrite ion, NO_2^-	N (+3 to +5)	NO_3^-
Sulfide ion, S^{--}	−2 to 0 (usually)	S
Iodide ion, I^-	−1 to 0 (usually)	I_2
Hydride ion, H^-	−1 to 0 or +1	H_2 or H^+ (bound)
Hydrogen peroxide, H_2O_2	O (−1 to 0)	O_2
Copper(I) ion, Cu^+	+1 to +2	Cu^{++}

1. How many electrons must be donated per atom by elemental sulfur, if the sulfur is to be oxidized completely?　If elemental oxygen is used as the oxidizing agent, how many oxygen atoms are necessary per atom of sulfur oxidized?

Since the oxidation number of sulfur must be increased from 0 to +6, a donation of 6 electrons per sulfur atom is necessary. Because each oxygen atom can accept no more than 2 electrons, at least 3 oxygen atoms are necessary.　However, at ordinary temperatures oxygen atoms always exist in pairs in oxygen molecules, so 3 oxygen molecules can oxidize completely 2 sulfur atoms.

$$2S + 3O_2 \rightarrow 2SO_3$$

2. In the reduction of nitrate ion, NO_3^-, how many electrons must the element nitrogen accept per atom to be reduced completely? If elemental zinc is the reducing agent, how many atoms of zinc are necessary per atom of nitrogen reduced?

Since the oxidation number of nitrogen must be decreased from $+5$ to -3, a total of 8 electrons must be accepted per nitrogen atom. Because elemental zinc always donates 2 electrons per atom, 4 atoms of zinc are necessary to reduce completely each nitrate ion. (In nitrate ion, oxygen is completely reduced.)

3. In the reduction of bromate ion, BrO_3^-, how many electrons must bromine accept per atom, if bromate ion is to be reduced to elemental bromine?

Since the oxidation number of bromine must be decreased from $+5$ to 0, each bromine atom must accept 5 electrons.

4. How many molecules of oxygen are necessary to oxidize completely each molecule of propane, C_3H_8 (a gas)?

The oxidation number of hydrogen is $+1$. Therefore in propane, hydrogen is completely oxidized. The total oxidation number of carbon in propane is -8, and that is the total oxidation number of 3 carbon atoms. If carbon is to be oxidized completely, then the total oxidation number of 3 carbon atoms must be increased to $(3)(+4)$ or $+12$. Therefore the total oxidation number increase is from -8 to $+12$, or the 3 carbon atoms in 1 molecule of propane must donate collectively 20 electrons. Since each oxygen atom in each oxygen molecule can accept no more than 2 electrons, 5 oxygen molecules are necessary to oxidize completely each molecule of propane.

$$C_3H_8 + 5O_2 \rightarrow 3CO_2 + 4HOH$$

5. How many moles of electrons must be donated by 3.3 moles of arsine, AsH_3, during its complete oxidation?

Only the arsenic can be oxidized, and the oxidation is from the -3 state to $+5$ state. This is 8 moles of electrons donated per mole of arsine oxidized, or 8×3.3, 26.4 moles of electrons donated by 3.3 moles of arsine. (Eight electrons donated per molecule is 8 moles of electrons per mole.)

20.8 BALANCING OXIDATION-REDUCTION EQUATIONS

a. *The oxidation-number-change method:*

Because many oxidation-reduction reactions are rather complex, it is often convenient to use an orderly method for balancing oxidation-reduction equations, rather than trial and error. Also, by assigning oxidation numbers to the elements involved in a given chemical reaction, it is possible to determine whether that reaction is an oxidation-reduction reaction.   Obviously if the oxidation number of any element changes during a reaction, that reaction is an oxidation-reduction.   If the oxidation numbers of all elements involved in a chemical reaction remain unchanged, the reaction is not an oxidation-reduction.

The oxidation-number–change method for balancing oxidation-reduction equations is based on the premise that the total number of electrons accepted by the oxidizing agent must equal the total number donated by the reducing agent.   In other words, if the oxidation number of an element in the oxidizing agent is decreased to a certain extent, the oxidation number of an element in the reducing agent is increased to the same extent.

The unbalanced equation for a reaction is:

$$NH_3 \quad + O_2 \rightarrow N_2 + HOH$$
ammonia (a gas)

The oxidation number of nitrogen changes from -3 to 0 (a donation of 3 electrons per atom).   The oxidation number of oxygen changes from 0 to -2 (an acceptance of 2 electrons per atom).

If the oxidation number increase of nitrogen must be equal to the oxidation number decrease of oxygen, then two atoms of nitrogen must donate six electrons to be accepted by three atoms of oxygen.

Unbalanced: $2NH_3 + \frac{3}{2}O_2 \rightarrow N_2 + HOH$

But if coefficients are to be integral numbers,

Unbalanced: $4NH_3 + 3O_2 \rightarrow N_2 + HOH$

These coefficients for ammonia and oxygen must not be altered, so to balance the equation it is necessary to choose the correct coefficients for N_2 and HOH on the product side.

Balanced: $4NH_3 + 3O_2 \rightarrow 2N_2 + 6HOH$

b. *The half-reaction or ion-electron method:*

Another method used for balancing some oxidation-reduction equations is the half-reaction or ion-electron method.   This is a convenient, if not always literal, scheme for balancing those reactions in which ions are involved.   The method highlights the concept that oxidation and reduction always occur simultaneously because the oxidation process is considered to be one-half of the overall reaction and the reduction process the other half.   A separate equation is balanced for each process; the two equations are adjusted so that the number of electrons donated in the oxidation half-reaction equals the number accepted in the reduction half-reaction; then these two half-reactions are added to produce the total oxidation-reduction equation.

Oxidation-reduction equations balanced by the half-reaction or ion-electron method usually include only those chemical entities actually involved in the reaction. In a sense, the balanced equation is a net equation; any "spectator" ions are not represented. Most reactions whose equations are balanced by the half-reaction method occur in aqueous solution; under such circumstances alkali metal ions, calcium ions, and barium ions are never reduced. Therefore it seems reasonable to omit such ions. However, most monatomic ions, especially those of the transition elements, interact with water molecules whenever they are in aqueous solutions. Although these interactions are significant, we shall disregard them for the moment because usually they do not affect the oxidation state of the element of the monatomic ion. Therefore in most simple oxidation-reduction equations the monatomic ions will be represented as such.

Occasionally the separation of oxidation and reduction in two different half-reactions may seem imaginary. However, in certain electrochemical systems called *voltaic cells*, it is possible to isolate at least partially the oxidation and reduction processes. In such cells, if the circuit is closed, electrons flow from the location at which oxidation occurs (the anode) to the location at which reduction occurs (the cathode). In other words, electrons flow from the seat of oxidation to the seat of reduction. The driving force of this stream of electrons is the voltage of the cell. This voltage depends partially on the electron-donor vigor of the reducing agent and the electron-acceptor ability of the oxidizing agent. (See p. 513.)

Each half-reaction must be balanced atomically and electrically. To balance a half-reaction electrically, we must use electrons. Frequently it will be necessary to use protons (H^+) in balancing a half-reaction because these are positively charged. If the redox reaction occurs in an aqueous solution, the water molecules may serve as sources of protons. (Each symbol H in the formula of water, HOH, represents a covalently bound proton.) Many covalent entities which contain the element hydrogen may serve as sources of protons because apparently their protons are bound rather loosely. These covalent entities are called acids, and every acidic aqueous solution contains such a covalent entity.

Frequently it is necessary to use a basic aqueous solution.   Such a solution contains hydroxide ions (OH^-).   Several ionic hydroxides, such as sodium hydroxide (Na^+OH^-), are direct sources of hydroxide ions.   (The relationship of the proton H^+ to the hydroxide ion OH^- is quite intimate.   If a water molecule loses or donates a proton, a hydroxide ion remains.   If a hydroxide ion accepts a proton, a water molecule is produced.)

An unbalanced redox equation is

$$BrO_3^- + \quad H^+ \quad + \quad Br^- \rightarrow Br_2 + HOH$$

bromate   proton, from   bromide
ion   some acid   ion

By assignment of oxidation numbers, we find that bromine in bromate ion is reduced and bromide ion is oxidized.   Therefore the oxidation half-reaction involves

$$Br^- \rightarrow Br_2$$
Balanced atomically: $2Br^- \rightarrow Br_2$
Balanced electrically: $2Br^- \rightarrow Br_2 + 2e^-$

The reduction half-reaction involves:

$$BrO_3^- + H^+ \rightarrow Br_2$$

Balanced atomically with respect to bromine: $2BrO_3^- + H^+ \rightarrow Br_2$

In order to balance the oxygen atoms, 6 HOH are placed on the product side.   Then to balance the 12 covalently bound protons in 6 HOH, 12 H^+ are placed on the reactant side.   Then

$$2BrO_3^- + 12H^+ \rightarrow Br_2 + 6HOH$$

Now to balance this electrically, 10 electrons are added to the reactant side, so that the net charge is zero on this side to balance the zero net charge on the product side.   Then the balanced reduction half-reaction is

$10e^- + 2BrO_3^- + 12H^+ \rightarrow Br_2 + 6HOH$
added to $5(2Br^- \rightarrow Br_2 + 2e^-)$ the oxidation half-reaction
$\overline{2BrO_3^- + 12H^+ + 10Br^- \rightarrow 6Br_2 + 6HOH}$

The total is the net balanced redox equation.   This reaction is frequently used to produce elemental bromine in aqueous solutions.

In balancing a specific half-reaction, it may be convenient to insert initially the necessary number of electrons, and then to balance the equation electrically by adding protons if necessary; finally, if protons are added, it may be necessary to add HOH to balance them.   For example,

$$Mn^{++} \rightarrow MnO_4^-$$

Since the oxidation number of Mn increases from $+2$ to $+7$, each Mn atom must donate 5 electrons. These are placed on the product side because this equation represents any oxidation. Then

$$Mn^{++} \rightarrow MnO_4^- + 5e^-$$

To balance this electrically, 8 protons must be placed on the product side. Then

$$Mn^{++} \rightarrow MnO_4^- + 5e^- + 8H^+$$

Assuming that HOH may serve as a source of protons, 4 HOH are placed on the reactant side.

$$Mn^{++} + 4HOH \rightarrow MnO_4^- + 5e^- + 8H^+$$

Perhaps we should note that the somewhat arbitrary and mechanical processes used in the conventional balancing of redox reactions by the half-reaction method are realistic and productive only when all actual reactants and products are known, and when each reactant leads directly to one of the actual products. A conventional unbalanced redox equation does not indicate whether intermediate reactions occur. If intermediate reactions are involved, the ion-electron or half-reaction method may be pointless.

20.9 A RELATIVE ACTIVITY SERIES

Within a general discussion of oxidation and reduction, it is customary to formulate a relative activity series for oxidizing and reducing agents. The order in a given series is valid only for the particular environmental conditions specified. For different sets of conditions, several different activity series may be formulated.

In the activity series presented in Table 20.4, the position of each chemical entity is related to a reference standard. For reducing agents this standard is the activity of elemental hydrogen as a reducing agent; for oxidizing agents it is the activity of the loosely bound proton, H^+, as an oxidizing agent. All entities in the left-hand column above hydrogen are more active electron donors than elemental hydrogen; all entities below it are less active. These comparisons are made under specified conditions in aqueous solutions.

The activity series in Table 20.4 is based on reactions in aqueous solutions in which ionic concentrations are 1 molal (1 m) and any gases are at 1 atm of pressure.

TABLE 20.4   An abridged activity series

Potential Reducing Agents		Potential Oxidizing Agents
Li	$\leftrightarrows$	Li^+
Cs	$\leftrightarrows$	Cs^+
Rb	$\leftrightarrows$	Rb^+
K	$\leftrightarrows$	K^+
Ba	$\leftrightarrows$	Ba^{++}
Sr	$\leftrightarrows$	Sr^{++}
Ca	$\leftrightarrows$	Ca^{++}
Na	$\leftrightarrows$	Na^+
Mg	$\leftrightarrows$	Mg^{++}
Be	$\leftrightarrows$	Be^{++}
Al	$\leftrightarrows$	Al^{3+}
Mn	$\leftrightarrows$	Mn^{++}
Zn	$\leftrightarrows$	Zn^{++}
Cr	$\leftrightarrows$	Cr^{3+}
Fe	$\leftrightarrows$	Fe^{++}
Cd	$\leftrightarrows$	Cd^{++}
Co	$\leftrightarrows$	Co^{++}
Ni	$\leftrightarrows$	Ni^{++}
Sn	$\leftrightarrows$	Sn^{++}
Pb	$\leftrightarrows$	Pb^{++}
H_2	$\leftrightarrows$	$2H^+$
Sb	$\leftrightarrows$	Sb^{3+}
Bi	$\leftrightarrows$	Bi^{3+}
As	$\leftrightarrows$	As^{3+}
Cu	$\leftrightarrows$	Cu^{++}
$2I^-$	$\leftrightarrows$	I_2
H_2O_2	$\leftrightarrows$	$O_2 + 2H^+$
Fe^{++}	$\leftrightarrows$	Fe^{3+}
$2Hg$	$\leftrightarrows$	Hg_2^{++}
Ag	$\leftrightarrows$	Ag^+
Hg	$\leftrightarrows$	Hg^{++}
Hg_2^{++}	$\leftrightarrows$	$2Hg^{++}$
$NO + 2HOH$	$\leftrightarrows$	$NO_3^- + 4H^+$
$2Br^-$	$\leftrightarrows$	Br_2
$2Cl^-$	$\leftrightarrows$	Cl_2
$2Cr^{3+} + 7HOH$	$\leftrightarrows$	$Cr_2O_7^{--} + 14H^+$
Au	$\leftrightarrows$	Au^{3+}
$Mn^{++} + 4HOH$	$\leftrightarrows$	$MnO_4^- + 8H^+$
$Cl_2 + 2HOH$	$\leftrightarrows$	$2HOCl + 2H^+$
$2HOH$	$\leftrightarrows$	$H_2O_2 + 2H^+$
Co^{++}	$\leftrightarrows$	Co^{3+}
$2F^-$	$\leftrightarrows$	F_2

INCREASING TENDENCY TO BE OXIDIZED OR

INCREASING ACTIVITY AS A REDUCING AGENT

INCREASING TENDENCY TO BE REDUCED OR

INCREASING ACTIVITY AS AN OXIDIZING AGENT

Whenever a reducing agent is oxidized, the oxidation product is a potential oxidizing agent because under the appropriate conditions this oxidation product can accept electrons, thereby reproducing the original reducing agent.   In other words, every oxidation is a reversible process as is every reduction.   In the activity series, an arrow pointing from left to right indicates the direction of an oxidation process (fate of a reducing agent), and an arrow pointing from right to left indicates a reduction process (fate of an oxidizing agent).   For example,

$$Cs \leftrightarrows Cs^+$$

The arrow pointing from left to right indicates that a Cs atom is oxidized to a Cs^+ ion; the arrow pointing from right to left shows that a Cs^+ ion is reduced to a Cs atom.   The double arrow is a conventional sign used to symbolize two reversible processes.

It should be evident that if a particular entity is an active reducing agent, the product of its oxidation is a relatively inactive, or weak, oxidizing agent.   Also if an entity is an active oxidizing agent, the product of its reduction is a relatively weak reducing agent.   For example, elemental cesium is a very active reducing agent, whereas its oxidation product, Cs^+, is an extremely inactive oxidizing agent.   Elemental fluorine is an exceedingly active oxidizing agent, but its reduction product, F^-, is such a weak reducing agent that it cannot reduce any known chemical substance.

Inspection of Table 20.4 reveals that the most active reducing agent is the top of the left-hand column and the most active oxidizing agent, F_2, is at the bottom of the right-hand column.

If a covalent entity, such as an acid, contains one or more loosely bound protons per molecule, it can oxidize any entity listed above H_2 in the left-hand column.   Therefore if any metallic element listed above H_2 in the left-hand column is added to an aqueous solution of an active source of loosely bound protons (an acid), elemental hydrogen is produced because hydrogen in its $+1$ oxidation state (H^+) is reduced to its 0 oxidation state.   Whenever elemental sodium or any metal above it is added to water at room temperature, gaseous hydrogen is produced because these relatively active reducing agents can reduce at least one potential proton per water molecule involved.   Those metals or entities below H_2 in the left-hand column are unable to reduce hydrogen from its $+1$ oxidation state to its elemental state.

With only a few exceptions, a reducing agent that resides at a certain level in the left-hand column can reduce any oxidizing agent below that level in the right-hand column. The higher the reducing agent resides in the left-hand column, the easier it can reduce an oxidizing agent lower in the right-hand column. For example, elemental aluminum, Al^0, can reduce iron(III), Fe^{3+}, more easily than it can reduce iron(II), Fe^{++}. Of course, this statement could read: Since Fe^{3+} is a better oxidizing agent than Fe^{++}, Fe^{3+} can oxidize Al^0 better than Fe^{++}. Potassium (K) can reduce loosely bound protons more easily than it can reduce Fe^{++} ions.

Generally an oxidizing agent which resides at a certain level in the right-hand column can oxidize any reducing agent above that level in the left-hand column. The lower the oxidizing agent resides in the right-hand column, the easier it can oxidize a reducing agent higher in the left-hand column. For example, elemental chlorine can oxidize bromide ion, Br^-, but it cannot oxidize fluoride ion, F^-. Also Cl_2^0 can oxidize iodide ion, I^-, more readily than it can oxidize Br^-.

20.10 CORROSION

The undesirable or unwanted oxidation of metals to yield either their oxides or their positive ions is a phenomenon called *corrosion*. Since the metallic atoms are frequently converted to ions, the products often are much more soluble in water than are the metals themselves. Therefore, if sufficient water is present, many metals undergo dissolution during corrosion. In fact, it seems that water is a necessary factor in corrosion phenomena. The higher a metal resides in the left column of the activity series (p. 487), the more susceptible it is to corrosion (more easily oxidized).

The oxidation of metals during corrosion is often caused either by acids (H^+ being the probable oxidizing agent) or by atmospheric oxygen. Industrial acid fumes can cause serious corrosion of some metals. The rusting of iron, which consumes thousands of tons of iron per year, seems to require both oxygen and moisture. The presence of ions in the water that is in contact with the metal greatly facilitates transfer of electrons from metal to oxidizing agent (p. 501).

The presence of elemental mercury greatly enhances the dissolution (in water) of lead in plumbing. This contact between lead and mercury is one in which a metal is in contact with another metal less readily oxidized than it, that is, a metal below it in the activity series (p. 487). The electrons that accumulate on the lead during its oxidation ($Pb^0 \rightarrow Pb^{++} + 2e^-$) apparently flow from the lead to the metal in contact with it if the other metal is below lead in the activity series. A negative charge is thereby built on the metal that is less readily oxidized. This phenomenon enhances the oxidation of the lead by favoring the reaction given above.

If metal X is in electrical contact with another metal Y that is below it in the activity series, oxidation (corrosion) of metal X is enhanced. With this in mind, it seems reasonable to accept the fact that if metal X is in contact with a metal above it in the activity series, corrosion of metal X is inhibited. The corrosion of iron is, in fact, significantly inhibited by contact with metals above it in the activity series (such as Mg, Zn, Cr). The metals that are more readily oxidized do corrode preferentially to the iron; hence they gradually disappear. Under these conditions such metals are called *sacrificial metals*. The over-all phenomenon is called *galvanic action*, similar to that in certain galvanic cells (p. 510).

Occasionally the products of corrosion yield a protective coating so that initial corrosion inhibits further corrosion. The greenish-blue coloration that appears eventually on new copper roofs is a protective coating of basic copper(II) carbonate, $Cu(OH)_2 \cdot CuCO_3$. A fresh surface of aluminum slowly corrodes in moist air, but after a protective coating of oxide has formed, further corrosion is markedly inhibited.

Many kinds of protective coatings are used to prevent corrosion of metals, the most economical being paint, oils, waxes, or lacquers. Iron may be coated with metallic zinc to yield what is called galvanized iron. Such a coating is applied by dipping the iron (previously surface-cleaned by acids) in molten zinc. Another method is to apply a coating of zinc dust and then heat so that the metallic zinc is absorbed into the surface of the iron. This method, called *sherardizing*, is used in the protection of small iron objects. The zinc coating is not only protective; it is also corroded preferentially, thereby acting as a sacrificial metal.

Metals may be alloyed to yield resistant materials. Stainless steel (Fe, Cr, C) and Defirust (Fe, Cr, Mn, Ni, C) are iron alloys that are very resistant to corrosion.

20.11 GRAM-EQUIVALENT WEIGHT OF AN ELEMENT

The quantitative relationship between the oxidizing agent and the reducing agent in a specific oxidation-reduction reaction is based on the concept that a given amount of the oxidizing agent can oxidize an equivalent amount of the reducing agent. In other words, each equivalent of oxidizing agent can oxidize one equivalent of reducing agent. A more specific, practical viewpoint is: each gram-equivalent of oxidizing agent can oxidize one gram-equivalent of reducing agent.

Since we realize that in every redox reaction the number of electrons accepted by the oxidizing agent is equal to the number of electrons donated by the reducing agent, let us identify the term *gram-equivalent weight*, the mass of one gram-equivalent.

The gram-equivalent weight of the oxidizing agent in a given reaction is the amount, in grams, that accepts one mole of electrons. The gram-equivalent weight of the reducing agent in a given reaction is the amount, in grams, that donates one mole of electrons.

In the reaction during which ionic silver oxidizes elemental tin, $2Ag^+ + Sn \rightarrow Sn^{++} + 2Ag$, 2 moles of silver ion are needed to oxidize one mole of tin. Each mole of silver ion can accept only one mole of electrons, and each mole of tin can donate 2 moles of electrons. The balanced equation indicates that 1 gram-equivalent of silver ion oxidize 1 gram-equivalent of tin. The gram-equivalent weight of silver is therefore 107.9 g, whereas the gram-equivalent weight of tin is 59.35 g.

The gram-equivalent weight of an element should be assigned only after inspection of the equation of the reaction in question. Often an element may have two or more different gram-equivalent weights, the actual value depending on the fate of the element. For example, elemental oxygen may act as an oxidizing agent in at least three different ways:

1. $O_2 + 4e^- \rightarrow 2O^{--}$ oxide ion
2. $O_2 + 2e^- \rightarrow O_2^{--}$ peroxide ion
3. $O_2 + e^- \rightarrow O_2^-$ superoxide ion

In the first case, the gram-equivalent weight of oxygen is 8 g, in the second it is 16 g, and in the third it is 32 g.

For some elements the gram-equivalent weight is constant. Each alkali metal element (1a) has a gram-equivalent weight numerically equal to its atomic weight. For each alkaline-earth metal element (2a), it is almost always numerically equal to one-half of its atomic weight. Whenever a halogen element acts as an oxidizing agent, its gram-equivalent weight is numerically equal to its atomic weight. Representative reactions for these three families of elements are

$$Na \rightarrow Na^+ + 1e^-$$
$$Ca \rightarrow Ca^{++} + 2e^-$$
$$F_2 + 2e^- \rightarrow 2F^-$$

20.12 GRAM-EQUIVALENT WEIGHT OF AN ACTIVE METAL

The elements above hydrogen in the activity series (see Table 20.4) are called the *active metals*, partly because they are the best electron donors and partly because they are able to reduce loosely bound protons on certain covalent entities. These covalent entities are usually called *acids*. Therefore the active metals can reduce the protons of certain acids to yield gaseous hydrogen. The simplified reduction reaction is $2H^+ + 2e^- \rightarrow H_2$. It is evident that each mole of gaseous hydrogen requires the acceptance of two moles of electrons by two moles of protons. One mole of electrons accepted would yield only one-half mole of hydrogen.

The gram-equivalent weight of an active metal is that amount of the metal which, under the correct conditions, can cause the production of one-half mole of hydrogen, or one gram-atom of hydrogen. Two gram-equivalents of metal are needed to yield one mole of gaseous hydrogen. The gram-equivalent weight of an active metal is numerically equal to its atomic weight divided by the number used to designate the oxidation state of the element after it is oxidized by the protons in aqueous solution. For example, iron is oxidized to iron(II) ions, Fe^{++}, by protons in aqueous solution. The gram-equivalent weight of iron is 55.85 g/2, or 27.93 g.

For an active metal it is possible to predict the approximate volume, corrected to standard conditions, of gaseous hydrogen produced during a complete reaction between an active metal and an excess of some active source of protons. Each gram-equivalent of metal can yield 11.2 liters of hydrogen measured at standard conditions, because this is the volume of one-half mole of hydrogen under these conditions.

20.13   GRAM-EQUIVALENT WEIGHT OF AN OXIDIZING OR REDUCING AGENT

Since hundreds of oxidizing agents and reducing agents contain two or more different elements, it is important to be able to identify the gram-equivalent weights of such substances. The chemical behavior of many of them depends on the reaction conditions. Thus the gram-equivalent weight of a specific oxidizing or reducing agent may vary, depending on the fate of the reagent.

Potassium permanganate ($K^+MnO_4^-$) is a common, direct source of the extremely strong oxidizing agent, permanganate ion, MnO_4^-. If MnO_4^- behaves as an oxidizing agent in acidic aqueous solutions, the MnO_4^- is reduced to Mn^{+2} (manganese(II) ion).

$$MnO_4^- + 8H^+ + 5e^- \rightarrow Mn^{+2} + 4HOH$$

Therefore under these conditions the gram-equivalent weight of $K^+MnO_4^-$ is equal to the molar weight of $K^+MnO_4^-$ divided by 5, 158 g/5, or 31.6 g. The milliequivalent weight of $K^+MnO_4^-$ is 31.6 mg.

However, if permanganate ion acts as an oxidizing agent in nonacidic solutions, the MnO_4^- is reduced to manganese dioxide, MnO_2.

$$MnO_4^- + 2HOH + 3e^- \rightarrow MnO_2 + 4OH^-$$

Under these conditions the gram-equivalent weight of $K^+MnO_4^-$ is equal to the molar weight of $K^+MnO_4^-$ divided by 3, 158 g/3, or 52.7 g. The milliequivalent weight is 52.7 mg.

In an acidic aqueous solution MnO_4^- can oxidize iron(II), Fe^{++}. Since the oxidation of iron(II) to iron(III) is a one-electron change, the gram-equivalent weight of Fe^{++} is numerically equal to the atomic weight of iron, 55.8 g. The complete oxidation of one gram-equivalent of Fe^{++} requires one gram-equivalent of MnO_4^-, let us say from potassium permanganate. Since one mole of potassium permanganate, $K^+MnO_4^-$, is the source of five gram-equivalents of permanganate ion, the complete reduction of one mole of permanganate ion by iron(II) ion requires five gram-equivalents of Fe^{++}.

$$5Fe^{++} + MnO_4^- + 8H^+ \rightarrow Mn^{++} + 5Fe^{++} + 4HOH$$

20.14   A SUMMARY OF COMMON TERMS

Oxidation is a chemical change—
  (a) during which an entity donates one or more electrons.
  (b) during which an element's oxidation number is increased.
  (c) caused by an oxidizing agent.
  (d) always accompanied by reduction.
  (e) which a reducing agent undergoes.
  (f) which occurs at the anode of an electrochemical cell.

Reduction is a chemical change—
  (a) during which an entity accepts one or more electrons.
  (b) during which an element's oxidation number is decreased.
  (c) caused by a reducing agent.
  (d) always accompanied by oxidation.
  (e) which an oxidizing agent undergoes.
  (f) which occurs at the cathode of an electrochemical cell.

An *oxidizing agent* is a chemical entity which during an oxidation-reduction reaction—
  (a) causes oxidation.
  (b) accepts one or more electrons.
  (c) is reduced.
  (d) contains at least one element whose oxidation number is decreased.

A *reducing agent* is a chemical entity which during an oxidation-reduction reaction—
  (a) causes reduction.
  (b) donates one or more electrons.
  (c) is oxidized.
  (d) contains at least one element whose oxidation number is increased.

Problems

1. A few substances that contain the element nitrogen are $(K^+)_3N^{3-}$, $K^+NO_3^-$, $NH_4^+Cl^-$, $K^+NO_2^-$, NH_2OH, $N_2H_5^+$, N_2H_4, NO, N_2, HN_3, $Cs^+NH_2^-$, $NH_2OH_2^+HSO_4^-$, N_2O_4, NH_3, $HONO_2$. (a) Indicate the oxidation state of nitrogen in each substance. (b) Relative to the element nitrogen, which can behave as oxidizing agents? (c) Relative to nitrogen, which can act as reducing agents? (d) In which substances is the nitrogen completely oxidized? (e) In which is nitrogen in its lowest oxidation state? (f) Identify each substance that can, relative to nitrogen, act both as a reducing agent and as an oxidizing agent.

2. Some entities are O_2, Ca, H_2, He, Rb, O^{--}, O_2^{--}, Sr^{++}, P_4, Se^{--}, H^-, I^-, C_2^{--}, Li^+, F_2, F^-, N^{3-}. (a) Which cannot be oxidized? (b) Which cannot be reduced? (c) Which can behave as electron acceptors? (d) Which can act as electron donors? (e) Which can act both as an oxidizing agent and as a reducing agent? (f) Which can act only as oxidizing agents?

3. Of the elements Rb, Al, In, Pb, N, As, Bi, Be, which is (a) the best reducing agent; (b) the best oxidizing agent; (c) the poorest reducing agent; (d) the poorest oxidizing agent?

4. Some common entities are Fe^{3+}, Sn^{++}, Cu^{++}, Ni^{++}, Fe, Co, Cd, Fe^{++}. By considering aqueous solutions of unit concentrations, which is (a) the poorest reducing agent; (b) the poorest oxidizing agent; (c) the best reducing agent; (d) the best oxidizing agent? (e) Can iron(III) oxidize Pb? (f) Can elemental lead reduce iron(II)? (g) Can Cd^{++} oxidize elemental iron? (h) Can nickel(II) oxidize tin(II)? (i) Can elemental iron reduce tin(II)? (j) Can tin(II) oxidize elemental iron?

5. Atoms of element 81 react with those of element 16 to yield a compound. During the reaction the oxidizing agent is reduced completely, and the reducing agent is oxidized completely. (a) Write the formula of the compound. (b) Which element acted as the reducing agent? (c) How many moles of electrons must be accepted by the oxidizing agent during the production of 3.3 moles of the compound? (d) What is the oxidation state of each atom of element 16 in the compound? (e) How many grams of the compound must be decomposed completely to yield as many atoms as are in 42 g of carbon-12 atoms?

6. What is the minimum amount of elemental nitrogen (in grams) needed to oxidize completely 7 moles of elemental barium?

7. How many g-atoms of elemental calcium are needed to convert 25 moles of carbonate ion, CO_3^{--}, to carbide ion, C_2^{--}?

8. (a) How many electrons must the bromine in one bromate ion, BrO_3^-, accept to be reduced completely? (b) How many electrons must 8 molecules of phosphine, PH_3, donate to be oxidized completely? (c) How many moles of electrons must be donated by 4 moles of butene, C_4H_8, if oxidation of the butene is to be complete? (d) How many moles of electrons must be accepted by 3.3 moles of chlorite ion, ClO_2^-, if the ions are to be reduced completely? (e) How many moles of electrons are needed to reduce completely 4.4 g of CO_2?

9. How many moles of electrons are involved in the following transformations? (a) Six moles of P_4O_{10} is reduced completely. (b) Twenty grams of elemental phosphorus is reduced completely. (c) One mole of chloride ion is oxidized to yield one mole of perchlorate ion, ClO_4^-. (d) One-half mole of bromate ion, BrO_3^-, is converted to elemental bromine. (e) Forty grams of hydroxylamine, NH_2OH, is converted completely to nitric acid, $HONO_2$.

10. How many moles of oxygen, O_2, are needed to oxidize completely 0.33 mole of $C_3H_8O_3$?

11. How many grams of elemental magnesium are needed to reduce completely 30.8 g of elemental nitrogen?

12. During a chemical reaction 4.5 moles of hydrazine, N_2H_4, donated 45 moles of electrons and was, thereby, converted to compound X. In X there is 1 g-atom of nitrogen per mole. What is the oxidation state of nitrogen in X?

13. A compound Z that consists solely of nitrogen and oxygen atoms contains 2 g-atoms of nitrogen per mole. Four and one-half moles of Z are reduced completely by 18 g-atoms of elemental aluminum. The reducing agent is oxidized completely. What is the formula of Z?

14. How many grams of elemental oxygen are needed to oxidize completely 60 g of pentane, C_5H_{12}?

15. Identify the oxidizing agent and reducing agent, if any, in each of the following equations.
(a) $CO + 2H_2 \rightarrow CH_3OH$
(b) $2H_2S + SO_2 \rightarrow 3S + 2H_2O$
(c) $3NO_2 + H_2O \rightarrow 2HNO_3 + NO$
(d) $2K + H_2 \rightarrow 2KH$
(e) $N_2O_5 + H_2O \rightarrow 2HNO_3$
(f) $3Br_2 + 6OH^- \rightarrow BrO_3^- + 5Br^- + 3H_2O$
(g) $H_2CO_2 + H_2SO_4 \rightarrow CO + OH_3^+ + HSO_4^-$
(h) $C_2H_2 + H_2 \rightarrow C_2H_4$
(i) $Fe + S \rightarrow FeS$
(j) $2CrO_4^{--} + 2H^+ \rightarrow Cr_2O_7^{--} + H_2O$

16. Each pair of elements listed below will, under certain conditions, interact chemically to yield a compound. Identify the compound, assuming that the oxidizing agent is reduced completely and the reducing agent is oxidized completely.
(a) Ba and I
(b) Rb and P
(c) Sn and Cl
(d) As and F
(e) Ge and O
(f) Fe and Br
(g) Cs and N
(h) In and Cl
(i) Se and O
(j) Zn and I

17. Balance the following equations by the oxidation-number–change method.

(a) $HNO_2 + HI \rightarrow H_2O + I_2 + NO$

(b) $C_4H_6 + O_2 \rightarrow CO_2 + H_2O$

(c) $PH_3 + N_2O \rightarrow H_3PO_4 + N_2$

(d) $HPO_3 + C \rightarrow H_2 + CO + P_4$

(e) $NH_3 + O_2 \rightarrow NO + H_2O$

(f) $C_3H_6(OH)_2 + O_2 \rightarrow CO_2 + H_2O$

(g) $SF_6 + H_2S \rightarrow HF + S$

(h) $H_2S + HNO_3 \rightarrow S + NO + H_2O$

(i) $NH_3 + O_2 \rightarrow NH_2OH$

(j) $NO_2 + H_2O \rightarrow HNO_3 + NO$

18. Balance the following equations by using the half-reaction (ion-electron) method.

(a) $Fe^{++} + H^+ + NO_3^- \rightarrow Fe^{3+} + NO_2 + H_2O$

(b) $Fe + H^+ + NO_3^- \rightarrow Fe^{++} + NH_4^+ + H_2O$

(c) $Cl^- + MnO_4^- + H^+ \rightarrow Mn^{++} + Cl_2 + H_2O$

(d) $Br_2 + SO_2 + H_2O \rightarrow H_2SO_4 + HBr$

(e) $PbO_2 + Mn^{++} + H^+ \rightarrow Pb^{++} + MnO_4^- + H_2O$

(f) $IO_3^- + SO_3^{--} + H^+ \rightarrow SO_4^{--} + I_2 + H_2O$

(g) $Bi^{3+} + SnO_2^{--} + OH^- \rightarrow Bi + SnO_3^{--}$

(h) $Cu + H^+ + NO_3^- \rightarrow Cu^{++} + NO + H_2O$

(i) $Cu + H^+ + NO_3^- \rightarrow Cu^{++} + NO_2 + H_2O$

(j) $Cl_2 + H_2O \rightarrow OCl^- + Cl^- + H^+$

(k) $ClO_3^- + H^+ + Fe^{++} \rightarrow Fe^{3+} + Cl^- + H_2O$

(l) $I_2 + S_2O_3^{--} \rightarrow I^- + S_4O_6^{--}$

(m) $SH^- + H^+ + NO_3^- \rightarrow S + NO + H_2O$

(n) $H^+ + Cr_2O_7^{--} + Fe^{++} \rightarrow Cr^{3+} + Fe^{3+} + H_2O$

(o) $Fe^{3+} + Sn^{++} \rightarrow Fe^{++} + Sn^{4+}$

(p) $MnO_4^- + H^+ + H_2O_2 \rightarrow O_2 + Mn^{++} + H_2O$

(q) $Fe^{++} + H_2O_2 \rightarrow H_2O + Fe^{3+}$

19. What is the gram-equivalent weight of (a) iron in reaction (b) in Problem 18? (b) iron in reaction (a) in Problem 18? (c) nitrate ion in reaction (h) in Problem 18? (d) nitrate ion in reaction (i) in Problem 18? (e) chlorate ion in reaction (k) in Problem 18?

20. Ten grams of a metal reacts completely in an acidic aqueous solution to yield 0.231 g of hydrogen. What is the gram-equivalent weight of the metal?

21. How many gram-equivalents of a metal are needed to reduce completely 70.4 g of elemental sulfur?

22. How many moles of elemental chlorine are needed to oxidize completely 10 gram-equivalents of bismuth?

21

ELECTROCHEMISTRY

21.1 A PERSPECTIVE

Many of the oxidation-reduction reactions mentioned in Chapter 20 involve ions. In each case we suggested that the over-all reaction be divided into two half-reactions, one the oxidation, the other the reduction. This separation of the two phenomena is not only a matter of convenience in balancing redox equations; it can also be done mechanically. That is, half-reactions can occur in individual compartments in electrochemical systems, compartments called cells.

This chapter consists of some descriptions about the extension of the concept of oxidation-reduction to practical industrial and commercial applications. We know that redox reactions involve the transfer of electrons from the reducing agent to the oxidizing agent. Hence it seems likely that if this transfer is spontaneous we should be able to devise a means to put to use the energy evolved.

Since nearly every redox reaction is reversible, one of the oxidation-reduction systems in the pair is, at ordinary temperature and pressure, spontaneous, and the other redox system is not. For instance, let us consider the formation of water from its elements.

$$H_2(g) + \tfrac{1}{2} O_2(g) \leftrightarrows H_2O(g) \qquad \Delta H = -57.8 \text{ kcal}$$

At ordinary temperature and pressure, the reaction reading from left to right is spontaneous and exothermic. Hence this redox reaction, if it occurs in a suitable electrochemical cell, yields electrical energy. Electrochemical cells that yield electrical energy are called either *voltaic* or *galvanic cells* (p. 510).

The reaction reading from right to left is, at ordinary temperature and pressure, nonspontaneous and endothermic. Therefore if this reaction is to occur in an ordinary electrochemical cell, energy must be expended continually. Electrochemical cells that employ electrical energy to produce redox reactions are called *electrolytic cells;* the over-all redox reaction is called *electrolysis.*

While you read this chapter, it is imperative that you keep in mind the fact that the major reactions in all electrochemical cells are oxidation-reduction. It might be helpful to review the definitions stated earlier concerning electrolytes, pseudoelectrolytes, and nonelectrolytes (p. 368). Figure 21.1 depicts certain kinds of systems that exhibit electrolytic conductances.

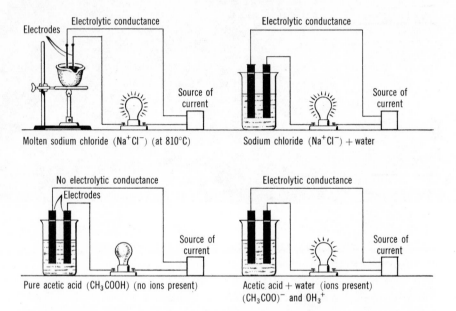

FIGURE 21.1 Diagrams of experiments which indicate that molten sodium chloride and an aqueous solution of sodium chloride conduct an electric current. Sodium chloride is an electrolyte, but acetic acid is a pseudoelectrolyte because it is a nonconductor in the pure state and a conductor in aqueous solution. Note that these experiments indicate the occurrence of conductance in a liquid system which contains ions (charged particles).

21.2 ELECTROLYSIS

Electrolysis is a phenomenon in which electrical energy is used to change the chemical identity of certain electrolytes and pseudoelectrolytes. Actually an electrolysis involves two distinct physical processes and each causes a chemical transformation. The two physical processes occur at two different electrodes in a liquid medium. The two electrodes are immersed in or are in contact with the liquid medium, which is part of an electrical circuit. Since the liquid medium contains ions, it is an electrolytic conductor. By means of a battery or a source of direct current, electricity (electrons) is "pumped" from one electrode, the anode, to the other, the cathode. In the liquid medium the mobile positive ions (cations) are attracted to the cathode, and the mobile negative ions (anions) to the anode. At the anode the negative ions transfer (donate) electrons to the anode; at the cathode the positive ions receive (accept) electrons from the cathode. Because of this migration of the ions and their eventual fate at the electrodes, the liquid appears to conduct an electric current. Actually this conductance is an electrolytic phenomenon; during electrolysis in an electrolytic cell, no electrons flow through the electrolyte. In fact, electrolytic conductance of a direct current is always accompanied by electrolysis. During electrolysis, every time an electron is received from an ion by the anode, another electron is discharged to an ion by the cathode. Therefore oxidation occurs at the anode and reduction at the cathode.

The electrolytic cell (in which electrolysis occurs) is an apparatus the design for which depends in part on the nature of the electrolyte, the chemical and physical properties of the solid materials that compose the electrodes, the chemical and physical properties of the substances produced at the electrodes, and the temperature at which the electrolysis is performed. In the interest of simplicity, we shall consider only the general structural characteristics of an electrolytic cell. Every electrolytic cell consists of a suitable vessel to contain the electrolytic liquid, two suitable electrodes, some means of collecting the products individually, and an arrangement to "pump" electrons from the anode to the cathode.

Actually an electrolytic cell is a device used to perform an oxidation and a reduction by physical means. In essence, electrons are "pulled" from ions at the anode, and electrons are "pushed" into ions at the cathode. If a positive ion has a weak tendency to accept electrons and a negative ion a weak tendency to donate, electrolysis can usually be accomplished by increasing the electrical potential between the electrodes. By increasing the electromotive force (emf) of the cell, the driving force of the electrons is increased.

21.3   OXIDATION OF FLUORIDE ION BY ELECTROLYSIS

Since elemental fluorine is the most avid electron acceptor, the fluoride ion, F^-, is the weakest electron donor.   Because of fluorine's extraordinary chemical activity, this element exists in nature in its -1 oxidation state only. Therefore, in order to prepare elemental fluorine, it is necessary to transform fluorine by oxidation from its -1 to its zero oxidation state. No ordinary chemical transformation can supply enough energy to oxidize fluoride ion. This can be accomplished only by a process in which ample energy is available. Electrolysis is the ideal choice because by using electrical energy an electron can be forcibly "yanked" from a fluoride ion. The "bath" liquid in the electrolytic cell is a molten mixture of hydrogen fluoride, H—F, and potassium fluoride, K^+F^-, usually at a temperature of 300°C. Since less energy is required to reduce a loosely bound proton (in H—F) than a potassium ion, elemental hydrogen is produced at the cathode while fluoride ions are oxidized to elemental fluorine at the anode.   (See Fig. 21.2.)

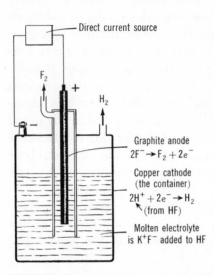

Direct current source

F_2

$+$

H_2

Graphite anode
$2F^- \rightarrow F_2 + 2e^-$

Copper cathode
(the container)
$2H^+ + 2e^- \rightarrow H_2$
(from HF)

Molten electrolyte
is K^+F^- added to HF

FIGURE 21.2 Diagram of an electrolytic cell used for the production of elemental fluorine. Fluoride ion is oxidized at the anode, and hydrogen in its $+1$ oxidation state is reduced to the elemental state at the copper cathode, which also serves as the cell wall.

21.4   ELECTROLYSIS OF IONIC CHLORIDES

The alkali metal elements and the alkaline-earth metal elements are extremely active reducing agents.   They are therefore always found in nature in a combined state, never in their elemental state. Generally they exist in nature as positively charged ions.   To produce the elemental form, it is necessary to reduce the positive ion.

The least expensive method for the production of metallic sodium, lithium, calcium, and magnesium is the electrolysis of their molten chlorides. Since these ionic chlorides have relatively high melting points, an "inert" substance is usually added to the molten electrolyte to lower the fusion temperature. The elemental form of the metal is produced at the cathode and elemental chlorine at the anode. (See Fig. 21.3.)

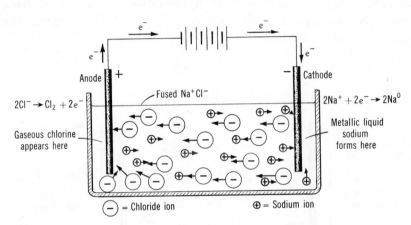

FIGURE 21.3 Electrolysis of molten sodium chloride. Sodium ions migrate in the liquid toward the cathode; chloride ions move toward the anode. Reduction of sodium ion occurs at the cathode; oxidation of chloride ion occurs at the anode.

At present, nearly all metallic sodium is prepared by the *Downs process*. The two electrode reactions are

$$\text{At the anode:}\quad 2Cl^- \rightarrow Cl_2 + 2e^-$$
$$\text{At the cathode:}\quad 2Na^+ + 2e^- \rightarrow 2Na$$

During the electrolysis, the production of 1 g-atom of sodium is accompanied by the simultaneous production of 1 g-atom of chlorine.

In the Hooker electrolytic cell, in which a brine (aqueous Na^+Cl^-) is the electrolyte, gaseous chlorine is produced at the anode ($2Cl^- \rightarrow Cl_2 + 2e^-$) and gaseous hydrogen at the cathode ($2H^+$ [from $2HOH$] $+ 2e^- \rightarrow H_2$). Since less energy is needed to reduce a loosely bound proton than to reduce a sodium ion, hydrogen rather than metallic sodium is produced at the cathode. Whenever a proton, from a water molecule, is reduced at the cathode, a hydroxide ion, OH⁻, is left behind in solution. As electrolysis proceeds, the concentration of hydroxide ions increases in the solution in the vicinity of the cathode. Since the sodium ions are "spectators" during the electrolysis, at the cathode the solution eventually contains mostly sodium ions and hydroxide ions. This cathode solution drips slowly and continuously from the electrolytic cell. Upon evaporation of the water, sodium hydroxide (white solid) is obtained. The electrolysis of aqueous sodium chloride is a profitable venture because three important industrial chemicals— hydrogen, chlorine, and sodium hydroxide—are produced from inexpensive sodium chloride. Of course, electrical energy is the major expense. (See Fig. 21.4.)

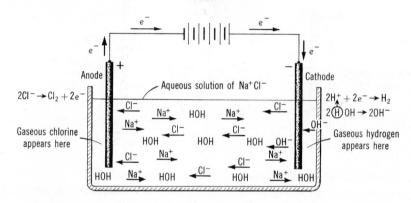

FIGURE 21.4 Electrolysis of an aqueous solution of sodium chloride. Although chloride ions are oxidized at the anode, hydrogen ions, H⁺ (not sodium ions) are reduced at the cathode. (The energy necessary to reduce H⁺ in aqueous solution is less than that needed to reduce Na⁺ in water.) Whenever an H⁺ ion is reduced, a hydroxide ion, OH⁻, appears in the solution.

21.5 ELECTROLYSIS OF WATER

Hydrogen and oxygen can be produced by the electrolysis of water. A small quantity of sulfuric acid, H_2SO_4, is added to the water, because the latter is an extremely poor electrolytic conductor. The protolytic dissociation of sulfuric acid produces ions, and apparently these ions make electrolysis possible. During the electrolysis of water, gaseous hydrogen is produced at the cathode, owing to the reduction of hydrogen from its +1 oxidation state to its elemental state, and gaseous oxygen is produced at the anode, owing to the oxidation of oxygen from its -2 oxidation state to its elemental state. The production of 2 g-atoms (2 g-equiv) of hydrogen at the cathode is accompanied by the simultaneous production at the anode of 1 g-atom (2 g-equiv) of oxygen. Therefore whenever 1 mole of hydrogen is produced, 0.5 mole of oxygen is produced. (See Fig. 21.5.)

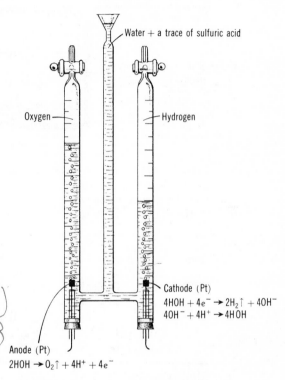

Water + a trace of sulfuric acid

Oxygen —

— Hydrogen

Cathode (Pt)
$$4HOH + 4e^- \rightarrow 2H_2\uparrow + 4OH^-$$
$$4OH^- + 4H^+ \rightarrow 4HOH$$

Anode (Pt)
$$2HOH \rightarrow O_2\uparrow + 4H^+ + 4e^-$$

21.6   INDUSTRIAL APPLICATIONS

Electrolysis is widely used as a means of producing elemental substances by oxidation or reduction. Aluminum (see Fig. 21.6) and sodium are produced exclusively by electrolysis, as is nearly all of the magnesium made industrially. Chlorine is produced almost entirely by the electrolysis of sodium chloride (either molten or aqueous); practically all of the sodium hydroxide (caustic soda) pro-

FIGURE 21.5 Electrolysis of water. A small amount of sulfuric acid is added to increase conductance.

duced commercially is a by-product of the electrolysis of aqueous sodium chloride. All elemental fluorine is also made by electrolysis.

Some examples of electrolysis are tabulated very briefly in Table 21.1. The examples illustrate the fact that although oxidation and reduction always occur simultaneously, they can be separated in certain ionic systems.

Certain metals must be produced in a very pure state if they are to be useful for specific purposes. For example, the electronic conductance of copper is retarded appreciably by the presence of small quantities of other elements. A relatively inexpensive and convenient process for production of metals in a high state of purity is called *electrolytic refining* or *electrorefining*.

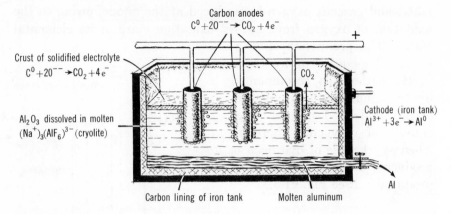

FIGURE 21.6 Cross-sectional diagram of the cell used in the commercial production of aluminum. The cell operates at an elevated temperature, and the carbon electrodes are continually consumed by the oxygen formed at the anode.

TABLE 21.1 Typical industrial electrolyses

Principal Electrolyte	Reaction at the Anode (Oxidation)	Reaction at the Cathode (Reduction)
Molten mixture of Al_2O_3 (from bauxite) and Na_3AlF_6 (cryolite)	$3O^{--} \rightarrow 3O + 6e^-$	$2Al^{3+} + 6e^- \rightarrow 2Al$
Molten $Mg^{++}(Cl^-)_2$	$2Cl^- \rightarrow Cl_2 + 2e^-$	$Mg^{++} + 2e^- \rightarrow Mg$
Molten Na^+Cl^-	$2Cl^- \rightarrow Cl_2 + 2e^-$	$2Na^+ + 2e^- \rightarrow 2Na$
Molten Li^+Br^-	$2Br^- \rightarrow Br_2 + 2e^-$	$2Li^+ + 2e^- \rightarrow 2Li$
Molten $Ca^{++}(Cl^-)_2$	$2Cl^- \rightarrow Cl_2 + 2e^-$	$Ca^{++} + 2e^- \rightarrow Ca$
Molten mixture of K^+F^- and HF	$2F^- \rightarrow F_2 + 2e^-$	$2H^+ + 2e^- \rightarrow H_2$
Aqueous Na^+Cl^-	$2Cl^- \rightarrow Cl_2 + 2e^-$	$2H^+ + 2e^- \rightarrow H_2$
Water plus a trace of H_2SO_4	$2HOH \rightarrow O_2 + 4e^- + 4H^+$	$4H^+ + 4e^- \rightarrow 2H_2$
Aqueous $Cu^{++}SO_4^{--}$	*Cu $\rightarrow Cu^{++} + 2e^-$	$Cu^{++} + 2e^- \rightarrow Cu$
Aqueous $Ag^+NO_3^-$	†Ag $\rightarrow Ag^+ + 1e^-$	$Ag^+ + 1e^- \rightarrow Ag$

* Anode is impure copper.
† Anode is impure silver.

In essence, electrolytic refining is an ingenious example of controlled electrolysis. In the cell the anode is a sheet or bar of the impure metal and the cathode a thin sheet of the pure metal. The electrolyte in the cell liquid contains some ionic compound of the metal. During the operation of the cell, metal atoms leave the anode because they are oxidized to positive ions. By carefully controlling the voltage of the cell, only the atoms of the metal being refined are deposited on the pure cathode.

In electrolytic refining of copper, the only reaction at the pure copper cathode is $Cu^{++} + 2e^- \rightarrow Cu^0$. At the impure copper anode, several metals, along with copper, may be oxidized to positive ions. However, only copper(II) ions are reduced at the cathode. All impurities either remain in solution or produce an undissolved sludge near the anode. In certain instances this anode sludge contains valuable elements such as gold, silver, and platinum. The anode sludge may contain any element below copper in the activity series; the elements above copper are in the solution as positive ions. (See Fig. 21.7.)

In the electrolytic refining of nickel, the anode is made of the impure nickel and the cathode is a sheet of pure nickel. As in the refining of copper, the cell is operated so that only nickel(II) ions are reduced at the cathode, while nickel ions are produced con-

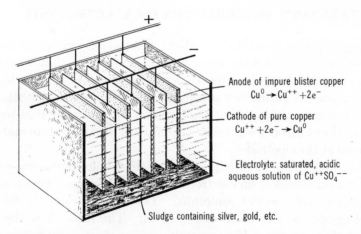

Anode of impure blister copper
$Cu^0 \rightarrow Cu^{++} + 2e^-$

Cathode of pure copper
$Cu^{++} + 2e^- \rightarrow Cu^0$

Electrolyte: saturated, acidic aqueous solution of $Cu^{++}SO_4^{--}$

Sludge containing silver, gold, etc.

FIGURE 21.7 Schematic sketch of the type of cell used in the electrolytic refining of copper. During electrolysis the over-all result is the transfer of copper from an impure anode to a pure copper cathode.

tinuously from nickel atoms at the impure nickel anode. The electrolyte is a nickel-containing salt.

The phenomenon of *electroplating* is an example of electrolysis. In essence, it is somewhat similar to electrolytic refining. During electroplating a thin film or deposit of a metal is produced electrolytically on the surface of another metal which serves as the cathode.

Metallic silver and nickel seem to plate on or adhere to copper surfaces more readily than to some other surfaces. Therefore, if the object to be plated is iron or steel, a thin film of copper is often deposited first, before the object is plated with silver or nickel. In silver-plating the object to be plated is the cathode, the anode is pure silver, and the electrolyte is a suitable ionic compound of silver. During electroplating silver ions are reduced to silver atoms at the cathode, while silver atoms are oxidized to silver ions at the anode. The process of nickel-plating is essentially identical to silver-plating.

The electroplating of chromium is frequently most practical on nickel surfaces. The object to be plated is the cathode because the elemental chromium is deposited at this electrode. The electrolytic solution contains ionic compounds that contain chromium and the anode is made of lead, platinum, or chromium.

21.7 FARADAY'S OBSERVATIONS ON ELECTROLYSIS

The quantitative observations about electrolysis first published in 1834 by Michael Faraday are classic. He noticed that whenever one gram-equivalent of a substance was produced at the anode, one gram-equivalent of another substance was produced at the cathode. Faraday also recognized that the quantity of electricity that passed between the electrodes was related directly to the amounts of material produced at the electrodes.

The amount of electricity required to produce one gram-equivalent of a substance at an electrode is called a *faraday*. One faraday is approximately 96,500 coulombs. This is equivalent to 6.02×10^{23} electrons, or one mole of electrons. The *coulomb* is the unit amount of electricity. If a coulomb passes a given point per second, the electric current is flowing at the rate of one ampere.

During the electrolysis of molten magnesium chloride, for instance, the electrode reactions are

Does the numerical value of a coulomb vary?

the anode: $2Cl^- \rightarrow Cl_2 + 2e^-$
the cathode: $Mg^{++} + 2e^- \rightarrow Mg$

The anode equation states that the production of 1 mole of chlorine requires the loss of 2 moles of electrons by 2 moles of chloride ion. Two faradays of electricity contain 193,000 coulombs, or 2 moles of electrons. The cathode equation states that 1 mole of magnesium ion must accept 2 moles of electrons to yield 1 mole of magnesium. Two faradays of electricity will supply these 2 moles of electrons. The production of 6.08 g of magnesium metal, actually 0.25 mole, requires 0.5 faraday, or 48,250 coulombs.

Some typical problems are given below.

a. How many grams of metallic chromium would be deposited by the reduction of chromium(III) ions during the passage of 4.8×10^3 coulombs through the cell?

The process $Cr^{3+} + 3e^- \rightarrow Cr$ requires 3 moles of electrons per mole of chromium deposited; or the number of moles of Cr obtained is $\frac{1}{3}$ the number of moles of electrons used in the cell. Therefore we must determine how many moles of electrons passed through the cell. Since 9.65×10^4 coulombs is equivalent to 1 mole of electrons,

$$\frac{4.8 \times 10^3}{9.65 \times 10^4} = 4.98 \times 10^{-2} \text{ mole of electrons}$$

Since the number of moles of Cr produced is $\frac{1}{3}$ the number of moles of electrons, $4.98 \times 10^{-2}/3 = 1.66 \times 10^{-2}$ mole of Cr obtained. Since 52.01 g is 1 mole of Cr, $(52.01)(1.66 \times 10^{-2}) = 86.4 \times 10^{-2}$ g, or 0.864 g of Cr obtained.

b. How many hours would be needed to deposit 356 g of copper from Cu^{++} if a current of 150 amperes is flowing through the cell?

Since 356 g of Cu is 5.6 moles, 11.2 moles of electrons will be needed. $Cu^{++} + 2e^- \rightarrow Cu$. Each mole of electrons is in 9.65×10^4 coulombs; therefore $(11.2)(9.65 \times 10^4) = 10.82 \times 10^5$ coulombs are necessary. Since coulombs = amperes $\times$ seconds,

$$\frac{10.82 \times 10^5}{150} = 7.2 \times 10^3 \text{ seconds} = \text{time required}$$

Since each hour is 3.6×10^3 sec, 2 hours will be needed.

21.8 AVOGADRO'S NUMBER

Previously (p. 29) we referred to Avogadro's number, the number of atoms in one gram-atom of any element and the number of molecules in one mole of a covalent substance. The number of electrons in a faraday is actually an Avogadro's number of electrons. Using Faraday's generalizations and the charge on a single electron, we can calculate quite accurately the number of electrons in one faraday. This number of electrons corresponds to one of the most accurate values of Avogadro's number.

A precise value of a faraday is 96,493 coulombs. The most precise value of the charge of an electron is 1.6018×10^{-19} coulomb. Therefore the number of electrons necessary to supply 96,493 coulombs is

$$\frac{\text{coulombs/faraday}}{\text{coulomb/electron}} = \frac{9.6493 \times 10^4}{1.6018 \times 10^{-19}}$$

$$= 6.0238 \times 10^{23} \text{ electrons/faraday}$$

$$\text{Avogadro's number} = 6.0238 \times 10^{23}$$

21.9 VOLTAIC (GALVANIC) CELLS

Most of the material in the preceding sections of this chapter is concerned with electrolytic cells and the redox reactions that occur therein. This section and those following pertain to descriptions and discussions of electrochemical cells in which chemical changes produce electrical energy. Such cells are either called *voltaic cells* (in recognition of Alessandro Volta (Italian), who in 1800 constructed the first such cell), or called *galvanic cells* (in homage to Luigi Galvani (Italian), who, shortly before Volta's experiments, investigated novel electrical phenomena by using frogs). Nearly all of the ordinary types of wet and dry batteries used today are voltaic (galvanic) cells. In each of these batteries there is an anode at which oxidation occurs and a cathode at which reduction takes place.

In the more practical voltaic cells, the source of electrons is some active metallic element. Transformation of the metal's atoms to positive ions is an important aspect.

$$\text{Metal atom} \leftrightarrows \text{metal ion}^{n+} + ne^-$$

where n is a small integer.

<u>Water is the fluid medium in all ordinary voltaic cells.</u> We recall that the more active metals tend strongly to behave as reducing agents in the presence of water, thereby being converted to their water-soluble ions. If an alkali metal is placed in water, the reaction reading from left to right appears to be so greatly favored that the conversion of metal atoms to positive ions appears complete. This conversion is favored because electrons are continually removed from the metal by the loosely bound protons of the water molecules.

If a strip of metallic zinc is placed in water, no appreciable amount of zinc is oxidized because the reaction, $Zn \leftrightarrows Zn^{++} + 2e^-$, attains equilibrium after only a very few ions are formed. Nevertheless, the liberated electrons impart a negative charge to the strip of zinc.

If a piece of metallic zinc is placed in an aqueous solution of copper(II) sulfate, $Cu^{++}SO_4^{--}$, metallic copper is deposited on the zinc: $Cu^{++} + 2e^- \leftrightarrows Cu^0$. Zinc ions enter the solution: $Zn \leftrightarrows Zn^{++} + 2e^-$. These reactions attain equilibrium as the surface of the zinc is covered by metallic copper. (See Fig. 21.8.) This indicates that copper(II) ion can oxidize metallic zinc and that electrons are transferred from the zinc to copper-(II) ions. Let us now describe a simple voltaic cell with which we can demonstrate and use the actual flow of electrons from elemental zinc to copper(II) ions.

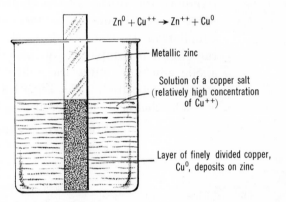

$$Zn^0 + Cu^{++} \rightarrow Zn^{++} + Cu^0$$

— Metallic zinc

Solution of a copper salt (relatively high concentration of Cu^{++})

Layer of finely divided copper, Cu^0, deposits on zinc

FIGURE 21.8 Deposition of metallic copper on a strip of zinc immersed in a solution containing copper(II) ions. For every copper atom deposited, a zinc ion appears in solution.

21.10 THE ZINC-COPPER CELL (THE DANIELL CELL)

A porous partition is placed in a suitable vessel to divide it into two compartments of approximately equal volume. Into one compartment is poured an aqueous solution of zinc sulfate, $Zn^{++}SO_4^{--}$; into the other is poured an aqueous solution of copper(II) sulfate. The porous partition prevents complete mixing of the two solutions,

Know!

KNOW!

but when a current is drawn from the cell, ions can diffuse through the partition. A strip of metallic zinc is placed in the solution that contains zinc ions. A strip of metallic copper is placed in the solution containing copper(II) ions. The strip of zinc serves as the anode and the copper as the cathode. Since the zinc is a better electron donor than copper, the anode becomes the negative electrode: $Zn \leftrightarrows Zn^{++} + 2e^-$.

If the two electrodes are connected correctly, an electric current may be taken from the cell. If a voltmeter is placed in the external circuit, the voltage of the cell can be determined. If the solutions in the electrode compartments are one molal (p. 371) in the respective ions, the voltage of the Daniell cell is approximately one volt. After the electrodes are connected, electrons flow in the external circuit from the zinc anode to the copper cathode; within the cell the circuit is completed by the migration of sulfate ions. At the anode zinc ions enter the solution, and at the cathode metallic copper is deposited. (See Fig. 21.9.)

The chemical reactions are

At the anode: $Zn \rightarrow Zn^{++} + 2e^-$
At the cathode: $Cu^{++} + 2e^- \rightarrow Cu$

m = modality - g/liter

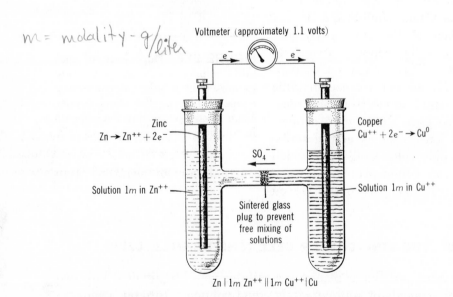

FIGURE 21.9 Electrochemical cell (Daniell cell) in which the anode system is Zn^0, $1\ m\ Zn^{++}$, and the cathode system is Cu^0, $1\ m\ Cu^{++}$. The approximate emf of this cell is 1.1 volts.

21.11 THE VOLTAGE OF VOLTAIC CELLS

The voltage or electromotive force (emf) of a voltaic cell is dependent on (1) the electron-donor vigor of the anode metal; (2) the electron-acceptor vigor of the entities reduced at the cathode; (3) the concentration of the solutions surrounding the electrodes; (4) the temperature. Let us consider a voltaic cell in which the anode system is a magnesium rod in contact with a one molal (1 m) solution of magnesium nitrate, $Mg^{++}(NO_3^-)_2$. The cathode system is a silver rod in contact with a 1 m solution of silver nitrate, $Ag^+NO_3^-$. The reaction at the anode is $Mg \leftrightarrows Mg^{++} + 2e^-$. The reaction at the cathode is $2Ag^+ + 2e^- \leftrightarrows 2Ag$. The voltage of this magnesium-silver cell is approximately 3.1 volts. This is a greater emf than that of the zinc-copper cell because magnesium is a more active electron donor than zinc, and silver ion is a more active electron acceptor than copper(II) ion. Since the voltages of such voltaic cells are related to the activities of the metals used, the activity series of the metals (p. 516) is often called an *electromotive series*.

By constructing various kinds of voltaic cells, it is possible to demonstrate the following generalizations:

a. The more active electron-donor metals can under most circumstances reduce the positive ions of the less active electron donors.
b. The positive ions of the less active metals can oxidize the atoms of the more active metals.
c. The easier the oxidation of the metal, the more difficult the reduction to the metal of its positive ions.
d. The more difficult the oxidation of the metal, the easier the reduction to the metal of its positive ions.

21.12 SINGLE ELECTRODE POTENTIALS

The zinc-copper cell, like all voltaic cells, consists of two half-cells, or couples: the anode half-cell, $Zn \leftrightarrows Zn^{++} + 2e^-$ (zinc half-cell) and the cathode half-cell, $Cu^{++} + 2e^- \leftrightarrows Cu$ (copper half-cell). The over-all oxidation-reduction reaction that occurs during operation of the cell is the sum of the two half-reactions at the two half-cells. The voltage of the cell is approximately the sum of the single electrode potentials of the two half-cells. (The potential difference between the half-cells is usually measured with a potentiometer.)

An abbreviated notation of the zinc-copper cell is Zn | Zn^{++}(1 m) || Cu^{++}(1 m) | Cu.

It is impossible at present either to measure the actual voltage (emf) of a half-cell or to designate a sign to the single electrode potential, but it is possible to compare one single electrode potential with another.   Using a standard hydrogen electrode, with which all other electrodes (half-cells) can be compared, an arbitrary scale of single electrode potentials has been formulated.   The half-reaction at the standard hydrogen electrode is H$_2 \leftrightarrows$ 2H$^+$ + 2e$^-$. This half-cell is arranged by using a spongy platinum electrode surrounded by hydrogen gas at 1 atm, immersed in an acidic aqueous solution whose effective proton (hydrogen ion) concentration is 1 m. This hydrogen electrode is arbitrarily assigned a voltage (emf) of zero.   (See Fig. 21.10.)

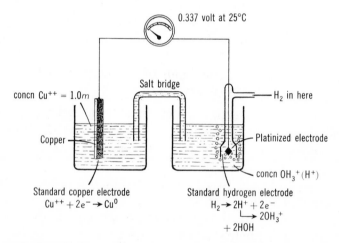

0.337 volt at 25°C

concn Cu^{++} = 1.0m

Salt bridge

H$_2$ in here

Copper

Platinized electrode

concn OH$_3^+$ (H$^+$)

Standard copper electrode
Cu^{++} + 2e$^- \rightarrow$ Cu^0

Standard hydrogen electrode
H$_2 \rightarrow$ 2H$^+$ + 2e$^-$
$\rightarrow$ 2OH$_3^+$
+ 2HOH

FIGURE 21.10 Cell used in determining the single electrode potential of the standard copper electrode, Cu^0, 1 m Cu^{++}.   The standard hydrogen electrode is used as the reference electrode.

The single electrode potential of the zinc half-cell (Zn $\leftrightarrows$ Zn^{++} + 2e$^-$) is determined by constructing a voltaic cell in which one half-cell is the zinc electrode (in 1 m Zn^{++} solution) and the other, the standard hydrogen electrode.   Since the potential of the hydrogen electrode is zero, the voltage, 0.76 volts, of the zinc-hydrogen cell is the single electrode potential of zinc (zinc half-cell). The zinc-hydrogen cell may be noted as Zn | Zn^{++}(1 m) || H$^+$(1 m)

| H_2(1 atm). The hydrogen electrode is positive with respect to the zinc electrode, but there are two conventions in regard to the sign of the zinc electrode potential. By one convention it is $+0.76$ volts, and by the other it is -0.76 volts. In the United States the positive sign is more commonly used.

By constructing a copper-hydrogen cell, Cu | Cu^{++}(1 m) || H^+ (1 m) | H_2 (1 atm), the single electrode potential of copper is found to be -0.34 volts. The emf of the copper half-cell has a negative sign because the hydrogen electrode is negative with respect to it.

Table 21.2 lists some single electrode potentials and the corresponding half-cell reactions. Using these values, we can calculate the voltage of certain voltaic cells. In a magnesium-copper cell: at the magnesium half-cell (anode), $Mg \leftrightarrows Mg^{++} + 2e^-$; at the copper half-cell (cathode), $Cu^{++} + 2e^- \leftrightarrows Cu$. Since copper(II) ions are reduced at the cathode, the half-cell reaction is the reverse of that noted in Table 21.2. The electrode potential of this copper half-cell is $+0.34$ (the reverse of -0.34). Hence the voltage of the magnesium-copper cell is $+0.34 + 2.34 = 2.68$. The voltage of a tin-silver cell, Sn | Sn^{++}(1 m) || Ag^+(1 m) | Ag, is $0.14 + 0.80 = 0.94$ volts.

Table 21.2 lists the standard electrode potentials (acidic solutions at 25°C) of some half-cells as they are determined in conjunction with the standard hydrogen electrode (p. 514). The electrode potential ($+0.762$) of a $Zn \leftrightarrows Zn^{++}$(1 m) electrode implies that metallic zinc in acidic solutions is a better reducing agent than metallic nickel because the potential of the electrode, $Ni \leftrightarrows Ni^{++}$ (1 m), is only $+0.250$. The electrode potentials may be considered as molar oxidation potentials. The more positive the value, the better the reducing agent; the less positive the value, the poorer the reducing agent. Each electrode potential is therefore the voltage of a specific half-cell, and it is a measure of the tendency for the specific half-reaction to occur in the stated direction.

The voltage of a given galvanic cell is a measure of the tendency for the over-all oxidation-reduction to occur. The over-all redox reaction is the total of the two half-cell half-reactions. The voltage of the magnesium-silver ion cell (3.1 volts) is greater than that of the zinc-copper cell (1.1 volts), which indicates that the reaction

$$Mg^\circ + 2Ag^+ \rightarrow Mg^{++} + 2Ag^\circ$$

has a greater driving force (under the conditions measured) than the reaction

$$Zn^\circ + Cu^{++} \rightarrow Zn^{++} + Cu^\circ$$

TABLE 21.2 Standard electrode (oxidation-reduction) potentials in the electromotive series

Half-Reaction	Electrode Potential, in Volts
$Li \leftrightarrows Li^+ + e^-$	+3.05
$Cs \leftrightarrows Cs^+ + e^-$	+2.92
$Rb \leftrightarrows Rb^+ + e^-$	+2.92
$K \leftrightarrows K^+ + e^-$	+2.92
$Ba \leftrightarrows Ba^{++} + 2e^-$	+2.90
$Sr \leftrightarrows Sr^{++} + 2e^-$	+2.89
$Ca \leftrightarrows Ca^{++} + 2e^-$	+2.87
$Na \leftrightarrows Na^+ + e^-$	+2.71
$Mg \leftrightarrows Mg^{++} + 2e^-$	+2.34
$Be \leftrightarrows Be^{++} + 2e^-$	+1.85
$Al \leftrightarrows Al^{3+} + 3e^-$	+1.67
$Mn \leftrightarrows Mn^{++} + 2e^-$	+1.18
$Zn \leftrightarrows Zn^{++} + 2e^-$	+0.762
$Cr \leftrightarrows Cr^{3+} + 3e^-$	+0.73
$Fe \leftrightarrows Fe^{++} + 2e^-$	+0.44
$Cd \leftrightarrows Cd^{++} + 2e^-$	+0.402
$Co \leftrightarrows Co^{++} + 2e^-$	+0.277
$Ni \leftrightarrows Ni^{++} + 2e^-$	+0.250
$Sn \leftrightarrows Sn^{++} + 2e^-$	+0.136
$Pb \leftrightarrows Pb^{++} + 2e^-$	+0.126
$H_2 \leftrightarrows 2H^+ + 2e^-$	0.0000
$Sb \leftrightarrows Sb^{3+} + 3e^-$	−0.10
$Bi \leftrightarrows Bi^{3+} + 3e^-$	−0.20
$As \leftrightarrows As^{3+} + 3e^-$	−0.30
$Cu \leftrightarrows Cu^{++} + 2e^-$	−0.345
$Cu \leftrightarrows Cu^+ + e^-$	−0.521
$I^- \leftrightarrows \frac{1}{2}I_2 + e^-$	−0.53
$H_2O_2 \leftrightarrows O_2 + 2H^+ + 2e^-$	−0.682
$Fe^{++} \leftrightarrows Fe^{3+} + e^-$	−0.771
$Hg \leftrightarrows \frac{1}{2}Hg_2^{++} + e^-$	−0.799
$Ag \leftrightarrows Ag^+ + e^-$	−0.800
$Hg \leftrightarrows Hg^{++} + 2e^-$	−0.854
$\frac{1}{2}Hg_2^{++} \leftrightarrows Hg^{++} + e^-$	−0.910
$NO + 2HOH \leftrightarrows NO_3^- + 4H^+ + 3e^-$	−0.96
$Br^- \leftrightarrows \frac{1}{2}Br_2 + e^-$	−1.065
$Mn^{++} + 2HOH \leftrightarrows MnO_2 + 4H^+ + 2e^-$	−1.23
$Cl^- \leftrightarrows \frac{1}{2}Cl_2 + e^-$	−1.358
$2Cr^{3+} + 7HOH \leftrightarrows Cr_2O_7^{--} + 14H^+ + 6e^-$	−1.36
$Au \leftrightarrows Au^{3+} + 3e^-$	−1.50
$Mn^{++} + 4HOH \leftrightarrows MnO_4^- + 8H^+ + 5e^-$	−1.52
$\frac{1}{2}Cl_2 + HOH \leftrightarrows HOCl + H^+ + e^-$	−1.63
$HOH \leftrightarrows \frac{1}{2}H_2O_2 + H^+ + e^-$	−1.77
$Co^{++} \leftrightarrows Co^{3+} + e^-$	−1.84
$F^- \leftrightarrows \frac{1}{2}F_2 + e^-$	−2.85

21.13 FREE-ENERGY CHANGES IN VOLTAIC CELLS

In Section 21.11 we stated that the emf (voltage) of a given voltaic cell is an indication of the tendency for a specific redox reaction to occur. A positive value indicates that the reaction proceeds spontaneously in the direction written. This means, of course, that the reaction proceeds with a decrease in free energy (ΔF is negative). Hence the free-energy change (ΔF) of the reaction is related to the emf of the cell. A negative value of emf indicates an increase in free energy (ΔF is positive), and the redox reaction is not spontaneous.

Consider the zinc-copper cell (p. 512). $m = molality$

$$Zn^\circ + Cu^{++}(1\,m) \leftrightarrows Zn^{++}(1\,m) + Cu^\circ \qquad (at\ 25^\circ C)$$

The standard emf may be written as $E^\circ = 1.10$ volts.

$$E^\circ = E^\circ_{Zn} - E^\circ_{Cu} \qquad or \qquad E^\circ = E^\circ_{Zn} + E^\circ_{Cu^{++}}$$
$$+1.10 = +0.76 - (-0.34) \qquad (at\ 25^\circ C)$$

Since the value of the emf of the cell is positive, we conclude that under standard conditions the reaction proceeds spontaneously to the right. Zinc spontaneously reduces copper(II) ion, but Cu° does not spontaneously reduce Zn^{++}.

Consider the cell in which each substance is in its standard state.

$$\tfrac{1}{2} I_2(s) + Fe^{++}(1\,m) \leftrightarrows I^-(1\,m) + Fe^{3+}(1\,m)$$

The emf of this cell is

$$E^\circ = E^\circ_{Fe^{++}} - E^\circ_{I^-} = -0.771 - (-0.53) = -0.241$$
or $$E^\circ = E^\circ_{Fe^{++}} + E^\circ_{I_2} = -0.771 + (+0.53) = -0.241$$

Since the value of the emf of the cell is negative, we conclude that under standard conditions the reaction does not proceed spontaneously to the right. Iron(II) does not spontaneously reduce I_2, but I^- does reduce Fe^{3+} spontaneously.

The previous discussion is based on a thermodynamic viewpoint. Although the sign of the emf of a cell may indicate the direction of the reaction, this is no indication of the velocity of the reaction. The reaction might be so slow that its rate is immeasurably small. Also if the over-all reaction proceeds in two or more steps, one step, perhaps the initial, may have a positive ΔF although the free-energy change for the over-all reaction is negative. In such a case the initial step cannot occur spontaneously.

The expression that relates the standard free-energy change ($\Delta F°$) to the standard emf (voltage) of a voltaic cell is

$$\Delta F° = -n\mathfrak{F}E°$$

where n is the number of moles of electrons, or faradays, transferred as stated in the chemical equation; $\mathfrak{F}$ is the number of coulombs in a faraday, 96,500; $E°$ is the standard emf of the cell. $\Delta F°$ is the standard free-energy change (p. 449) of the over-all redox reaction in the cell at 25°C, of any gases at 1 atm, and of ionic concentrations at $1\ m$.

Let us consider again the zinc-copper cell (Daniell cell) under standard conditions.

Anode	$Zn° \leftrightarrows Zn^{++} + 2e^-$	$E° = +0.76$
Cathode	$Cu^{++} + 2e^- \leftrightarrows Cu°$	$E° = +0.34$
Over-all reaction	$Zn° + Cu^{++} \leftrightarrows Zn^{++} + Cu°$	$E° = +1.10$

$$\Delta F° = -n\mathfrak{F}E° = -(2)(96,500)(+1.10) = -51\ \text{kcal}$$

The negative value of ΔF is a further sign that the reaction proceeds spontaneously to the right.

In Chapter 19 (p. 466) we presented an expression that relates the free-energy change of a reaction to the equilibrium constant.

$$\Delta F° = -RT \ln K$$

If the reaction involves reactants and products in their standard states (25°C and 1 atm), the equation relates the standard free energy $\Delta F°$.

$$\Delta F° = -RT \ln K$$

Since $\Delta F° = -n\mathfrak{F}E°$, then $-RT \ln K = -n\mathfrak{F}E°$.   Therefore

$$E° = \frac{RT}{n\mathfrak{F}} \ln K$$

If $T = 298°$ (25°C), $\mathfrak{F} = 96,500$, $R = 1.99$, and if $\ln K$ to $\log K$,

$$E° = \frac{0.059}{n} \log K$$

or

$$\text{Log } K = \frac{nE°}{0.059}$$

Let us consider the redox reaction and calculate K.

$$Ag° + Hg^{++} \leftrightarrows Ag^+ + \tfrac{1}{2} Hg_2^{++}$$

$$E^\circ = E^\circ_{Ag,Ag^+} - E^\circ_{Hg_2^{++},Hg^{++}}$$
$$E^\circ = -0.80 - (-0.91) = +0.11$$

$$\log K = \frac{nE^\circ}{0.059} = \frac{(1)(+0.11)}{0.059} = 1.8$$

$$K = 10^{1.8} = 6.3 \times 10^1 = 63$$

The relatively large value for the equilibrium constant, K, indicates that the reaction has a distinct tendency to proceed from left to right, as written in the chemical equation.

Let us consider a generalized reaction system expressed by the chemical equation

$$aA + bB \leftrightharpoons cC + dD$$

By applying the equilibrium law, we can derive the expression for the equilibrium constant K.

$$K = \frac{C^c\,D^d}{A^a\,B^b}$$

which if stated more accurately in terms of activities (effective concentrations) reads

$$K = \frac{a_C^c\,a_D^d}{a_A^a\,a_B^b}$$

where a_C^c means activity of C raised to the cth power.
Then, since $\Delta F^\circ = -RT \ln K$,

$$\Delta F = \Delta F^\circ + RT \ln \frac{a_C^c\,a_D^d}{a_A^a\,a_B^b} = \Delta F^\circ + RT \ln Q$$

Because $\Delta F = -n\mathfrak{F}E$ and $\Delta F^\circ = -n\mathfrak{F}E^\circ$,

$$E = E^\circ - \frac{RT}{n\mathfrak{F}} \ln \frac{a_C^c\,a_D^d}{a_A^a\,a_B^b} = E^\circ - \frac{RT}{n\mathfrak{F}} \ln Q$$

This relation, called the *Nernst equation*, can be abbreviated since most of the redox systems are at 25°C and logarithms to the base 10 are used.

$$E = E^\circ - \frac{0.059}{n} \log Q$$

In this equation E is the emf of the cell (oxidation potential of the reaction system) under the concentration conditions; E° is the corresponding emf under standard activity conditions; n is the number of faradays involved in the redox reaction; Q is the reaction quotient as defined by the equilibrium law.

Although activities are effective concentrations only and are less than stoichiometric concentrations in most solutions, we may state that the emf of a cell does vary with the activities and the concentrations of the redox reaction participants. It will be well to keep in mind that the activity of a pure elemental form of matter is unity, and that the activity of an ion in a very dilute solution is very nearly equal to the concentration of the ion. For rough calculations it is possible to use concentrations in the Nernst equation because these yield valid qualitative statements. Values of E (the emf) computed in this manner will, of course, be only approximate.

In dilute solutions the activity of water may be considered unity and hence dropped from the reaction quotient expression.

Let us consider the reaction system

$$Sn(s) + Pb(aq)^{++} = Sn(aq)^{++} + Pb(s) \qquad \text{(at 25°C)}$$

$$E = E° - \frac{RT}{2} \ln \frac{a_{Sn^{++}}}{a_{Pb^{++}}} = 0.136 - (+0.126) - \frac{0.059}{2} \log \frac{a_{Sn^{++}}}{a_{Pb^{++}}}$$

$$E = 0.010 - \frac{0.059}{2} \log \frac{a_{Sn^{++}}}{a_{Pb^{++}}}$$

If activity of Sn^{++} = activity of Pb^{++}, or $a_{Sn^{++}} = a_{Pb^{++}}$, it is evident that elemental tin can reduce lead ion.

Let us assume that in a specific cell $a_{Sn^{++}} = 1.2$ and that $a_{Pb^{++}} = 0.2$ at 25°C. Then

$$E = 0.010 - \frac{0.059}{2} \log \frac{1.2}{0.2} = 0.010 - 0.023 = -0.013$$

The emf of the cell with the activities as indicated is negative in this case. Therefore the spontaneous reaction in such a cell is the reduction of Sn^{++} by elemental Pb. Apparently the ionic activities play a significant role as we consider the redox reactions in specific cells.

21.14 CONCENTRATION CELLS

The voltage of any voltaic cell may be varied by changing the ion concentrations of the solutions that surround the electrodes because the positive ion of the electrode metal is one of the factors in a reversible reaction which can, under certain conditions, attain a state of equilibrium. In the determination of single electrode potentials, the effective concentration of the solutions surrounding the electrodes must be one molal in the ion related to the electrode element. The effective proton (hydrogen ion) concentration of an aqueous solution may be measured by observing the change in voltage of a hydrogen electrode placed in the solution, since the half-reaction, $H_2 \leftrightarrows 2H^+ + 2e^-$, is affected by the H^+ concentration of the solution.

By applying Le Châtelier's principle, we see why a single electrode potential varies with the concentration of the solution surrounding the electrode. In the half-cell reaction, $Cu \leftrightarrows Cu^{++} + 2e^-$, we note that Cu^{++} ion is a factor in a reversible process which can attain a state of equilibrium. By increasing the concentration of Cu^{++} from 1 m to 2 m, the process $Cu^{++} + 2e^- \rightarrow Cu$ is favored. This causes the single electrode potential of copper to change to a value higher than the assigned potential noted in Table 21.2. In the case of the zinc half-cell reaction, $Zn \leftrightarrows Zn^{++} + 2e^-$, if the concentration of Zn^{++} is increased from 1 m to 2 m, the process favored is $Zn^{++} + 2e^- \leftrightarrows Zn$. This causes the zinc electrode potential to decrease below the assigned value noted in Table 21.2.

A copper concentration cell is constructed with two copper electrodes, one in contact with a dilute solution of copper(II) sulfate and the other with a concentrated solution of the same substance.

$$Cu \mid Cu^{++} \text{ (low concn)} \parallel Cu^{++} \text{ (high concn)} \mid Cu$$

Since the reduction of Cu^{++} in the presence of copper is favored by a high concentration of Cu^{++}, the more positive electrode is the pole in contact with the concentrated solution of copper(II) sulfate. Although this concentration cell has a rather small voltage, electrons flow in the external circuit from the electrode in the dilute solution to the one in the concentrated solution.

21.15   DRY CELLS

The dry cell, used in portable radios and flashlights, is a primary voltaic cell. It is not really dry because in all electrochemical cells there must be a fluid medium in which ions may migrate to complete the electrical circuit. The dry cell contains a wet paste of ammonium chloride, $NH_4^+Cl^-$, and zinc chloride, $ZnCl_2$, mixed with some filler, such as sawdust. This paste is separated from the metallic zinc container by blotting paper. Between the wet paste and a carbon rod (the positive electrode) there is a mixture of graphite and manganese dioxide, MnO_2. The zinc container serves as the anode of the cell. (See Fig. 21.11.)

During operation of a dry cell, electrons leave the metallic zinc. The half-cell reaction is $Zn \leftrightarrows Zn^{++} + 2e^-$. At the carbon rod manganese dioxide is reduced. One probable representation of the reaction is

$$2NH_4^+ + 2MnO_2 + 2e^- \rightarrow$$
$$2NH_3 + 2HOMnO(?)$$

The ammonia apparently combines with zinc ions to produce the zinc-ammonia complex ion, $Zn(NH_3)_4^{++}$. The voltage of the cell is approximately 1.5 volts. As a current is withdrawn from the cell, the metallic zinc exterior of the cell is oxidized to Zn^{++}. As in the case of all primary cells, this oxidation of the electrode is essentially irreversible under the conditions in the cell.

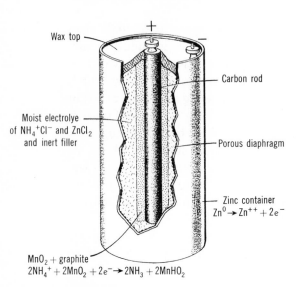

Wax top

Carbon rod

Moist electrolye of $NH_4^+Cl^-$ and $ZnCl_2$ and inert filler

Porous diaphragm

Zinc container
$Zn^0 \rightarrow Zn^{++} + 2e^-$

MnO_2 + graphite
$2NH_4^+ + 2MnO_2 + 2e^- \rightarrow 2NH_3 + 2MnHO_2$

FIGURE 21.11 Cross section of a simple dry cell.

21.16 LEAD STORAGE BATTERIES

In contrast to the dry cell, the lead storage battery is a secondary cell because the reactions at the electrodes can be reversed, or the cell may be recharged.

The main features of a common fully charged lead storage battery are grids of metallic lead on which is supported spongy lead (the anodes); grids of lead on which is supported lead dioxide, PbO_2 (the cathodes); separators or insulating strips that separate the electrodes and an aqueous solution of sulfuric acid whose density is approximately 1.25 g/ml. Voltage is approximately 2 volts per "cell." (In some automobile batteries there are 3 "cells" arranged in series, yielding a total voltage of about 6 volts, while others have 6 "cells" yielding 12 volts.)

When a current is withdrawn from the cell, electrons depart from the lead anode: $Pb \rightarrow Pb^{++} + 2e^-$. As the lead ions and sulfate ions, SO_4^{--}, come in contact, lead sulfate, $PbSO_4$, is deposited on the anode. When electrons enter the cathode, lead dioxide is reduced.

$$PbO_2 + 4H^+ + 2e^- \rightarrow Pb^{++} + 2HOH$$

The lead ions so formed and the sulfate ions of the electrolyte combine to form a deposit of lead sulfate on the cathode.

The two electrode reactions, when added, compose the over-all redox reaction which describes the chemical changes when the battery is discharging. We must recall, however, that the reducing agent, Pb, never comes in actual contact with the oxidizing agent, PbO_2.

During discharge of the lead storage battery, the density of the aqueous sulfuric acid gradually decreases because sulfate ions leave the solution (as solid $PbSO_4$), and hydrated protons are reactants in the reduction (cathode) reaction. The density of the solution in the battery is an indication of the extent to which the battery is charged. By using a hydrometer to measure the density of the solution, the "charge" of the battery can be checked. If the density is less than 1.05 g/ml, the battery should be recharged.

To charge the battery, it is necessary to reverse those reactions which occur during discharge. This is done by changing the cells into electrolytic cells. Direct current is "pumped" into the battery so that electrons flow in a direction opposite to that during discharge. (The positive pole or cathode becomes the anode and the negative pole becomes the cathode.) When the battery is charging, oxidation $(Pb^{++} + 2HOH \rightarrow PbO_2 + 4H^+ + 2e^-)$ occurs at the positive pole and reduction $(Pb^{++} + 2e^- \rightarrow Pb)$ at the negative pole.

21.17   FUEL CELLS

Although current interest in fuel cells is much greater than that shown during the first half of this century, the first gaseous fuel cell was constructed in 1829 by William Grove, an Englishman. The energy produced by this apparatus was the by-product of the combination of gaseous hydrogen and oxygen to yield water (gaseous).

$$H_2 + \tfrac{1}{2} O_2 \leftrightarrows H_2O \qquad \Delta H = -57.82 \text{ kcal}$$

We know that since the reaction reading from left to right is exothermic, it is spontaneous at ordinary temperatures. Obviously it proceeds in the direction of lower energy. The energy evolved during the formation of one mole of water, an oxidation-reduction reaction, can just as well be converted to electrical energy if suitable means are arranged. Ordinarily if gaseous hydrogen is burned in oxygen, most of the energy is evolved as heat and most of the remainder as kinetic energy of the product molecules.

The reaction reading from right to left is not spontaneous at ordinary temperatures, but it can proceed by expenditure of electrical energy. This reaction is, in fact, the simple electrolysis of water. It is not surprising, therefore, that electrical energy is available from the reaction that is the reverse of the electrolytic change.

Fuel cells are ordinary voltaic (galvanic) cells. There are two electrodes—an anode at which oxidation occurs and a cathode at which reduction occurs. Because the common reductants (reducing agents) used in fuel cells, such as hydrogen, alcohols, ethane, and other hydrocarbons, formaldehyde and coal, are often used as fuels burned to yield energy, voltaic cells in which these reductants are used came to be called *fuel cells*. The reductants and oxidants in fuel cells are covalent compounds, not ionic as in most ordinary voltaic cells. Because these reactants usually require more energy of activation than do ionic reactants, catalysts are used at the electrodes to lower the energy of activation and thereby increase the rate of activation of the reactant molecules.

Some fuel cells operate at high temperatures and pressures. F. T. Bacon's hydrogen-oxygen cell operates at 200°C and 400 psi, and is the center of a 7 kilowatt unit. In 1959 the Allis-Chalmers Company (American) demonstrated a low-pressure–low-temperature 15 kilowatt cell that could power a farm tractor.

A major feature of the fuel cells is their relatively high efficiency, between 65 and 80 per cent. They are not heat engines, whose efficiency is usually between 20 and 40 per cent, and they have no moving parts. The cells can utilize very inexpensive oxidizing and reducing agents.

Problems

1. During an electrolysis 19.55 g of potassium was produced at the cathode. How many coulombs passed through the cell?

2. How many grams of water would be decomposed electrolytically during the passage of 10 faradays of electricity?

3. If 1 faraday is considered to be 96,500 coulombs, how many electrons are there in 10 coulombs of electricity?

4. How many minutes must pass if 12.7 g of metallic copper is to be deposited from a copper(II) electrolyte in a cell when a current of 15 amp is flowing?

5. A metal has an equivalent weight of 56.2. Three faradays of electricity passed through an electrolytic cell in which the metal was the anode. How many grams of the element were oxidized?

6. Identify the products obtained by the electrolysis of each of the following systems: (a) aqueous solution of rubidium bromide; (b) fused $Ba^{++}(Cl^-)_2$; (c) aqueous solution of potassium chloride; (d) molten lithium bromide; (e) deuterium oxide + trace of sulfuric acid.

7. A given amount of electricity passed through two cells simultaneously; one cell contained copper(II) ions, the other contained chromium(III) ions. During electrolysis the current was 10 amp, and 2.542 g of copper was deposited. (a) How many grams of chromium were deposited? (b) How much electricity (coulombs) passed through the cells? (c) How many moles of electrons passed through the electron pump? (d) How long, in minutes, did the electrolysis occur?

8. (a) What volume, in milliliters, of chlorine measured at STP would be produced by the passage of 3.86×10^4 coulombs of electricity during the electrolysis of molten lithium chloride? (b) How many grams of lithium would be produced simultaneously? (c) How many milligrams of chlorine would be produced?

9. During the electrolysis of water, (a) how many grams of hydrogen (measured at 25°C and 2.0 atm) are produced during the passage of 1.93×10^6 coulombs? (b) How many moles of oxygen are produced simultaneously?

10. An aqueous electrolyte contains iron(III) ions. How many grams of metallic iron would be deposited electrolytically in a cell through which a current of 50 amp flowed for 3 hours?

11. What would you observe visually if a clean strip of iron were immersed in an aqueous solution of silver nitrate?

12. What would you observe visually if a stiff (aqueous) paste of mercury(I) chloride (white, slightly soluble solid) were rubbed on the surface of a clean strip of aluminum?

13. What would you observe visually if a clean strip of silver were immersed in an aqueous solution of magnesium sulfate?

14. Predict the voltage of a cell in which one electrode is metallic zinc in a solution containing zinc ions (1.0 m), and the other electrode is metallic silver in a solution that is 1.0 molal in silver ions.

15. Consider the three electrochemical cells X, Y, and Z:

$$X \text{ is Ni} \,|\, \text{Ni}^{++} \,(1\ m) \,\|\, \text{H}^+ \,(1\ m) \,|\, \text{H}_2 \,(1\ \text{atm})$$
$$Y \text{ is Fe} \,|\, \text{Fe}^{++} \,(1\ m) \,\|\, \text{H}^+ \,(1\ m) \,|\, \text{H}_2 \,(1\ \text{atm})$$
$$Z \text{ is Sn} \,|\, \text{Sn}^{++} \,(1\ m) \,\|\, \text{Ag}^+ \,(1\ m) \,|\, \text{Ag}$$

(a) Which has the highest voltage? (b) Which has the lowest voltage? (c) What occurs at the anode of Z? (d) What occurs at the cathode of Z?

16. Using Table 21.2 (p. 516) and assuming that all ions are at unit concentrations in aqueous solutions, answer the following questions. (a) Will elemental manganese reduce cadmium(II) ion? (b) Will copper(II) ion oxidize silver ion? (c) Can cobalt(III) ion oxidize chloride ion? (d) Can iron(II) ion reduce mercury(II) ion? (e) Will hydrogen peroxide reduce silver ion? (f) Can elemental lead reduce iron(III) ion? (g) Can mercury(I) ion reduce permanganate ion, MnO_4^-, in acidic solutions?

17. (a) What would be the voltage (emf) of a zinc-copper cell (similar to the Daniell cell) in which the concentration of the Zn^{++} ions is 100 times greater than that of the copper(II) ions? (b) What would be the voltage of a zinc-copper cell in which the concentration of copper(II) ions is 100 times that of the zinc ions? (c) What would be the voltage of a zinc-copper cell in which both the copper(II) ion and zinc ion concentrations are 0.1 m?

18. What is the approximate value of the equilibrium constant for the reaction $\text{Cu}^{++} + \text{Zn} \leftrightarrows \text{Cu}^\circ + \text{Zn}^{++}$ as it exists in the Daniell cell?

19. Calculate the approximate equilibrium constant for the reduction of cadmium ions Cd^{++} by elemental iron. Assume unit concentrations and the data in Table 21.2 (p. 516).

22

ACIDS AND

22.1 A PERSPECTIVE

Since an introduction to current acid-base concepts has already been presented in Chapter 9, we shall in this chapter review only the major terms and expand our viewpoint. The importance of a knowledge of acid-base phenomena is evident because the majority of chemical reactions can be classed as either acid-base or redox reactions.

It may be helpful, as you review the concepts in question, to recall (1) that every base is an electron-pair donor, and (2) that every electron-pair donor is classed as a base. Another important axiom is that an entity can act as a base only in the presence of an acid. Hence any entity that can cause a molecule to act as a base is called an acid. If the previous comment seems awkward, it will be well to recall that the behavior of any molecule is dependent not only on its structure and

BASES: I

inherent tendencies, but also on its environment. For instance, water molecules can act either as acids or as bases, depending on the character of the molecules in contact with them.

A study of acid-base behavior can serve as an admirable means of emphasizing the value of logical reasoning and the need for rigid allegiance to established rules. The material in this chapter and Chapter 23 is presented both as information and as food for thoughtful reasoning based on valid concepts.

22.2 SOME BRÖNSTED-LOWRY CONVENTIONS

Conventions relative to Brönsted acids

a. Brönsted acids are classified according to the number of protons donated per molecule in aqueous solutions. If 1 proton is donated per molecule, the acid is *monoprotic;* 2 protons per molecule, the acid is *diprotic;* 3 protons per molecule, the acid is *triprotic;* and so on. The terms *monobasic, dibasic,* and *tribasic* are used occasionally as synonyms for *monoprotic, diprotic,* and *triprotic* respectively.

b. Brönsted acids are commonly classified according to their ability to donate protons when added to water to yield a dilute solution (0.1 M or less). A proton donor is classed as a *strong* acid if all of its molecules apparently disappear, because of proton donation, when they are added to water to yield a dilute solution. (Hydrogen chloride is a strong acid because if 0.01 mole is added to water to yield 1 liter of solution, the oxonium ion concentration is 0.01 M.) A proton donor is called a *weak* acid if it is incompletely dissociated when added to water to yield a dilute solution. (Hydrogen cyanide is a weak acid because if 0.01 mole is added to water to yield 1 liter of solution, the oxonium ion concentration is much less than 0.01 M.)

c. Whenever a Brönsted acid reacts with a base, another B-acid and another base are produced. Every B-acid has a conjugate base, the molecule that remains after the acid has donated a proton. Every B-acid is the conjugate acid of some base because when the base accepts a proton a B-acid is formed. (Water, HOH, is the conjugate base of oxonium ion, OH_3^+, and OH_3^+ is the conjugate acid of water.) The conjugate acid of a strong base does not act as an acid when added to water, whereas the conjugate acid of a weak base does act as an acid when added to water. (Ammonia, NH_3, is the conjugate acid of amide ion, NH_2^-. Since amide ion is a strong base, its conjugate acid, NH_3, does not act as an acid when added to water. Because ammonia is a weak base, its conjugate acid, NH_4^+, ammonium ion, acts as an acid when added to water.)

d. Each Brönsted acid has at least one covalently bound proton, usually attached to either an oxygen, a nitrogen, or a halogen kernel (see Fig. 22.1). Some B-acids have protons attached to either carbon, sulfur, selenium, or tellurium kernels. Every oxy-acid—an acid that contains oxygen atoms—has at least one pair (usually more) of unshared electrons. Therefore every oxy-acid is a potential base.

e. If a molecule can act both as an acid and as a base in aqueous solutions, it is said to be *amphoteric*. An amphoteric B-acid is *amphiprotic* (a H^+ donor and acceptor).

f. Nearly every acid-base reaction in aqueous solutions is reversible, and the relative significance of each reaction may vary considerably with the concentrations of the entities in the system.

g. The oxonium ion, OH_3^+, is the strongest acid that can exist in dilute aqueous solutions. If any acid stronger than OH_3^+ is added to water, the acid is destroyed by the water, thereby yielding oxonium ions.

Conventions relative to bases

a. Bases may be classified according to their ability to add covalently bound protons in aqueous solutions. If 1 proton is accepted per molecule, the base is a *mono-acid* base; 2 protons per molecule, a *diacid* base; and so on.

b. Bases are commonly classified according to their ability to accept protons when added to water to yield dilute solutions. A base is classed as *strong* if all of its molecules accept at least one proton when the base is added to water to yield a dilute solution. A base is said to be *weak* if its molecules are only partially protonated when added to water to yield a dilute solution. (Amide ion, NH_2^-, is a strong base because when it is added to water to yield a dilute solution, all of the amide ions seem to accept protons from the water molecules. However, if ammonia is added to water, many unprotonated ammonia molecules exist in the solution. Hence ammonia is a weak base.)

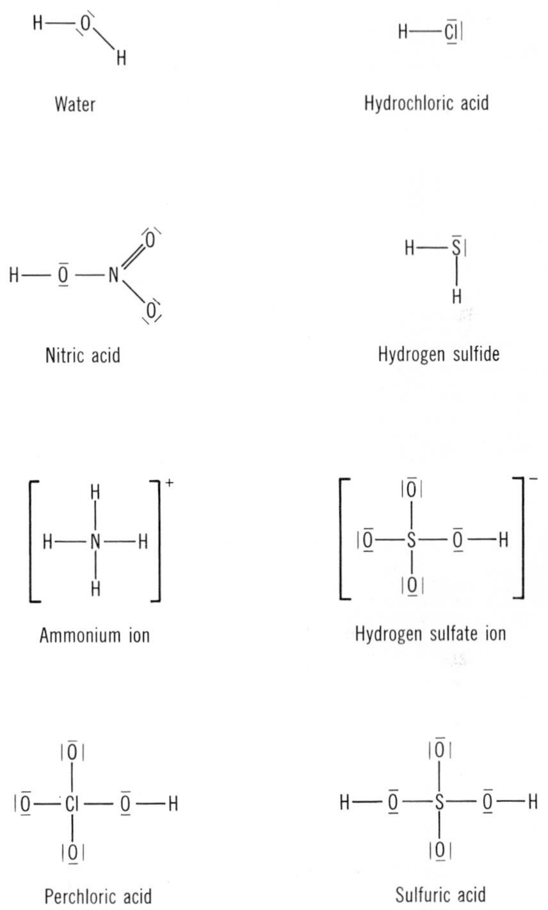

c. Every base has a conjugate acid, the molecule that remains after the base has accepted a proton. Every base is the conjugate base of some B-acid because it is what is left behind when the acid

Water

Hydrochloric acid

Nitric acid

Hydrogen sulfide

Ammonium ion

Hydrogen sulfate ion

Perchloric acid

Sulfuric acid

FIGURE 22.1 Some common acids.

donates a proton. The conjugate base of a strong acid never acts as a base when added to water to yield a dilute solution. But the conjugate base of a weak acid always acts as a base when added to water. (Chloride ion, Cl^-, is the conjugate base of the strong acid HCl; hence Cl^- does not act as a base when added to water to yield a dilute solution. Cyanide ion, CN^-, is the conjugate base of the weak acid HCN, so it acts as a base when added to water.)

Water

Hydroxide ion

Ammonia

Hydrosulfide ion

Cyanide ion

Acetate ion

Carbonate ion

Phosphate ion

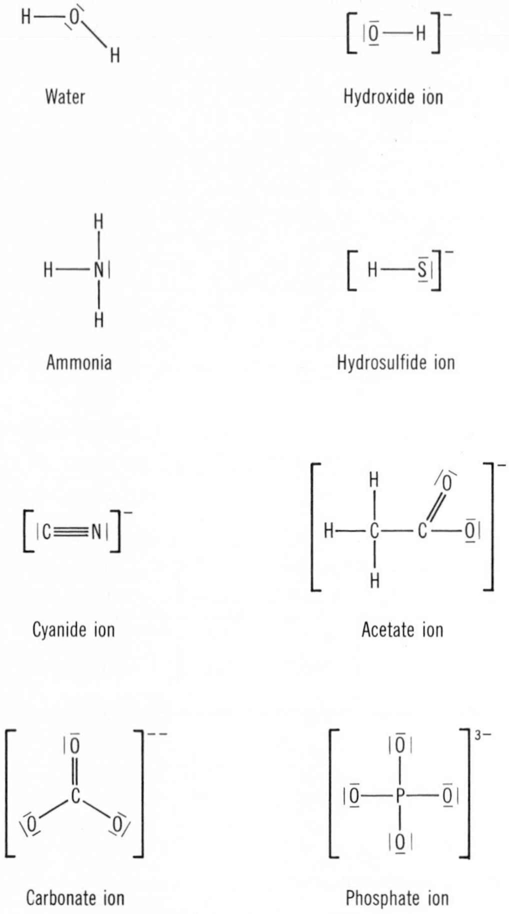

FIGURE 22.2 Some common bases.

d. Each base has at least one unshared pair of electrons or a pair not used directly in covalent bonding. Every molecule that contains the element oxygen has at least one unshared pair of electrons at each oxygen kernel (usually there are two). Therefore all such molecules are potential bases. Every common negatively charged ion is a potential base. (See Fig. 22.2.)

e. Some bases are amphoteric; they can act as acids under certain conditions and as bases under other conditions.

f. Since nearly every acid-base reaction is reversible in solution, the extent of proton acceptance shown by a base in a given solution may vary considerably with the concentrations of the reaction participants.

g. Hydroxide ion, OH^-, is the strongest base that can exist in dilute aqueous solutions. If any base stronger than OH^- is added to water, the base is protonated by the water, thereby converting water molecules to hydroxide ions.

22.3   A SYSTEM IN EQUILIBRIUM

In a sample of pure water the molecules are interacting to produce oxonium and hydroxide ions at the same rate that these ions are interacting to yield water molecules.   This is a dynamic equilibrium.

$$HOH + HOH \leftrightarrows OH_3^+ + OH^-$$

The expression for the equilibrium constant of this system is

$$K_{HOH} = \frac{[OH_3^+][OH^-]}{[HOH]^2}$$

Since the concentration of undissociated water molecules is much larger than that of the ions, it is generally assumed that the factor $[HOH]^2$ remains essentially constant in the case of dilute aqueous solutions, as it does in pure water.   The simplified expression of the equilibrium constant then becomes

$$K_{HOH} = [OH_3^+][OH^-]$$

At 25°C the value of the ion-product constant of water is found to be 1×10^{-14}.   Then for pure water and all dilute aqueous solutions,

$$[OH_3^+][OH^-] = 1 \times 10^{-14}$$

This simplified expression indicates that if the hydroxide ion concentration (moles/l) of a dilute aqueous solution is increased 10 times, the oxonium ion concentration is decreased to 1/10 that of the original.   Since the ion-product equation involves only two variables, if the concentration of one of the ions is known, the concentration of the other can be easily calculated.

In pure water the oxonium ion concentration is equal to the hydroxide ion concentration.   The concentration of each is 1×10^{-7} M (0.0000001 M).   In many aqueous solutions the concentration of the oxonium ion is much different from that of the hydroxide ion.   In subsequent sections we shall describe some of these. We must continually remember that in pure water and in all aqueous solutions, oxonium ions and hydroxide ions are in equilibrium with water molecules.

22.4 ACIDIC AND BASIC AQUEOUS SOLUTIONS

Long before chemists were certain about the correct formula of water, arbitrary classifications of aqueous solutions existed. They were often based more on the chemical behavior of the aqueous solution than on its composition. An acidic solution was frequently described in these terms: It contains an acid, it has a sour taste, it reacts with certain metals to yield hydrogen, it reacts with a base to produce a salt, and it is neutralized by the addition of an appropriate amount of base. A basic solution was often described thus: It contains a base, it feels slippery (soapy) when rubbed between the fingers, it is caustic (corrosive) to living tissues, it reacts with an acid to produce a salt, and it is neutralized by the addition of an appropriate amount of acid. If a solution was neither acidic nor basic, it was called a neutral solution. Basic solutions were also called alkaline solutions, and bases were often called alkalies. (The alkali metal and alkaline-earth metal elements and also oxides of these elements react with water to yield basic or alkaline solutions.)

We shall assume that any aqueous solution can be placed in one of three classes, acidic, basic or neutral, and then differentiate them in the light of present knowledge of the composition of pure water.

a. An acidic aqueous solution is a system in which the oxonium (hydronium) ion concentration is greater than that of pure water. (Oxonium ion concentration is greater than 1×10^{-7} M. Oxonium ion concentration is greater than hydroxide ion concentration.)

b. A basic aqueous solution is a system in which the hydroxide ion concentration is greater than that of pure water. (Hydroxide ion concentration is greater than 1×10^{-7} M. Hydroxide ion concentration is greater than oxonium ion concentration.)

c. A neutral aqueous solution is a system in which the oxonium ion concentration is equal to the hydroxide ion concentration. (Oxonium and hydroxide ions have the concentration 1×10^{-7} M.)

We recall that an acidic aqueous solution contains more oxonium ions than does pure water. This means that if we increase the oxonium ion concentration of pure water, we create an acidic solution. This can be accomplished either by adding OH_3^+ ions directly to water or by causing a chemical reaction in water that yields OH_3^+ ions. We know that whenever a water molecule accepts a proton, an OH_3^+ ion is produced. Therefore if an entity reacts as a proton donor in water, oxonium ions are produced.

By applying Le Châtelier's principle to the autoprotolysis of water, we notice that any process that specifically decreases the hydroxide ion, OH^-, concentration of pure water will upset the system to yield an acidic solution.

We know that a basic aqueous solution contains more hydroxide ions, OH^-, than does pure water. Therefore we can create a basic solution either by adding OH^- directly to water or by causing a reaction in the water that yields hydroxide ions. Whenever a water molecule loses or donates a proton, a hydroxide ion remains. If an entity reacts as a proton acceptor in water, hydroxide ions are left behind.

Application of Le Châtelier's principle leads to the conclusion that any process that specifically decreases the oxonium ion concentration of pure water will upset the system to yield a basic solution.

Let us consider a special case in which a pure compound is added to water and a neutral solution is obtained. One explanation is that the compound neither accepted protons from nor donated protons to the water molecules. Neither oxonium ions nor hydroxide ions are produced. Another explanation is that water molecules did react chemically with the ions of the compound, but the number of water molecules acting as proton donors was equal to the number acting as proton acceptors. That is, neither OH_3^+ nor OH^- increased in concentration.

The discussion in this and the previous section indicates rather clearly that water is both a Brönsted acid and a base. Also, water is amphoteric, although, according to the conventions stated in Section 22.2, it is only weakly acidic and basic.

22.5 SOME TYPICAL ACIDS AND BASES

Let us use, as examples, two hypothetical monoprotic acids: HAS, which is strong, and HAW, which is weak. We shall prepare two separate solutions and describe their character.

Solution A is prepared by adding 0.01 mole of HAS to water to yield 1.0 l of solution.

$$HAS + HOH \leftrightharpoons AS^- + OH_3^+$$

(a strong   0.01 M 0.01 M
acid)

Since the concentrations of OH_3^+ and AS^- are 0.01 M, all of the HAS molecules have apparently dissociated. Because there are no HAS molecules in solution A, oxonium ion is the only acid present, other than water. The AS^- ion does not appear to be acting as a base in the solution. If the compound Na^+AS^- is added to water, a neutral solution is obtained. The conjugate base of a strong acid does not act as a base when added to water.

Solution B is prepared by adding 0.01 mole of HAW to water to yield 1.0 l of solution.

$$HAW + HOH \leftrightharpoons AW^- + OH_3^+$$

  (a weak   0.001 M 0.001 M
  acid)
  0.009 M

There are many undissociated HAW molecules, indicat'ng that dissociation of the weak acid HAW is incomplete. Since the concentration of AW^- ions in solution B is 1×10^{-3} M, only 10 per cent of HAW is dissociated. There are two acids other than water, HAW and OH_3^+. The AW^- ions are definitely acting as bases in the solution. If the compound Na^+AW^- is added to water, a basic solution is obtained.

Since AS^- (the conjugate base of the strong acid HAS) does not act as a base when it is added to water, but AW^- does, we conclude that AW^- is a stronger base than AS^-.

Let us use, as examples, two hypothetical bases: SB, which is strong, and WB, which is weak. We shall prepare two separate solutions and describe their character.

Solution C is prepared by adding 0.01 mole of SB to water to yield 1.0 of solution.

$$SB + HOH \leftrightharpoons SBH^+ + OH^-$$

  (a strong   0.01 M 0.01 M
  base)

There appear to be no unprotonated SB molecules in solution C; hence protonation of the strong base is complete. The hydroxide ion is the only base other than water. The conjugate acid of SB, which is SBH^+, does not appear to be acting as an acid in the solution. If the compound SBH^+Cl^- is added to water, a neutral solution is obtained. The chloride ion, being the conjugate base of a strong acid (hydrogen chloride, HCl), does not act as a base when added to water.

Solution D is prepared by adding 0.01 mole of WB to water to yield 1.0 l of solution.

$$WB + HOH \leftrightarrows WBH^+ + OH^-$$

(a weak   0.0005 M 0.0005 M
base)
0.0095 M

There are many unprotonated WB molecules in solution D; hence WB is a weak base. Since the concentration of WBH$^+$ is 5×10^{-4} M, only 5 per cent of the base WB has accepted protons. There are two bases, other than water, in solution D, WB and OH$^-$. The WBH$^+$ ions are definitely acting as acids in the solution. If the compound WBH$^+$Cl$^-$ is added to water, an acidic solution is obtained.

Since SBH$^+$ ions do not act as acids when added to water, but WBH$^+$ ions do, we conclude that WBH$^+$ is the stronger acid.

22.6 SOME MONOPROTIC ACIDS

In Table 22.1 are listed some of the common monoprotic acids. An idealized symbolism of the behavior of hydrogen chloride is shown in Fig. 22.3.

A generalized equation representing the addition of an uncharged monoprotic acid, HA, to water is

$$HA + HOH \leftrightarrows OH_3^+ + A^-$$

monoprotic   conjugate
acid   base of HA

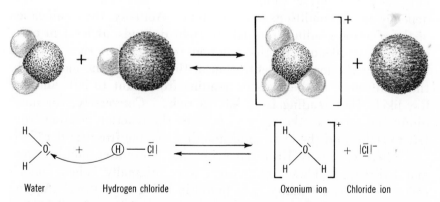

Water   Hydrogen chloride   Oxonium ion   Chloride ion

FIGURE 22.3 Protolytic dissociation of hydrogen chloride in the presence of water.

TABLE 22.1   Some common monoprotic acids

Acid	Relative Strength	Conjugate Base
Hydrofluoric, HF	Weak	F^-, fluoride ion
Hydrochloric, HCl	Strong	Cl^-, chloride ion
Hydrobromic, HBr	Strong	Br^-, bromide ion
Hydriodic, HI	Strong	I^-, iodide ion
Nitric, $HONO_2$	Strong	NO_3^-, nitrate ion
Iodic, $HOIO_2$	Strong	IO_3^-, iodate ion
Perchloric, $HOClO_3$	Strong	ClO_4^-, perchlorate ion
Sulfamic, $HOSO_2NH_2$	Strong	$SO_3NH_2^-$, sulfamate ion
Acetic, CH_3COOH	Weak	CH_3COO^-, acetate ion
Ammonium ion, NH_4^+	Weak	NH_3, ammonia
Benzoic, C_6H_5COOH	Weak	$C_6H_5COO^-$, benzoate ion
Chlorous, $HOClO$	Weak	ClO_2^-, chlorite ion
Cyanic, $HOCN$	Weak	OCN^-, cyanate ion
Formic, $HCOOH$	Weak	$HCOO^-$, formate ion
Hydrocyanic, HCN	Weak	CN^-, cyanide ion
Hydrogen sulfate ion, $HOSO_3^-$	Weak	SO_4^{--}, sulfate ion
Hydrogen sulfite ion, $HOSO_2^-$	Weak	SO_3^{--}, sulfite ion
Hypochlorous, $HOCl$	Weak	OCl^-, hypochlorite ion
Hypophosphorous, $H_2PO(OH)$	Weak	$H_2PO_2^-$, hypophosphite
Metaboric, $HOBO$	Weak	BO_2^-, borate ion
Nitrous, $HONO$	Weak	NO_2^-, nitrite ion

This equation identifies only the reaction participants and the fact that the dissociation of the acid HA is reversible. It does not indicate the relative significance of each reaction because this depends on the conditions in the system. Actually, the significance of the reaction reading from left to right depends, at least in part, on the insignificance of the reaction reading from right to left. The higher the ionic concentration of the solution, the more likely the significance of the reaction reading from right to left, and the less likely that reading from left to right. Conversely, the more dilute the solution, the more significant the reaction reading from left to right, and the less significant that reading from right to left.

There are many Brönsted acids that contain carbon, oxygen, and hydrogen. These compounds were originally called *organic compounds* because many were found in living organisms. Among the thousands of organic compounds, there is a large family called carboxylic acids, each member of which has at least one carboxyl

group, $-\overset{\displaystyle O}{\overset{\|}{C}}-OH$.   The hydrogen kernel in this structural grouping
is fairly easily removed from most carboxylic acids, especially by
strong bases.   Most of the water-soluble carboxylic acids, however,
behave as weak acids in pure water.   The conjugate base (a negative ion) of a carboxylic acid is usually named by dropping the
suffix *-ic* from the name of the acid and substituting *-ate* in its place
(the conjugate base of form*ic* acid is form*ate* ion).

Some carboxylic acids are:

formic acid, $H-\overset{\displaystyle O}{\overset{\|}{C}}-OH$, monoprotic (in certain insects)

acetic acid, $H_3C-\overset{\displaystyle O}{\overset{\|}{C}}-OH$, monoprotic (in vinegar)

lactic acid, $H_3C-\overset{\overset{\displaystyle OH}{|}}{\underset{|}{C}}-\overset{\displaystyle O}{\overset{\|}{C}}-OH$, monoprotic (in sour milk and sauer-

kraut)

butyric acid, $H_3C-CH_2-CH_2-\overset{\displaystyle O}{\overset{\|}{C}}-OH$, monoprotic (in rancid
butter)

When formic acid is added to water, it behaves as a fairly
active acid.

$$H-\overset{\displaystyle O}{\overset{\|}{C}}-OH + HOH \leftrightarrows OH_3^+ + [H-\overset{\displaystyle O}{\overset{\|}{C}}-O]^-$$
formate ion

Acetic acid is a weaker acid than formic acid.

$$H_3C-\overset{\displaystyle O}{\overset{\|}{C}}-OH + HOH \leftrightarrows OH_3^+ + [H_3C-\overset{\displaystyle O}{\overset{\|}{C}}-O]^-$$
acetate ion

Acetate ion is a stronger base than formate ion.

There are hundreds of organic compounds that contain hydroxyl groups but no carboxyl groups.   Among these the phenols

are the principal acids. Most water-soluble phenols behave as weak acids in water. Phenol (carbolic acid), C_6H_5OH, a monoprotic acid, is called the parent phenol.

$$C_6H_5OH + HOH \leftrightarrows OH_3^+ + C_6H_5O^-$$

phenol　　　　　　　　　　　　　phenoxide ion

Picric acid, $C_6H_2(NO_2)_3OH$, behaves as a fairly strong acid when added to water.

$$C_6H_2(NO_2)_3OH + HOH \leftrightarrows OH_3^+ + C_6H_2(NO_2)_3O^-$$

picrate ion

Among the organic acids are the sulfonic acids. Each sulfonic

acid has the group, $\begin{matrix} & O \\ & \diagup \\ S & \!\!\!\!-OH \\ & \diagdown \\ & O \end{matrix}$, in its molecular structure. This group

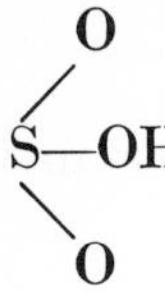

is covalently attached to a carbon kernel. Aqueous solutions of water-soluble sulfonic acids are acidic. Benzenesulfonic acid, $C_6H_5SO_2OH$, behaves as a strong monoprotic acid when added to water.

$$C_6H_5SO_2OH + HOH \leftrightarrows OH_3^+ + C_6H_5SO_3^-$$

benzenesulfonate ion

Hydrogen cyanide, HCN, is a weak acid. In this molecule the hydrogen kernel is covalently attached to a carbon kernel.

$$HCN + HOH \leftrightarrows OH_3^+ + CN^-$$

cyanide ion

22.7 SOME DIPROTIC ACIDS

Although a diprotic acid yields two protons per molecule, the protons leave in a stepwise fashion, never simultaneously. Let us use sulfuric acid as a model.

Step 1:　　$H_2SO_4 + HOH \leftrightarrows HSO_4^- + OH_3^+$

　　　　　　　sulfuric　　　　　　　hydrogen
　　　　　　　acid　　　　　　　　 sulfate
　　　　　　　　　　　　　　　　　 ion

Step 2:　　$HSO_4^- + HOH \leftrightarrows SO_4^{--} + OH_3^+$

　　　　　　　　　　　　　　　　　sulfate
　　　　　　　　　　　　　　　　　ion

Since Step 1 is practically complete, sulfuric acid is classed as a strong acid. Step 2 is incomplete. Therefore hydrogen sulfate ion is a weaker acid than sulfuric acid. It is also a weaker base than sulfate ion. Actually hydrogen sulfate ion is amphoteric because in the "reverse" of Step 1 it acts as a base and in the "forward" reaction of Step 2 it acts as an acid.

A generalized pair of equations that represent the addition of an uncharged diprotic acid to water are:

$$\text{Step 1:} \quad H_2A + HOH \rightleftharpoons HA^- + OH_3^+$$
$$\text{Step 2:} \quad HA^- + HOH \rightleftharpoons A^{--} + OH_3^+$$

a. Step 1 is always more nearly complete than Step 2. The concentration of HA^- is often greater than that of A^{--}.
b. H_2A is always a stronger acid than HA^-.
c. HA^- is always amphoteric.
d. A^{--} is always a stronger base than HA^-. Some common diprotic acids are listed in Table 22.2.

TABLE 22.2 Some common diprotic acids*

Acid	Formula	Conjugate Bases
Sulfuric	$(HO)_2SO_2$	$HOSO_3^-$, hydrogen sulfate ion SO_4^{--}, sulfate ion
Sulfurous	$(HO)_2SO$	HSO_3^-, hydrogen sulfite ion SO_3^{--}, sulfite ion
Disulfuric	$(HO)_2S_2O_5$	$HOS_2O_6^-$, hydrogen disulfate $S_2O_7^{--}$, disulfate ion
Phosphorous	$HPO(OH)_2$	HPO_2OH^-, hydrogen phosphite ion HPO_3^{--}, phosphite ion
Dihydrogen phosphate ion	$(OH)_2PO_2^-$	$(OH)PO_3^{--}$, monohydrogen phosphate PO_4^{3-}, phosphate ion
Carbonic	$(HO)_2CO$	$HOCO_2^-$, hydrogen carbonate CO_3^{--}, carbonate ion
Hydrogen sulfide	H_2S	HS^-, hydrosulfide ion S^{--}, sulfide ion
Chromic	$(HO)_2CrO_2$	$HOCrO_3^-$, hydrogen chromate ion CrO_4^{--}, chromate ion
Oxalic	$(COOH)_2$	CO_2COOH^-, hydrogen oxalate ion $(COO)_2^{--}$, oxalate ion
Tartaric	$C_4H_4O_4(OH)_2$	$C_4H_4O_5OH^-$, hydrogen tartrate $C_4H_4O_6^{--}$, tartrate ion

* All acids are weak except sulfuric, disulfuric, and chromic.

22.8 TRIPROTIC ACIDS

Phosphoric acid, H_3PO_4, is the most common triprotic acid. It yields its three protons stepwise as does every triprotic acid. The behavior of phosphoric acid when added to water is used as a model.

$$H_3PO_4 + HOH \leftrightarrows H_2PO_4^- + OH_3^+$$
$$\text{dihydrogen phosphate ion}$$

$$H_2PO_4^- + HOH \leftrightarrows HPO_4^{--} + OH_3^+$$
$$\text{monohydrogen phosphate ion}$$

$$HPO_4^{--} + HOH \leftrightarrows PO_4^{3-} + OH_3^+$$
$$\text{phosphate ion}$$

The third step is quite incomplete; hence phosphate ion is an active base.

Arsenic acid, H_3AsO_4, is a weaker triprotic acid than phosphoric acid. Citric acid, $C_3H_5O(COOH)_3$, (in citrous fruits) is weaker than arsenic acid.

22.9 SOME COMMON BASES

Water is the most common (abundant) base. Among the uncharged molecules other than water, ammonia, NH_3, is the most common base. Ammonia is a weak base, so there are many ammonia molecules in an aqueous solution of ammonia. Ammonia's conjugate acid, NH_4^+, acts as a weak acid in water.

$$NH_3 + HOH \leftrightarrows NH_4^+ + OH^-$$
$$\text{ammonium ion}$$

Most of the common bases are negative ions, the most common being the conjugate bases of water, OH^- and O^{--} (oxide ion). In fact, any common negative ion can be called the conjugate base of some Brönsted acid. Although the negative ions related to the strong acids do not act as bases when added to water, they do accept protons in the presence of some acids much stronger than water.

The behavior of a given negative ion in the presence of water may be determined by adding to water a soluble ionic compound that consists in part of the negative ion in question. The alkali metal salts are the best choices because the alkali metal ions never react chemically with water. These ions are "spectator" ions. Since radium, calcium, strontium, and barium ions do not react chemically with water, simple water-soluble compounds of these may be used to test the behavior of a specific negative ion (see p. 545).

In Table 22.3 are listed some common bases. If a salt consisting of an alkali metal ion and any one of the ions listed is added to water, a basic solution is obtained. Since a chemical change has been initiated by water molecules, the salt is said to be hydrolyzed. This hydrolysis reaction is actually a proton-transfer reaction. Alkali metal salts of strong monoprotic acids do not undergo hydrolysis, but those of weak acids always do.

TABLE 22.3   Some common bases

Base	Symbol	Relative Strength	Conjugate Acid
Acetate ion	CH_3COO^-	Weak	Acetic acid, CH_3COOH
Amide ion	NH_2^-	Strong	Ammonia, NH_3
Arsenate ion	AsO_4^{3-}	Weak	Hydrogen arsenate ion, $HAsO_4^{--}$
Benzoate ion	$C_6H_5COO^-$	Weak	Benzoic acid, C_6H_5COOH
Borate ion	BO_2^-	Weak	Metaboric acid, HBO_2
Carbide ion (diatomic)	C_2^{--}	Strong	Acetylene, C_2H_2
Carbide ion (monatomic)	C^{4-}	Strong	Methane, CH_4
Carbonate ion	CO_3^{--}	Weak	Hydrogen carbonate ion, HCO_3^-
Cyanide ion	CN^-	Weak	Hydrogen cyanide, HCN
Hydride ion	H^-	Strong	Hydrogen, H_2
Hydrogen carbonate	HCO_3^-	Weak	Carbonic acid, H_2CO_3
Hydrosulfide ion	HS^-	Weak	Hydrogen sulfide, H_2S
Hydroxide ion	OH^-	Strong	Water, HOH
Hypochlorite ion	OCl^-	Weak	Hypochlorous acid, HOCl
Nitride ion	N^{3-}	Strong	NH_3 and NH_2^-
Nitrite ion	NO_2^-	Weak	Nitrous acid, HNO_2
Oxide ion	O^{--}	Strong	Hydroxide ion, OH^-
Phosphate ion	PO_4^{3-}	Weak	HPO_4^{--} and $H_2PO_4^-$
Sulfide ion	S^{--}	Strong	Hydrosulfide ion, SH^-
Sulfite ion	SO_3^{--}	Weak	Hydrogen sulfite ion, HSO_3^-

Some organic compounds that contain nitrogen behave as bases when added to water. Many of these may be considered relatives of ammonia. A few organic bases are methylamine, CH_3NH_2; ethylamine, $C_2H_5NH_2$; ethylenediamine, $H_2N-CH_2-CH_2-NH_2$; aniline, $C_6H_5NH_2$; piperidine, $C_5H_{11}N$; guanidine, $HCN(NH_2)_2$. In each of these molecules an unshared pair of electrons resides at each nitrogen kernel.

Methylamine is a stronger base than ammonia and is fairly soluble in water.

$$CH_3NH_2 + HOH \leftrightarrows \underset{\text{methylammonium ion}}{CH_3NH_3^+} + OH^-$$

Guanidine is a strong base and is very soluble in water.

$$HNC(NH_2)_2 + HOH \leftrightarrows \underset{\text{guanidinium ion}}{H_2N-C(NH_2)_2^+} + OH^-$$

An essentially ionic hydroxide is a direct source of hydroxide ions. If an alkali metal hydroxide, such as sodium hydroxide, Na^+OH^-, is added to water, the ionic solid disintegrates. The number of moles of hydroxide ion then present in the solution is equal to the number of moles of alkali metal hydroxide added. For example,

$$Na^+OH_{(s)}^- \xrightarrow[\substack{\text{excess of} \\ \text{water}}]{\text{in an}} \underset{\substack{\text{ions randomly distributed} \\ \text{in solution}}}{Na^+ + OH^-}$$

Magnesium, calcium, strontium, and barium hydroxides are much less soluble than the alkali metal hydroxides, although they are essentially ionic. Each mole of alkaline-earth metal hydroxide, $M^{++}(OH^-)_2$, is a direct source of 2 moles of hydroxide ion. If 0.05 mole of barium hydroxide is dissolved in water to prepare a liter of solution, the solution contains 0.1 mole of hydroxide ion.

The hydroxides of the electropositive elements in the 3a, 4a, and 5a families and the transition elements are generally less ionic than the hydroxides of the alkali metal and alkaline-earth metal elements. Therefore the 1a and 2a hydroxides are the most soluble hydroxides. Hydroxides only slightly soluble in water do not dissociate appreciably when added to water, and so their aqueous solutions contain relatively few hydroxide ions.

The alkali metal hydroxides have long been classified as strong bases. The alkaline-earth metal hydroxides, except beryllium hydroxide, are usually considered fairly strong bases. Any very slightly soluble hydroxide is called a weak base. In this classification a hydroxide is typed by its tendency to dissolve, when added to water, to yield hydroxide ions.

Every ionic hydroxide contains two different individual entities, the metallic positive ion and the hydroxide ion. Since this positive ion never behaves as a base, the basic character of an ionic hydroxide is due solely to the hydroxide ion. According to the Brönsted and Lewis concepts, an alkali metal hydroxide is not, in its entirety, a base; the hydroxide ion is the base. Although hydroxide ions behave as strong bases when added to water, they do not disappear because the acid with which they are reacting is their conjugate acid.

Earlier (p. 532) we stated that the conjugate base of a weak B-acid always acts as a base when it is added to water. There are many alkali metal compounds (all ionic and therefore salts) whose negative ions (anions) are the conjugate bases of weak acids. The aqueous solutions of all such alkali metal salts are basic, providing that the salts in question are the only solutes in solution. All of these salts therefore undergo hydrolysis when added to water, but in all cases involving alkali metal salts the positive ion is a "spectator." (M^+ will denote any alkali metal ion.) A few examples are given below.

Alkali metal cyanides, M^+CN^-.

$$CN^- + HOH \leftrightharpoons HCN + OH^-$$

cyanide ion　　　　　　hydrogen cyanide

Alkali metal sulfites, $(M^{++})_2SO_3^{--}$.

$$SO_3^{--} + HOH \leftrightharpoons HOSO_2^- + OH^-$$

sulfite ion　　　　　　hydrogen sulfite ion

Alkali metal phosphates (normal), $(M^+)_3PO_4^{3-}$.

$$PO_4^{3-} + HOH \leftrightharpoons HOPO_3^{--} + OH^-$$

phosphate ion　　　　　monohydrogen phosphate ion

Alkali metal arsenates (normal), $(M^+)_3AsO_4^{3-}$.

$$AsO_4^{3-} + HOH \leftrightharpoons HOAsO_3^{--} + OH^-$$

arsenate ion　　　　　　monohydrogen arsenate ion

Alkali metal metaborates, $M^+BO_2^-$.

$$BO_2^- + HOH \leftrightharpoons HBO_2 + OH^-$$

metaborate ion　　　　　metaboric acid

Alkali metal acetates, $M^+C_2H_3O_2^-$.

$$C_2H_3O_2^- + HOH \leftrightarrows C_2H_3O_2H + OH^-$$

acetate ion   acetic
acid

The examples of acid-base behavior presented in this chapter and in Chapter 23 document an extremely important generalization, namely that during *every* acid-base reaction a "new" covalent bond is produced. There are many redox reactions during which *no* "new" covalent bonds are formed.

22.10   ACIDITY AND BASICITY OF AQUEOUS SOLUTIONS

The actual acidity of a dilute aqueous solution is usually the oxonium ion concentration, expressed as moles per liter or millimoles per milliliter. The actual basicity of a dilute aqueous solution is the hydroxide ion concentration, which may also be expressed as molarity.

Because we must use dilute solutions to minimize physical interactions between the ions, we shall be concerned mainly with solutions in which either the oxonium ion concentration or the hydroxide ion concentration varies from 1×10^{-1} M (0.1 M) to 1×10^{-13} M. The ion product of water is $[OH_3^+][OH^-] = 1 \times 10^{-14}$ at $25°$. Therefore we can compute the hydroxide ion concentration of a solution if we know the oxonium ion concentration, and vice versa.

We can prepare a typical standard acidic solution by dissolving 0.01 mole of a strong monoprotic acid in water to yield a liter of solution. By definition we shall assume that the oxonium ion concentration of this solution is 0.01 M or 1×10^{-2} M. We say that the stoichiometric concentration of the strong acid in the solution is 0.01 M, although we realize that the solute is practically completely dissociated.

Similarly we can prepare a typical standard basic solution by dissolving 0.01 mole of an alkali metal hydroxide in water to yield a liter of solution. Since each 0.01 mole of the hydroxide supplies 0.01 mole of hydroxide ions, the hydroxide ion concentration of this reference standard is 0.01 M.

22.11 THE pH SCALE

Oxonium ion concentrations of dilute solutions are very often expressed as powers of ten. For example, a concentration of 0.01 M is often written as 1×10^{-2} M. In 1909 Sören Sörensen (Danish) suggested a simplified notation, the pH. The pH is defined as the negative logarithm (to the base 10) of the oxonium ion concentration, $[OH_3^+]$.

$$pH = -\log_{10} [OH_3^+] = \log_{10} \frac{1}{[OH_3^+]}$$

$$[OH_3^+] = 10^{-pH} = \text{antilog}\,(-pH)$$

If $[OH_3^+] = 1 \times 10^{-7}$ M,   pH = 7
If $[OH_3^+] = 1 \times 10^{-2}$ M,   pH = 2
If $[OH_3^+] = 1 \times 10^{-14}$ M,   pH = 14
If $[OH_3^+] = 1 \times 10^{0}$ M,   pH = 0
If $[OH_3^+] = 3.09 \times 10^{-4}$ M,   pH $= -\log (3.09 \times 10^{-4})$
                                            $= -[0.49 + (-4)] = 3.51$

If the pH of a solution is 5.5, the $[OH_3^+]$ is calculated as

$$[OH_3^+] = \text{antilog of } -5.5, \text{ or antilog of } 0.5 - 6.0$$

where antilog of 0.5 = 3.16, antilog of $-6.0 = 10^{-6}$, then

$$[OH_3^+] = 3.16 \times 10^{-6} \ M$$

Figure 22.4 indicates that the higher the value of the pH of a solution, the lower the oxonium ion concentration.

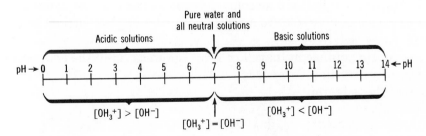

FIGURE 22.4   The pH scale used to identify the acidity or basicity of dilute aqueous solutions.

22.12 ACID-BASE INDICATORS

When chemists first determined the chemical properties of acids and bases, they noted that these substances caused changes in the colors of certain colored compounds. *Litmus*, a colored substance obtained from lichens, has a red color in most acidic solutions and a blue color in basic solutions. It is a typical acid-base indicator.

Each acid-base indicator is either a weak acid or a weak base or both. In aqueous solutions, it is able to act either as a weak acid or a weak base. If it is a weak acid, or in its acidic from, its color must be different from that of its conjugate base. If it is a weak base, or in its basic form, its color must be different from that of its conjugate acid. *Phenolphthalein* is a colorless weak acid; its conjugate base is red. *Methyl orange* is a weak base (yellow); its conjugate acid is red. The color change of an acid-base indicator is the result of a structural change in the molecule. In the case of methyl orange, the red form has an electronic structure different from the yellow form. Most acid-base indicators have definite limitations: they can be used only in colorless solutions; they are often easily oxidized or reduced, so active oxidizing and reducing agents must be absent; they are useful only in specific limited pH ranges.

To describe the essential characteristics of most acid-base indicators, let us use methyl orange as an example. We shall first consider a few facts and then interpret them logically. (We shall assume that the indicator is added to colorless solutions containing no active reducing or oxidizing agents.) The facts about methyl orange are: it imparts a red color to any solution whose pH value is 3 or less; it imparts a yellow color to any solution whose pH value is 4.5 or greater; it imparts an orange color to a solution of pH 3.7; it imparts a reddish-orange color to a solution of pH 3.4; it imparts a yellowish-orange color to a solution of pH 4.2. Let us now interpret these facts.

Methyl orange in its yellow form is a weak base; the conjugate acid of this yellow form is red. Using the symbol, InH^+, to represent the red form,

$$InH^+ \quad + HOH \leftrightarrows \quad In \quad + OH_3^+$$

acidic form
of indicator
(red for methyl
orange)

basic form
of indicator
(yellow for
methyl orange)

According to Le Châtelier's principle, a high concentration of oxonium ion favors the formation of acidic form, InH^+. A high hydroxide ion concentration favors the formation of the basic form, In. According to the facts just presented, in a solution whose pH is 4.5 the amount of InH^+ (acidic form) is so small that no red color is detectable by the eye. In solutions whose pH values are higher than 4.5, the amount of acidic form present is much less than at pH 4.5. In all such solutions the main form of the indicator is the basic form, In. In a solution whose pH is 4.2, there is some of the acidic form, InH^+ (perhaps 25 per cent), because the color of the solution is different from that of the pH 4.5 solution. At pH 3.7 the orange color is due to nearly equal amounts of the acidic and basic forms (50 per cent InH^+ and 50 per cent In). At pH 3.4 there are more acidic form than basic form entities; hence the solution is reddish-orange. At pH 3 or lower, there are practically no basic form entities, In.

Methyl orange is an effective indicator only in the pH range 3.0 to 4.5. Within this range the pH of a colorless solution may be approximately determined by adding methyl orange and then matching the color to that of another solution of known pH containing the same amount of methyl orange. Colored glass disks and color charts having various indicator colors differing by about 0.2 of a pH unit are available.

Methyl orange is useless for solutions whose pH is over 4.5 because it imparts the same yellow color to all of them, as only the basic form molecules are present. Methyl orange is equally ineffective in solutions whose pH values are less than 3.0 because to all such solutions this indicator imparts the same red color.

Some indicators are weak acids; most of these have effective pH ranges above 7. The effective range of phenolphthalein is very limited because its acidic form is colorless. It is thus colorless in solutions of pH 8.5 or less; it is red in solutions of pH 8.8 to 14. In very strongly basic solutions phenolphthalein is colorless.

An extremely simplified representation of the behavior of the indicator phenolphthalein (abbreviated PPN) is

$$HIn \ + OH^- \leftrightarrows \ In^- \ + HOH$$

acidic form	basic form
of PPN	of PPN
(colorless)	(red)

Phenolphthalein appears to behave as an acid in the presence of sufficient hydroxide ions (pH 8.8).

Table 22.4 lists some acid-base indicators and their effective pH ranges. When selecting an acid-base indicator for a particular task, it will be well to recall that an indicator is effective only in those solutions which contain both its basic and acidic forms.

TABLE 22.4 Some common acid-base indicators

Indicator	Effective pH Range	
Methyl violet	0.2 (yellow)......	3.0 (violet)
Thymol blue	1.2 (red).........	2.8 (yellow)
Methyl orange	3.1 (red).........	4.4 (orange-yellow)
Congo red	3.0 (blue)........	5.0 (red)
Bromcresol green	3.8 (yellow)......	5.4 (blue)
Methyl red	4.4 (red).........	6.2 (yellow)
Chlorphenol red	4.8 (yellow)......	6.8 (red)
Bromcresol purple	5.2 (yellow)......	6.8 (purple)
Litmus	4.5 (red).........	8.3 (blue)
Bromthymol blue	6.0 (yellow)......	7.6 (blue)
Thymol blue	8.0 (yellow)......	9.6 (blue)
Phenolphthalein	8.3 (colorless).....	10.0 (red)
Alizarin yellow R	10.0 (yellow)......	12.0 (red)
Indigo carmine	11.4 (blue)........	13.0 (yellow)

22.13 LEVELING EFFECT OF THE SOLVENT

We have previously noted that strong monoprotic acids are nearly completely dissociated (protolytically) in dilute aqueous solutions. It is evident therefore that the oxonium ion is the only acid (other than water) present in a dilute solution of a strong monoprotic acid. No matter how strong the monoprotic acid, when it is dissolved in water to prepare a dilute solution, the strength of the acid is leveled to that of oxonium ion. Perchloric acid, $HOClO_3$, is much stronger than either nitric acid or hydrochloric acid, but in dilute aqueous solutions the strength of each is leveled to that of oxonium ion. Oxonium ion is the strongest acid that can exist in appreciable concentration in a dilute aqueous solution.

There are several bases that are much stronger than hydroxide ion. Some of these are oxide ion, O^{--}; amide ion, NH_2^-; nitride ion, N^{3-}; the carbide ions, C_2^{--} and C^{4-}; and the hydride ion, H^-. If any one of these is added to water to prepare a dilute solution, the strength of the base is leveled to that of hydroxide ion, OH^-.   Hydroxide ion is the strongest base that can exist in appreciable concentration in a dilute aqueous solution.

In chemical research pure liquid ammonia is often used either as a solvent or as a reagent.   Since ammonia is a stronger base than water, many acids that behave as weak acids in water behave as strong acids when dissolved in liquid ammonia.   Acetic acid, for example, is nearly completely dissociated in liquid ammonia.

$$CH_3COOH + NH_3 \leftrightarrows CH_3COO^- + NH_4^+$$
$$\text{acetic acid} \qquad\qquad \text{acetate ion}$$

The ammonium ion, NH_4^+ (the conjugate acid of ammonia), is the strongest acid that can exist in appreciable concentration in liquid ammonia.   The amide ion, NH_2^- (the conjugate base of ammonia), is the strongest base that can exist in appreciable concentration in liquid ammonia.

By considering the fate of acids in the typical solvents water and ammonia, we realize that an acid retains its maximum strength only when alone or when in those solvents in which it is undissociated.

22.14   ACTUAL, POTENTIAL, AND TOTAL ACIDITY OF A SOLUTION

As arbitrarily defined, the actual acidity of an aqueous solution is its oxonium ion concentration.   Considering this definition, let us recall the essential characteristics of dilute acidic solutions in which (a) a strong monoprotic acid is dissolved in water, and (b) a weak monoprotic acid is dissolved in water.

a. The actual acidity and the total acidity of a dilute aqueous solution of a strong monoprotic acid are identical.   Each is represented practically by the oxonium ion concentration because the strong acid is nearly completely dissociated.   There is no potential (reserve) acidity in a solution of a strong monoprotic acid because practically every molecule of the acid has reacted with a water molecule to form an oxonium ion.   The actual acidity and the total acidity of an aqueous solution of a strong monoprotic acid are each equal to the stoichiometric concentration of the strong acid. (In $0.1\ M$ HCl, the actual acidity $= 0.1\ M =$ oxonium ion concentration $=$ total acidity.)

b. The actual acidity is never equal to the total acidity in an aqueous solution of a weak monoprotic acid because the undissociated acid molecules constitute a sort of potential (reserve) acidity. In a solution of a weak acid, the total acidity = the actual acidity (oxonium ion concentration) + the potential acidity (contration of undissociated acid). The actual acidity of a solution of a weak acid is always less than the stoichiometric concentration of the acid. The total acidity of a solution of a weak acid is equal to the stoichiometric concentration of the acid. (In 0.1 M acetic acid, the total acidity is 0.1 M; the actual acidity is approximately 0.0013 M; the potential (reserve) acidity is approximately 0.0987 M.)

22.15 ACTUAL, POTENTIAL, AND TOTAL BASICITY OF A SOLUTION

The actual basicity of an aqueous solution is its hydroxide ion concentration. With this definition in mind, let us consider solutions prepared by adding bases to water in which the added base is monoacidic, or yields a maximum of one mole of hydroxide ion per mole of base when the base is dissolved in excess water.

a. The actual basicity and the total basicity of a dilute aqueous solution of a strong monoacidic base are identical. This fact results from the convention that a strong base is completely protonated when it is added to water to yield a dilute solution. Since hydroxide ions are the only bases other than water in the solution, no reserve (potential) basicity is present.

b. The actual basicity of an aqueous solution is never equal to the total basicity if the solution contains a weak base. An aqueous solution made by adding a weak base to water contains molecules of the base; thus two bases are present, hydroxide ions and the base itself. The molecules of the base constitute the potential (reserve) basicity, the hydroxide ions the actual basicity. Therefore total basicity = actual basicity + potential basicity.

22.16 DETERMINATION OF TOTAL ACIDITY OR BASICITY OF AN AQUEOUS SOLUTION

To determine the total acidity of an aqueous solution, we choose the strongest base that can exist in appreciable concentration in water— the hydroxide ion. The total acidity of a dilute solution of a strong acid is easily determined by using hydroxide ions because the reaction $OH_3^+ + OH^- \leftrightarrows 2HOH$ is practically complete. The total acidity of a dilute solution of a weak acid can be determined by using hydroxide ions only if the hydroxide ions (in ordinary concentrations) can cause the weak acid to dissociate nearly completely.

The total basicity of a solution is often determined by using an aqueous solution of a strong monoprotic acid, because the acidity of such a solution is due solely to oxonium ions, and the oxonium ion is the strongest acid that can exist in appreciable concentration in dilute aqueous solution.

It is conventional to state that if an acid-base reaction is complete, each equivalent of an acid reacts with an equivalent of a base. To interpret this, let us consider for the moment those reactions that occur when aqueous solutions of Brönsted acids are added to solutions of the water-soluble ionic hydroxides (usually alkali metal and barium hydroxides). It is evident that the acid and/or oxonium ion serve as the source of protons and the solid ionic hydroxide as the original source of the hydroxide ions. When a solution of the acid is added to a solution of the ionic hydroxide the major reaction is

$$\underset{\substack{\text{from either} \\ \text{the B-acid} \\ \text{or oxonium} \\ \text{ion}}}{H^+} + OH^- \leftrightarrows HOH$$

Under ordinary conditions this reaction is essentially complete because those compounds, usually classified as acids, are stronger acids than water. Hydroxide ion is therefore a stronger base than the conjugate bases of these acids.

22.17   THE EQUIVALENT WEIGHTS
OF ACIDS AND BASES

Since one mole of proton reacts completely with one mole of hydroxide ion, then one equivalent of B-acid supplies one mole of protons and one equivalent of ionic hydroxide supplies one mole of hydroxide ion. The mass of one equivalent (equivalent weight) of a B-acid is the amount that will supply one mole of protons. The mass of one equivalent (equivalent weight) of an ionic hydroxide is the amount that will supply one mole of hydroxide ions. The equivalent weight of a monoprotic acid is equal to its molar weight.

The equivalent weight of a diprotic acid is one-half of its molar weight. The equivalent weight of an alkali metal hydroxide is equal to its molar weight; of an alkaline-earth metal hydroxide, one-half of its molar weight. The equivalent weight of an uncharged covalent base is equal to its molar weight divided by the number of protons it can accept per molecule. The equivalent weight of an alkali metal salt of a weak acid is equal to its molar weight divided by the number of protons that the negative ion of the salt can accept per ion. [For sodium carbonate, $(Na^+)_2CO_3^{--}$, the equivalent weight = one-half the molar weight of the salt because carbonate ion, CO_3^{--}, can accept two protons per ion.]

22.18 THE NORMALITY OF ACIDIC
AND BASIC SOLUTIONS

The concentrations of acidic and basic solutions are often expressed in terms of normality, N, rather than molarity, M. The normality of a solution of an acid or a base is the number of equivalents either of acid or of base per liter of solution. Liter volumes are cumbersome in arithmetical calculations, so practically we measure normality as the number of milliequivalents of acid or base per milliliter of solution. The mass of one milliequivalent (me.) of an acid or a base is its equivalent weight expressed in milligrams. (The milliequivalent weight of Na^+OH^- is 40 mg; of HCl, 36.5 mg. The numerical notation of the equivalent weight of Na^+OH^- is identical to that of its milliequivalent weight; in each case the value is 40, but the equivalent weight is 40 g, and the milliequivalent weight is 40 mg.)

The normality of a solution of a Brönsted acid is the number of moles of available protons per liter or the number of millimoles per milliliter. The normality of a solution of an ionic hydroxide is the number of moles of hydroxide ions per liter or the number of millimoles per milliliter. If 20 ml of a 0.1 N solution of a B-acid is added to 20 ml of a 0.1 N solution of an ionic hydroxide, the 2 millimoles of available protons (20 ml $\times$ 0.1 millimole/ml) in the acidic solution react completely with the 2 millimoles of hydroxide ion in the basic solution.

Let us now consider a possible method of preparing 350 ml of a 0.15 N solution of hydrochloric acid. For a 0.15 N solution, 0.15 me. of acid is needed per milliliter of prepared solution. To prepare 350 ml of 0.15 N solution, we need 52.5 me. of HCl (350 ml $\times$ 0.15 me./ml).   Since each milliequivalent of HCl has a mass of 36.5 mg, 52.5 me. weighs 1916 mg or 1.916 g.   We then dissolve 1.916 g of HCl in enough water to prepare 350 ml of solution.

22.19 ACID-BASE TITRATIONS

The fundamental basis for the quantitative determination of the amount of acid (or base) in a solution depends on the fact that if an acid-base reaction is essentially complete, then

number of equivalents of acid = number of equivalents of base

or

number of me. of acid = number of me. of base

Since the normality of a solution identifies the number of milliequivalents per milliliter (N = me./ml),

$$\underset{\substack{\text{of acidic}\\\text{solution}}}{\text{ml} \times N} = \underset{\substack{\text{of basic}\\\text{solution}}}{\text{ml} \times N}$$

The quantitative determination of the amount of acid in a solution or as a liquid or a solid is most frequently performed in aqueous solutions.   Since careful measurements of volumes are necessary, the procedure is called a *volumetric analysis*.

An acid-base titration is a volumetric procedure during which a solution of an acid or a base of known concentration is added carefully to another solution of unknown concentration (or containing an unknown amount of acid or base) until a specific acid-base reaction is essentially complete.   The volume of the solution added to the "unknown" solution is measured by using a buret.   In every titration we must know exactly when equivalent (stoichiometric) amounts of acid and base have been mixed.   If no electrical devices are used, it is necessary to employ some indicator in the solution being titrated so that the endpoint can be identified.   The titration endpoint should if possible coincide with the stoichiometric endpoint (equivalence point).

Let us briefly describe a typical titration of a solution of a strong acid with a solution of an ionic hydroxide (strong base).   We have 30 ml of the acidic solution, but we do not know its normality nor how much acid was used to prepare the solution.   We have on hand a 0.15 N solution of sodium hydroxide (a standard solution).

A few drops of a dilute solution of the acid-base indicator, phenolphthalein, are added to the acidic solution. The indicator is colorless in this solution. Some of the basic solution is put in the buret and then added slowly to the acidic solution which is being agitated (swirled). At the moment that the solution has a faint pink coloration the addition of basic solution is stopped. (The endpoint of the titration is the appearance of the basic form of the indicator.) By reading the buret the volume of basic solution used is found to be 25.5 ml.

The normality of the original acidic solution is calculated by the expression

$$\underset{\substack{\text{of basic} \\ \text{solution}}}{\text{ml} \times N} = \underset{\substack{\text{of acidic} \\ \text{solution}}}{\text{ml} \times N}$$

$$(25.5)(0.15) = (30.0)(N \text{ of acidic solution})$$

The acidic solution is $0.127 \ N$.

The milliequivalent weight (mass of 1 me.) of an acid may be determined by titrating a known mass of the acid (in solution) with an ionic hydroxide solution of known normality. Let us solve two typical problems of this type.

1. Three hundred and twenty milligrams of a monoprotic acid is dissolved in 50 ml of water. In a correct titration of the acid, 32.5 ml of $0.125 \ N \ Na^+OH^-$ is used. What are the molecular and equivalent weights of the acid?

   The milliequivalent of base used $= (32.5 \text{ ml})(0.125 \text{ me./ml}) = 4.06$ me. Therefore 4.06 me. of acid is present in 320 mg of the acid. The mass of 1 me. (me. wt) of the acid is 78.8 mg (320 mg/4.06 me.). Since the acid's milliequivalent weight is 78.8 mg, its equivalent weight is 78.8 g; because it is monoprotic, its molar weight is 78.8 g. The molecular weight of the acid is 78.8.

2. A solid is a mixture of sulfamic acid, H_2NSO_2OH (monoprotic), and some inert water-soluble material. To 0.255 g of this mixture 100 ml of water is added. By performing a correct titration, it is found that 21.2 ml of $0.11 \ N \ K^+OH^-$ is needed to react completely with the acid in the sample. What percentage of the mixture is sulfamic acid?

   The milliequivalent of base used $= (21.2 \text{ ml})(0.11 \text{ me./ml}) = 2.33$ me. Therefore the milliequivalent of sulfamic acid titrated $= 2.33$ me. Since 97 mg $=$ mass of 1 me. of sulfamic acid, the mass of 2.33 me. is 226 mg (0.226 g).   The total mass of the solid mixture (the sample) is 255 mg.   Then

$$\frac{226}{255} \times 100 = 88.6\% \text{ sulfamic acid}$$

22.20 CHOICE OF INDICATORS FOR ACID-BASE TITRATIONS

In performing acid-base titrations, the choice of a correct indicator is extremely important.

a. During the titration of a strong acid with an ionic hydroxide (and vice versa), a neutral solution is obtained at the endpoint because the only ions then present in appreciable concentrations are the positive ions of the ionic hydroxide and the negative ions related to the strong acid.   (Evaporation of the endpoint solution yields an alkali metal—or alkaline-earth metal—salt of a strong acid; such a salt does not undergo hydrolysis.)   The best indicator to use in such a titration is a substance that exhibits a color change at or near pH 7.   Litmus and bromthymol blue include pH 7 in their most effective range.   Since additions of very small amounts of oxonium or hydroxide ion cause marked changes in the pH of solutions which contain only "spectator" ions, it is permissible (error is quite small) to use either methyl orange or phenolphthalein when titrating strong acids with ionic hydroxides.

b. During the titration of a moderately weak acid with an ionic hydroxide, a basic solution is obtained at the endpoint because the most abundant negative ions then present are derived from a weak acid.   (Evaporation of the endpoint solution yields an alkali metal—or alkaline-earth metal—salt of a weak acid; such salts undergo hydrolysis.)   An indicator for such titration should not exhibit a color change until the pH of the solution being titrated is well above pH 7.   Phenolphthalein (effective range 8.5–10.0) is one of the best indicators to use when titrating a moderately weak acid with an ionic hydroxide.

In the case of some quite weak acids, it is impossible to titrate the weak acid completely by using ordinary concentrations of hydroxide ion.   Although phosphoric acid, $(HO)_3PO$, is a triprotic acid, it is impossible, under ordinary conditions, to titrate the monohydrogen phosphate ion, $HOPO_3^{--}$, completely because this acid is so weak that ordinary concentrations of hydroxide ion cannot cause its complete dissociation. The phosphate ion, PO_4^{3-} (conjugate base of $HOPO_3^{--}$), is such a strong base that it competes strongly with hydroxide ion in its search for protons.

c. During the titration of a moderately weak uncharged base with a strong acid, an acidic solution is obtained at the endpoint because the most abundant positive ions then present are derived from a weak base. (Evaporation of the endpoint solution yields a salt of a weak base and a strong acid; such a salt undergoes hydrolysis. The positive ions act as acids and the negative ions are "spectators.") Methyl orange (effective pH range 3.0–4.5) is a suitable indicator to use when titrating a moderately weak base (such as ammonia) with a strong acid. If hydrogen carbonate ion, HCO_3^-, is titrated with a strong acid, the endpoint solution contains carbonic acid (CO_2 and H_2O). Since the endpoint solution is definitely acidic, methyl orange is used.

22.21 HEAT OF NEUTRALIZATION

If 25 ml of a 0.1 N aqueous solution of a strong monoprotic Brönsted acid is added to 25 ml of a 0.1 N aqueous solution of an ionic hydroxide, a neutral solution is obtained. It is customary to call such a reaction a neutralization because the acidic and basic solutions are neutralized.

Whenever one mole (one equivalent) of a strong monoprotic acid is added to an aqueous solution containing one equivalent of an ionic hydroxide, the amount of heat evolved is approximately 13.7 kcal. The net reaction during each neutralization is $H^+ + OH^- \leftrightarrows HOH$. We see that whenever a mole of protons reacts with a mole of hydroxide ions (in aqueous solution) 13.7 kcal of heat is evolved per mole of water produced. The heat of neutralization of one equivalent of a strong acid (in water) by one equivalent of an ionic hydroxide is 13.7 kcal.

Problems

1. (a) Indicate the equations that represent the dissociation of hydrogen selenide when this substance is added to water. (b) What two molecules in the solution are present in similar concentrations? (c) What

two entities in the solution are acting as amphoteric molecules?
(d) What molecules in the solution are definitely acting as acids?
(e) What molecules in the solution are definitely acting as bases?
(f) What is the strongest acid in the solution? (g) If the solution
were evaporated to dryness, what, if anything, would remain? (h)
What chemical reactions would occur in the solution if 2.0 M Na^+OH^-
were added? (i) Of the negative ions in the solution, which is the
weakest base? (j) If 100 ml of the solution were boiled to evaporate
enough water to have 85 ml of solution remaining, would the final
solution be more acidic or less acidic than the original?

2. What occurs chemically when:
  (a) ammonium bromide is added to water?
  (b) rubidium sulfite is added to water?
  (c) potassium amide is added to water?
  (d) carbon dioxide is added to aqueous ammonia solution?
  (e) sodium acetate is added to aqueous acetic acid?
  (f) piperidine is added to water?
  (g) methyl violet is added to a solution whose pH is 1.0?
  (h) cesium phosphate is added to water?
  (i) methylammonium bromide is added to water?
  (j) lithium hydride is added to water?

3. Write the formula of the conjugate acid of·
  (a) ethylamine   (e) sulfamic acid
  (b) nitrite ion   (f) hydrogen sulfite ion
  (c) dihydrogen phosphate ion   (g) hydrogen bromide
  (d) carbonate ion

4. If 0.1 mole of the hypothetical compound K^+AP^- is added to water
   to yield 1.0 l of solution, the hydroxide ion concentration of the solution is 1×10^{-3} M. When 0.2 mole of the hypothetical compound
   Na^+OP^- is added to water to yield 2.0 l of solution, the hydroxide ion
   concentration of the solution is 2×10^{-4} M. Which is the stronger
   acid, HAP or HOP?

5. When dimethylamine is added to water, a basic solution is obtained.
   What are the proper names of the two molecules in the solution that
   are present in practically identical concentrations?

6. A solution X is prepared by adding pure ammonia to pure water.
   Among the various entities in X, identify each one that is able individually to decrease the hydroxide ion concentration of X when it is
   added to a fresh portion of X.

7. If the hypothetical compound K^+AT^- is added to pure water, the resultant solution RS has an oxonium ion concentration of 4.0×10^{-9} M.

(a) When 2.6 millimoles of HAT are added to water to yield 65 ml of solution, is the oxonium ion concentration of the solution equal to, less than, or greater than $4 \times 10^{-2} M$? (b) What is the hydroxide ion concentration of solution RS? (c) What molecules in RS are present in nearly identical concentrations?

8. Solution E is prepared by adding the hypothetical monoprotic acid HUM to pure water. The hydroxide ion concentration of solution E is $2.5 \times 10^{-12} M$. Thirty milliliters of E is titrated correctly with 25 ml of $0.015\ N\ Ba^{++}(OH^-)_2$. (a) What is the actual acidity of E? (b) What is the potential acidity, if any, of E? (c) What is the total acidity of E? (d) After the titration is complete, is the resultant solution acidic, basic, or neutral?

9. Four hundred and fifty milligrams of the diprotic chronic acid (molar weight 50) was added to pure water to yield solution A. A portion of A was titrated correctly with 40 ml of $0.15\ N\ Na^+OH^-$. What fraction of A was actually titrated?

10. A covalent compound has the formula $C_2H_6O_4$. If 0.05 mole of the compound is added to pure water to yield 500 ml of solution S, the pH of S is 1.0. Among the various kinds of uncharged and charged molecules in S, there are exactly three different kinds of negatively charged ions. (a) Is the compound a weak acid or a strong acid? (b) Is the compound monoprotic, diprotic, triprotic, etc.? (c) What is the hydroxide ion concentration of S? (d) What entities in S are definitely acting as amphoteric molecules? (e) Among the various molecules in S that are acting as acids, which is most abundant in S? (f) What molecules in S are definitely acting as bases? (g) Among the molecules that are acting as bases in S, which is the least abundant?

11. List all of the molecules present in an aqueous solution made by dissolving gaseous hydrogen sulfide in pure water at room temperature. (a) Which molecule (excluding water) is most abundant in the solution? (b) Which entity is least abundant? (c) If a current of gaseous nitrogen is bubbled through a saturated solution of hydrogen sulfide in water for a period of one hour, what effect, if any, will this have on the pH of the solution? (d) What is observed if a $6\ M$ solution of hydrogen chloride is added to 25 ml of a saturated solution of H_2S in water at room temperature?

12. An aqueous solution was prepared by adding 6.395 mg of hydrogen iodide to pure water to yield 500 l of solution. What was the oxonium concentration of the solution?

13. An ionic compound A consists of only two kinds of ions. These ions are those of the element potassium and of the conjugate base of a monoprotic acid, here called *psychic acid*. The mass of one-fifth of a mole of A is 22.0 g. If 50 g of A is added to water to yield 500 ml of water, the solution has an oxonium ion concentration of $5 \times 10^{-10} M$. (a) Eighteen grams of psychic acid was added to pure water to yield 2.5 l of solution. Was the oxonium ion concentration in the solution equal to, less than, or greater than 0.1 M? (b) How many milliliters of 0.05 N aqueous barium hydroxide solution are needed to titrate correctly 151 mg of psychic acid? (c) An aqueous solution of psychic acid has a pH of 3.0. What is the concentration of psychate ion in this solution?

14. Without adding oxonium ions to the system, how might you decrease the hydroxide ion concentration of an aqueous solution of ammonia?

15. Four hundred milligrams of a monoprotic acid is dissolved in pure water to yield 100 ml of solution A. Fifty millimoles of potassium hydroxide is added to water to yield 600 ml of solution B. Experimentation yields the fact that 30 ml of B is needed to titrate correctly 40 ml of solution A. What is the molar weight of the acid?

16. A student dissolved 269 mg of an alkali metal hydroxide in 35 ml of water. He found that 17.5 ml of 0.15 N HCl was needed to titrate correctly all of the base in the basic solution. Which alkali metal hydroxide did the student use?

17. How many millimoles of the strong monoprotic acid HAS are needed to prepare 328 ml of a 0.17 N solution?

18. If 472 ml of water is added to the solution mentioned in Problem 17, what is the oxonium ion concentration of the resultant solution?

19. (a) How many milligrams of sulfuric acid are needed to prepare 345 ml of a 0.23 N solution? (b) What is the molarity of this solution? (c) How many milliliters of water must be added to this solution to change the normality to 0.04 N? (d) What is the mass of 7.46 me. of sulfuric acid?

20. A student added some oxalic acid to some pure water. With this solution he performed a correct titration by adding 28.6 ml of 0.05 N K^+OH^-. How many milligrams of oxalic acid did the student use?

21. A solution was made by adding 5 me. of an acid to pure water to yield 50 ml of solution. Student X was given 18 ml of the solution, and student Y was given 27 ml. Each student correctly titrated his solution with 0.06 N Na^+OH^-. (a) What volume of the basic solution was used by each student? (b) What was the normality of the acidic solution?

22. Solution A, whose pH is 2, is made by adding 0.01 mole of the hypothetical monoprotic acid, HAMP, to pure water to yield 1000 ml of solution. Solution B, whose oxonium ion concentration is $1 \times 10^{-2} M$, is made by adding one mole of the hypothetical monoprotic acid, HUMP, to pure water to yield 10 l of solution. (a) Which is the stronger acid, HAMP or HUMP? (b) Which acid has the stronger conjugate base? (c) What is the formula of the conjugate acid of HAMP?

23. (a) What color would the indicator Congo red impart to pure water? (See Table 22.4, p. 550.) (b) What color would Congo red impart to a colorless solution whose pH is 4? (c) If Congo red is added to a solution whose oxonium ion concentration is $1 \times 10^{-4} M$, what entities are definitely present in the resulting solution? (d) Congo red is added to a colorless solution, and a red solution is obtained. What correct, positive statement can you make about the oxonium ion concentration of this solution?

23.1 DISSOCIATION CONSTANTS OF WEAK ACIDS

The equilibrium constant for the reversible dissociation of a monoprotic acid is usually called its *dissociation (ionization) constant.* Since the strong monoprotic acids are nearly completely dissociated in dilute solutions, their dissociation constants are large. There is no simple means of contrasting these acids with respect to their behavior in the presence of water. Since the weak monoprotic acids are incompletely dissociated in water, their dissociation constants are relatively small (usually much less than unity). The relative strength of a weak acid may be ascertained by contrasting its dissociation constant with those of other weak acids.

The expression for the dissociation constant of acetic acid (a typical weak monoprotic acid) is derived by using the chemical equation and the equilibrium law.

BASES: II

$$CH_3COOH + HOH \leftrightarrows OH_3^+ + CH_3COO^-$$

acetic acid   acetate ion

The equilibrium expression is

$$K = \frac{[OH_3^+][CH_3COO^-]}{[HOH][CH_3COOH]}$$

In dilute solutions (ion concentrations small) the concentration of water remains practically constant at 55.5 M, so let us combine the factor [HOH] with the equilibrium constant. (This is done whenever the dissociation constant of a weak acid is being derived.) Then

$$K_{equil} \times [HOH] = \frac{[OH_3^+][CH_3COO^-]}{[CH_3COOH]} = K_{dissoc}$$

$$= 1.8 \times 10^{-5} \quad \text{(at 25°C)}$$

The notation, K_{dissoc}, of a weak acid is often symbolized as K_a. Hence the K_a of acetic acid is 1.8×10^{-5}.

If oxonium ions are added (say, by using 6 M HCl) to a 0.1 M solution of acetic acid, the acetate ion concentration of this solution decreases and the concentration of undissociated acetic acid increases. If acetate ions are added (say, by using solid sodium acetate) to a 0.1 M solution of acetic acid, the oxonium ion concentration of this solution decreases and the concentration of undissociated acetic acid increases. Since the equilibrium in the 0.1 M acetic acid can be upset (displaced) by the addition of an ion common to the equilibrium system, this phenomenon is often called the *common ion effect* (see p. 465). It is pertinent to all solutions of weak acids; the changes noted for 0.1 M acetic acid are typical.

If hydroxide ions are added (say, by using 1 M Na$^+$OH$^-$) to a 0.1 M solution of acetic acid, the concentration of oxonium ion decreases, the concentration of acetate ion increases, and the concentration of undissociated acetic acid decreases. If a sufficient number of hydroxide ions is added, nearly all of the acetic acid is dissociated.

In a 0.1 M acetic acid solution the concentration of undissociated acetic acid is nearly 0.1 M, mainly because of the prominence of the reaction, $OH_3^+ + CH_3COO^- \rightarrow HOH + CH_3COOH$, which maintains a relatively high concentration of acetic acid molecules in the solution. The relative prominence of this reaction (the degree of interaction between oxonium ions and acetate ions) may be decreased by diluting the solution of acetic acid, thereby making it more and more difficult for the oxonium and acetate ions to interact chemically. It is a known fact that the degree of dissociation of acetic acid progressively increases as a 0.1 M solution is progressively diluted. In a 0.1 M solution, 1.36 per cent of the acetic acid is dissociated; in a 0.01 M solution, 4.3 per cent is dissociated; in a 0.001 M solution, about 14 per cent is dissociated.

The dissociation constant, K_a, of a weak monoprotic acid may be determined experimentally by measuring the oxonium ion concentration of a 0.1 M solution. Let us apply this method, as a typical example, to the determination of the K_a of acetic acid.

In a 0.1 M solution of acetic acid the oxonium ion concentration, $[OH_3^+]$, is 1.34×10^{-3} M. Since the amount of oxonium ion produced by the autoprotolysis of water is negligible in contrast with that resulting from the dissociation of acetic acid, we shall assume that all oxonium ions present arise from the dissociation of the acetic acid. (This assumption is made in determining approximate K_a values of most weak acids.)

The values of the concentration factors to be placed in the K_a expression are

$$[OH_3^+] = 1.34 \times 10^{-3}\ M$$
$$[CH_3COO^-] = 1.34 \times 10^{-3}\ M$$
$$[CH_3COOH] = 0.099 = (0.10 - 0.001)$$

Then $\qquad K_a = (1.34 \times 10^{-3})^2/0.099 = 1.80 \times 10^{-5}$

A general rule is: The oxonium ion concentration of a 1.0 M solution of a weak monoprotic acid (prepared by adding the acid to pure water) is approximately equal to the square root of the K_a of the acid. Symbolizing this approximation,

$$[OH_3^+]^2 = K_a,\ \sqrt{K_a} = [OH_3^+]$$

The dissociation constants of weak monoprotic acids are given in Table A.3, page A-4. The pK_a value of an acid is equal to $-\log K_a$ ($pK_a = -\log K_a$). The pK_a of acetic acid is 4.7.

Oxalic acid, $(HO)_2C_2O_2$, is a weak diprotic acid. Since the first and second dissociations are incomplete, K_1 and K_2 are small.

Step 1: $\qquad (HO)_2C_2O_2 + HOH \leftrightharpoons HOC_2O_3^- + OH_3^+$

hydrogen
oxalate ion

$$K_1 \text{ for oxalic acid} = \frac{[OH_3^+][HOC_2O_3^-]}{[(HO)_2C_2O_2]} = 3.8 \times 10^{-2}$$

$$= K_a \text{ of oxalic acid}$$

Step 2: $\qquad HOC_2O_3^- + HOH \leftrightharpoons OH_3^+ + C_2O_4^{--}$

oxalate ion

$$K_2 \text{ for oxalic acid} = \frac{[OH_3^+][C_2O_4^{--}]}{[HOC_2O_3^-]} = 4.9 \times 10^{-5}$$

$$= K_a \text{ of hydrogen oxalate ion}$$

The second dissociation constant, K_2, of an uncharged diprotic acid is always much less than the first dissociation constant, K_1, mainly because of the following factors: the diprotic acid molecule has twice as many expendable protons as its singly negative conjugate base; an uncharged molecule releases a proton more readily than does a negative ion; the acid's doubly negative conjugate base, because of its greater negative charge, attracts protons more readily than does the acid's singly negative conjugate base. The singly negative conjugate base of a diprotic acid is amphiprotic, whereas the acid's doubly negative conjugate base can behave only as a base.

Phosphoric acid, $(HO)_3PO$, is a weak triprotic acid, but since its third dissociation step involves the protolytic dissociation of a doubly negative ion, the K_3 of phosphoric acid is very small. When considering dilute aqueous solutions of phosphoric acid, it is customary to disregard this third step.

Step 1: $(HO)_3PO + HOH \leftrightarrows OH_3^+ + \quad (HO)_2PO_2^-$

$\qquad\qquad\qquad\qquad\qquad\qquad\qquad$ dihydrogen phosphate ion

$$K_1 = \frac{[OH_3^+][(HO)_2PO_2^-]}{[(HO)_3PO]} = 7.5 \times 10^{-3} = K_a \text{ of phosphoric acid}$$

Step 2: $(HO)_2PO_2^- + HOH \leftrightarrows OH_3^+ + HOPO_3^{--}$

$$K_2 = \frac{[OH_3^+][HOPO_3^{--}]}{[(HO)_2PO_2^-]} = 6.2 \times 10^{-8}$$

$$= K_a \text{ of dihydrogen phosphate ion}$$

Step 3: $HOPO_3^{--} + HOH \leftrightarrows OH_3^+ + PO_4^{3-}$

$$K_3 = \frac{[OH_3^+][PO_4^{3-}]}{[HOPO_3^{--}]} = 1 \times 10^{-12}$$

$$= K_a \text{ of monohydrogen phosphate ion}$$

It is interesting to note that for phosphoric acid the ratio of any two successive dissociation constants is about $1 \times 10^{-5}:1$. This ratio is frequently manifested by other weak polyprotic acids.

23.2 IONIZATION CONSTANTS OF WEAK BASES

The ionization constant (basic constant), K_b, of a weak base is readily calculated by using the equilibrium expression for the ionization of the weak base. A solution is prepared by dissolving a known amount of the base in pure water, so that the stoichiometric concentration of the base is known. The hydroxide ion concentration of this solution is determined, and with this information the K_b of the base is calculated.

For ammonia:

$$NH_3 + HOH \leftrightarrows NH_4^+ + OH^-$$

(The symbol, NH_3, represents free and hydrated ammonia molecules.)

$$K_b = \frac{[NH_4^+][OH^-]}{[NH_3]} = 1.8 \times 10^{-5} \qquad \text{(at 25°C)}$$

Let us calculate the hydroxide ion concentration of a 0.1 M aqueous solution of ammonia by a procedure applicable to all such problems concerning solutions of weak acids and bases.

According to the expression for K_b of ammonia, $[NH_4^+] = [OH^-]$ in any solution prepared by dissolving ammonia in pure water. In a 0.1 M solution of ammonia, the concentration of un-ionized ammonia is $0.1 - [OH^-]$. Since the hydroxide ion concentration is unknown, we set up the expression

$$[NH_4^+] = [OH^-] = x$$

Then
$$[NH_3] = 0.1 - x$$

and
$$K_b = \frac{x^2}{0.1 - x} = 1.8 \times 10^{-5}$$

A simplifying assumption is: x in the factor $0.1 - x$ is so small (compared with 0.1) it may be disregarded. Then $0.1 - x = 0.1$.

$$\frac{x^2}{0.1} = 1.8 \times 10^{-5} \quad \text{or} \quad x^2 = 1.8 \times 10^{-6}$$

$$x = \sqrt{1.8 \times 10^{-6}} = [OH^-] = 1.34 \times 10^{-3} \, M = [NH_4^+]$$

Therefore the concentration of hydroxide ion in a 0.1 M aqueous solution of ammonia is $1.34 \times 10^{-3} \, M$.

Among the hundreds of different negative ions (anions) there are many, in fact the majority, that act as bases when added to water. Although each of these bases is the conjugate base of some weak B-acid, some act as weak bases, some as strong bases. A rule of thumb is: The weaker the acid, the stronger its conjugate base; the stronger the acid, the weaker its conjugate base. These statements neither state nor imply that every weak acid has a strong conjugate base.

For example, amide ion, NH_2^-, the conjugate base of ammonia, acts as a strong base when added to water,

$$NH_2^- + HOH \leftrightharpoons NH_3 + OH^-$$

whereas acetate ion, CH_3COO^-, the conjugate base of acetic acid, acts as a weak base.

$$CH_3COO^- + HOH \leftrightharpoons CH_3COOH + OH^-$$

The most common direct sources of basic anions are specific alkali metal and alkaline-earth metal compounds that are ionic and called salts. Previously (p. 545) we described briefly the hydrolyses of such salts, and we stressed the fact that these phenomena are simple acid-base reactions in which the anion of the compound acts as a base. Since the cation in each such hydrolysis is a "spectator" ion and since the compound is ionic, the salt does not actually undergo hydrolysis. Instead, only the anion constituents of the salt act as bases.

The relative basic strength of an anion is determined by the strength of its conjugate acid. For instance, the K_a of hydrocyanic acid, HCN, is 4.0×10^{-10}, whereas the K_a of hydrofluoric acid, HF, is 6.9×10^{-4}. Since HCN is by far the weaker acid, cyanide ion, CN^-, is a much stronger base than is fluoride ion, F^-. If it is said that the hydrolysis of Na^+CN^- is more extensive than that of Na^+F^-, we interpret this as meaning that cyanide ions react as bases with water more extensively than do fluoride ions.

Let us now derive an expression for the equilibrium constant for the reaction system in which the conjugate base of a weak acid is added to water. The base must be a weak base if the equilibrium law is to apply. The weak base is A^-.

$$A^- + HOH \leftrightarrows HA + OH^-$$

$$K = \frac{[HA][OH^-]}{[A^-][HOH]}$$

If the factor $[HOH]$ is considered as part of K,

$$K_b \text{ of } A^- = \frac{[HA][OH^-]}{[A^-]}$$

Multiplication of numerator and denominator by $[OH_3^+]$ yields

$$\frac{[OH_3^+][OH^-][HA]}{[OH_3^+][A^-]} = K_w \times \frac{1}{K_a \text{ of HA}}$$

$$K_b \text{ of } A^- = \frac{K_w}{K_a \text{ of HA}}$$

where $K_w = 1 \times 10^{-14}$.

If we wish to calculate the K_b of a conjugate base of a weak acid, we simply use the relation K_w/K_a, where K_a is the dissociation constant of the weak acid to which the base is related. The K_b of acetate ion, for instance, is determined by using the expression

$$K_b \text{ of } CH_3COO^- = \frac{1 \times 10^{-14}}{1.8 \times 10^{-5}} = 5.5 \times 10^{-10}$$

where $1.8 \times 10^{-5} = K_i$ of CH_3COOH, and $K_w =$ ionic product of water.

23.3 BUFFERS

A *buffer system* is a solution that has the unique property of resisting attempts to change its pH or oxonium ion concentration. That is, the buffer has a tendency to maintain its actual acidity or basicity. If small amounts of oxonium ions are added to the buffer, the oxonium ion concentration of the solution neither increases nor decreases. This means that although the oxonium ions disappear, the base that caused their disappearance is apparently not hydroxide ion. If hydroxide ions are added to the same buffer, they disappear. They are not destroyed solely by oxonium ions because the pH of the solution is constant.

The only valid conclusion is that the buffer system contains an acid other than OH_3^+ and a base other than OH^-. The buffer actually has both reserve acidity and reserve basicity, a weak acid and a weak base together in solution.

An aqueous solution that contains undissociated acetic acid and acetate ion together in relatively high concentration is a specific buffer. *The buffering substances are undissociated acetic acid (the reserve acidity) and acetate ion (the reserve basicity).* The acetic acid (weak) acts as a good proton donor when hydroxide ions are added, and the weak base, acetate ion, eventually acts as a good proton acceptor when oxonium ions are added. The acetic acid-acetate ion buffer is a typical example of a system consisting of a weak acid and its conjugate base together in appreciable concentrations.

There are two ways to prepare an acetic acid-acetate buffer: (1) half-neutralize an aqueous solution of acetic acid by using sodium hydroxide; (2) add solid sodium acetate to aqueous acetic acid.

The efficacy of a buffer depends, in part, on the concentration of the buffering substances, high concentrations being the most favorable. Each buffer has a range of pH in which it is most effective. For an acetic acid-acetate buffer the effective range is pH 3.6–5.6. This buffer is most effective at pH 4.7 (1.8×10^{-5} M oxonium ion concentration). Inspection of the expression for the dissociation of acetic acid (p. 565) indicates that if the concentrations of the buffering substances are identical, the oxonium ion concentration is numerically equal to the dissociation constant of the acid.

In the animal organism, blood and nearly all other physiologic solutions are well-buffered. There are several buffer systems in blood; one is the hydrogen carbonate-carbonic acid system. In a healthy human the pH of the blood varies only in the pH range 7.3–7.45. The importance of buffer action in blood is appreciated when we realize that death (in humans) usually occurs if the pH of the blood drops below 6.9 or rises above 7.7.

23.4 RELATIVISTIC CHARACTER OF ACID-BASE BEHAVIOR

Up to this point certain substances have been classified either as acids or as bases because of their behavior when added to water. We have used the amphoteric substance water as the reference standard in determining the relative strengths of the common acids and bases.

We might well expect, however, that if we used a reference base other than water to contrast the common acids, we should have to revise our original classification. Let us now consider a few statements of fact which emphasize the relativistic character of acid-base behavior.

All of the hydrogen halides (HF, HCl, etc.), nitric acid, sulfuric acid, and sulfamic acid act as bases in the presence of perchloric acid. In fact, nitric acid seems to accept two protons per molecule when in perchloric acid.

$$2HClO_4 + HNO_3 \leftrightarrows H_3NO_3^{++} + 2ClO_4^-$$
$$\text{perchloric acid}$$

The behavior of these molecules might have been predicted because each has unshared pairs of electrons, the only structural requisite of a base. (See Fig. 22.2.)

Most of the acids in Table 22.1 (p. 538) act as bases in pure sulfuric acid. Acetic acid is an example.

$$CH_3COOH + H_2SO_4 \leftrightarrows [CH_3COOH_2]^+ + HSO_4^-$$

All the acids in Tables 22.1 (p. 538) and 22.2 (p. 541) act as strong acids (complete dissociation) in pure liquid ammonia, although many are weak in water.

Nearly every base listed in Table 22.3 (p. 543) is unable to exhibit any basic character in liquid ammonia.

In Table 23.1 some common acids are arranged in order of decreasing strength. Their conjugate bases are placed in order of increasing strength. In this list of acids, disulfuric acid is the strongest acid, and water is the weakest acid. Hydroxide ion is the strongest base, and hydrogen disulfate ion, $HS_2O_7^-$, is the weakest base.

TABLE 23.1   Relative strengths of some Brönsted acids and bases*

Name	Formula	Conjugate Base
Disulfuric acid	$H_2S_2O_7$	$HS_2O_7^-$
Perchloric acid	$HClO_4$	ClO_4^-
Sulfuric acid	H_2SO_4	HSO_4^-
Hydriodic acid	HI	I^-
Hydrobromic acid	HBr	Br^-
Hydrochloric acid	HCl	Cl^-
Nitric acid	HNO_3	NO_3^-
Oxonium ion	H_3O^+	H_2O
Sulfurous acid	H_2SO_3	HSO_3^-
Hydrogen sulfate ion	HSO_4^-	SO_4^{--}
Phosphoric acid	H_3PO_4	$H_2PO_4^-$
Acetic acid	CH_3COOH	CH_3COO^-
Hydrogen sulfite ion	HSO_3^-	SO_3^{--}
Carbonic acid	H_2CO_3	HCO_3^-
Hydrogen sulfide	H_2S	HS^-
Dihydrogen phosphate ion	$H_2PO_4^-$	HPO_4^{--}
Hydrocyanic acid	HCN	CN^-
Ammonium ion	NH_4^+	NH_3
Hydrogen carbonate ion	HCO_3^-	CO_3^{--}
Monohydrogen phosphate ion	HPO_4^{--}	PO_4^{3-}
Hydrosulfide ion	HS^-	S^{--}
Water	H_2O	OH^-

* Acids are arranged in order of decreasing strength; bases, in order of increasing strength.

23.5   THE LEWIS CONCEPT OF ACIDS AND BASES

In Chapter 9 we introduced the Lewis concept of acid-base behavior, which is more general than the Brönsted-Lowry concept.
According to the Brönsted-Lowry theory, a base is the entity that
donates, by sharing, a pair of electrons to a proton, thereby acting
as a proton acceptor.   The base is therefore the electron-pair donor;
the proton is the electron-pair acceptor.   Lewis realized that many
different substances act as electron-pair acceptors.   Hence he
proposed that any electron-pair acceptor be called an acid.   The
Lewis classifications are: an electron-pair acceptor is an acid; an
electron-pair donor is a base.   Whenever a Lewis acid reacts with a
base, the acid accepts, by sharing, at least one electron-pair from

the base. Thereby the acid becomes covalently attached to the base.

A typical Lewis acid-base reaction is

$$HO^- + CO_2 \rightarrow HOCO_2^-$$

hydroxide   carbon   hydrogen
ion   dioxide   carbonate
ion

in which CO_2 is the acid and OH^- the base. The product, $HOCO_2^-$, is a Brönsted acid (p. 213).

$$HOCO_2^- + OH^- \leftrightarrows HOH + CO_3^{--}$$

Carbon dioxide dissolves in water to yield an acidic solution. The initial reaction, wherein water is the base and CO_2 the Lewis acid, probably is the formation of carbonic acid.

$$H_2O + CO_2 \leftrightarrows H_2CO_3$$

carbonic
acid

The carbonic acid acts as a weak diprotic acid in excess water.

$$H_2CO_3 + HOH \leftrightarrows HCO_3^- + OH_3^+$$

hydrogen
carbonate
ion

$$HCO_3^- + HOH \leftrightarrows CO_3^{--} + OH_3^+$$

carbonate
ion

Some other acid-base reactions in which carbon dioxide acts as a Lewis acid are

$$HO^- + CO_2 \rightarrow HOCO_2^-$$

$$CO_2 + O^{--} \rightarrow CO_3^{--}$$

oxide
ion

$$H_2N^- + CO_2 \rightarrow H_2NCO_2^-$$

amide   carbamate
ion   ion

$$H^- + CO_2 \rightarrow HCO_2^-$$

formate
ion

23.6   WATER AS A LEWIS BASE

Whenever water acts as a base in the presence of a Lewis acid, the initial product always has the structural requisites of a Brönsted acid.   This is evident because the initial product has, in part, the structural elements of a water molecule.   Since water is electronically satisfied, it does not, as a unit, act as a Lewis acid.

$$H_2O + LA \leftrightarrows H_2O - LA$$

Lewis   initial
acid   product

Several covalent oxides of the electronegative elements act as Lewis acids when added to water (see p. 219).   The compounds produced act as Brönsted acids if excess water is used; hence aqueous solutions of these oxides are distinctly acidic.   Some of the reactions are given below.

$$SO_2 + H_2O \leftrightarrows H_2SO_3$$

sulfur   sulfurous
dioxide   acid

$$SO_3 + H_2O \leftrightarrows H_2SO_4$$

sulfur   sulfuric
trioxide   acid

$$P_2O_3 + 3H_2O \leftrightarrows 2H_3PO_3$$

diphosphorus   phosphorous
trioxide   acid

$$P_4O_{10} + 6H_2O \leftrightarrows 4H_3PO_4$$

tetraphosphorus   phosphoric
decaoxide   acid

$$Cl_2O + H_2O \leftrightarrows HOCl$$

dichlorine   hypochlorous
monoxide   acid

$$N_2O_3 + H_2O \leftrightarrows 2HNO_2$$

dinitrogen   nitrous
trioxide   acid

$$N_2O_5 + H_2O \leftrightarrows 2HNO_3$$

dinitrogen   nitric
pentoxide   acid

$$As_2O_5 + 3H_2O \leftrightarrows 3H_3AsO_4$$

diarsenic   arsenic
pentoxide   acid

Sulfur trioxide (p. 273) and tetraphosphorus decaoxide should be handled with care because they react vigorously even with cool water.

Some covalent molecules that contain one or more halogen atoms react readily with excess water to yield acidic solutions.   The hydrolysis of any one of these compounds initially yields a Brönsted acid that dissociates to yield protons.   (See p. 537.)   The water molecules that act as electron-pair donors displace at least one, often all, of the halogens as halide ion. The oxygen kernel of each participating water molecule thereby becomes an integral part of one of the product molecules. The covalent halide therefore acts as a Lewis acid.

The hydrolysis of phosphorus trichloride, PCl_3 (liq), is a typical example.

$$PCl_3 + 3HOH \leftrightarrows H_3PO_3 + 3HCl$$
phosphorous
acid

All of the different phosphorus(III) halides hydrolyze completely in excess water to yield phosphorous acid and the hydrogen halide.

In Table 23.2 are listed some of the common covalent halides that hydrolyze in water to yield acidic solutions. These halides are Lewis acids.

23.7 AMPHOTERIC HYDROXIDES

The hydroxides of the transition elements and of the electropositive elements of Groups $3a$ and $4a$ are only slightly soluble in water. Therefore they are neither strongly acidic nor strongly basic. The behavior of these hydroxides is due, in part, to the fact that they are much less ionic than the alkali metal hydroxides (strong bases).

Some of the slightly soluble metal hydroxides are *amphoteric;* that is, they act as weak bases in acidic solutions and as weak acids in basic solutions. This dual acid-base character might be expected since the amphoteric hydroxides have hydroxyl (—O—H) groups, each with a covalently bound proton and two unshared pairs of electrons. The amphoteric character of an amphoteric hydroxide is easily demonstrated visually. The undissolved solid hydroxide dissolves readily in acidic as well as in basic solutions.

The slightly soluble amphoteric hydroxides dissolve in acidic solutions because they accept protons to yield positive ions. Zinc hydroxide may be used as an example.

$$Zn(OH)_2 + OH_3^+ \leftrightarrows Zn(OH)OH_2^+ + HOH$$

Such a hydroxide dissolves in basic solutions because it either donates protons (Brönsted acid) or accepts hydroxide ions (Lewis acid) to yield negative ions.

TABLE 23.2   Some covalent halides that hydrolyze in excess water

Name	Formula	Major Initial Product plus the Hydrogen Halide
Phosphorus trihalides	PX_3	H_3PO_3, phosphorous acid
Phosphorus pentahalides	PX_5	POX_3, phosphorus oxyhalides (except the iodide)
Arsenic trihalides	AsX_3	H_3AsO_3, arsenous acid
Arsenic pentahalides	AsX_5	$AsOX_3$, arsenic oxyhalides
Antimony(III) chloride	$SbCl_3$	$SbOCl$, antimony(III) oxychloride
Antimony(V) chloride	$SbCl_5$	$SbOCl_3$, antimony(V) oxychloride
Bismuth(III) chloride	$BiCl_3$	$BiOCl$, bismuth oxychloride
Silicon tetrafluoride	SiF_4	H_2SiO_3, silicic acid
Tin(II) chloride	$SnCl_2$	$SnOHCl$ and $Sn(OH)_2$
Tin(IV) chloride	$SnCl_4$	$(H_2O)_2Sn(OH)_4$, tin(IV) hydroxide
Lead(IV) chloride	$PbCl_4$	PbO_2, lead dioxide
Boron fluoride	BF_3	HBO_2 and BF_4^-
Aluminum chloride	$AlCl_3$	$Al(OH_2)_6^{3+}$, $Al(OH)(OH_2)_5^{++}$, etc.
Iron(III) chloride	$FeCl_3$	$Fe(OH_2)_6^{++}$, $Fe(OH)(OH_2)_5^{++}$, etc.
Titanium(IV) chloride	$TiCl_4$	$TiO_2 \cdot xH_2O$, hydrous(IV) oxide
Sulfur chloride	S_2Cl_2	SO_2, sulfur dioxide
Thionyl chloride	$SOCl_2$	$H_2SO_3 \leftrightarrows H_2O + SO_2$
Sulfuryl chloride	SO_2Cl_2	H_2SO_4, sulfuric acid
Chlorsulfonic acid	$HOSO_2Cl$	H_2SO_4, sulfuric acid
Acetyl chloride	CH_3COCl	CH_3COOH, acetic acid
Benzoyl chloride	C_6H_5COCl	C_6H_5COOH, benzoic acid
Benzenesulfonyl chloride	$C_6H_5SO_2Cl$	$C_6H_5SO_3H$, benzenesulfonic acid

$$Zn(OH)_2 + OH^- \leftrightarrows ZnO_2H^- + HOH$$
$$Zn(OH)_2 + OH^- \leftrightarrows Zn(OH)_3^-$$
$$Zn(OH)_3^- + OH^- \leftrightarrows Zn(OH)_4^{--}$$

The acid-base reactions involved in the dissolving of an amphoteric hydroxide are reversible. Applying Le Châtelier's principle, we notice that if the hydroxide is dissolved in a basic solution, it can be reprecipitated by adding oxonium ions. If the hydroxide is dissolved in an acidic solution, it can be reprecipitated by adding hydroxide ions.

Table 23.3 lists the simplified formulations of some common, very slightly soluble amphoteric hydroxides and the most probable ions produced when they dissolve in acidic and basic solutions. Few if any unhydrated ions are present in solution.

TABLE 23.3   Some amphoteric hydroxides and their related ions

Probable Ion in Acidic Solutions (Excess OH_3^+)		Amphoteric Hydroxide	Probable Ion in Basic Solutions (Excess OH^-)	
Unhydrated	*Hydrated*		*Hydroxo form*	*Oxo form*
(Cr^{3+})	$Cr(OH_2)_6^{3+}$	$Cr(OH)_3$ chromium(III)	$Cr(OH)_4^-$	(CrO_2^-) chromite ion
(Pb^{++})	$Pb(OH_2)_6^{++}$	$Pb(OH)_2$ lead(II)	$Pb(OH)_3^-$	(PbO_2H^-) plumbite ion
(Al^{3+})	$Al(OH_2)_6^{3+}$	$Al(OH)_3$ aluminum	$Al(OH)_4^-$	(AlO_2^-) aluminate ion
(Sn^{++})	$Sn(OH_2)_6^{++}$	$Sn(OH)_2$ tin(II)	$Sn(OH)_3^-$	(SnO_2H^-) stannite ion
(Sn^{4+})	$Sn(OH_2)_6^{4+}$	$Sn(OH)_4$ tin(IV)	$Sn(OH)_6^{--}$	(SnO_3^{--}) stannate ion
(Be^{++})	$Be(OH_2)_4^{++}$	$Be(OH)_2$ beryllium	$Be(OH)_4^{--}$	(BeO_2^{--}) beryllate ion

The formulas of the hydroxides that appear in the central column of Table 23.3 are the unhydrated formulations. Because most amphoteric hydroxides are voluminous, gelatinous solids when freshly precipitated, it seems likely that they are hydrated, especially under these conditions. Therefore it appears more nearly correct to represent the amphoteric hydroxides in their hydrated formulations.

A probable hydrated formulation of zinc hydroxide is

$$Zn(OH)_2(OH_2)_2$$

Since the Brönsted acid-base character of this formulation is evident, let us write some probable equations to depict amphoteric behavior.

In acidic solutions:

$$Zn(OH)_2(OH_2)_2 + OH_3 \leftrightarrows Zn(OH)(OH_2)_3^+ + HOH$$
$$\text{hydroxotri-}$$
$$\textbf{aquozinc ion}$$

$$Zn(OH)(OH_2)_3^+ + OH_3^+ \leftrightarrows Zn(OH_2)_4^{++} + HOH$$

tetraquozinc ion

In basic solutions:

$$Zn(OH)_2(OH_2)_2 + OH^- \leftrightarrows Zn(OH)_3(OH_2)^- + HOH$$

tri-hydroxoaquozincate ion

$$Zn(OH)_3(OH_2)^- + OH^- \leftrightarrows Zn(OH)_4^{--} + HOH$$

tetrahydroxozincate ion

The Brönsted acid-base character of every hydrated amphoteric hydroxide can be represented by equations similar to those written for zinc hydroxide. A useful generalization is: Whenever an amphoteric hydroxide dissolves in an acidic aqueous solution, a positively charged aquo-hydroxo-complex ion is produced during the initial step; whenever such a hydroxide dissolves in a basic aqueous solution, the initial step is the production of a negatively charged aquo-hydroxo-complex ion. In acidic solutions an aquo-complex ion is probably produced eventually, whereas in basic solutions a hydroxo-complex ion is produced.

23.8 COMPLEX IONS

Many positive ions that have relatively large charge densities and/or unfilled d orbitals exhibit strong tendencies to group around them certain negative ions and neutral molecules. Many of these complex ions are sufficiently stable in their specific environments so that we may identify them as distinct entities having specific formulations.

Some complex ions such as sulfate (SO_4^{--}), nitrate (NO_3^-), phosphate (PO_4^{3-}), permanganate (MnO_4^-), and perchlorate (ClO_4^-) are extremely stable because of strong covalent bonding. In a sense, these ions are complex oxide ions. The oxonium ion (OH_3^+) and the ammonium ion (NH_4^+) are familiar complex ions. In this section we shall describe some less stable complex ions and show that many are produced by typical Lewis acid-base reactions.

In Chapter 17 (p. 405) we described the general tendency shown by water molecules to hydrate ions. It seems very likely that every ion in every aqueous solution is hydrated. If, for example, we think of a hydrated sodium ion as a unit (p. 405), we may call it an aquo-complex ion—a water-complex ion. The simple sodium ion, Na^+, is said to be complexed with the ligand water. The number of bonding sites at which the ion is complexed is called the ligancy of the ion. The ligancy of the sodium ion in the aquo-complex ion shown in Fig. 17.3 (p. 405) is 6.

Several positive ions of the metallic elements act as Lewis acids when they complex with water molecules. The aquo-complex ions produced by this complexing often act as Brönsted acids in excess water. If iron(III) chloride, $FeCl_3$, is added to water, an acidic solution is obtained. A possible interpretation of the formation of oxonium ions is

$$FeCl_3 + \underset{\text{(excess)}}{H_2O} \leftrightharpoons Fe(OH_3)_6^{3+} + 3Cl^-$$

$$Fe(OH_2)_6^{3+} + H_2O \leftrightharpoons Fe(OH)(OH_2)_5^{++} + OH_3^+.$$

A solution made by adding iron(III) chloride to water usually yields, on standing, an appreciable amount of a reddish-brown, gelatinous precipitate of iron(III) hydroxide, $Fe(OH)_3$, or more properly, hydrous iron(III) oxide $(Fe_2O_3 \cdot xH_2O)$. A possible simplified formulation for the over-all reaction is:

$$Fe(OH_2)_6^{3+} + \underset{\text{(excess)}}{H_2O} \leftrightharpoons Fe(OH)_3(OH_2)_3 \downarrow + 3OH_3^+$$

From Le Châtelier's principle it is evident that the production of the iron(III) hydroxide can be inhibited practically completely by adding sufficient oxonium ions to the solution.

If a small amount of iron(III) chloride is added to a large volume of hot water, a visually clear, red solution is obtained. This solution is a colloidal system consisting of the colloid hydrous iron(III) oxide suspended in water. This iron(III) oxide sol coagulates easily on addition of monohydrogen phosphate ion, HPO_4^{--}.

Some other metal positive ions that act as Lewis acids when they complex with water are: Co^{++}, Ni^{++}, Cr^{3+}, Cu^{++}, Hg^{++}, Zn^{++}, Sn^{++}, Sn^{4+}, and Al^{3+}. The nitrates, sulfates, and in many cases the chlorides and bromides of these Lewis acid cations dissolve in water to yield acidic solutions. The behavior of the aquo-complex ions of these cations seems to be analogous to that of the aquo-iron(III) ion.

Among the common representative-element positive ions that yield complex ions sufficiently stable to be identified are Al^{3+}, Si^{4+}, Sn^{++}, Sn^{4+}, and Pb^{++}. Nearly every common positive ion of each transition element forms one or more complex ions.

Some of the most common bases that act as ligands during the formation of complex ions are all of the halide ions, OH^-, NO_2^-, CN^-, SCN^- (thiocyanate), NH_3, H_2O, CO_3^{--}, SO_3^{--}, $C_2O_4^{--}$ (oxalate), $S_2O_3^{--}$ (thiosulfate), and $H_2NCH_2CH_2NH_2$ (ethylenediamine).

Cobalt(III) ion, Co^{3+}, which has a ligancy of 6, yields different complexes containing one or more of these ligands. Some of the cobalt(III) complex ions are unusually stable. In fact, the Co^{3+} ion generally yields the most stable complex ions of any of the common cations. This stability of the Co^{3+} complex ions seems to be a result of the acceptance of 12 electrons by the Co^{3+} ion to yield around the Co^{3+} nucleus the same electronic structure as that of the krypton atom. The tendency exhibited by several of the transition element cations to form complex ions seems to be an attempt to add electrons to attain a stabilized electronic configuration and to decrease charge density.

The charge on a complex ion is equal to the algebraic sum of the charges of the entities that compose the ion. For example, iron(III) ion has a ligancy of 6 when it complexes with cyanide ion, CN^-; hence $Fe(CN)_6^{3-}$ has a charge of -3.

A few complex ions are listed below.

of iron(III): $Fe(CN)_6^{3-}$, FeF_6^{3-}, $Fe(C_2O_4)_3^{3-}$, $Fe(SCN)_6^{3-}$, $Fe(NO)(CN)_5^{--}$

of iron(II): $Fe(CN)_6^{4-}$, $Fe(C_2O_4)_2^{--}$, $Fe(NO)^{++}$

of mercury(II): $HgBr_3^-$, $HgBr_4^{--}$, $Hg(CN)_4^{--}$, $HgCl_4^{--}$, $Hg(NCS)_4^{--}$, HgS_2^{--}, HgI_4^{--}

of copper(II): $Cu(NH_3)_4^{++}$, $Cu(CN)_4^{--}$, $Cu(C_2O_4)_2^{--}$

of zinc ion: $Zn(NH_3)_4^{++}$, $Zn(OH)_4^{--}$, $Zn(OH)_3^-$, $ZnCl_4^{--}$

of silver ion: $AgCl_2^-$, $Ag(NH_3)_2^+$, AgI_2^-, $Ag(S_2O_3)_2^{3-}$, $Ag(CN)_2^-$

The most common spatial arrangements of complex ions are shown in Fig. 23.1.

The discussion of complex ions in this and in subsequent sections is only cursory, but it can serve as an introduction to a very significant aspect of the chemistry of the positive ions (either real or incipient) of some of the metallic elements.

On the basis of the preliminary discussion, we shall define a *complex ion* as a charged molecular aggregate consisting of a metallic atom or ion to which is attached one or more molecules (either charged or uncharged). Since all of the attached molecules are bases, each individually has at least one unshared pair of electrons. The attached molecules (bases) are called *ligands* (donor groups); the number of sites where ligands are attached to the central atom is called the *ligancy* of the central element. The ligands are said to be complexed (coordinated) to the central ion or atom in the first complexing (coordination) sphere. For instance, the tetraquo-

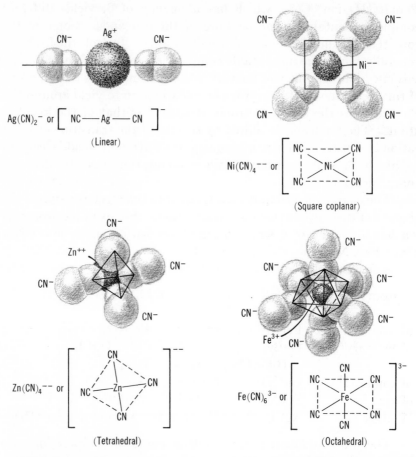

FIGURE 23.1 Spatial arrangements of four different cyanide complex ions. Nearly all common complex ions have spatial configurations similar to one of the above types.

copper(II) ion $[Cu(OH_2)_4]^{++}$ is a complex ion in which the ligands are water molecules, the ligancy (coordination number) of the copper(II) ion is 4, and the complexing sphere is "bounded" by the brackets. If a ligand is attached by one unshared pair of electrons during complexing, it is said to be *monodentate*.

Certain ligands have two or more unshared pairs of electrons separated from each other in the molecule (distinctly separated sites of basicity). If two of these sites are used to attach the ligand to a given positive ion, the ligand is said to be *bidentate*, a chelate ligand. The complexing process is called *chelation* and the complex ion is often called a *chelate complex*. A tridentate ligand has three separate basic sites by which to attach itself to the central ion. The chelation exhibited by polydentate ligands is identified by the prefixes, *mono*(1), *bis*(2), *tris*(3), *tetrakis*(4).

A typical bidentate ligand, ethylenediamine, $H_2NCH_2CH_2NH_2$, complexes with several transition metal cations. If three of these molecules complex with a cobalt(III) ion, the complex ion $[Co(H_2NCH_2CH_2NH_2)_3]^{3+}$ or $[Co(en)_3]^{3+}$, tris(ethylenediamine)-cobalt(III), is obtained. This ion is octahedral and the suggested bonding is d^2sp^3. (See p. 194 and Figs. 23.1 and 23.4.) This ion will later be described more fully (p. 588).

The actual nature of the bonding that holds the ligands to the central ion or atom is complex. However, the geometry of the complex ions, as related to the ligancy of the central ion, seems to suggest an electrostatic force not too unlike that of covalent bonding. The types of covalent hybrid bonds mentioned earlier (p. 195) are suggested for many of the common types of complex ions. Some are listed below.

Ligancy of 2:

Linear (*sp* bonding): Ag^+, Au^+

Ligancy of 4:

Tetrahedral (sp^3 bonding): Cu^+, Be^{++}, Zn^{++}, Cd^{++}, Hg^{++}, B^{3+}

Square planar (dsp^2 bonding): Ni^{++}, Cu^{++}, Pt^{++}, Pd^{++}

Ligancy of 6:

Octahedral (d^2sp^3 bonding, inner complex): Cr^{++}, Cr^{3+}, Mn^{++}, Fe^{3+}, Fe^{++}, Co^{3+}, Ni^{++}, Pt^{4+}

Octahedral (sp^3d^2 bonding, outer complex): Al^{3+}, Ga^{3+}, Fe^{3+}, In^{3+}, Tl^{3+}, Zn^{++}, Cd^{++}, Hg^{++}, Ge^{4+}

An example of d^2sp^3 bonding is suggested for the ion called hexacyanoferrate(III) ion, $[Fe(CN)_6]^{3-}$. An example of sp^3d^2 bonding is suggested for the hexafluoroferrate(III) ion, $[Fe(F)_6]^{3-}$. The orbitals involved are depicted below.

	3d	*3d*	*3d*	*3d*	*3d*	*4s*	*4p*	*4p*	*4p*	*4d*	*4d*
Fe atom	(..)	(.)	(.)	(.)	(.)	(..)					
Fe^{3+}	(.)	(.)	(.)	(.)	(.)	( )					
or	(..)	(..)	(.)	( )	( )	( )					
$Fe(CN)_6^{3-}$	(..)	(..)	(.)	(..)	(..)	(..)	(..)	(..)	(..)		
				d^2sp^3 bonding							
$Fe(F)_6^{3-}$	(.)	(.)	(.)	(.)	(.)	(..)	(..)	(..)	(..)	(..)	(..)
						sp^3d^2					

The $[Fe(CN)_6]^{3-}$ ion appears to have only one unpaired electron, whereas the $[Fe(F)_6]^{3-}$ ion seems to have five unpaired electrons. In order to explain these apparent facts, the bonding indicated has been suggested. The orbitals involved are those indicated, but this does not mean that the bonds are ordinary hybrid covalent bonds. In fact, many indications lead to a suspicion that they are not.

23.9 NOMENCLATURE OF COMPLEX IONS

Although the specific nomenclature used in identifying complex ions may seem rather arbitrary, its necessity is obvious because of the complicated nature of many complex ions and their compounds. The most important nomenclature rules are listed below.

a. All negatively charged ligands have the suffix -*o*. Uncharged ligands have no characteristic suffixes. (See Table 23.4.)

TABLE 23.4 Some common ligands and their names as prefixes

Ligand*	Name as Prefix
NH_3	ammine
CH_3NH_2	methylamine
$H_2N(CH_2)_2NH_2$	ethylenediamine
HOH	aquo
CH_3OH	methanol
C_2H_5OH	ethanol
CO	carbonyl
NO	nitroso
CN^-	cyano
SCN^-	thiocyanato
OH^-	hydroxo
O^{--}	oxo
F^-, Cl^-, Br^-, I^-	fluoro, chloro, etc.
$C_2O_4^{--}$	oxalato
CO_3^{--}	carbonato
NO_2^-	nitro
C_5H_5N	pyridyl
SO_3^{--}	sulfito
SO_4^{--}	sulfato

* All are monodentate except ethylenediamine and oxalate ion, which are bidentate.

b. In a given complex ion negative ligands are named before uncharged ligands.

c. In cations and uncharged complexed compounds, the name of the central metal ion or atom is used in ordinary compounds. In anions the name of the central metal ion or atom has the suffix -*ate*.

d. For complexed (coordination) compounds, the cation is always named before the anion.

Some examples are given below.

$Co(NH_3)_4(CN)_2^+$ is dicyanotetrammine cobalt(III) ion.
HgI_4^{--} is tetraiodomercurate(II) ion.
$Cu(CN)_2^-$ is dicyanocuprate(I) ion.
$(K^+)_2[(PtCl_6)]^{--}$ is potassium hexachloroplatinate(IV).
$[Pt(NH_3)_3Cl_3]^+Cl^-$ is trichloro-triammineplatinum(IV) chloride.
$(K^+)_3[Fe(CN)_6]^{3-}$ is potassium hexacyanoferrate(III).

Various degrees of amination of cobalt(III) and platinum(IV) chlorides create different complexed (coordination) compounds which, because of their different compositions, yield differing numbers of ions in aqueous solutions. Two specific combinations of ammonia and chloride ion ligands yield nonionic compounds. The formulas of some of these complexed compounds are given in Table 23.5.

TABLE 23.5 Some cobalt(III) and platinum(IV) complexed compounds

Compound	Number of Ions in Solution
$[Co(NH_3)_6]^{3+}(Cl^-)_3$	4
$[Co(NH_3)_5Cl]^{++}(Cl^-)_2$	3
$[Co(NH_3)_4(Cl)_2]^+Cl^-$	2
$[Co(NH_3)_3Cl_3]$	0
$K^+[Co(NH_3)_2Cl_4]^-$	2
$[Pt(NH_3)_6]^{4+}(Cl^-)_4$	5
$[Pt(NH_3)_5Cl]^{3+}(Cl)_3$	4
$[Pt(NH_3)_4Cl_2]^{++}(Cl^-)_2$	3
$[Pt(NH_3)_3Cl_3]^+(Cl^-)$	2
$[Pt(NH_3)_2Cl_4]$	0

Later, in Chapter 27, we shall elaborate the fact that the concept of isomerism yields a logical explanation for the existence of the hundreds of thousands of compounds of carbon. Two compounds are said to be *isomers* if they have different chemical and/or physical properties but identical compositions. That is, there are two different compounds butane and isobutane that have the same compositional formula, C_4H_{10}. These compounds are isomers in that they exhibit isomerism. The difference in properties is due to difference in structure. (See p. 669.)

There are three complexed compounds of chromium(III) that have identical empirical (stoichiometric) formulas. Since they are ionic, each consists of positive and negative ions. The ions in the compounds are not isomeric; however, the empirical formulas are identical. Hence in one sense they are isomeric. These compounds are hexaquochromium(III) chloride, $[Cr(OH_2)_6]^{3+}(Cl^-)_3$ (violet color); monochloro-pentaquochromium(III) chloride-1-water, $[Cr(OH_2)_5Cl]^{++}(Cl^-)_2 \cdot HOH$ (green); dichloro-tetraquochromium(III) chloride-2-water, $[Cr(OH_2)_4Cl_2]^+Cl^- \cdot 2HOH$ (green).

Two compounds that exhibit ligand group isomerism are tetramminecopper(II) tetrachloroplatinate(II), whose formula is $[Cu(NH_3)_4]^{++}[PtCl_4]^{--}$, and tetrammineplatinum(II) tetrachlorocuprate(II), $[Pt(NH_3)_4]^{++}[CuCl_4]^{--}$.

23.10   STEREOISOMERISM IN COMPLEX IONS

The arrangement of the ligands in three dimensions about the central metal ion can, in many cases, lead to a type of isomerism called *stereoisomerism*. That is, the geometry of the complex ions—their spatial representation—leads to the prediction of isomers. The initial work done by Alfred Werner between 1893 and 1918 on the composition and isomerism of many kinds of complexed (coordination) compounds is one of the most brilliant examples of the use of spatial perception in considering the possible configurations of some of the most complicated complexed compounds and ions. Whenever there are four or more ligands about a central ion, there is a possibility that stereoisomerism may be an important factor.

Let us first consider the complex ions that have a square planar configuration, those that we said apparently showed dsp^2 hybrid bonding. If a platinum(II) ion has two different ligands complexed with it in dsp^2 bonding, there are two possible formulations of the ion. An example is the diaquo-diammineplatinum(II) ion, $[Pt(NH_3)_2(H_2O)_2]^{++}$. There are two stereoisomeric forms of this ion, one called *cis* (like ligands at adjacent corners), the other called *trans* (like ligands at opposite corners).

$$
\begin{array}{ccc}
H_3N & & OH_2 \\
& \diagdown\diagup & \\
& Pt & \\
& \diagup\diagdown & \\
H_3N & & OH_2 \\
\end{array}
\qquad
\begin{array}{ccc}
H_2O & & NH_3 \\
& \diagdown\diagup & \\
& Pt & \\
& \diagup\diagdown & \\
H_3N & & OH_2 \\
\end{array}
$$

cis form *trans* form

This type of stereoisomerism is usually called *geometric isomerism*, and the *cis* and *trans* forms are geometric isomers.

If there are three different ligands in a planar platinum(II) complex ion, there are two possible geometric isomers. For example, the chloroaquodiammineplatinum(II) ion exists in two different stereoisomeric forms.

$$
\left[\begin{array}{ccc}
H_3N & & OH_2 \\
& \diagdown\diagup & \\
& Pt & \\
& \diagup\diagdown & \\
H_3N & & Cl \\
\end{array}\right]^{+}
\qquad
\left[\begin{array}{ccc}
H_2O & & NH_3 \\
& \diagdown\diagup & \\
& Pt & \\
& \diagup\diagdown & \\
H_3N & & Cl \\
\end{array}\right]^{+}
$$

Cis *Trans*

If there are four different ligands in a planar platinum(II) complex ion, three isomers are predicted. Several different compounds are known for which there are three stereoisomers each, as predicted. For the compound chlorobromopyridylammineplatinum(II), the three isomers are

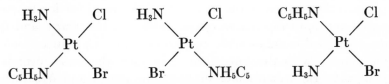

If there are two different ligands complexed about a cobalt(III) complex ion in an octahedral arrangement so that there are four of one kind and two of another, geometric isomers are possible. That is, there is a *cis* form and a *trans* form of dichlorotetramminecobalt(III) ion. These are shown in Fig. 23.2.

The complex ion dichloro-bis(ethylenediamine)cobalt(III) ion shows rather unusual stereoisomerism in that the *cis* form exhibits *optical isomerism*. For the *cis* form there are two stereoisomers that are nonsuperimposable mirror images of each other. Each of these ions has the ability to rotate plane polarized light. One of the optically active forms rotates the plane of polarized light a certain extent to the right; the other ion rotates the polarized light to the left by an identical extent. Therefore the former is said to be *dextrorotatory*, the latter, *levorotatory*. One is the *dextro* form, the other the *levo* form. An equimolar mixture of the *dextro* and *levo* forms is called a *racemic modification*. It is optically inactive because there are equal numbers of identical mirror images in the molecular population.

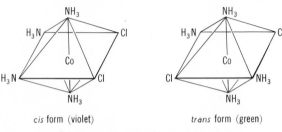

cis form (violet)   *trans* form (green)

FIGURE 23.2 Diagrams showing the *cis* and *trans* forms (geometric isomers) of dichloro-tetramminecobalt(III) ion, an octahedral structure. These two different ions exhibit a type of isomerism called *stereoisomerism*, in which spatial arrangements are involved.

The *trans* form of dichloro-bis(ethylenediamine)cobalt(III) ion has no optical isomers; hence it is optically inactive. Although the molecule has a mirror image, of course, its mirror image is superimposable on itself. Also, an extremely important different aspect of the *trans* form is that it is symmetric, whereas the *cis* form is asymmetric. All symmetric molecules are optically inactive, whereas all asymmetric molecules are optically active. Since the *trans* form consists of symmetric molecules, all of the mirror images are identical, or each is superimposable on each other.

Figure 23.3 indicates the *cis* and *trans* forms of the ion in question and the optically active configurations. The *dextro* and *levo* forms are called *enantiomorphs* or *enantiomers*. Of course, each is stereoisomeric with the *trans* form. In fact, the *trans* form is a nonenantiomeric stereoisomer of both the *dextro* and *levo* forms. Enantiomers are optically active mirror image isomers.

Tris(ethylenediamine)cobalt(III) ion exists in two enantiomeric forms, one the *dextro*, the other the *levo*. These are shown in Fig. 23.4.

We shall refer to optical isomerism again in Chapter 27 because thousands of organic compounds exhibit this type of stereoisomerism. In our discussion of the optical isomerism of organic compounds, we shall notice that many compounds of carbon are

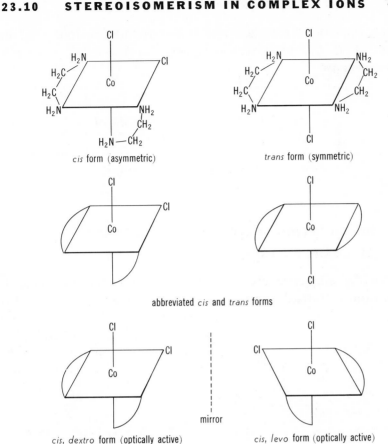

cis form (asymmetric)   *trans* form (symmetric)

abbreviated *cis* and *trans* forms

mirror

cis, dextro form (optically active)   *cis, levo* form (optically active)

FIGURE 23.3 Diagrams showing the *cis* and *trans* forms dichloro-bis(ethylenediamine)cobalt(III) ion and the two enantiomeric forms (nonsuperimposable mirror images) of the *cis* form.   Because the *cis* form is asymmetric, it has two optically active stereoisomers that are enantiomeric.

optically active because a specific carbon kernel has surrounding it, in a tetrahedral arrangement, four different kernels or groups of kernels. This configuration leads to molecular asymmetry, the apparent cause of optical activity.

If a specific complex ion has tetrahedral geometry and there are four different ligands around the central atomic kernel, the ion exhibits optical isomerism. There are two different complex ions for each such case, one *dextro* and one *levo*. Each is the mirror image of the other, but the mirror images are nonsuperimposable.

Let us assume that a central kernel M is surrounded by four different ligands, A, B, C, and D, in a tetrahedral arrangement. The two enantiomers are

$$\begin{bmatrix} B \\ | \\ A-M-C \\ | \\ D \end{bmatrix}^+ \qquad \begin{bmatrix} B \\ | \\ C-M-A \\ | \\ D \end{bmatrix}^+$$

dextro form   *mirror*   *levo* form

23.11 DISSOCIATION (INSTABILITY) CONSTANTS OF COMPLEX IONS

Each of the simpler complex ions exists, in aqueous solutions, in equilibrium with its dissociation products (its constituent entities). An equilibrium expression can be formulated for the reversible dissociation of a complex ion. For the silver ammonia complex ion,

$$Ag(NH_3)_2^+ \leftrightarrows Ag^+ + 2NH_3$$

$$K = \frac{[Ag^+][NH_3]^2}{[Ag(NH_3)_2^+]} = K_{dissoc}$$

$$= 6.8 \times 10^{-8} \qquad (at\ 25°C)$$

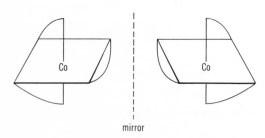

mirror

FIGURE 23.4 Diagrams showing the two optically active forms of the tris(ethylenediamine)cobalt(III) ion. Because these are nonsuperimposable mirror images, they are called *enantiomers*. Each is an asymmetric charged molecule.

Because of the magnitude of this dissociation (instability) constant, we realize that the silver ion concentration, $[Ag^+]$, of the solution is much less than that of the complex ion. If the concentration of ammonia, $[NH_3]$, is increased, the concentration of silver ions decreases and the concentration of complex ion increases. If the ammonia concentration is decreased by the addition of oxonium ions, the silver ion concentration increases and the concentration of complex ion decreases.

For the cadmium cyanide complex ion, the dissociation (instability) constant expression is

$$Cd(CN)_4^{--} \leftrightarrows Cd^{++} + 4CN^-$$

$$K_{\text{dissoc}} = \frac{[Cd^{++}][CN^-]^4}{[Cd(CN)_4^{--}]} = 1.4 \times 10^{-17} \quad (\text{at } 25°C)$$

Table 23.6 lists the dissociation (instability) constants of some complex ions. Contrasting the figures for the complex ions

TABLE 23.6 **Dissociation (instability) constants of complex ions**

Complex Ion	Dissociation Constant (Instability Constant)	pK_{dissoc}
$Ag(NH_3)_2^+$	6.8×10^{-8}	7.2
$Ag(CN)_2^-$	8×10^{-23}	22.1
$Cd(NH_3)_4^{++}$	1×10^{-7}	7.0
$Cd(CN)_4^{--}$	1.4×10^{-17}	16.9
$Zn(NH_3)_4^{++}$	2.6×10^{-10}	9.6
$HgBr_4^{--}$	2.2×10^{-22}	21.7
HgI_4^{--}	5.0×10^{-32}	31.3
$Hg(CN)_4^{--}$	4×10^{-42}	41.4
$Hg(SCN)_4^{--}$	1.0×10^{-22}	22.0

$Ag(NH_3)_2^+$ and $Ag(CN)_2^-$, we see that the silver cyanide complex ion is the more stable. This means that, mole for mole, cyanide ions are more effective than ammonia molecules in decreasing the silver ion concentration of an aqueous solution.

It is impossible, simply by inspecting the instability constants, to compare directly the relative stabilities of the complex ions $Ag(CN)_2^-$ and $Cd(CN)_4^{--}$, because in the instability constant expression for the $Ag(CN)_2^-$ ion the cyanide ion concentration term is to the second power, whereas in the corresponding expression for the $Cd(CN)_4^{--}$ ion the cyanide ion concentration term is to the fourth power. It is possible, however, to make a direct comparison of the complex ions $HgBr_4^{--}$, HgI_4^{--}, $Hg(CN)_4^{--}$, and $Cd(CN)_4^{--}$. In this group $Hg(CN)_4^{--}$ is the most stable, $Cd(CN)_4^{--}$, the least stable, and HgI_4^{--}, more stable than $HgBr_4^{--}$ ($pK_{\text{dissoc}} = -\log_{10} K_{\text{dissoc}}$).

The value of the dissociation constant of a complex ion implies the strength of bonding in the complexion.

23.12 HOMOATOMIC NEGATIVE IONS

Although iodine is very slightly soluble in water, it is quite soluble in a solution of potassium iodide. Iodide ions apparently form complex ions by sharing with iodine molecules pairs of electrons. The most common such ion is the triiodide ion, I_3^-.

$$I_2 + |\underline{I}|^- \leftrightarrows I_3^-$$

This complex ion is the one formed in aqueous solutions. A solution containing the triiodide ion has a dark brown coloration.

A small quantity of iodine dissolves in water; iodine is fairly soluble in ethanol (tincture of iodine). Each solution has a brown coloration similar to that of a solution which contains the triiodide ion. It seems likely that iodine molecules complex to some extent with water, and to a greater extent with ethanol molecules. If iodine is dissolved in a relatively nonpolar solvent (chloroform, $CHCl_3$, or carbon tetrachloride, CCl_4), the solution has a purple coloration similar to iodine vapor. Here all the iodine seems molecular.

If iodine is added to solid potassium iodide, the complex ions I_5^-, I_7^-, and I_9^- appear to be present. These and the triiodide ion are called homoatomic ions because they are polyatomic and composed of chemically identical atoms.

Sulfur is practically insoluble in water but is fairly soluble in solutions containing relatively high concentrations of sulfide ion, S^{--}. Each participating sulfide ion forms a complex ion by sharing a pair of electrons with one or more sulfur atoms. The simplest homoatomic ion of this type is the disulfide ion, S_2^{--} ($S^{--} + S \leftrightarrows S_2^{--}$). There is evidence that the ions S_3^{--}, S_4^{--}, and S_5^{--}, are often present with the disulfide ion. If hydrogen sulfide is bubbled into a solution of aqueous ammonia, a solution is produced that contains a fairly high concentration of ammonium ions and sulfide ions (also hydrosulfide ions). Sulfur is quite soluble in this solution (due to formation of S_2^{--}, etc.). The yellow solution so obtained is usually called ammonium polysulfide solution and is useful in certain qualitative analysis procedures.

To be consistent in regard to the Lewis concept of acid-base behavior, elemental iodine and sulfur can apparently act as Lewis acids. Sulfur, apparently acting as a Lewis acid, reacts with sulfite ion, $|SO_3^{--}$, to yield the thiosulfate ion, $S\!-\!SO_3^{--}$ ($S_2O_3^{--}$).

There are several homoatomic negative ions whose methods of

preparation are rather different in character from those of the triiodide and disulfide ions. These ions are peroxide ion, O_2^{--}; superoxide ion, O_2^-; ozonate ion, O_3^-; carbide ion, C_2^{--}; and azide ion, N_3^-. We should not infer any acid-base behavior with respect to their formation.

23.13   NONAQUEOUS ACID-BASE PHENOMENA

Throughout our discussions of acid-base phenomena we have described primarily reactions occurring in aqueous solutions or in the presence of stoichiometric amounts of water. Some gaseous phase reactions are acid-base, as are certain heterogeneous reactions between gases and solids. (It is interesting to note that very small amounts of water greatly accelerate many reactions involving the heterolytic fission—rupture to yield two ions—of some covalent bond in a reactant molecule. The water molecules may, by some physical or chemical interaction, increase the polarity of the bond that undergoes heterolytic fission. The actual, apparently catalytic, role of water in such reactions is incompletely understood.)

Let us now mention a few gaseous acid-base reactions in which the base, ammonia, is a reactant molecule.

a. Gaseous ammonia and hydrogen chloride, in the presence of a relatively small amount of water vapor, react at room temperature to yield the white solid, ammonium chloride. This reaction is definitely reversible at temperatures around 400°–500°C.

$$NH_3(g) + HCl(g) \leftrightarrows (NH_4^+ + Cl^-)(s)$$

b. The commercial preparation of sulfamic acid and its ammonium salt is

$$NH_3(g) + SO_3(g) \leftrightarrows H_2N—SO_2OH(s)$$
sulfamic acid

$$H_2N—SO_2OH + NH_3 \leftrightarrows \quad (H_2N—SO_3)^-NH_4^+$$
ammonium sulfamate, "Ammate"

c. One of the important industrial preparations of urea is

$$NH_3(g) + CO_2(g) \leftrightarrows [H_3N—CO_2] \leftrightarrows (H_2N—\overset{\overset{\displaystyle O}{\|}}{C}—OH)$$
carbamic acid (unstable)

$$HOH + H_2N—\overset{\overset{\displaystyle O}{\|}}{C}—NH_2(s) \leftrightarrows H_2N—\overset{\overset{\displaystyle O}{\|}}{C}—O^-NH_4^+(s) \longleftarrow \Big] + NH_3$$
urea   ammonium
(carbamide)   carbamate

Urea is extensively used as a fertilizer because of its solubility and its high percentage (47 per cent) of nitrogen. It is also used to synthesize barbiturates (Phenobarbital, Nembutal, Amytal, Veronal, etc.) and urea-formaldehyde resins (Plaskon, Bettle products, etc.). Urea and formaldehyde, H_2CO, polymerize (combine) to form relatively large molecules that compose the resins. In the animal body, urea is the major nitrogenous product of metabolism (mainly of proteins).

d. Since boron trifluoride, a gas, is a strong Lewis acid,

$$NH_3(g) + BF_3(g) \leftrightharpoons H_3N\!-\!BF_3$$

Certain typical heterogeneous reactions involve carbon dioxide and oxide ion of some ionic oxide. The essentially ionic oxides are the alkali metal oxides, $(M^+)_2O^{--}$, and calcium, strontium, and barium oxides. The positive ion is a "spectator" during the reaction.

$$O^{--} + CO_2 \leftrightharpoons CO_3^{--}$$

in a solid   in a
ionic oxide   carbonate salt

The hydroxide ion of the ionic hydroxide related to the ionic oxide reacts with the carbon dioxide.

$$OH^- + CO_2 \leftrightharpoons HOCO_2^-$$

in a solid   in a hydrogen
ionic hydroxide   carbonate salt

Sulfur trioxide reacts with ionic oxides and hydroxides in a manner exactly analogous to the behavior of carbon dioxide, but sulfur trioxide is the stronger acid. The net reactions are

$$O^{--} + SO_3 \leftrightharpoons SO_4^{--}$$

in a solid   in a sulfate
ionic oxide   salt

$$OH^- + SO_3 \leftrightharpoons HOSO_3^-$$

in a solid   in a hydrogen
ionic hydroxide   sulfate salt

Sulfur trioxide reacts with certain weakly basic oxides to yield salts. A few examples are

$$PbO + SO_3 \leftrightharpoons Pb^{++}SO_4^{--}$$
$$ZnO + SO_3 \leftrightharpoons Zn^{++}SO_4^{--}$$
$$Ag_2O + SO_3 \leftrightharpoons (Ag^+)_2SO_4^{--}$$

There are many organic liquids (compounds of carbon) that serve as solvents for a wide variety of acid-base reactions. We have previously identified the main types of organic acids and mentioned that many covalent organic compounds containing nitrogen can behave as bases because of the unshared pair of electrons around each nitrogen kernel.

Among the thousands of organic compounds, there are many substances usually classed as neutral because under ordinary conditions they behave neither as acids nor as bases. Among them are hundreds of compounds containing oxygen; in nearly all of these substances there are two unshared pairs of electrons around each oxygen kernel. Since these compounds have the structural requirements of a base, this suggests that in the presence of strong acids they might behave as bases. It is well known that many, if not most, organic compounds containing oxygen atoms do behave as bases in the presence of either pure sulfuric acid or disulfuric acid. Their solubility in sulfuric acid is usually due mainly to the formation of ions. For example, ethyl ether, $(C_2H_5)_2O$, dissolves in pure sulfuric acid although it is only slightly soluble in water.

$$(C_2H_5)_2O + (HO)_2SO_2 \leftrightarrows (C_2H_5)_2OH^+ + HOSO_3^-$$

ethyl ether   conjugate acid
                          of ethyl ether

The strong Lewis acids, aluminum chloride and boron trifluoride, usually behave as acids in the presence of the neutral organic compounds containing oxygen atoms.

Among the common neutral organic compounds are the alcohols (such as methanol, CH_3OH, and ethanol, C_2H_5OH); the ethers (such as methyl ether, $(CH_3)_2O$); the aldehydes (such as acetalde-

hyde, $CH_3-\overset{\displaystyle H}{\underset{\displaystyle }{\diagdown}}C{=}O$); the ketones (such as acetone, $(CH_3)_2C{=}O$); the esters (such as ethyl acetate, $CH_3COOC_2H_5$); and the hydrocarbons (such as hexane, C_6H_{14}, and benzene, C_6H_6). As we have just mentioned, most of those compounds containing oxygen are bases relative to sulfuric acid. Benzene acts as a base in the presence of sulfur trioxide.

$$C_6H_6 + SO_3 \rightarrow \qquad C_6H_5SO_2OH$$

benzenesulfonic acid
(as strong as hydrochloric acid)

Let us consider the organic liquid, ethanol, C_2H_5OH, as a suitable liquid in which to perform certain acid-base reactions. We shall create an environment in ethanol similar to that of an aqueous solution of sodium hydroxide. We shall produce the conjugate base of ethanol, $C_2H_5O^-$ (just as we can produce hydroxide ions in water) by adding metallic sodium to an excess of pure ethanol. The reaction is

$$2C_2H_5OH + 2Na \rightarrow 2C_2H_5O^- + 2Na^+ + H_2 \uparrow$$

ethanol   ethoxide
(in excess)   ion

The ethanolic solution containing sodium ions and ethanol's conjugate base, $C_2H_5O^-$, is exactly analogous to an aqueous solution containing sodium ions and water's conjugate base, OH^-. Since ethanol is a fairly good solvent for many organic compounds, we can use this ethanolic solution of the strong base, ethoxide ion, to illustrate many organic acid-base phenomena, just as we use an aqueous solution of the strong base, hydroxide ion, to illustrate many inorganic acid-base reactions. (Ethoxide ion is at least as strong a base as hydroxide ion.)

A few reactions involving ethoxide ion are given below (reactions are nearly complete).

$$\overset{\displaystyle O}{\overset{\|}{CH_3C}}\!-\!OH + C_2H_5O^- \leftrightharpoons CH_3COO^- + C_2H_5OH$$

acetic acid   ethoxide   acetate   ethanol
                ion   ion

$$C_6H_5OH + C_2H_5O^- \leftrightharpoons C_6H_5O^- + C_2H_5OH$$

phenol   phenoxide
                     ion

$$HOH + C_2H_5O^- \leftrightharpoons OH^- + C_2H_5OH$$

Problems

1. Write chemical equations illustrating the amphoteric character of (a) $Cr(OH_2)_3(OH)_3$; (b) $Sn(OH)_2(OH_2)_2$; (c) $Pb(OH_2)_2(OH)_2$; (d) ZnO. (Initial steps only are necessary in representing the acid-base reactions.)

2. A strongly basic, clear solution contains a relatively high concentration of the complex ion called tetrahydroxoaluminate ion. (a) What is observed visually when 12 M hydrochloric acid is added slowly to the solution until the system is distinctly acidic? (b) Write an equation representing the initial acid-base reaction. (c) What is the proper name of the immediate conjugate acid of tetrahydroxoaluminate ion?

3. Suggest a simple test that might be used to differentiate an aquo-complex ion from an ammine-complex ion.

4. What structural characteristics endow sulfuric acid molecules with the ability to behave both as acids and as bases?

5. In the absence of liquid water, with what molecules can sulfur trioxide react to yield the conjugate base of sulfamic acid?

6. Considering the fact that addition of sulfur trioxide to pure sulfuric acid yields disulfuric acid, suggest an electronic formula for disulfuric acid.

7. Assuming the absence of water as a solvent, write plausible equations representing reactions between acids and bases that would yield (a) formate ion; (b) hydrogen sulfite ion; (c) the conjugate acid of hydrogen chloride; (d) hydrogen chloride; (e) carbonate ion; (f) carbon monoxide (p. 666); (g) sulfamate ion; (h) methoxide ion, OCH_3^-.

8. Suggest a simple preparation of a buffer solution by using sodium monohydrogen phosphate as the principal compound (other than water).

9. Write suitable equations illustrating the following reactions.
   (a) The conjugate acid of ammonia acts as an acid in the presence of ethoxide ion, $OC_2H_5^-$.
   (b) Sulfur dioxide acts as an acid in the presence of hydroxide ions.
   (c) Hydrogen chloride acts as a base in the presence of sulfuric acid.
   (d) The conjugate acid of ethylamine, $C_2H_5NH_2$, yields an acidic solution when added to water.
   (e) Bromide ion acts as a base in pure sulfuric acid.
   (f) The conjugate base of methanol (methanol is CH_3OH) acts as a base when added to water.
   (g) Thionyl chloride is added to water to yield an acidic solution.
   (h) The conjugate base of ammonia acts as a base in pure CH_3OH.
   (i) Sodium oxide is added to water.
   (j) Sulfuric acid acts as an acid when added to pure sodium chloride.

10. Several different solutions are identified as 0.1 N HBr, 0.1 M HI, 0.1 N H_2SO_4, 0.1 M CH_3COOH, 0.25 M HCN, 0.15 M CH_3COOH, 0.1 N $HClO_4$, 0.1 M H_2SO_4.   (a) Which solutions have practically identical actual acidities?   (b) Which solution has the lowest pH value?   (c) Which solution has the lowest hydroxide ion concentration?   (d) Which solution has the highest total acidity?   (e) Which solution has the largest number of milliequivalents of acid per milliliter?   (f) Which solution has the highest potential (reserve) acidity?

11. In a specific solution the concentration of undissociated HCN is identical to that of cyanide ion.   What is the oxonium ion concentration of the solution?

12. A solution was made by adding 50 g of sodium cyanide, Na^+CN^-, to 500 ml of 0.15 M HCN. What was the oxonium concentration of the resultant solution? (Assume no volume change on addition of the solid.)

13. Two hundred millimoles of an acid HA was added to water to yield 4 l of solution. The oxonium concentration of the solution was 5×10^{-4} M. What was the dissociation constant of the acid HA?

14. One hundred millimoles of sodium cyanide NaCN was added to water to yield 1 l of solution. What was the hydroxide ion concentration?

15. Three hundred millimoles of acetic acid was added to water to yield 4.5 l of solution. What was the oxonium concentration of the solution?

16. What was the potential acidity of a solution made by adding 5 ml of 6 M HCl to 100 ml of a 0.1 M solution of acetic acid?

17. What was the actual acidity of the final solution mentioned in Problem 16?

18. What was the total acidity of the final solution mentioned in Problem 16?

19. Suggest a method of preparing an acetic acid-acetate ion buffer in which the actual acidity is 5×10^{-4} M.

20. A metallic element, here called M, exists in its $+4$ oxidation state in a hydrated amphoteric hydroxide, HAH. HAH dissolves in a given aqueous Na^+OH^- solution to yield a doubly negative complex ion X in which the ligancy of M is 6. What is the formula of X?

21. Which is the stronger base, hydrogen sulfite ion or monohydrogen phosphate ion?

22. Whenever a molecule acts as a Lewis acid in liquid ammonia, what chemical elements are always present in the initial product?

23. What is the conjugate acid of carbamate ion?

24. Predict the geometry of the following complex ions.
(a) dichlorogold(I) ion
(b) tetraiodomercurate(II) ion
(c) tetrachlorocuprate(II) ion
(d) diamminesilver(I) ion
(e) dichlorotetraquoaluminum(III) ion
(f) hexacyanoferrate(II) ion
(g) trichlorotriammineplatinum(IV) ion
(h) tetrachlorodiamminecobaltate(III) ion
(i) diaquodiammineplatinum(II) ion
(j) monobromotriaquocadmium(II) ion

25. Write the formula for each of the following complex ions or compounds.

   (a) sodium tetrachlorodiamminecobaltate(III)

   (b) dibromotetramminecobalt(III) chloride

   (c) monochloropentammineplatinum(IV) chloride

   (d) mononitrosopentacyanoferrate(III) ion

   (e) di-pyridyl-bis(ethylenediamine)cobalt(III) ion

   (f) dithiocyanatotetraquoiron(III) ion

   (g) tetramminecopper(II) sulfate-1-water

   (h) sodium dioxozincate(II)

   (i) tribromotriamminecobalt(III)

   (j) dihydroxotetraquoaluminum chloride

26. Identify the type(s) of stereoisomerism exhibited by each of the following complex ions or compounds.

   (a) dichlorodiaquocopper(II)

   (b) dicyano-bis(ethylenediamine)platinum(IV) ion

   (c) tris(ethylenediamine)platinum(IV) ion

   (d) dichlorotetrammineindium(III) ion

   (e) tetracyanodiaquoferrate(III) ion

24

24.1 A PERSPECTIVE

Since it is difficult to classify all elements explicitly, let us contrast the metals and nonmetals as to certain properties. We can then suggest some practical means of classification.

a. The general chemical distinction between the metals and nonmetals is related to their valence-electronic configurations. At least some valence electrons are removed more easily from a metal atom than from a nonmetal atom. This conclusion is reached by inspection of the ionization potentials (p. 152) of the common elements. The values for the metals are generally much lower than those of the nonmetals. The metals are nearly always electron donors, whereas the nonmetals act either as acceptors or donors, depending on the environment. (Fluorine accepts only.) As we have mentioned earlier, the metallic

600

METALS

elements reside in the periodic chart to the left of the "stairway," the nonmetallic to the right of the "stairway." In nearly all of their compounds, the metals are assigned positive oxidation numbers. Each nonmetal has at least one oxidation state identified by a negative number.

b. The type of bonding in the elemental forms of the metals is contrasted with that of the nonmetals on page 178.

c. The appearance of most metals at room temperature is much different from that of most nonmetals. No metal is completely gaseous at room temperature and 1 atm, and only mercury is distinctly liquid at 25°C. Several nonmetals are gaseous at room temperature and 1 atm, and a few are fluid far below room temperature. Smooth metallic surfaces have a luster or sheen that is very different from that of most solid nonmetals. The valence electrons in the metals are essentially unlocalized; hence they are more mobile than those of the nonmetals in which some valence electrons are localized in bonding. Radiant energy is reflected from a metallic surface more readily than from a nonmetallic surface, probably because of electron mobility.

d. Metals are good conductors of heat and electricity, whereas most nonmetals are very poor conductors. The greater mobility of the valence electrons in the metals seems to be the reason for their superior conductance.

e. In the solid state, metals are much more plastic and more readily deformed than the solid nonmetals. The nonmetals are more brittle. The malleability and ductility of most metals is apparently due to the absence of strong bonding in the crystal.

24.2 OCCURRENCE OF METALS

The metals, either free or combined, are found mainly in the mineral kingdom. The minerals used as sources of the metals are usually called *ores*. Ores frequently are mixtures of compounds, some of complex composition.

A few of the metals occur in their elemental form in nature, mainly because they are such poor reducing agents. Among those that occur in their native states are gold, silver, platinum, and copper. Iron is found free in meteorites.

Some typical mineral oxides and oxy-salts are listed on page 260, the sulfide ores on page 270. Halite, NaCl, and cerargyrite, AgCl, are important chloride minerals. These may be called ores because NaCl is the major source of metallic sodium, and silver chloride is an important source of silver.

The oceans and certain brine wells contain huge amounts of dissolved salts. Magnesium ions are sufficiently abundant in sea water so that their extraction is a practical enterprise (p. 609).

24.3 GENERAL METALLURGY

In this section we shall present very briefly the major aspects in the over-all process of converting an ore to the free metal. The general pattern is: (a) beneficiation of the ore either by removal of useless ore or by conversion to a chemically more suitable form;

(b) reduction of the metal from some positive oxidation state to its elemental state; (c) refining or purification of the impure metal.

a. *Beneficiation* of an ore often involves a simple mechanical separation of the unwanted material (gangue).   If the wanted ore is more dense (and it often is) than the worthless solids, the finely crushed mixture is made into a slurry in water and shaken vigorously.   The more dense ore settles to the bottom, the gangue is removed at the top.   Gold may be separated (panned) by this gravity method.

Some ores of very low grade, usually sulfides, are upgraded by a process that is opposite to the gravity method.   *Ore flotation* is a mechanical separation in which the finely crushed ore is mixed with water and a small amount of oil.   The mixture is agitated with air and the more dense ore particles are preferentially attached to the air bubbles.   The concentrated froth that forms at the surface is skimmed off and dried to yield a solid that is often ten to twenty times richer than the cruder ore.

Most sulfide ores are converted to oxides prior to reduction of the metal ion.   This process, called *roasting*, involves heating the sulfide in air.   For copper(II) sulfide,

$$2CuS + 3O_2 \rightarrow 2CuO + 2SO_2$$

Roasting of sulfide ores is used in the metalurgy of copper, lead, mercury, and zinc.

b. *Reduction* of the metal cation in the ore to yield the free metal is the main chemical step in metallurgy.   The two types of reduction are (1) the use of common active reducing agents, and (2) the electrolytic reduction at a cathode.

The use of coke or charcoal, both forms of carbon, is common in metallurgy.   The coke is usually mixed with the oxide ores and heated in a furnace.   If the reduction temperature is high, the process is called *smelting*.   Among the metals produced by reduction of their oxides by carbon are bismuth, cadmium, cobalt, iron, lead, nickel, tungsten, and zinc.

$$ZnO + C \rightarrow CO + Zn$$
$$2PbO + C \rightarrow 2Pb + CO_2$$
$$Fe_2O_3 + 3C \rightarrow 3CO + 2Fe$$

Hydrogen is used in certain reductions.   This method usually yields a powdered form of the metal.

Aluminum is used as a reducing agent in the Goldschmidt

process. Chromium(III) oxide, Cr_2O_3, manganese(IV) oxide, MnO_2, and cobalt(II) oxide, CoO, are reduced by aluminum to yield the metal. Magnesium and calcium can be used as well.

$$Cr_2O_3 + 2Al \rightarrow 2Cr + Al_2O_3$$
$$3MnO_2 + 4Al \rightarrow 2Al_2O_3 + 3Mn$$
$$3CoO + 2Al \rightarrow 3Co + Al_2O_3$$

When ignited, a powdered mixture, called *Thermit*, of iron(III) oxide, Fe_2O_3, and metallic aluminum yields molten iron and aluminum oxide. The reaction is extremely vigorous and exothermic.

$$Fe_2O_3 + 2Al \rightarrow Al_2O_3 + 2Fe + \Delta$$

Metallic calcium is used as the reducing agent in the production of metallic potassium, rubidium, and cesium at high temperature. Although the reactions are reversible, the continuous removal of the vapor of the alkali metal from the reaction system favors the production of the metal. The boiling point of calcium is about 1200°C, that of cesium is 670°, and that of potassium, 760°.

$$Ca + 2(K^+Cl^-) \leftrightarrows Ca^{++}(Cl^-)_2 + 2K$$

Since the boiling point of sodium is above 880°C, sodium can be substituted for calcium in this process.

The electrolytic reduction of aluminum(III) to the metal (p. 506), of magnesium ion to the metal (p. 505), and of the alkali metal and alkaline-earth metal ions (p. 503) are mentioned elsewhere. (See Fig. 24.1.)

c. The *refining* of an impure metal is either a method of purification or a treatment to yield a more suitable material. Purification is often necessary for metallic conductors. The electrolytic refining of copper, for example, is described on page 507. Among the other metals refined by electrolysis are aluminum, gold, iron, lead, nickel, silver, and tin.

Mercury is refined by distillation because it is a liquid.

24.4 ALLOYS

Nearly all of the metals we use are actually mixtures, either because the metal is impure or because it is a prepared mixture. The various metallic solid solutions are called *alloys*. A thorough discussion of even a few alloys would be too lengthy for this book. Most alloys

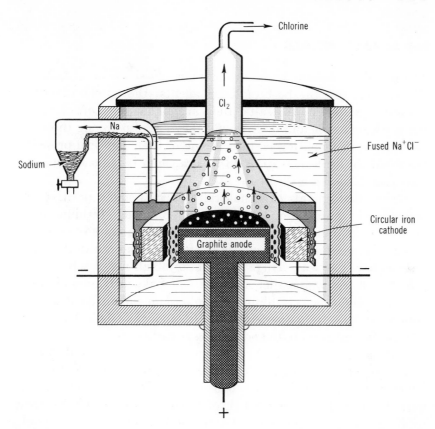

FIGURE 24.1   The Downs cell is the electrolytic cell in which is produced most of the sodium used commercially. Fused sodium chloride is the electrolyte. Since this cell operates around 800°C, molten sodium rises to the surface of the electrolyte in the cathode compartment.

are prepared to achieve a metal having specific properties. For instance, two soft metals may yield a hard alloy. Two or more metals when mixed often yield an alloy whose melting point is lower than that of any one of the constituents. Wood's metal (p. A-3), which contains Bi, Pb, Sn, and Cd, melts at 70°C. Some alloys are more resistant to corrosion than is the most abundant metal in the mixture. Stainless steel (p. A-3) is more resistant by far than is cast iron.

Alloys are usually classified as either *ferrous* (containing iron) or *nonferrous* (containing no iron). The steels are ferrous alloys; the brasses and bronzes are nonferrous.

Some of the more common alloys are listed on page A-2.

24.5 ALKALI METALS

The metals of Group 1*a* in the periodic classification (Li, Na, K, Rb, Cs, Fr) are the best reducing agents; they yield the widest variety of water-soluble salts; they are among the softest metals, the most malleable and ductile, and they are also among those that have the lowest melting points. Some of their physical properties are listed in Table A.9 (p. A-13). Francium is radioactive and so rare that it will be neglected.

The alkali metals exist naturally only as singly positive ions. Sodium and potassium are the most common. Lithium ion is present in small amounts in many rocks, but rubidium and cesium ions are rare. Sodium chloride is an abundant mineral in the earth's crust and in the sea. Huge amounts of alkali metal salts occur in inland bodies of water, such as Great Salt Lake in Utah and Searles Lake in California. Lithium and potassium salts are extracted in large quantities from Searles Lake, although the lake's deposits are mainly sodium carbonate and hydrogen carbonate.

Metallic sodium and potassium were discovered by Sir Humphrey Davy (English) in 1807. He produced the metals by electrolysis from their fused hydroxides. Rubidium and cesium were discovered around 1860 through spectroscopic evidence prior to their chemical isolation. Francium was not discovered until 1939.

The only chemical uses of the elemental alkali metals are as reducing agents because this is their only chemical property. Since sodium is the cheapest, it is used most commonly, especially in organic chemistry. Sodium reacts vigorously either with water or oxygen, as do all of the alkali metals.

$$2Na + 2H_2O \rightarrow 2(Na^+OH^-) + H_2$$
$$2Na + O_2 \rightarrow (Na^+)_2O_2^{--}$$
sodium
peroxide

$$4Na + O_2 \rightarrow 2(Na^+)_2O^{--}$$
sodium
oxide

Because of their reactivity, the alkali metals are usually stored under kerosene or in hermetically sealed containers.

Alkali metals dissolve in liquid ammonia (p. 250) to yield blue solutions. If the solutions are allowed to stand, or if a catalyst such as platinum ent, the metal reacts with the ammonia. For sodium,

$$a + 2NH_3 \rightarrow 2(Na^+NH_2^-) + H_2$$

sodium amide

The oxiroxides, and superoxides of the alkali metals are listed on pa$

All of t li metals react with hydrogen to yield hydrides.

$$2Na + H_2 \rightarrow 2(Na^+H^-)$$

Because the e ion, H^-, is a very strong base, it easily accepts protons from molecules. Therefore the alkali metal hydrides react vigoro th water.

$$,^+H^- + HOH \rightarrow Na^+OH^- + H_2$$

The alkals react violently with the halogens to yield ionic halides, M^+ Many of these halides occur widely in nature and have extensi in the chemical industry.

Becauseesium's low ionization potential, its $6s$ valence electron leavlily on the absorption of light. This property of cesium is use hotoelectric cells.

The flart colors imparted by the alkali metal ions are: lithium, red um, yellow; potassium, violet; rubidium, red; cesium, blue.

It will b to recall that each alkali metal ion is isoelectronic (same electronfiguration) with some inert gas atom and its neighboring e-earth metal ion. Although an alkali metal ion is hydrated ier, it never undergoes any chemical changes in ordinary aquolutions. Alkali metal compounds are very useful chemicall use so many of them are soluble in water.

Sodium xide (caustic soda) and potassium hydroxide, K^+OH^-, (cauotash or potash lye) are produced industrially in large quantit. 505). Over 6 million tons of sodium hydroxide are producedially in the United States, mainly as flakes and pellets.

Sodium nate, $(Na^+)_2CO_3^{--}$, and its close relative, sodium hydrogen cate, $Na^+HCO_3^-$, are among the most important sodium saltsiese compounds are made industrially by the Solvay proces289) and by the passage of carbon dioxide through aqueous sodivdroxide.

$$CO_2 + Na^+OH^- \rightarrow Na^+HCO_3^-$$
$$2(NaO_3^-) + \Delta \rightarrow (Na^+)_2CO_3^{--} + CO_2 + H_2O$$

Sodium hydrogen carbonate is an ingredient of ng powders. An acidic constituent in the powder cause ydrogen carbonate ions, HCO_3^-, to act as bases, thereby yieater and carbon dioxide.

$$HCO_3^- + H^+ \leftrightarrows H_2CO_3 \leftrightarrows H_2O + ($$

from some
acid

The carbon dioxide bubbles make the dough poro he acidic constituent of alum baking powders is an alumi ompound (p. 613) that hydrolyzes in water to yield oxoni s, OH_3^+. Phosphate baking powders contain calcium dihydraosphate, $Ca^{++}(H_2PO_4^-)_2$. The dihydrogen phosphate ions he acidic entities in the mixtures. The acid tartrate or hydro trate ion, $HC_4H_4O_6^-$, is the acidic constituent of the tartrate l powders. The hydrogen tartrate ions donate protons either ly or indirectly to the hydrogen carbonate ions.

$$HC_4H_4O_6^- + HCO_3^- \leftrightarrows C_4H_4O_6^{--} + H_2O -$$

tartrate ion

Some of the slightly soluble (in water) salts of tali metals are lithium fluoride, Li^+F^-; potassium fluoride, ; sodium fluorosilicate, $(Na^+)_2SiF_6^{--}$; lithium orthophospha i^+)_3PO_4^{3-}$; sodium tetraborate (borax), $(Na^+)_2B_4O_7^{--}$; potass lloroplatinate, $(K^+)_2PtCl_4^{--}$; potassium hydrogen tartrate (cof tartar), $K^+(HC_4H_4O_6)^-$; potassium fluorosilicate, $(K^+)_2Si$ potassium cobaltinitrite, $(K^+)_3Co(NO_2)_6^{3-}$.

24.6 ALKALINE-EARTH METALS

The metals in Group 2a (Be, Mg, Ca, Sr, Ba, Ra among the better reducing agents, although they are less activ a the alkali metals. Their only chemical property, in the el al state, is that of a reducing agent. They are harder, less ma b, and have higher melting points than their Group 1a neighbor heir physical constants are listed in Table A.9 (p. A-13).

The alkaline-earth metals exist naturally only a ly positive ions. Each ion is isoelectronic with its neighboring li metal ion and with the nearest inert gas. Calcium ion is mos ndant, and magnesium is next most abundant. Beryllium io widespread, but the total amount is small.

Electrolytic reduction is the most common means of winning the metals from their compounds.

The major production of magnesium in the United States comes from sea water. The magnesium ions are precipitated as magnesium hydroxide, $Mg(OH)_2$, by using calcium oxide obtained by calcining oyster shells. The suspension is filtered and the $Mg(OH)_2$ is converted to magnesium chloride by using hydrochloric acid. The dried $MgCl_2$ is electrolyzed to yield 99.9 per cent pure metal.

The major reactions involved in the production of magnesium from sea water are

$$CaCO_3 + \Delta \rightarrow CaO + CO_2$$
$$\underset{\text{from oyster}}{\text{shells}} \qquad \underset{\text{quick}}{\text{lime}}$$

$$CaO + H_2O \rightarrow Ca(OH)_2 \leftrightharpoons Ca^{++} + 2OH^-$$
$$Mg^{++} + 2OH^- \rightarrow Mg(OH)_2$$
$$Mg(OH)_2 + 2OH_3^+ + 2Cl^- \rightarrow Mg^{++} + 2Cl^- + 4H_2O$$
$$\text{hydrochloric acid}$$

$$\left.\begin{array}{l} Mg^{++} + 2e^- \rightarrow Mg \\ 2Cl^- \rightarrow 2e^- + Cl_2 \end{array}\right\} \begin{array}{l} \text{electrolysis of} \\ \text{dry } MgCl_2 \end{array}$$

The hydrogen carbonates, $M^{++}(HOCO_2^-)_2$, of the Group $2a$ cations are appreciably soluble in water. "Temporary hardness" of water is due to appreciable concentrations of the ions Ca^{++} and $HOCO_2^-$ and occasionally Mg^{++}. Acidic ground water in limestone districts may contain relatively high concentrations of calcium and hydrogen carbonate ions, so that the "hardness" of such water may be appreciable. Hardness of water is due mainly to the ions Ca^{++}, Mg^{++}, and Fe^{++}. Hard water is the term used to identify water which causes ordinary soaps to form slightly soluble precipitates. These solids are calcium, magnesium, and iron(II) salts of large carboxylic acids (such as stearic acid, $C_{17}H_{35}COOH$). If the hardness of water is removed, the water is said to be "softened."

Water of "temporary hardness" may be softened by boiling, during which precipitation of the ions, Ca^{++} and Mg^{++}, as their carbonates is favored by the continual expulsion of carbon dioxide.

$$\Delta + Ca^{++} + 2HOCO_2^- \leftrightharpoons Ca^{++}CO_3^{--} + HOH + CO_2 \uparrow$$

Addition of sodium carbonate to hard water softens the water more economically and practically by causing the precipitation of calcium carbonate, magnesium carbonate and iron(II) and iron(III) hydroxides. If the hardness of water is due to an appreciable concentration of calcium ions accompanied by sulfate ions, the hardness cannot be removed by boiling; this kind of hard water can be softened by other means.

An ingenious and intriguing method for the softening of hard water employs certain alumino-silicates (such as $Na_2Al_2Si_4O_{12}$) called *zeolites*. These zeolites have rigid, "open" structural patterns built by the aluminum, silicon, and oxygen atoms. Within the "open spaces" of this molecular framework, the sodium ions seem to have a significant freedom of motion. If hard water is passed over fine granules of zeolite, many of the sodium ions in the zeolite escape into the water. Since the zeolite then has a net negative charge it attracts calcium, magnesium, and iron(II) ions. These ions leave the hard water and displace sodium ions in the zeolite; thus the water is softened. As more and more hard water is passed over the zeolite, the "concentration" of sodium ions in the zeolite gradually decreases and equilibrium is eventually reached: the rate at which calcium ions in the water are displacing sodium ions in the zeolite is equal to the rate at which sodium ions in the water are displacing calcium ions in the zeolite. At this point the zeolite must be recharged with sodium ions. This is accomplished by placing the "spent" zeolite in contact with a saturated solution of sodium chloride. The high concentration of sodium ions outside the zeolite (in the saturated solution) reverses the water softening process, with sodium ions now displacing most of the calcium, magnesium, and iron(II) ions from the zeolite. The zeolite is then ready to "soften" more "hard" water.

24.7 CHEMICAL DETECTION OF ALKALINE-EARTH METAL IONS

The hydrated ions of the alkaline-earth metal elements do not impart a color to aqueous solutions. Although the hydrogen carbonates of the alkaline-earth metals are fairly soluble in water, the carbonates are only slightly soluble. The precipitates are easily soluble in distinctly acidic solutions. All of the carbonates are white. Among the alkaline-earth carbonates, strontium carbonate is the least soluble in water, and magnesium carbonate is the most soluble. Beryllium carbonate is actually more soluble than magnesium carbonate, but beryllium is often omitted from a list of the Group 2a metals because of its unique character. (See p. 159.)

The chromates of barium, strontium, and calcium can be precipitated in aqueous solutions that have relatively high concentrations of chromate ion, CrO_4^{--}. Since chromate ion imparts a yellow color to aqueous solutions, the slightly soluble alkaline-earth metal chromates are yellow solids. Among these chromates, calcium chromate, $Ca^{++}CrO_4^{--}$, is the most soluble, and barium chromate, $Ba^{++}CrO_4^{--}$, is the least soluble. Magnesium chromate is so soluble that it usually does not precipitate in ordinary aqueous solutions. The slightly soluble alkaline-earth chromates are soluble in aqueous solutions of strong acids, and, except for barium chromate, they are appreciably soluble in aqueous acetic acid. The basicity of chromate ion is easily evident in strongly acidic solutions.

$$M^{++}CrO_4^{--}(s) \leftrightarrows M^{++} + CrO_4^{--} \qquad \text{(the saturated solution)}$$

the alkaline-earth
metal chromate

$$\updownarrow \; +OH_3^+$$

$$HCrO_4^- \leftrightarrows \tfrac{1}{2}Cr_2O_7^{--} + HOH$$

dichromate ion
(orange)

24.8 ALUMINUM

Although metallic aluminum is not found in nature, its compounds occur in nearly all of the common rocks except the calcium carbonate minerals, such as limestone and marble. Clay soils are mainly aluminum silicate. Bauxite, $Al_2O_3 \cdot 2H_2O$ (usually with Fe_2O_3) is the major ore used commercially. Other common minerals are corundum, Al_2O_3, and cryolite, Na_3AlF_6.

Most of the current production of aluminum uses bauxite and cryolite as sources of the metal. In the beneficiation of certain bauxites, the unwanted iron is removed before reduction of the aluminum oxide, Al_2O_3. The crude bauxite is dissolved in concentrated sodium hydroxide solution, whereupon the Al_2O_3 dissolves but the Fe_2O_3 does not.

$$Al_2O_3 \cdot xH_2O + OH^- \leftrightarrows 2Al(OH)_4^- + yH_2O$$

(excess)

The solution that contains the aluminum hydroxide complex ion, $Al(OH)_4^-$, also called tetrahydroxoaluminate ion, is diluted to yield a precipitate of the hydrous aluminum oxide, $Al_2O_3 \cdot xH_2O$. The hydrous oxide is heated to obtain the dry oxide. The dry oxide is electrolyzed, as described on page 506, to yield the metallic aluminum.

Aluminum is ductile and malleable at 150°C, but it is so brittle at high temperatures that it may be ground to a powder (its physical constants are listed on p. A-13). The metal oxidizes in the presence of air at ordinary temperatures, but a protective layer forms on the surface thereby inhibiting extensive corrosion. Aluminum cooking utensils are protected from oxygen and from dilute acids and bases by this protective coating. However, prolonged contact with acids and bases may destroy the protective layer and seriously attack the metal itself.

The use of aluminum as a structural metal continues to grow at a rapid pace. During the period from 1935 to 1962, the production in the United States increased from 80,000 tons to 2,000,000 per annum.

Aluminum is called a strong reducing agent, but the metals of groups $1a$ and $2a$ are generally better. Aluminum burns in air, if ignited, to yield the oxide, Al_2O_3, and the nitride, AlN. The interaction of aluminum and oxygen yields much heat.

$$4Al + 3O_2 \rightarrow 2Al_2O_3 \qquad \Delta H = -779 \text{ kcal}$$

Aluminum reacts vigorously with aqueous mineral acids and alkali metal hydroxides to yield hydrogen.

$$2Al + 6OH_3^+ + H_2O \rightarrow 2Al(OH_2)_6^{3+} + 3H_2$$
$$\text{(excess)}$$

$$2Al + 8OH^- + H_2O \rightarrow 2Al(OH)_4^- + 3H_2$$
$$\text{(excess)}$$

Concentrated sulfuric and nitric acids in contact with metallic aluminum cause the formation of a protective coating. Therefore these acids may be stored and shipped in aluminum-lined containers.

Aluminum ion, Al^{3+}, has a large charge density; hence it strongly attracts water molecules and many negative ions. Most aluminum compounds are hydrolyzed readily by water because of the aluminum ion's strong tendency to be hydrated. The sulfide, Al_2S_3, is hydrolyzed to yield hydrogen sulfide, H_2S.

$$Al_2S_3 + H_2O \rightarrow Al_2O_3 \cdot xH_2O + 3H_2S$$
$$\text{(excess)}$$

The hydroxide, $Al(OH)_3$, is amphoteric. It yields the complex hydroxide ion $Al(OH)_4^-$ in strongly basic solutions, and the hydrated ion $Al(OH_2)_6^{3+}$ in acidic solutions. (See p. 579.)

Aluminum chloride, $AlCl_3$, is actually a dimer, Al_2Cl_6, at ordinary temperatures. The aluminum kernels, or ions, tend to gather four chloride ions around them.

$$
\begin{array}{ccc}
\text{Cl} & \text{Cl} & \text{Cl} \\
\diagdown \;\; \diagup & \diagdown \;\; \diagup \\
\text{Al} & \;\;\; \text{Al} \\
\diagup \;\; \diagdown & \diagup \;\; \diagdown \\
\text{Cl} & \text{Cl} & \text{Cl}
\end{array}
$$

Since aluminum chloride sublimes readily at 178°C, it is purified by sublimation. It is easily hydrolyzed by water and it fumes in moist air. Since it is a strong Lewis acid, it is used widely as an acidic catalyst, especially in organic chemistry.

Potassium alum, $KAl(SO_4)_2 \cdot 12H_2O$, is a double salt which crystallizes during the evaporation of a solution containing potassium sulfate, K_2SO_4, and aluminum sulfate, $Al_2(SO_4)_3$. Ammonium alum, $NH_4Al(SO_4)_2 \cdot 12H_2O$, is obtained if ammonium sulfate, $(NH_4)_2SO_4$, is substituted for potassium sulfate. These two alums hydrolyze in dilute aqueous solutions and, since aluminum hydroxide is produced, the alums are commercially useful as mordants in the dyeing and printing of cloth, in water purification, and in the sizing and weighting of paper. As a mordant the undissolved gelatinous aluminum hydroxide assists in fixing dye to cloth because the dye is strongly adsorbed to the undissolved hydroxide. In water purification the gelatinous precipitate adsorbs certain dissolved impurities. As the solid falls to the bottom of the settling basin, suspended solids are carried down with it. In the sizing and weighting of paper, the undissolved hydroxide precipitates between the cellulose fibers, thereby increasing the weight and stability of the paper.

The chemical detection of aluminum ion is not easily accomplished. The ion does precipitate a white amphoteric hydroxide $Al(OH)_3$, but the precipitate is often so gelatinous that it is not readily detected visually. It does not appear, of course, if the solution is too basic. A common test for aluminum hydroxide as a precipitate is to add to the suspension an aqueous solution of an organic dye, called the aluminon reagent. The dye is adsorbed on the precipitate to yield what is called a *red lake*. It is wise to run a comparative test using a solution known to contain aluminum ions.

24.9 LEAD AND TIN

The most common mineral of lead is galena, PbS, a shiny, black cubic solid. The sulfide is roasted to yield the oxide, PbO. The oxide is reduced by coke (p. 603). Lead is refined electrolytically by the Betts process, a method similar to that used for copper.

Lead has a brilliant luster at a freshly formed surface, but oxidation, by oxygen, quickly yields a dull gray color. The metal is soft and reasonably malleable, but not ductile. It is plastic at 300°C.

The hydroxide, $Pb(OH)_2$, and lead(II) oxide, PbO (litharge), are only slightly soluble in water, but they dissolve in acidic and in basic solutions. Lead(IV) oxide (dioxide) is a brown solid obtained by the oxidation of lead(II) oxide with hypochlorite ion.

$$PbO + ClO^- \rightarrow PbO_2 + Cl^-$$

Lead(IV) oxide is a strong oxidizing agent. Red lead (minium), Pb_3O_4, is made by roasting PbO at 400°C.

Among the other slightly soluble lead compounds are lead chloride, $PbCl_2$ (white); lead chromate, $PbCrO_4$ (yellow); lead sulfide, PbS (black); lead sulfate, $PbSO_4$ (white). The nitrate and acetate are quite soluble in water. The basic carbonate, $Pb(OH)_2 \cdot 2PbCO_3$, is the paint pigment, white lead.

Lead chloride precipitates along with silver chloride and mercury(I) chloride in Group I in the common scheme of qualitative analysis. Lead chloride is sufficiently soluble in hot water so that the lead ion can be leached, as lead chloride, from the solid mixture. If $PbCl_2$ does not crystallize from the cold aqueous extract, the Pb^{++} can be detected by adding chromate ions to yield a yellow, slightly soluble lead chromate, $PbCrO_4$.

The most important ore of tin is a very dense mineral, cassiterite, SnO_2. The oxide is reduced by coke to yield the metal. By any one of several methods of refining, tin of a 99.8 per cent purity is obtained.

Tin has a low melting point, 232°C. Since it is crystalline, the process of bending a rod yields a squeaking sound (tin "cry") as the crystals slip over each other. It is malleable at ordinary temperatures, but it becomes brittle when heated. When cooled it slowly changes to a gray powder (tin "disease").

Tin(II) oxide, SnO, is prepared by heating the hydroxide, $Sn(OH)_2$. The oxide burns when ignited in air to yield the tin(IV) oxide, SnO_2. The tin(II) oxide is amphoteric, and its alkaline solutions are strong reducing agents. The major ion in these solutions is probably $Sn(OH)_4^{--}$.

Tin(IV) oxide, SnO_2, when fused with sodium hydroxide, yields sodium stannate, Na_2SnO_3. This stannate is soluble in water, but if the solution is acidified, a precipitate of the tin(IV) hydrous oxide is formed. The hydrous oxide is soluble in both acidic and basic solutions, but only slightly soluble in water.

Tin(II) chloride is a white solid that melts at 247°C, whereas the tin(IV) chloride, $SnCl_4$, is a colorless liquid that melts at −30°C. Each of the chlorides is readily hydrolyzed even by cold water. The tin(IV) chloride fumes in moist air. Solutions of these chlorides must be acidified with dilute hydrochloric acid to prevent hydrolysis. Tin(II) chloride yields solutions that serve as good reduction media.

Tin(II) sulfide, SnS, is brown and only very slightly soluble in water. It is soluble on addition of hot dilute nitric acid. Tin(IV) sulfide, SnS_2, is yellow and only slightly soluble in water. This sulfide does dissolve easily in high sulfide ion concentration solutions and in dilute acidic solutions of nitric and hydrochloric acids.

$$SnS_2 + S^{--} \rightarrow SnS_3^{--}$$
$$SnS_2 + OH_3^+ \rightarrow Sn(OH_2)_6^{4+} + 2H_2S$$
$$\text{(excess)}$$

Tin(IV) sulfide is obviously amphoteric.

Problems

1. List the common ions that are isoelectronic with barium ion.

2. Suggest a reason why the alkali metals are softer than their alkaline-earth neighbors.

3. Which would you expect to be the better electronic conductor, cesium or barium?

4. Considering the "Thermit" process, which is the better reducing agent, iron or aluminum?

5. What is the major by-product obtained during the roasting of an ordinary sulfide ore?

6. Why will it always be more difficult to extract potassium ions from sea water than to extract magnesium ions?

7. (a) How many tons (minimum amount) of hydrochloric acid, 36 per cent HCl, will be needed during the production of each ton of metallic magnesium from sea water? (b) If the specific gravity of the acid is

1.12, what minimum volume of acid, in liters, is needed per ton of magnesium ion extracted?

8. Why is the oxide coating on metallic aluminum more protective against corrosion than is the oxide coating on metallic sodium?

9. What negative ions are isoelectronic with Sr^{++}?

10. What elemental metals melt either at or below body temperature, $37°C$? (Use Table A.9 in the Appendix.)

11. Although metallic calcium may be used to reduce cesium ions to elemental cesium, it is not practical to reduce lithium ions with calcium metal. Why?

12. Whenever elemental potassium undergoes a chemical change, a specific equation may be written to represent the change. What is it?

13. How many grams of gaseous hydrogen (maximum yield) can be obtained by adding 5 g of lithium hydride to excess water?

14. Write the chemical equation representing the reaction that occurs when sodium dihydrogen phosphate is added to an aqueous solution containing hydrogen carbonate ions.

15. What would you probably observe visually during the reaction mentioned in Problem 14?

16. How many faradays of electricity are needed for the production of one ton of aluminum?

17. How many calories of heat are evolved during the burning of 10 g of aluminum in oxygen?

18. A certain mixture consists of sodium chloride (mp, 800°C) and aluminum chloride. Suggest the simplest practical separation of these compounds.

19. What is observed visually when concentrated hydrochloric acid is added slowly with agitation to a clear solution of sodium stannate until the solution is strongly acidic?

20. Write the chemical equation representing the dissolving of lead hydroxide in a basic aqueous solution.

21. What is observed visually when a 6 M HCl solution is added to a solution that contains a high concentration of SnS_3^{--} ions?

22. Suggest a logical reason for a precipitate of lead chromate usually dissolving in excess sodium hydroxide solution.

23. Predict what would occur when concentrated hydrochloric acid is added to the clear supernatant solution of a saturated solution of lead chloride.

24. A solution consists of either barium ions or calcium ions and chloride ions. What simple test could be used to determine which cation is present?

25. A solid is either magnesium chloride or sodium chloride. How would you determine its identity?

26. Suggest a reason for magnesium hydroxide being the least soluble alkaline-earth metal hydroxide, and magnesium chromate being the most soluble chromate of the alkaline-earth metals.

25

THE TRANSITION

25.1 A PERSPECTIVE

The transition element metals have several general characteristics that differentiate them from the representative elements. For one thing, they are in the short vertical columns in the periodic chart, whereas the representative metals are in the long vertical columns. The transition metals are in the b series, the representative metals in the a series. Some of the electrons involved in the chemical reactions of the transition elements are in d subgroups as well as s and p subgroups. Generally the electrons involved in the chemical reactions of the representative elements are in the s and p subgroups. The electronic configurations of the $3d$ transition elements are shown on page 123; the electronic configurations of the other elements are shown on page A-9.

Since the $3d$ transition series (Sc–Cu) is the most

METALS

important, we shall confine most of our remarks to the metals in it. All of the metals in the $3d$ series, except scandium, exhibit two or more oxidation states, one of which is the $+2$ state. This behavior is expected because the $4s$ electrons are on the average slightly farther from the nucleus than are the $3d$ electrons. Therefore the $4s$ electrons may frequently be donated more readily than the $3d$ electrons. There are four stable oxidation states of vanadium, $+2$, $+3$, $+4$, and $+5$. Some compounds are VO, V_2O_3, VO_2, and V_2O_5. The oxidation states $+2$, $+3$, $+4$, $+6$, and $+7$ are identified in the various compounds of manganese, for example, $Mn(OH)_2$, $Mn(OH)_3$, MnO_2, MnO_3^-, MnO_4^{--}, and MnO_4^-. Manganite ion, MnO_3^-, and manganate ion, MnO_4^{--}, are less common than permanganate ion, MnO_4^-. Among the compounds of chromium, CrS, Cr_2O_3, and CrO_3 exhibit the $+2$, $+3$, and $+6$ oxidation states of chromium.

The atoms of some transition elements (all of which are metals) can exist in complex oxide ions, just as can the atoms of most non-metallic elements. For instance, chromate ion, CrO_4^{--}, is similar to sulfate ion, SO_4^{--}; permanganate ion, MnO_4^-, is similar to perchlorate ion, ClO_4^-; vanadate ion, VO_4^{3-}, is similar to phosphate ion, PO_4^{3-}.

Many compounds of the $3d$ elements are paramagnetic (attracted to a magnet, p. 184) because of unpaired electrons (p. 184). Some of the various ions of the $3d$ metals that have at least one unpaired electron are V^{3+}, Co^{++}, Cu^{++}, Mn^{3+}, Mn^{++}, Cr^{3+}, Fe^{3+}, Ni^{++}. Compounds of these ions are attracted to a magnet more strongly than compounds in which all electrons are paired.

Most of the compounds of the $3d$ metals, except those of scandium and titanium, are colored, especially the hydrates. The $3d$ subgroup energy level is so close to the next higher energy level, $4p$, that excitation by visible light raises $3d$ electrons to the higher level. As the electrons fall back to the lower energy level, light is emitted. The absorption by matter of white light of only specific wave lengths yields the phenomenon of color to the eye.

Nearly all of the $3d$ element ions have a strong tendency to react with certain entities that have one or more pairs of unshared electrons to yield complex ions. The ions therefore act as Lewis acids. (See p. 580.)

Most of the $3d$ ions react with excess water to yield acidic solutions (p. 580). Nearly all the chlorides of the $3d$ metals are readily hydrolyzed in the presence of excess water to yield acidic solutions. (See Table 23.2, p. 577.) Some anhydrous chlorides that seem to be more covalent than ionic and that hydrolyze in water are $TiCl_4$, colorless liquid; VCl_4, red liquid; $CrCl_3$, pink solid; $MnCl_4$, green solid; $FeCl_3$, dark brown solid; $CoCl_2$, blue solid; $NiCl_2$, yellow solid; $CuCl_2$, dark brown solid. The formulas given for these chlorides are the empirical formulas. The chlorides are actually polymers of the ones given here in which the central metal kernel, or ion, is complexed with the chloride ions. In the case of $CuCl_2$, for instance,

Several of the $3d$ metal oxides are used as catalysts, and some of the $3d$ metal ions in aqueous solution show distinct catalytic activity. Manganese(IV) oxide, MnO_2, has been mentioned as a catalyst in the pyrolysis of chlorate ion, ClO_3^-. Copper(II) ion catalyzes the oxidation of sulfite ion, SO_3^{--} (see p. 234). Metallic nickel, palladium (a $4d$ element), and platinum ($5d$) are used industrially as contact catalysts (p. 435). The presence of unfilled d orbitals and of unpaired electrons seems to endow the transition element atoms and ions with catalytic properties.

25.2 TITANIUM

Elemental titanium is a silver-white metal that is quite resistant to corrosion because of a protective layer of oxide and nitride. The most important ores of titanium are rutile, TiO_2, and ilmenite, $FeTiO_3$. Metallic titanium is produced industrially by reduction of the tetrachloride, $TiCl_4$, by magnesium at 1000°C either in an inert atmosphere or in a vacuum.

$$TiCl_4 + 2Mg \rightarrow Ti + 2MgCl_2$$

The excess magnesium and $TiCl_4$ are removed by using dilute acid. The spongy titanium melts at 1800° to yield a solid mass on cooling.

Titanium is being used increasingly as a structural metal in aircraft frames and engines because of its tensile strength. Since it is resistant to corrosion, it is ideal for marine construction and in jet engines.

Titanium(II) oxide, TiO, is made by reducing titanium(IV) oxide, TiO_2, by carbon or magnesium.

$$TiO_2 + C \rightarrow TiO + CO$$

Compounds of titanium(II) are easily oxidized to titanium(IV) in acidic solutions.

Titanium(III) oxide, Ti_2O_3, is prepared by the reduction of TiO_2 with hydrogen.

$$2TiO_2 + H_2 \rightarrow Ti_2O_3 + H_2O$$

Titanium(III) hydroxide, $Ti(OH)_3$, is a very strong reducing agent, being able to reduce nitrate ion to ammonia in basic solutions.

Titanium(IV) chloride, $TiCl_4$, is used in making smoke screens (p. 290). The anhydrous titanium chlorides, bromides, and iodides react with water to yield the oxide.

$$TiCl_4 + 2H_2O \rightarrow 4HCl + TiO_2$$

Titanium(IV) oxide, TiO_2, is an excellent white pigment because of its extreme whiteness and its unusual opacity.

25.3 VANADIUM

Elemental vanadium is usually produced by reducing the oxide, V_2O_5, with aluminum.

$$3V_2O_5 + 10Al \rightarrow 5Al_2O_3 + 6V$$

Because this process is difficult, very little pure vanadium is made commercially. An alloy of vanadium and iron, ferrovanadium, is added to steel to combine with the oxygen and nitrogen and also to increase the toughness, elasticity, and tensile strength of the metal. Vanadium is brittle and rather resistant to most acids, but it is vulnerable to attack by strong bases.

Vanadium is found combined in carnotite,

$$K_2O \cdot 2UO_3 \cdot V_2O_5 \cdot 3H_2O$$

deposits in Arizona, Colorado, and Utah. Vanadium sulfide is found in Peru.

The reddish-yellow vanadium(V) oxide, V_2O_5, dissolves in basic solutions to yield complex negative ions and in acidic solutions to yield complex positive ions. It is a catalyst in the contact process (p. 435) for the manufacture of sulfuric acid.

25.4 CHROMIUM

Metallic chromium, a very hard metal, is produced by reducing chromium(III) oxide, Cr_2O_3, with aluminum by the Goldschmidt process. Magnesium and calcium can also be used.

$$Cr_2O_3 + 2Al \rightarrow Al_2O_3 + 2Cr$$

The major ore is chromite, $Fe(CrO_2)_2$, much of which is used in making alloy steels, such as the stainless steels (p. A-3). The electroplating of chromium is an important application of the metal. Although the electrolytic metal is malleable, that produced by chemical reduction is brittle. The metal is unusually resistant to corrosion; hence it is an excellent protective metal.

The stable oxidation states of chromium and the common

oxides are mentioned on p. 259. The chromium(III) hydroxide is amphoteric.

$$Cr(OH)_3 + OH^- \leftrightarrows Cr(OH)_4^-$$
$$Cr(OH)_3 + 3OH_3^+ \leftrightarrows Cr(OH_2)_3^{3+}$$

The sulfide, Cr_2S_3, is readily hydrolyzed in aqueous solution to yield the hydrous oxide and hydrogen sulfide.

$$Cr_2S_3 + H_2O \rightarrow Cr_2O_3 \cdot xH_2O + 3H_2S$$
$$\text{(excess)}$$

Anhydrous chromium(III) chloride (p. 407) and the colored chromate, CrO_4^{--}, and dichromate ions, $Cr_2O_7^{--}$ (p. 259), are mentioned elsewhere. Lead chromate, $PbCrO_4$, is a yellow salt which is only sparingly soluble in water.

Chromium(III) oxide, Cr_2O_3, is a green solid often used as a paint and ceramic pigment.

25.5   MANGANESE

Manganese is a hard, brittle gray-red metal. It may be made by reduction of pyrolusite, MnO_2, through the use of either carbon or aluminum.

$$MnO_2 + 2C \rightarrow Mn + 2CO$$
$$3MnO_2 + 2Al \rightarrow 3Mn + 2Al_2O_3$$

The carbon-reduction product is contaminated by carbon. The impure metal is refined electrolytically to yield 99.9 per cent purity. Most of the current ore production is used to prepare alloys of manganese and iron and in the manufacture of steel.

The oxidation states of manganese are listed on pages 619 and A-16. The manganese(II) sulfide is a flesh-pink color and is only very slightly soluble in water. The most common oxide, MnO_2, is brown when precipitated as its hydrous form in water, but it is black when dry. The formula does not indicate the exact nature of the oxide because the composition as indicated by the formula is very rarely, if ever, achieved.

Manganate ion, MnO_4^{--}, is produced by the oxidation of MnO_2 in strongly basic solutions.

$$2MnO_2 + 4OH^- + O_2 \rightarrow 2MnO_4^{--} + 2H_2O$$

Manganic acid, H_2MnO_4, and permanganic acid, $HMnO_4$, are too unstable to be isolated. Manganese(VII) oxide, Mn_2O_7, is a highly explosive dark brown liquid. It can be made by carefully treating potassium permanganate, $K^+MnO_4^-$, with concentrated sulfuric acid. Permanganate ion, MnO_4^-, imparts a purple color to water, whereas manganate ion imparts a green color. The ability of permanganate ion to act as an oxidizing agent has been mentioned earlier (p. 493).

Manganese(II) ion in basic solutions is slowly oxidized by atmospheric oxygen to yield manganese(III) hydroxide, $Mn(OH)_3$. Manganese(II) ion in acidic solutions is oxidized to permanganate ion by bismuthate ion, BiO_3^-.

25.6 IRON

The most abundant iron ore is hematite, Fe_2O_3, which in its hydrated form is called limonite, $2Fe_2O_3 \cdot 3H_2O$. The huge Mesabi range in northern Minnesota is by far the most important current source of iron ore in the United States.

The metallurgy of iron is somewhat less complex than that of most metals, as is attested by records indicating the use of iron more than 4000 years ago. Except in meteorites, iron is found in nature on'y in its combined state; hence it seems very likely that early man did prepare the metal from one of its ores. Perhaps charcoal was used as the reducing agent.

In the blast furnace (see Fig. 25.1) used in the metallurgy of iron, the coke (mostly carbon) that is the reducing agent is burned at the bottom to yield carbon dioxide and carbon monoxide. The carbon monoxide reduces the iron(III) oxide to iron.

$$Fe_2O_3 + 3CO \rightarrow 3CO_2 + 2Fe$$

The blast furnace yields a product called *pig iron*. This pig iron is refined to produce the various forms of iron and steel. A typical pig iron is approximately 92 per cent iron, 3–4 per cent carbon, 2–3 per cent silicon, 1 per cent manganese, and 1 per cent phosphorus. The amounts of carbon, silicon, and manganese are lowered, by oxidation to their oxides, to yield steels. This conversion is performed either by a Bessemer converter (see Fig. 25.2) or in an open-hearth furnace (see Fig. 25.3). The open-hearth process yields the better steels because it allows more careful control. However, the modern treatment of molten pig iron with high purity O_2 in basic oxygen furnaces greatly accelerates the steel-making process.

Cast iron is unrefined pig iron that has been remelted and cast. Wrought iron is a refined pig iron that has a carbon content of 0.1–0.2 per cent. There are many different steels, each being an alloy containing various elements which endow the steel with special properties. Most steels have a carbon content of 0.75–0.10 per cent.

The two main oxidation states of iron are $+2$ and $+3$. The

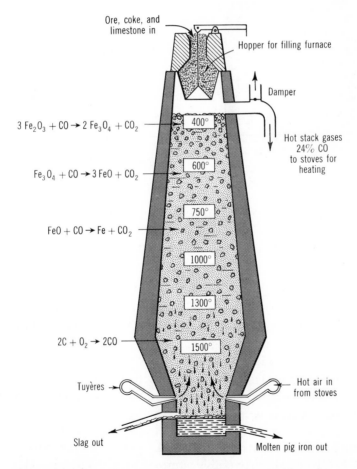

Ore, coke, and limestone in

Hopper for filling furnace

Damper

$3 Fe_2O_3 + CO \rightarrow 2 Fe_3O_4 + CO_2$ 400°

Hot stack gases 24% CO to stoves for heating

$Fe_3O_4 + CO \rightarrow 3 FeO + CO_2$ 600°

750°

$FeO + CO \rightarrow Fe + CO_2$ 1000°

1300°

$2C + O_2 \rightarrow 2CO$ 1500°

Tuyères

Hot air in from stoves

Slag out

Molten pig iron out

FIGURE 25.1 The chemical reactions in the blast furn-ace are more complex than is indicated in this diagram, but those listed do occur. During a 24-hour period an av-erage blast furnace will yield about 1000 tons of pig iron and 500 tons of slag, the latter being mainly $CaSiO_3$.

compounds of iron(II) are less common than those of iron(III) because Fe^{++} ion is easily oxidized to Fe^{3+}. Iron(II) nitrate does not exist in the solid state; the nitrate ions in the acidic solution

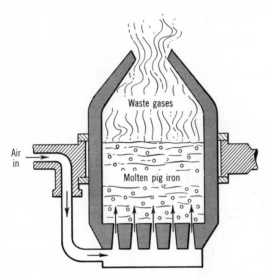

Air in

Waste gases

Molten pig iron

FIGURE 25.2 The Bessemer converter uses an air blast to oxidize most of the impurities in the pig iron from the blast furnace. Only a part of the carbon is oxidized. Although the Bessemer process is rapid and easy, accurate control of the composition of the product steel is difficult.

from which the solid would have to be crystallized oxidize the Fe^{++} ions to Fe^{3+}.

Iron(II) ammonium sulfate hexahydrate,

$$Fe(NH_4)_2(SO_4)_2 \cdot 6H_2O$$

also called Mohr's salt, is used frequently as a source of iron(II) because it is more resistant to oxidation than most other compounds of iron(II). Since iron(II) ions are easily oxidized, Mohr's salt is a commonly used reducing agent.

Iron(II) chloride, $FeCl_2$, is colorless, but the tetrahydrate is pale green. Iron(II) sulfide, FeS, is dark and nearly insoluble.

Iron(III) chloride is dark brown, whereas the hexahydrate, $FeCl_3 \cdot 6H_2O$, which is much more common, is yellow. The anhydrous chloride is prepared by treating iron with chlorine.

Both iron(II) ions and iron(III) ions combine with cyanide ions, CN^-, to yield fairly stable complex ions. The iron(II)cyanide complex ion is $Fe(CN)_6^{4-}$; the iron(III)cyanide complex ion is $Fe(CN)_6^{3-}$. Potassium iron(II)cyanide, $K_4Fe(CN)_6$, is a yellow solid; potassium iron(III)cyanide, $K_3Fe(CN)_6$, is a red solid. If iron(II) ions are added to a solution containing iron(III)cyanide ion, a blue compound $Fe_2[Fe(CN)_6]_2$, called Turnbull's blue, is obtained.

One of the most sensitive tests for the presence of iron(III) ion

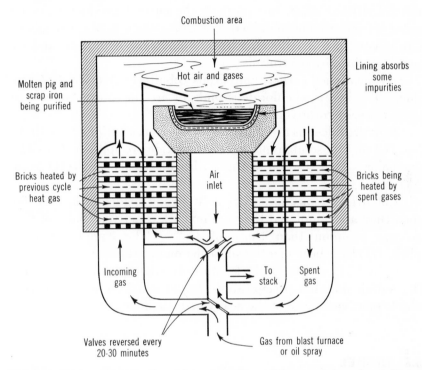

Combustion area

Hot air and gases

Molten pig and scrap iron being purified

Lining absorbs some impurities

Bricks heated by previous cycle heat gas

Air inlet

Bricks being heated by spent gases

Incoming gas

To stack

Spent gas

Valves reversed every 20-30 minutes

Gas from blast furnace or oil spray

FIGURE 25.3 The open-hearth process is used in supplying about 90 per cent of the current production of steel. Scrap iron, high-grade ore, and limestone are added to the pig iron. About 8 to 12 hours are required for the oxidation of the impurities in each batch of pig iron. The capacity of a large furnace is about 500 tons. The process can be carefully controlled.

is the formation of a red coloration in the presence of thiocyanate ion, SCN^-. A probable structure of the complex ion produced is $FeSCN^{++}$. Iron(II) ions yield no color with SCN^-.

Iron(III) compounds are generally good oxidizing agents because they are so readily reduced to iron(II).

Gaseous carbon monoxide, CO, combines with iron to yield a yellow viscous liquid, $Fe(CO)_5$, called iron pentacarbonyl. There are other iron carbonyls of varying compositions.

Iron(III) hydroxide has been mentioned previously (p. 580).

25.7 COBALT

Elemental cobalt is white or faintly pink, very hard, malleable, ductile, and slightly magnetic.   The major ores are smaltite, $CoAs_2$, and cobaltite, CoAsS, but most of the current production of the metal is from residues obtained in working the ores of other metals. The roasted ore is reduced with aluminum or hydrogen, and the metal is refined by electrolysis.

As mentioned earlier, anhydrous cobalt(II) chloride, $CoCl_2$, is blue.   The hydrated chloride is pink, as are the solutions made by adding the anhydrous chloride to water.

If hydroxide ions are added to an aqueous solution of cobalt(II) ions, the slightly soluble cobalt(II) hydroxide precipitates, $Co(OH)_2$, blue color.   Dehydration of this hydroxide yields cobalt(II) oxide, CoO.

Cobalt(III) ions are extremely strong oxidizing agents, but when they are complexed they are much less active.   Salts of Co^{3+} are less common than those of Co^{++}.   The complex ions of cobalt(III) have been mentioned earlier on p. 581.

Cobalt(II) sulfide is black and only slightly soluble in water. This sulfide does not precipitate in acidic solutions because it is so soluble relative to most of the heavy metal sulfides.

25.8 NICKEL

Metallic nickel is a white, hard, magnetic solid quite resistant to corrosion.   It is used in alloys (p. A-3), is electroplated extensively, and is used widely as a catalyst (p. 247).   Nickel combines with carbon monoxide to yield a tetracarbonyl, $Ni(CO)_4$, which boils at 43°C.   This carbonyl decomposes at 200°C to yield the pure nickel.

All of the common salts of nickel are those of nickel(II) because nickel(III) ion is such a strong oxidizing agent it cannot exist in aqueous solution.   Hydrated Ni^{++} ions impart a green color to aqueous solutions.   The nickel(II) hydroxide is green and only slightly soluble in water.   Anhydrous nickel(II) chloride, $NiCl_2$, is yellow and quite soluble in water.   Nickel(II) ion produces several different complex ions (p. 582).

If an aqueous solution that contains nickel(II) ions is treated with aqueous ammonia and dimethylglyoxime, $C_4H_6N_2O_2H_2$, a pink (red) precipitate of nickel dimethylglyoxime is obtained. Although this is a sensitive test for nickel(II) ion, other ions such as silver ion, manganese(II), iron(II) and (III), and cobalt(II) also yield precipitates in the presence of dimethylglyoxime.

Although nickel(II) sulfide (black) is only very slightly soluble in water, it is easily soluble in most ordinary acidic solutions.

25.9   COPPER

The most common ores from which copper is won are mixed sulfides usually of low copper content but of high iron content. The crude ore is concentrated by flotation, and then roasted to oxidize some of the iron sulfide to oxide. The roasted ore is mixed with silica and lime and then placed in an open-hearth furnace. The molten mass (matte), after removal of slag, is put into a Bessemer converter. Silica is added and hot air is blown through the molten mixture. The iron sulfide is oxidized by oxygen, and the resultant oxide yields a slag with the silica.

$$2FeS + 3O_2 \rightarrow 2FeO + 2SO_2$$
$$FeO + SiO_2 \rightarrow FeSiO_3 \text{ (slag)}$$

The copper(I) sulfide is converted to the (I) oxide, which is reduced by the copper(I) sulfide to yield blister copper.

$$2Cu_2O + Cu_2S \rightarrow 6Cu + SO_2$$

The blister copper is purified by electrorefining (p. 507).

The two main oxidation states of copper are +1 and +2. Copper(I) compounds are generally much less stable than those of copper(II). At high temperatures, however, copper(I) salts are the more stable. There are some binary copper(I) compounds such as copper(I) oxide, Cu_2O (red); copper(I) chloride, $CuCl$ (white); copper(I) iodide, CuI (red-brown); copper(I) cyanide, $CuCN$ (white).

Hydrated copper(II) ions impart a blue color to aqueous solutions, but uncomplexed Cu^{++} ions have no color. Anhydrous copper(II) sulfate is white, but the pentahydrate, $CuSO_4 \cdot 5H_2O$, is blue and the monohydrate is colorless. In the anhydrous halides of copper(II), the Cu^{++} ions are apparently complexed with the halide ions, because these halides are dark colored.

Copper(II) oxide, CuO, is black. It is obtained easily by heating the copper(II) hydroxide, $Cu(OH)_2$ (blue color).

$$Cu^{++} + 2OH^- \rightarrow Cu(OH)_2$$
$$Cu(OH)_2 + \Delta \rightarrow CuO + H_2O$$

Copper(II) sulfide, CuS, is brown-black and very slightly soluble in water. It is only slightly soluble in dilute acids, but it will dissolve in hot dilute nitric acid.

Copper(II) iodide, CuI_2, is very unstable. It dissociates to yield copper(I) iodide, CuI, and iodine.

$$2CuI_2 \rightarrow 2CuI + I_2$$

The greenish-blue solid that forms on copper surfaces exposed to the atmosphere is a basic copper(II) carbonate, $Cu(OH)_2 \cdot CuCO_3$, which is only slightly soluble in water.

Copper(II) ion forms an intensely blue complex ion with ammonia, $Cu(NH_3)_4^{++}$, and a brilliant green complex ion with chloride ions, $Cu(Cl)_4^{--}$. The latter is usually partially hydrated. Copper(I) forms a stable cyanide ion, $Cu(CN)_2^-$, as does copper(II), $Cu(CN)_4^{--}$.

Copper compounds are toxic to human beings and to most animals and insects. Bordeaux mixture, $CuSO_4 + Ca(OH)_2$, is used as a plant spray. Paris green, $Cu(C_2H_3O_2)_2 \cdot 3Cu(AsO_3)_2$, a mixed acetate-arsenite, is used as an insecticide and fungicide.

Fehling's solution and Benedict's solution contain complex copper(II) ions in basic solution. In the presence of many reducing agents, the complex Cu^{++} ions are reduced to copper(I), whereupon copper(I) oxide precipitates. Glucose (dextrose) in the presence of these solutions causes reduction of the copper(II) to Cu_2O. Sugar in urine is detected in this manner.

25.10 SILVER

At ordinary temperatures, silver is not oxidized by molecular oxygen, although it is oxidized by ozone. Hydrogen sulfide and sulfur-containing compounds in food do interact with silver to yield the familiar tarnish that we often see on silverware.

$$4Ag + 2H_2S + O_2 \rightarrow 2Ag_2S + 2H_2O$$

Silver dissolves in nitric acid and in concentrated sulfuric acid, gaseous oxides being the by-products.

$$Ag + 2HNO_3 \rightarrow AgNO_3 + H_2O + NO_2$$

If hydroxide ions are added to an aqueous solution that contains silver ions, a dark brown precipitate of silver oxide, Ag_2O, appears. The hydroxide, if it forms at all, is immediately dehydrated.

$$2Ag^+ + 2OH^- \rightarrow Ag_2O$$

If aqueous ammonia is added to the brown solid, it dissolves to form the silver ammonia complex ion, $Ag(NH_3)_2^+$, diamminesilver(I) ion.

$$Ag^+ + 2NH_3 \leftrightarrows Ag(NH_3)_2^+$$

Although silver chloride, AgCl, is only very slightly soluble in water, it dissolves readily in aqueous ammonia to yield the complex ammonia ion.

Silver nitrate, $AgNO_3$, is the most common soluble compound of silver. Silver sulfate, Ag_2SO_4, is somewhat soluble, but less than the nitrate. Silver sulfide, Ag_2S, is black and nearly insoluble.

The major use of silver, except that of electroplating and coinage, is in photography. Silver halides are especially unstable in the presence of light, and it is this instability that is used in the photographic process. The silver halides are supported in a gelatin vehicle that acts as a protective colloid or peptizing agent. As light reaches the supporting colloid, the silver ions are sensitized and thereafter they are more easily reduced than before exposure.

During the development of the exposed film, some reducing agent, the developer, reduces the sensitized silver ions that have been exposed to light. After the proper stage of development is attained, the silver halide not affected by exposure is removed from the emulsion by complexing the silver ions with thiosulfate ions, $S_2O_3^{--}$.

$$AgBr \leftrightarrows Ag^+ + Br^-$$
$$Ag^+ + S_2O_3^{--} \leftrightarrows Ag(S_2O_3)_2^{3-}$$

The thiosulfate ions are usually supplied by sodium thiosulfate, called hypo.

At least 200 tons of silver are used annually by the manufacturers of photographic films and papers.

25.11 ZINC, CADMIUM, AND MERCURY

Zinc, cadmium, and mercury are occasionally called the low melting trio because the melting point of mercury is $-39°C$; of cadmium, $321°$; of zinc, $419°$. The melting point of each alkali metal, however, is well below that of either cadmium or zinc. Of this trio, zinc is the most common and mercury the most expensive. Mercury is often called quicksilver because of its appearance and fluidity.

Zinc and cadmium have only one common oxidation state, $+2$, whereas mercury has a $+1$ state and a $+2$ state. Mercury(I) ion is much less stable than mercury(II), and many of the reactions that occur when reagents are added to a compound of mercury(I) are actually those of mercury(II) in equilibrium with mercury(I).

$$Hg_2^{++} \leftrightarrows Hg + Hg^{++}$$
$$\text{mercury(I) ion} \qquad \text{mercury(II) ion}$$

If aqueous ammonia is added to mercury(I) chloride, Hg_2Cl_2, the ammonia molecules react with the Hg^{++} ions to yield an ion that in the presence of chloride ions forms a precipitate of $HgNH_2Cl$ (white). During the formation of the white solid, metallic mercury appears as Hg^{++} ions are removed from the system in equilibrium. Hence the entire solid appears black.

If sulfide ions are added to a solution of Hg_2^{++}, black mercury(II) sulfide is the major product.

Mercury(II) chloride, $HgCl_2$, is soluble in water, but mercury(I) chloride, Hg_2Cl_2, is only very slightly soluble.

Mercury(II) sulfide, HgS, is almost insoluble in water, but it dissolves easily in a basic solution having a relatively high sulfide ion concentration. Since mercury(II) sulfide dissolves in aqua regia (concentrated HCl and HNO_3), the sulfide is amphoteric.

$$HgS + S^{--} \leftrightarrows HgS_2^{--}$$
$$\text{(soluble)}$$

$$HgS + OH_3^+ + NO_3^- + Cl^- \rightarrow Hg(Cl)_3^- + S + H_2S$$
$$\underbrace{\text{(excess)} \qquad\qquad \text{(excess)}}_{\text{(from aqua regia)}}$$

Zinc sulfide, ZnS, is white, whereas cadmium sulfide, CdS, is yellow. Each is only slightly soluble in water, but they dissolve in dilute nitric acid.

Zinc oxide and hydroxide are amphoteric.

$$ZnO + OH_3^+ \rightarrow Zn(OH_2)_6^{++}$$
$$\text{(excess)}$$
$$ZnO + OH^- \rightarrow Zn(OH)_4^{--}$$
$$\text{(excess)}$$

Cadmium and zinc ions yield many kinds of complex ions, the ammonia complex ions, $Cd(NH_3)_4^{++}$ and $Zn(NH_3)_4^{++}$, being the most common. Except for their oxides, hydroxides, and sulfides, many of the common compounds of zinc and cadmium are soluble in water. All of their common compounds are colorless, except CdS.

Problems

1. For each of the five oxidation states in which manganese can reside, there is an oxide. Write the formula of each.

2. By considering the electronic configuration of the titanium atom, explain why the compounds of the $+2$ and $+3$ oxidation states of titanium are oxidized so easily to the $+4$ state.

3. List the common ions that are isoelectronic with Sc^{3+}.

4. What transition element metals, in alloys, do you usually carry with you every day?

5. If aluminum is used in the Goldschmidt process to reduce chromium(III) to the metal, how many grams of aluminum are needed for each kilogram of chromium obtained?

6. A certain ore of titanium is 11 per cent rutile. What is the maximum yield of the metal from 1000 tons of the ore?

7. A clear acidic aqueous solution contains hydrated chromium(III) ions in 0.1 M concentration. What is observed visually if an aqueous solution of sodium hydroxide is added slowly by drops to the acidic solution until the solution is strongly basic?

8. Although manganese sulfide is only slightly soluble in water, it dissolves readily in dilute HCl. Why does it dissolve in the acidic solution?

9. Suggest an electronic representation for the permanganate ion.

10. What is the percentage of iron in Mohr's salt?

11. If you had to determine whether a solid sample of cobalt(II) chloride was dry or wet, how would you decide?

12. Write the formula of iron(II) chloride tetrahydrate.

13. What is the common ligancy of copper(II) ion?

14. Why is zinc hydroxide soluble in aqueous ammonia but only slightly soluble in water?

15. By using the rules of nomenclature listed on page 584, name the complex ions $[Cu(NH_3)_4]^{++}$, $[Cu(Cl)_4]^{--}$, $Ag(NH_3)_2^+$, $[Ni(CN)_4]^{--}$, $[Cu(OH_2)_2(NH_3)_2]^{++}$, $[Zn(OH_2)_4]^{++}$, $[Zn(OH)_4]^{--}$, $HgCl_3^-$, $[Mn(CN)_6]^{4-}$, ZnO_2^{--}.

16. You are told that a given white solid is either zinc sulfide or aluminum oxide. What single chemical test could be used to identify the solid?

17. What common negative ion, also a good oxidizing agent, is apparently closely analogous to bismuthate ion?

18. What single chemical test can be used to differentiate between cadmium hydroxide and aluminum hydroxide?

19. Predict the molecular geometry of nickel carbonyl, $Ni(CO)_4$.

26

26.1 A PERSPECTIVE

The chemical transformations we have previously described and classified are ordinary chemical reactions. During all of them the valence electrons of the participating atoms, ions, and molecules play the major roles; their atomic nuclei play the extremely minor (incidental) roles. (In the case of the element hydrogen, the protons and deuterons play major roles only when we feature these entities, but the valence electrons with which they interact are as important, if not more so, than the protons and deuterons themselves.)

In this chapter we shall comment very briefly on some of the major areas of man's current knowledge of nuclear phenomena. This chapter is therefore quite different from all of the others, which are almost exclusively devoted to extranuclear phenomena.

636

CHEMISTRY

Since ordinary chemical reactions involve extra-nuclear phenomena, we may state that nuclear phenomena are extraordinary chemical changes. Natural and artificial radioactivity are specific kinds of nuclear phenomena that seem rather extraordinary, at least when contrasted with ordinary chemical changes. The rate of radioactive disintegration of an atomic nucleus is completely independent of temperature and pressure. Except for a very few small variations, the rate is also independent of the element's chemical environment.

There are four main types of nuclear reactions:

a. Spontaneous radioactive nuclear disintegrations of unstable nuclides or isotopes (natural and artificial).

b. Nuclear reactions initiated by the bombardment of atomic nuclei by tiny high-velocity particles (some less massive than the alpha particle), with the resultant ejection from the target nucleus of some tiny particle or gamma radiation.

c. Nuclear fission reactions during which a large atomic nucleus undergoes cleavage, usually due to bombardment by neutrons, to yield two smaller nuclei having comparable (or very similar) masses. During such reactions an appreciable amount of mass of the original nucleus is converted to energy (atomic bombs).

d. Nuclear fusion reactions during which two small atomic nuclei of similar mass combine (fuse) to yield a more massive nucleus. During such reactions an appreciable amount of mass is converted to energy because the product nuclei have masses significantly less than the total masses of the "reactant" nuclei (thermonuclear or hydrogen bombs).

26.2 FUNDAMENTAL MATERIAL ENTITIES

In this section we shall again introduce the electron, the proton, and the neutron and briefly identify certain material entities not previously mentioned.

a. The *electron* (*negatron*) is such an important entity that it must head, at least in a chemistry textbook, the list of fundamental material entities. The mass of the electron is about 5.5×10^{-4} amu. The electron is the beta ray particle. The symbols used to identify it are β, e^-, $_{-1}e^0$.

b. The *proton* is the nucleus of the protium atom; its mass is approximately 1.0076 amu. Protons, present in all atomic nuclei, are usually identified by any one of the following symbols: p, $_1^1H$, ^1H.

c. The *neutron* is uncharged and its mass is approximately 1.0089 amu. Neutrons exist in all atomic nuclei (except in the protium atom). The usual symbols of a neutron are n, $_0^1n$, ^1n.

d. The *positron* is positively charged. Its mass is identical to that of the electron. The positron is, in a sense, a positive electron or an *antielectron*. When a positron encounters an electron, each is annihilated and a tremendous burst of energy (gamma radiation) is the result. Such a phenomenon is a perfect manifestation of the identity of matter and energy. A positron can exist as a free particle for time intervals usually no longer than one microsecond $(1 \times 10^{-6} \text{ sec})$. Several of the less massive unstable (artificially radioactive) nuclei are positron emitters. The symbols are β^+, $_{+1}^0e$.

e. The *antiproton* has a mass identical to that of the proton but it is negatively charged. (It is, in a sense, a negative proton.) When an antiproton encounters a proton, each is annihilated and only energy remains. Because antiprotons have an extremely transient existence, they are somewhat rarely identified. They have, however, been detected in cosmic radiation.

f. The *neutrino* has a very small mass and no charge. It seems to play an important role in nuclear architecture.

g. The *mesons* are produced by interactions between matter and cosmic radiation. (The cosmic radiation that reaches the earth's surface appears to consist mainly of protons, electrons, positrons, and mesons. These entities probably arise in the upper atmosphere as a result of nuclear interactions between different atomic nuclei and between high-energy photons and atomic nuclei. Because of their tremendous velocity in cosmic radiation, these particles have extremely high energies, 10^{15} to 10^{17} electron volts.) Mesons are very short-lived. They may be either positive, negative, or neutral. The approximate masses of the known mesons are: for mu (μ) mesons, 216 times the mass of an electron; for pi (π) mesons, 285 times the mass of an electron; for the more massive mesons, about 900 times the mass of an electron.

h. The *photon* (quantum of electromagnetic radiation) appears to be a discrete bundle of matter and energy. The energy of the photon varies with the wave length of the radiation. Since gamma radiation has the shortest wave lengths (highest frequencies) of the various types of radiation, it consists of the most energetic photons. The energy of a photon is equal to $h\nu$, where h is Planck's constant, 6.6×10^{-27} erg sec, and ν is the frequency of the radiation. ($\nu = c/\lambda$, where $c =$ velocity of light and λ is the wave length of the radiation in question.)

26.3 NATURAL RADIOACTIVITY

There are many naturally occurring nuclides whose nuclei disintegrate spontaneously. They are said to be radioactive because they emit radiation. In this section we shall consider natural radioactivity, and in Section 26.7 we shall discuss artificial radioactivity (the radioactivity of synthetic nuclides). All radioactive disintegrations are exothermic; hence a radioactive (unstable) nuclide decays to yield another nuclide having a more stable nucleus. (For a review of exothermic reactions, see p. 67.)

In most of the nonradioactive (stable) nuclei the number of protons is equal or comparable to the number of neutrons. In any case there seems to be a favorable neutron-to-proton ratio in stable nuclides. If the neutron-to-proton ratio in a given nucleus is much higher than the more favorable ratio, the nucleus usually emits (ejects) electrons, thereby increasing its nuclear charge (number of protons). If the neutron-to-proton ratio of a nucleus is much lower than the more favorable ratio, it has a tendency to decrease its nuclear charge. There are three ways to accomplish this: alpha particle (helium-4 nucleus) emission, positron emission, and K electron capture. (If a nucleus having a relatively high nuclear charge pulls an electron from the K shell of its atom, the nucleus is said to undergo K electron capture. During this type of radioactivity either x-radiation or gamma radiation is emitted.)

When the nucleus of a radioactive nuclide emits a material entity, a different nucleus of a different nuclide is formed; a spontaneous atomic transmutation occurs. Naturally radioactive substances emit three kinds of radiation consisting of three types of entities: (1) alpha particles, helium-4 nuclei (poor penetrating power, velocity of about 20,000 km/sec); (2) beta radiation, electrons (fair penetrating power, velocity of 100,000 km/sec); (3) gamma radiation, very high energy photons (high penetrating power, velocity of 300,000 km/sec). If an atomic nucleus emits an alpha particle, the nuclear charge decreases by two units and the mass number decreases by four units. An alpha particle emitter is transmuted spontaneously to an element whose position in the periodic chart is two columns to the left of it. If a nucleus emits a beta particle, the nuclear charge increases by one unit but the mass number is unchanged. A beta particle emitter is transmuted spontaneously to an element whose position in the periodic chart is one column to the right of it. If a nucleus emits gamma radiation, there are no changes in nuclear charge and mass number; hence no transmutation occurs. If a nucleus captures a K electron, the nuclear charge decreases by one unit. The nuclide is transmuted to an element whose position in the periodic chart is one column to the left of it.

The nuclear changes during radioactive disintegrations can be represented by equations in which charges and mass numbers balance. If you know the name and radioactive emanation(s) of a given nuclide, you can easily identify the nucleus that remains immediately after the emanation is ejected from the nucleus. Let us examine a few examples.

Uranium-238 is an alpha particle emitter. The equation representing its nuclear decay is

$$_{92}^{238}U \rightarrow {}_2^4He + {}_{90}^{234}Th$$

But thorium-234 is a beta particle emitter,

$$_{90}^{234}Th \rightarrow {}_{-1}^0e + {}_{91}^{234}Pa$$

protactinium-234 is a beta particle emitter,

$$_{91}^{234}Pa \rightarrow {}_{-1}^0e + {}_{92}^{234}U$$

and uranium-234 is an alpha particle emitter; the product of the decay of ^{234}U is thorium-230, and thorium-230 is unstable, etc. These disintegrations are parts of a series of successive radioactive disintegrations which commence with uranium-238 and end at nonradioactive lead-206—called the *uranium-radium series*. This radioactive disintegration series is often called the $4n + 2$ series because when the mass number of each nuclide in the series is divided by 4, a remainder of 2 is obtained in each case.

There are three other radioactive disintegration series similar to the uranium-radium one. (See Table A.6, p. A-8.)

a. The uranium-actinium series commences with uranium-235 and ends at stable lead-207. It is called the $4n + 3$ series. (Mass number of each nuclide is divisible by 4 with a remainder of 3.)

b. The thorium series commences with thorium-232 and ends at stable lead-208. It is called the $4n$ series. (Mass number of each nuclide is exactly divisible by 4.)

c. The neptunium series is not a naturally occurring one because the parent number, ^{241}Pu, does not exist in nature. This series, discovered during World War II, commences with plutonium-241 and ends at bismuth-209. This $4n + 1$ series is named for neptunium-237, the longest-lived member of the series.

There are relatively few naturally occurring radioactive nuclides whose atomic numbers are less than 82. Some of these are (half-life periods included in parentheses): potassium-40, beta particle emitter (1.4×10^9 yr); rubidium-87, beta emitter (6×10^{10} yr); and all of the known isotopes of technetium, Tc, and promethium, Pm.

The emanations ejected by radioactive nuclei are detected and identified by instruments such as Geiger counters, ionization chambers, electroscopes, Wilson cloud chambers, and scintillation counters. In the Geiger counter, ionic radioactive emanations ionize a gaseous phase, with the result that ideally an electrical discharge occurs each time an ion enters the gaseous phase in the counter.

The unit of radioactivity is the *curie*. One curie of a radioactive substance is the amount in which 3.7×10^{10} atomic nuclei of the substance undergo radioactive disintegration during each second. A *millicurie* is $\frac{1}{1000}$ of a curie. (One gram of radium is approximately one curie of radium.) One *roentgen*, named after W. C. Roentgen, is defined as the amount of radiation that yields 2 billion ion pairs after passing through 1 cm^3 of dry air (STP).

26.4 THE HALF-LIFE PERIOD OF A RADIOACTIVE NUCLIDE

The number of nuclei of any given nuclide that spontaneously disintegrate in a unit of time is a constant fraction of the total amount of nuclide present. The rate of radioactive disintegration of a given nuclide is expressed in terms of the nuclide's half-life period: the interval of time during which half the nuclei in a given sample disintegrate. If we have at a specific moment 100 g of a radioactive nuclide, immediately after one half-life period (of that nuclide) has passed we have 50 g of that nuclide; immediately after another half-life has passed we have 25 g. No matter how much of a radioactive nuclide may be present at a given moment, half of that amount will disintegrate during one half-life period of that nuclide.

It is important to realize that the concept of the half-life period of a radioactive nuclide is pertinent to the behavior only of huge aggregates of physically identical atoms. We have no way of determining the behavior of the nucleus of an isolated atom; hence we know very little about the actual life span of an individual nucleus.

By contrasting the half-life periods of two different radioactive nuclides, we see that the nuclide having the shorter half-life is the less stable nuclide and it emits, per unit of time, more radiation (particles) than the one with the longer half-life. Since radioactive emanations are very energetic (and some are very penetrating), prolonged exposure to such radiation is usually extremely injurious to living tissue. The danger of nuclear radiation is mainly dependent on the number of particles emitted per unit of time, the energy of the emanations (wave length if gamma radiation) and the penetration of the radiation. The nuclides with relatively short half-life periods are among the most dangerous radioactive substances.

Uranium-238 has a half-life period of 4.5×10^9 years. It is not considered dangerous, but prolonged direct exposure is to be avoided. There is a relatively large supply of this long-lived nuclide in the earth's crust. Therefore all the members of the uranium-radium disintegration series are always present in nature because each is continually produced by the constant decay of some nuclide in the series. The neptunium series is apparently absent from the earth's crust because the parent nuclide, plutonium-241, has a half-life of only 10 years and has long since practically disappeared.

26.5   THE AGE OF THE EARTH

The age of rocks containing uranium-238 may be estimated approximately by quantitative determination of the amount of lead-206 and uranium-238 currently present in them. One hundred grams of uranium-238 decomposes, during 4.5 billion years (half-life of ^{238}U, to yield 50 g of ^{238}U, 6.7 g of helium, and 43.3 g ($50 \times 207/238$) of ^{206}Pb. The currently observed ratios of helium to ^{238}U and ^{206}Pb to ^{238}U, as found by analysis of the oldest rocks, seem to indicate that their ages are approximately 3 to 3.5 billion years. These analyses are difficult, and the amount of gaseous helium found in a rock cavity may be much less than the amount actually formed after the rocks solidified during the formation of the earth's crust. Although these estimations of the ages of rocks are rather inaccurate and indefinite, they offer some clues as to the age of the earth.

26.6   ARTIFICIAL TRANSMUTATION

In 1919 Ernest Rutherford (British) noted that if alpha particles were discharged into a sample of nitrogen gas, small amounts of oxygen and hydrogen were formed. He concluded, after extensive investigations, that if an alpha particle effectively bombards the nucleus of an ordinary nitrogen atom, the nitrogen is transmuted to oxygen with a hydrogen atom as a sort of by-product. Rutherford's experiment is often considered the first artificially induced nuclear transmutation. This nuclear reaction may be represented by a nuclear equation in which nuclear changes and mass numbers are balanced.

$$\ce{^4_2He + ^{14}_7N -> ^{17}_8O + ^1_1H}$$

The mass numbers of the nuclides balance only because they are approximate nuclear masses. There actually is a change in the nuclear mass of the "target" nucleus, but this is quite small in such rather minor nuclear changes. Relatively large nuclear mass changes do occur, however, during some more drastic nuclear transformations.

In 1932 J. D. Cockcroft and E. T. S. Walton (British) bombarded lithium-7 with relatively high-energy (high-velocity) protons.

$$\ce{^7_3Li + ^1_1H -> ^4_2He + ^4_2He}$$

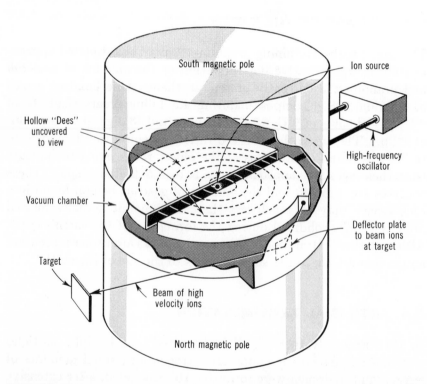

FIGURE 26.1 In the cyclotron the ions produced at the source between the two "dees" are accelerated as they go around inside the "dees." Each "dee" becomes alternately charged, positively then negatively, 12 million times a second; hence each ion is accelerated every time it comes to the gap between the "dees." After an ion attains sufficient velocity (kinetic energy), it leaves the "dee" and strikes the target.

Here the projectile is the proton, the target is the lithium-7 nucleus, and the alpha particles are the products of this artificial transmutation. The research of Cockcroft and Walton greatly stimulated research on nuclear reactions induced by the bombardment of atomic nuclei by projectiles having high energy. The most common projectiles used are protons, deuterons, electrons, alpha particles, and neutrons. A charged particle's energy can be increased in two ways: (1) by increasing the velocity of the particle, and (2) by allowing the particle to drop (fall) through a high potential difference. Van der Graaff generators are used to build up huge potential differences. The cyclotron is usually used to accelerate protons and deuterons (see Fig. 26.1). The 184-inch cyclotron at Berkeley, California, yields 200-million-volt deuterons. The betatron is used to obtain high-velocity electrons; the linear accelerator and the synchrotron yield charged particles of extremely high energies (velocities).

26.7 ARTIFICIAL RADIOACTIVITY

In 1934 F. Joliot and his wife Irene (the elder daughter of Pierre and Marie Curie) (French) reported they had produced, by artificial means, hitherto unknown radioactive nuclides. A typical example is

$$^{27}_{13}\text{Al} + {}^4_2\text{He} \rightarrow {}^{30}_{15}\text{P} + {}^1_0 n$$

Since phosphorus-30, a positron emitter, is not found in natural phosphorus, it is an artificial radioactive nuclide.

$$^{30}_{15}\text{P} \rightarrow {}^{30}_{14}\text{Si} + {}^0_{+1} e$$

Silicon-30 is a stable (nonradioactive) nuclide.

There are hundreds of currently known examples of artificial radioactivity. At least one radioactive isotope of every element has been produced in the laboratory. The general procedure involves the bombardment of various atomic nuclei with the common "light-weight" projectiles. It is customary to use shorthand abbreviations in identifying such reactions. Let us use, as an example, a specific nuclear reaction.

$$^{24}_{12}\text{Mg} + {}^4_2\text{He} \rightarrow {}^{27}_{14}\text{Si} + {}^1_0 n$$

This equation is abbreviated as $^{24}_{12}\text{Mg}\ (\alpha,\ n)\ ^{27}_{14}\text{Si}$, where $^{24}_{12}\text{Mg}$ is the "target" nucleus; α, the projectile; n, the ejected "light-weight" product; and $^{27}_{14}\text{Si}$, the major reaction product. Since the atomic number of magnesium is easily found by inspecting the periodic chart and we could determine the major reaction product by completing and balancing the nuclear equation, it is necessary only to use the symbols: $^{24}\mathrm{Mg}(\alpha, n)$.

When the shorthand representations of artificial nuclear transformations are written, the common "light-weight" particles are assigned these symbols: the proton, p; the deuteron, d; the electron, β; the neutron, n; the alpha particle, α.

Let us now write the complete balanced equation representing the nuclear reaction whose abbreviated identification is $^{207}\mathrm{Pb}(d, p)$, where the deuteron, d, is the projectile and the proton, p, is the ejected particle. The completed equation is

$$^{207}_{82}\mathrm{Pb} + {}^{2}_{1}\mathrm{H} \rightarrow {}^{1}_{1}\mathrm{H} + {}^{208}_{82}\mathrm{Pb}$$

The equation for an $^{40}\mathrm{Ar}(p, n)$ reaction is

$$^{40}_{18}\mathrm{Ar} + {}^{1}_{1}\mathrm{H} \rightarrow {}^{40}_{19}\mathrm{K} + {}^{1}_{0}n$$

Gamma radiation is occasionally ejected from the target nucleus during bombardment. In shorthand abbreviations a dash is often used to represent gamma radiation. For the nuclear reaction,

$$^{12}_{6}\mathrm{C} + {}^{1}_{1}\mathrm{H} \rightarrow {}^{13}_{7}\mathrm{N} + \gamma$$

the abbreviated notation is $^{12}\mathrm{C}(p, -)$.

In the primary steps of all artificial nuclear reactions, the "light-weight" ejected particles often have masses more than one amu. The very "light-weight" particles, electrons and positrons, are ejected during spontaneous disintegrations of the radioactive nuclides but apparently are infrequently ejected during the artificial transmutations. Electrons and positrons seem to be products of nuclear changes, rather than particles residing as such in atomic nuclei. When an electron is ejected from a nucleus, the nuclear charge increases by one unit. When a positron is emitted by a nucleus, the nuclear charge decreases by one unit.

The neutron is a particularly effective projectile to initiate nuclear transmutations, partly because it is uncharged. It is therefore repelled neither by the nucleus nor by the electron clouds surrounding the nuclei. Since the stability of an atomic nucleus seems to depend on the neutron-to-proton ratio, the addition of a neutron to a stable nucleus frequently results in the formation of an unstable nucleus (see Table 26.1).

TABLE 26.1   A few artificial radioactive nuclides (isotopes)

Nuclide	Nuclear Reaction Producing It	Radiation Emitted	Half-Life Period
^{24}Na	^{24}Mg(n, p)	beta	14.8 hr
^{14}C*	^{14}N(n, p)	beta	5760 yr
^{32}P	^{31}P(d, p)	beta	14.3 days
^{3}H	^{2}H(d, p)	beta	11 yr
^{35}S	^{35}Cl(n, p)	beta	88 days
^{13}N	^{12}C(d, n)	positron	9.9 min
^{60}Co	^{59}Co$(n, -)$	beta	5.2 yr
^{59}Fe	^{58}Fe(d, p)	beta, gamma	47 days
^{82}Br	^{81}Br$(n, -)$	beta, gamma	34 hr
^{17}F	^{14}N(α, n)	positron	70 sec
^{197}Pt	^{196}Pt(d, p)	beta	18 hr

*Carbon-14 is continually formed in the atmosphere; therefore it is not actually an artificial nuclide.

Prior to the advent of the atomic pile or nuclear reactor (see Sec. 26.14, p. 656), streams of neutrons to be used as projectiles were obtained from a ^{9}Be(α, n) reaction. A few nuclear reactions induced by neutrons are

$$^{32}_{16}S + {}^{1}_{0}n \rightarrow {}^{32}_{15}P + {}^{1}_{1}H$$
$$^{16}_{8}O + {}^{1}_{0}n \rightarrow {}^{13}_{6}C + {}^{4}_{2}He$$
$$^{238}_{92}U + {}^{1}_{0}n \rightarrow {}^{239}_{92}U + \gamma \text{ radiation}$$
$$^{31}_{15}P + {}^{1}_{0}n \rightarrow {}^{30}_{15}P + 2{}^{1}_{0}n$$

26.8   PREPARATION OF THE TRANSURANIUM ELEMENTS

The elements whose atomic numbers are greater than 92 are rarely, if ever, found in the earth's crust. All the known transuranium (transuranic) elements have been synthesized in the laboratory. They were initially discovered as nuclear reaction products in the laboratory.

Neptunium-239 (atomic number 93) is the nuclide of a transuranium element that was first discovered in the laboratory. In 1940 E. M. McMillan and P. H. Abelson (American) prepared ^{239}Np by bombarding ^{238}U with high-velocity deuterons.

$$^{238}_{92}U + ^{2}_{1}H \rightarrow ^{239}_{92}U + ^{1}_{1}H$$
$$^{239}_{92}U \rightarrow ^{239}_{93}Np + ^{0}_{-1}e$$
(23.5 min)

It was soon discovered that ^{239}Np is a radioactive beta particle emitter.

$$^{239}_{93}Np \rightarrow ^{239}_{94}Pu + ^{0}_{-1}e$$
(2.3 days)

Plutonium-239 has been prepared in far greater quantities than have all other transuranic elements because it readily undergoes nuclear fission when bombarded by neutrons with the simultaneous evolution of neutrons and much energy. We will describe ^{239}Pu more completely in Section 26.14.

Plutonium-238 was discovered before plutonium-239, as a result of the reaction

$$^{238}_{92}U + ^{2}_{1}H \rightarrow ^{238}_{93}Np + 2^{1}_{0}n$$
$$^{238}_{93}Np \rightarrow ^{238}_{94}Pu + ^{0}_{-1}e$$

Neptunium-237 has a rather long half-life period, 2.2×10^{6} years—much longer than most of the other transuranic nuclides.

$$^{238}_{92}U + ^{1}_{0}n \rightarrow ^{237}_{92}U + 2^{1}_{0}n$$
$$^{237}_{92}U \rightarrow ^{237}_{93}Np + ^{0}_{-1}e$$
(6.8 days)

Some nuclides of the other transuranic elements are prepared by certain artificial transmutations and some are radioactive disintegration products of specific transuranic nuclides. A few of the nuclear reactions are

$$^{238}_{92}U + ^{4}_{2}He \rightarrow ^{241}_{94}Pu + ^{1}_{0}n$$
$$^{241}_{94}Pu \rightarrow ^{241}_{95}Am + ^{0}_{-1}e$$
$$^{241}_{95}Am \rightarrow ^{237}_{93}Np + ^{4}_{2}He$$
(500 yr)

$$^{239}_{94}Pu + ^{4}_{2}He \rightarrow ^{242}_{96}Cm + ^{1}_{0}n$$
$$^{242}_{96}Cm \rightarrow ^{238}_{94}Pu + ^{4}_{2}He$$
(5 mon)

$$^{239}_{94}Pu + ^{4}_{2}He \rightarrow ^{240}_{96}Cm + 3^{1}_{0}n$$
$$^{241}_{95}Am + ^{1}_{0}n \rightarrow ^{242}_{95}Am + \gamma \text{ radiation}$$
$$^{241}_{95}Am + ^{4}_{2}He \rightarrow ^{243}_{97}Bk + 2^{1}_{0}n$$
$$^{242}_{96}Cm + ^{4}_{2}He \rightarrow ^{244}_{98}Cf + 2^{1}_{0}n$$

Professor G. T. Seaborg and his colleagues at the University of California in Berkeley discovered the transuranic elements Pu, plutonium; Am, americium; Cm, curium; Bk, berkelium; and Cf, californium. Their identification and the determination of their chemical properties were masterpieces of chemical technique, mainly because only extremely minute quantities of materials were available.

Einsteinium-253, $^{253}_{99}$Es, and fermium-255, $^{255}_{100}$Fm, have been identified in radioactive debris collected after a thermonuclear test. Specific nuclides of these elements have been prepared by bombarding less massive nuclei with high-energy alpha particles.

Some recent synthetic methods are

$$^{238}_{92}U + {}^{14}_{7}N \rightarrow {}^{247}_{99}Es + 5{}^{1}_{0}n$$
$$^{253}_{99}Es + {}^{1}_{0}n \rightarrow {}^{254}_{99}Es$$
$$^{254}_{99}Es \rightarrow {}^{254}_{100}Fm + {}^{0}_{-1}e$$
$$^{253}_{99}Es + {}^{4}_{2}He \rightarrow {}^{256}_{101}Md + {}^{1}_{0}n$$
$$^{246}_{96}Cm + {}^{12}_{6}C \rightarrow {}^{254}_{102}No + 4{}^{1}_{0}n$$

26.9   THE DATING OF CARBONACEOUS MATERIALS BY USING CARBON-14

The current carbon-14 content of certain carbonaceous materials can be used as an indication of their approximate age, by using a technique developed by W. F. Libby (American). Although this dating technique is somewhat inaccurate and is not easily applicable to materials over 50,000 years old, it is very interesting and often leads to surprisingly informative results. This method of age determination checks well with other means of dating, such as the botanical tree-ring method (for trees) and certain geologic methods.

Carbon-14 is continually formed in the upper atmosphere by the cosmic-ray neutron bombardment of nitrogen-14 (ordinary nitrogen) nuclei. This carbon-14 is oxidized to carbon dioxide and the radioactive carbon dioxide thoroughly diffuses (with the aid of winds), so that the concentration of carbon-14 in the atmosphere is nearly constant (one atom of carbon-14 to 10^{12} atoms of nonradioactive carbon, mostly carbon-12). Since plants assimilate this radioactive carbon (as radiocarbon dioxide), all carbonaceous compounds formed within plants contain this constant ratio of carbon-14 to ordinary carbon. Animals eat the plants and thereby gain (and maintain) in their tissues the same ratio of carbon-14 to ordinary carbon as in the plants and the atmosphere. At the instant of death of a plant or animal, the amount of ^{14}C relative to the total carbon present is the same as that of the atmosphere. As time passes after death, the amount of ^{14}C radioactivity decreases steadily at a constant rate. After 5,760 years have passed (half-life of ^{14}C), half of the original radioactivity has disappeared. After 11,520 years, one-quarter of the original amount of ^{14}C remains; after 23,040 years, only one-sixteenth remains. The carbon-14 method for the dating of plant and animal remains identifies the approximate interval of time that has passed since the carbon in the remains was originally extracted from the atmosphere.

In performing the technique, a fairly large sample of the organic material is completely burned and the carbon dioxide reduced to elemental carbon. The radioactivity of this elemental carbon is then determined by using radiation detectors.

26.10 POTASSIUM-40–ARGON-40 DATING

Recent investigations of the rocks that occur in certain geologic beds in the Olduvai Gorge in Tanganyika, East Africa, indicate that a very ancient man, apparently even earlier than that called Zinjanthropus, lived and made crude tools at least 1,750,000 years ago. The rocks in question were dated by Garniss Curtis and Jack Evernden at the University of California in Berkeley, by using the potassium-40–argon-40 technique. The fossils of Olduvai man and his tools were unearthed and identified by Dr. and Mrs. Louis S. B. Leakey (American).

The potassium-40–argon-40 dating method is based on the fact that potassium-40, a long-lived radioactive nuclide (half-life of 1.3×10^9 yr), decays by K electron capture to yield argon-40. (Potassium-40 also decays by beta emission to yield calcium-40, but this knowledge is of no practical significance because of the prevalence of calcium-40 in so many minerals.) By measuring the amount of ^{40}Ar in a given potassium-bearing mineral, it is possible to determine the approximate date of origin of the mineral.

Curtis and Evernden found a volcanic tuff, or ash, that contains anorthoclase, a potassium-bearing rock. Fortunately, successive volcanic eruptions left layers of the volcanic tuff in the Olduvai gorge. Thus the mineral in a specific layer that contains either fossil man or man-made fossils can be given a specific date of formation as a volcanic tuff. The molten lava inside the earth did not collect gaseous argon-40, but as soon as the lava became cool volcanic tuff, it did begin to collect argon-40. The amount of argon-40 collected in a given layer is therefore a measure of the age of the specific portion of the geologic sandwich in which the fossils were found.

Since the half-life period of potassium-40 is extremely long, the amount of argon-40 in a given sample is very minute. It is detectable, however, by the mass spectrograph (p. 000).

The potassium-40–argon-40 dating method is much superior, in one respect, to that of carbon-14 dating, mainly because it can be used for measuring extremely ancient rocks and their neighbors. The carbon-14 technique is of doubtful value for objects older than 50,000 years. Since each method is used for a specific purpose, any contrasts are dubious.

26.11 MEDICAL USES OF RADIOACTIVE ISOTOPES

a. Use of radium in cancer therapy has been common for some time. Currently cobalt-60 is slowly replacing radium as the source of gamma radiation, mainly because cobalt-60 is considerably cheaper and more conveniently handled than radium. Cobalt-60 is shipped, stored, and used in specially designed containers occasionally called cobalt "bombs." They are not bombs in the usual sense, but are simply sources of intense gamma radiation.

b. Phosphorus-32 is useful in the location of certain types of cancer because rapidly growing cells absorb phosphorus more rapidly than do normal mature cells. This radiophosphorus has been used in treating leukemia and in locating malignant growths.

c. Sodium-24 is frequently used to determine whether blood circulation is normal or abnormal. By injecting a solution of sodium chloride (part of the sodium is sodium-24) into the patient's blood stream, the physician can follow the course of the radioactive sodium-24 ions with a radiation detector.

d. Iodine-131 is often used to treat and identify disorders of the thyroid gland (such as hyperthyroidism and cancer) because this gland absorbs and uses most of the combined iodine ingested by a human. If iodine-131 (as radioactive sodium iodide) is administered to a patient, the radioiodine goes directly to the thyroid gland. The beneficial radiation is thus taken to the "seat of the trouble." A distinct advantage of this therapy is that detrimental radiation effects in surrounding normal tissue are minimal.   Iodine in diiodofluorescein is used in the detection of brain tumors.

e. Gold-198 (in solution) is used in the treatment of certain types of cancer.

26.12   USE OF RADIOACTIVE ISOTOPES AS TRACERS

A radioactive isotope of any element has chemical properties practically identical to those of every other isotope of that element. Thus the radioactive isotope can often serve as an effective tracer of the element's course, either in the presence of chemically identical atoms or in combination with chemically different atoms.   Modern radiation detectors are so sensitive that they can detect and measure accurately an extremely small amount of an ordinary radioisotope; hence its path can be traced during all sorts of physical and chemical changes.

Because biological processes are complex, radioactive tracers find extensive use in the investigation of such matters as the fate of certain metabolites and drugs, the circulatory system of an organism, the extent to which the organism concentrates certain elements in specific organs, and the rate of diffusion of certain substances through the system.   Carbon-14 is rather widely used in organic chemical research and in biological and medical research. It has been quite helpful in the epic research on photosynthesis done by Professor M. Calvin and his co-workers at the University of California at Berkeley.

Radioactive tracers are used in analytical chemistry for such purposes as the determination of the completeness of the precipitation of a compound or element from solution and the extent of contamination of a precipitate during coprecipitation.

The rate and extent of diffusion of atoms into a solid metal can be determined by placing a radioisotope of the metal on its surface.   By using suitable detection instruments, an investigator can follow the movement of atoms from the surface into the interior of the metal.

26.13   MASS-ENERGY AND THE ATOMIC NUCLEUS

The actual atomic weight (physical scale) of a nuclide is usually not exactly equal to the sum of the masses of its constituent fundamental particles, the protons, neutrons, and electrons. The mass number of a nuclide usually is therefore slightly different from the sum of the masses of its nucleons (protons and neutrons). Since these differences in mass are in some cases relatively large, we can substantiate the validity of the fundamental relationship of mass and energy, $E = mc^2$, originally suggested by Einstein in 1907, long before it could be verified experimentally.

Let us now consider this concept of the equality of matter and energy. The helium-4 nucleus contains 2 protons and 2 neutrons. The sum of the masses of these four particles is $2(1.0073) + 2(1.0089) = 4.0324$ amu. Since the nuclear mass of helium-4 is 4.0017, it is evident that 0.0307 amu of mass is evolved as energy during the "construction" of a helium-4 nucleus by using 2 protons and 2 neutrons. This is an eminent example of the conversion of mass to energy. When one mole of helium-4 is formed by using the necessary protons and neutrons, 6.5×10^{11} calories of heat is evolved.

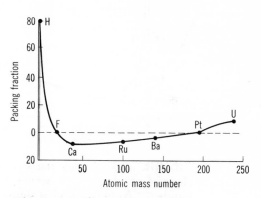

FIGURE 26.2 Packing fraction of an element vs. atomic mass number. All nuclear fissions of those elements having packing fractions less than zero are endothermic.

Since the atomic mass of nearly every nuclide is either less or greater than its mass number, we can appreciate the significance of Einstein's mass-energy concept. This difference between atomic mass and mass number is described by using a quantity called the "packing fraction": the difference in mass (mass number vs. atomic mass) relative to oxygen-16 as standard, per fundamental nuclear particle (proton or neutron). The packing fraction of a nuclide is

$$\frac{(\text{actual atomic mass}) - (\text{mass number})}{\text{mass number}} \times 10^4$$

A nuclide whose atomic mass is greater than its mass number has a positive packing fraction; a nuclide whose atomic mass is less than its mass number has a negative packing fraction. The nuclides of the elements from hydrogen to fluorine have positive packing fractions, as do the nuclides of the elements more massive than platinum. All elements between fluorine and platinum have negative packing fractions.   Fluorine has a zero packing fraction, which means that fluorine-19 has an atomic mass practically identical to its mass number.   (See Fig. 26.2.)

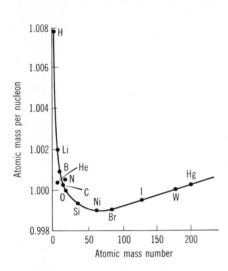

FIGURE 26.3   Atomic mass per nucleon of an element vs. atomic mass number.   Note that this is similar to the packing fraction vs. atomic mass number curve in Fig. 26.2.

If a nuclide is transmuted by a nuclear transformation to another nuclide having a smaller (algebraic) packing fraction, energy will be evolved. If a nuclide is transmuted to an element with a larger packing fraction, energy must be expended. The elements Mn, Fe, Co, Ni, and Cu have the smallest (largest negative) packing fractions; therefore energy must be expended to transmute them. These elements have the most stable atomic nuclei.   (See Fig. 26.3.)

The binding energy of a nucleus is the energy needed to disintegrate it to its constituent particles.   The binding energy is equivalent to a definite amount of mass: the difference between the nuclide's actual nuclear mass and the sum of the individual masses of the constituent protons and neutrons. The nuclei with the largest binding energy per nuclear particle (proton or neutron) are nuclides with the smallest (algebraic) packing fractions.

26.14   NUCLEAR FISSION

Early in 1939 O. Hahn and F. Strassman (German) reported in a physics journal the results of experiments during which they had bombarded with neutrons substances containing uranium.   They had found elements such as krypton and barium among the irradiation products.   Their report soon led Lise Meitner (German) to the correct conclusion that uranium nuclei undergo fission when bombarded by neutrons.

The first discovery by Hahn and Strassman and Lise Meitner's correct interpretation stimulated much investigation. In a short time many other laboratories reported evidence of the fission of uranium nuclei. It was evident to all scientists that much energy is evolved during the nuclear fission reactions because the fission products have smaller (algebraic) packing fractions than do the nuclides of uranium.

It is now known that uranium-235 undergoes fission in several different ways. Some of these are

$$^{235}_{92}U + ^{1}_{0}n \rightarrow ^{95}_{36}Kr + ^{140}_{56}Ba + ^{1}_{0}n$$
$$^{235}_{92}U + ^{1}_{0}n \rightarrow ^{93}_{38}Sr + ^{141}_{54}Xe + 2^{1}_{0}n$$
$$^{235}_{92}U + ^{1}_{0}n \rightarrow ^{89}_{37}Rb + ^{144}_{55}Cs + 3^{1}_{0}n$$

The fact that neutrons are products in all such fissions is extremely significant because these product neutrons can, under appropriate conditions, progressively initiate more and more fissions (chain reaction) until an explosive rate is reached (see Fig. 26.4).

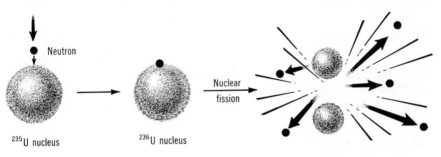

Neutron

^{235}U nucleus $\qquad$ ^{236}U nucleus $\qquad$ Nuclear fission

Two nuclei (atomic number between 30 and 60)
Five (more or less) neutrons

FIGURE 26.4 Nuclear fission of a uranium-235 nucleus initiated by the acceptance of a neutron. The fission yields neutrons which can in turn cause the fission of more uranium-235 nuclei, creating a chain reaction.

During the nuclear fission of uranium-235, the energy evolved is approximately 5×10^{12} cal/mole. Hence the complete fission of one pound (about 2 moles) of uranium-235 yields about 10×10^{12} cal. The complete combustion (an ordinary chemical reaction) of one pound of coal yields about 4×10^{6} cal. It is evident that the magnitude of the energy evolved during exothermic nuclear reactions far exceeds the energy evolved during ordinary exothermic chemical reactions, the main reason being that in the nuclear reactions there are much greater mass differences between the reactant and product systems.

Space does not permit a detailed description of the isolation of the kinds of matter that can undergo nuclear fission. The original most practical fissionable (fissile) substances for use in atomic bombs were uranium-235 and plutonium-239. (Uranium-233 undergoes fission by relatively slow neutrons, just as ^{235}U and ^{239}Pu do, but ^{233}U is present only in very small amounts in ordinary or natural uranium. Thorium-232 and uranium-238 undergo fission when bombarded with high-velocity neutrons.)

Ordinary uranium is approximately 99.3 per cent ^{238}U and about 0.7 per cent ^{235}U. Since these isotopes have practically identical chemical properties, they must be separated by physical means. The four methods used at Oak Ridge, Tennessee, during World War II were:

a. Gaseous diffusion through porous barriers; depends on the fact that gaseous compounds of ^{235}U (such as UF_6) diffuse more rapidly (Graham's law) than do corresponding compounds of ^{238}U.

b. Thermal diffusion; depends on the fact that in a sample of molten natural uranium the less massive ^{235}U isotope concentrates, due to convection, at the top of the vessel.

c. Centrifugation; depends on the fact that the two isotopes, because of their mass difference, may be separated in a centrifugal field.

d. Electromagnetic separation; depends on the fact that ^{235}U ions in a magnetic field are deflected more strongly than are ^{238}U ions (mass spectrometer).

Plutonium-239 is produced in an atomic pile (nuclear reactor). The principal nuclear reactions are

$$^{238}_{92}\text{U} + {}^{1}_{0}n \rightarrow {}^{239}_{92}\text{U}$$
$$\text{(slow)}$$

$$^{239}_{92}\text{U} \rightarrow {}^{239}_{93}\text{Np} + {}^{0}_{-1}e$$
$$\text{(23.5 min)}$$

$$^{239}_{99}\text{Np} \rightarrow {}^{239}_{94}\text{Pu} + {}^{0}_{-1}e$$
$$\text{(2.3 days)}$$

In the atomic pile, rods of natural uranium metal are inserted in aluminum cans, which are regularly distributed in a block of graphite. The graphite is called the moderator because it decelerates the neutrons so that nuclear fissions are less frequent and the

production of plutonium-239 favored.   The reactant neutrons come
from cosmic radiation and from the nuclear fission of the ^{235}U nuclei
present (0.7 per cent) with the ^{238}U nuclei.   The nuclear transformations are exothermic, so the evolved heat must be continually
removed by running water through the reactor (pile).   Since a
large quantity of cooling water is necessary, the huge plutonium-239
plant is located on the Columbia River near Hanford, Washington.
Plutonium-239 is fissile; thus long before all of the ^{238}U is converted
to ^{239}Pu the metallic uranium rods (which now contain ^{239}Pu,
among other substances) are removed from the reactor, and the
^{239}Pu is then separated by chemical means from the uranium and
all fission products.

26.15 NUCLEAR REACTORS

Nuclear reactors, similar to those used in the production of plu-
tonium-239, are essentially sources of neutrons (both fast and slow).
The nuclear reactor is therefore an excellent device in which to
perform neutron bombardments of all sorts of atomic nuclei (both
stable and unstable).   Since many artificial radioactive nuclides
are produced by neutron bombardments of specific nuclei, the nuclear reactor is an extremely valuable and relatively economical
means of preparing useful radioisotopes, such as cobalt-60, phos-
phorus-32, sodium-24, carbon-14, and scores of others.   While the
reactor is producing artificial nuclides, it may be used as a source of
thermal energy.

26.16 ATOMIC BOMBS

Although comparatively little official information has been released
about the technology of the uranium-235 bomb and the plutonium-
239 bomb, the theoretical aspects of nuclear fission (large energy
evolution and chain reaction character) were known by nearly all
physicists as early as 1940.   The technology of the atomic bombs
is one aspect, whereas the theoretical (purely scientific) aspect is
quite something else.
    The technology of the atomic bombs was developed primarily
at Los Alamos, New Mexico.   On July 16, 1945, at Alamogordo,
New Mexico, an epic application of the theoretical knowledge of

nuclear fission was eminently documented by the detonation of an atomic (nuclear) bomb. The fact that chain reactions lead to explosions was well known, but nuclear chain reactions must be handled more carefully than ordinary chemical chain reactions. The major problem in the development of the bomb apparently was the manner by which to attain instantaneously, at the moment of detonation, the critical mass of the fissile material. The critical mass is the minimum amount of matter necessary to confine enough neutrons so that the self-sustaining chain reaction practically instantly reaches an explosive rate, thereby detonating the entire mass. Samples of ^{235}U less massive than the critical mass will not detonate, but a terrific explosion occurs if two or more pieces of ^{235}U having a total mass equal to the critical mass are rapidly placed in intimate contact with each other. A stray cosmic-ray neutron is all that is necessary to trigger this nuclear chain reaction.

It should be noted that when ^{235}U undergoes nuclear fission, only about 0.1 per cent of the total mass of the uranium is converted to energy (88 per cent kinetic energy and 12 per cent radiation). It has been stated that when the first atomic bomb used in warfare detonated over Hiroshima, Japan, about one gram of mass was converted to energy. This means that the mass of the fissile material in this bomb was larger by one gram than the total mass of the fission products.

Nuclear reactions during which the most massive nuclides are transmuted to less massive nuclides are all exothermic because the packing fractions of the most massive nuclides are larger than those of the less massive ones.

26.17 NUCLEAR FUSION; HYDROGEN BOMBS

It was inevitable that man would consider nuclear fusion reactions to produce thermonuclear bombs. Nuclear fusion reactions involving the isotopes of hydrogen are especially exothermic because the packing fraction of a hydrogen nuclide is larger than that of any other nuclide.

Possible nuclear fusion reactions for use in hydrogen (thermonuclear) bombs are

$$\begin{aligned} {}^2_1\text{H} + {}^3_1\text{H} &\rightarrow {}^4_2\text{He} + {}^1_0n \\ {}^3_1\text{H} + {}^3_1\text{H} &\rightarrow {}^4_2\text{He} + 2{}^1_0n \end{aligned}$$

The first reaction yields the larger amount of energy. The fusion of hydrogen-2 and lithium-7 is another possible nuclear reaction. Since these reactions involve the interaction of entities of like charge and comparable mass, they have very high activation energies.

The technology of a hydrogen bomb is very different from the nuclear fission bombs. In the hydrogen bomb there is no critical mass, and no neutrons are necessary to trigger the explosion. Since the high activation energy necessary to start the nuclear fusion reaction may be derived from a nuclear fission bomb, the technology of the hydrogen bomb is, in a sense, indirectly concerned with the critical mass of the fissile material of the trigger mechanism. A hydrogen bomb can theoretically be of any practical size.

26.18 ATOMIC (NUCLEAR) ENERGY

Space does not permit a detailed discussion of all the possible sources and eventual uses of atomic energy. The practical use of neutron-induced nuclear reactions may very likely be limitless. There are relatively large amounts of uranium and thorium in the earth's crust; each of these elements is a potential source of a tremendous amount of energy. Most of us have read and heard much about atomic energy. Some may be excessively visionary; others, unduly pessimistic. Primitive man, during a forest fire, was probably rather dubious about the possible beneficial uses of fire, but he undoubtedly had hopeful visions as he gazed into his quiet campfire. No matter what our current sentiments may be, it is evident that in the relatively near future the earth's supply of fossil fuels, oil and coal, will be nearly exhausted or extremely expensive. It is comforting to know that nuclear fuels and solar energy are available. If they are used wisely, there will be ample energy for many generations. Primitive man realized how much he depended on the sun. Perhaps man in the twenty-first century will feel much as did his very ancient ancestors.

Problems

1. Write an equation to represent each of the following spontaneous nuclear changes:
   (a) Praseodymium-138 is a positron emitter.
   (b) Fermium-255 emits helium-4 nuclei.

(c) Zinc-62 undergoes K electron capture.

(d) Cadmium-115 is a beta emitter.

(e) Radon-220 is an alpha emitter.

(f) Calcium-45 is a negatron emitter.

(g) Bromine-75 is a positron emitter.

(h) Fluorine-21 undergoes beta emission.

(i) Astatine-212 undergoes alpha emission.

(j) Cadmium-104 decays by K electron capture.

2. The half-life of tin-110 is 4 hr. If you were given 80 mg of this nuclide at 9 A.M. on a Monday morning, how much of it would you have at 5 P.M. the next day?

3. Sulfur-37 is a negatron emitter, and its half-life is 5 min. At 9 A.M. on a certain morning a person had exactly 40 mg of this nuclide. How much of it was present at 9:55 A.M. the same morning?

4. The half-life period of a radioactive nuclide is 8 hr. At exactly 8 A.M. on a Tuesday morning there is 200 g of the nuclide. At what time and on what day of the week will exactly 1.5625 g of the nuclide be present?

5. Isobars that have consecutive atomic numbers are called *neighboring isobars*. According to a rule suggested by Mattauch, if two neighboring isobars exist, at least one is unstable. (There are some exceptions.) Using the table of stable nuclides (Table A.8, p. A-11), list the apparent exceptions to Mattauch's rule.

6. A generalization related to Mattauch's rule is: For a given *odd mass number*, there is only *one* stable nuclide. Using the table of stable nuclides, list the apparent exceptions to this generalization.

7. It is said that for a given *even mass number* there may be *two* stable isobars; that is, two stable nuclides may have the same even number. Using the table of stable nuclides, list the instances that substantiate this statement.

8. According to the Geiger-Nuttall rule, a plot of the logarithms of the half-life values of a group of alpha emitters vs. the logarithms of the initial energies of the emitted alpha particles yields a straight line. (The rule is only an approximate relationship.) How does this verify a logical expectation that the alpha particles of the highest energies are emitted by nuclei of nuclides having the shortest half-lives?

9. Let us consider that spontaneous radioactive decay is a chemical reaction. What is the order of this reaction? (See p. 430.)

10. Researchers have found that 1.0 g of radium emits enough alpha particles per year to yield 158 cu mm (measured at STP) of helium. By using a scintillation counter, other workers discovered that 1.0 g of radium emits 4.35×10^{18} alpha particles per year. With these data in mind, calculate a value of Avogadro's number. (Use 22,414 cu cm as the molar volume of helium at STP.)

11. Write equations representing the following nuclear transformations:
(a) $^{23}Na(d, \alpha)$
(b) $^{23}Na(d, p)$
(c) $^{23}Na(n, —)$
(d) $^{39}K(p, \alpha)$
(e) $^{58}Fe(d, p)$
(f) $^{238}U(d, 9n)$
(g) $^{255}Md(\alpha, 2n)$
(h) $^{3}H(d, n)$

12. When a lithium-7 nucleus is bombarded effectively by an alpha particle, a neutron is ejected. What nuclide is produced by this nuclear change?

13. If a copper-63 nucleus is hit effectively by a certain projectile, a neutron is ejected and a gallium-66 nucleus remains. What is the projectile?

14. An atomic nucleus is bombarded by a neutron to yield gamma radiation and a tellurium-131 nucleus. What is the target nucleus?

15. A mineral contains at least 5 per cent uranium-238. List all other chemical elements that definitely are present.

16. A person has 0.02 millicurie of a radioactive material. How many atomic nuclei in this sample are disintegrating per minute?

17. Indicate a preparative route from uranium-238 to californium-244.

18. How might the relative efficiencies of two different makes of vacuum cleaners be tested by using radioactive materials and a Geiger counter?

19. Would it be wise to attempt the construction of a nuclear fission bomb using elemental cobalt as the "active" material?

INTRODUCTION

27.1 A PERSPECTIVE

For nearly two centuries it has been customary to designate as organic compounds nearly all substances that contain the element carbon. Although the metal carbonates, the hydrogen carbonates, and the cyanides are usually considered inorganic (nonorganic) compounds, this distinction is arbitrary. The classification of chemical compounds into two classes, organic and inorganic, was originally motivated by the observations of the early chemists who noticed that most of the compounds of carbon then known to them were present primarily in living organisms. It seemed logical to differentiate the organic compounds from those other compounds (inorganic) that constitute the rocks and minerals.

Organic chemistry, the chemistry of the compounds of carbon, is an extremely important and extensive branch of chemistry, mainly because of the countless

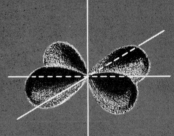

TO ORGANIC CHEMISTRY

number of organic compounds. At present there are at least one million known (characterized and named) organic compounds, and this is only a tiny fraction of the number of possible compounds. There are more compounds containing the element carbon than there are compounds of any other element except hydrogen. It is evident therefore that the number of organic compounds greatly exceeds the number of inorganic compounds. A huge segment of the chemical industry is now involved in the production of organic compounds.

In this chapter we can barely scratch the surface of organic chemistry, but we shall describe very briefly some of its important and interesting aspects.

27.2 ALLOTROPIC FORMS OF CARBON

The three allotropic forms of carbon are diamond, graphite, and amorphous carbon. Diamond often is transparent; it is one of the hardest substances known; it is relatively rare and expensive. Graphite is black (opaque); it is rather soft (used as a lubricant and in pencils); it is relatively inexpensive. Amorphous carbon (coke, charcoal, carbon black, etc.) is similar to graphite, but, as its name implies, it has no well-defined crystalline structure.

Diamond is a macromolecule in which each carbon kernel is covalently bound to four carbon kernels that reside about it at the corners (vertices) of a regular tetrahedron. The distance between any two carbon kernels is 1.54 A. Diamond is an elegant manifestation of the tetracovalence of carbon and of the tetrahedral arrangement of the four pairs of electrons (the octet) that surround the kernel of an electronically satisfied carbon atom (see Fig. 27.1). Since the valence electrons in diamond are localized essentially in nonpolar covalent bonding, diamond is a very poor electronic

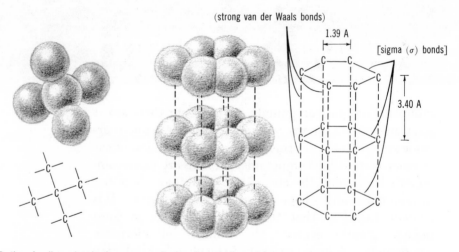

Portion of a diamond molecule   Portion of a graphite crystal

FIGURE 27.1 Greatly abbreviated depictions of the two major crystalline forms of carbon. Diamond has a cubic structure (p. 177) in which each carbon kernel is in the center of an imaginary tetrahedron. In graphite the carbon kernels are arranged to form regular planar hexagons which lie in large parallel sheets in the crystal. These diagrams indicate only the conventional covalent bonds; the pi electron clouds that yield the pi bonds are not indicated (see Fig. 27.3). The electronic arrangement at each hexagon seems to be the same as for a benzene molecule. In the actual graphite lattice the carbon kernels in a given plane are not directly over and under those in the two adjacent planes. Instead they are displaced in the plane by 0.7 A.

conductor. Diamond is the most dense form of carbon (3.5 g/ml at 20°C). It is made by heating graphite to high temperatures under high pressures. There are thousands of organic compounds in which the carbon atoms are tetracovalent and tetrahedral, just as they are in diamond. These are called *aliphatic compounds*.

Graphite has a planar structure; within the planes the carbon kernels are arranged in regular hexagonal patterns, each carbon kernel being covalently attached to three carbon kernels. The length of each carbon-to-carbon bond within the planes is 1.42 A, and the planes are separated by a distance of 3.40 A. (The density of graphite is 2.35 g/ml at 20°C.) The attractive forces between the planes are relatively weak. Graphite cleaves easily to yield thin sheets. Since each carbon kernel in graphite is covalently bonded to only three carbon kernels, there are many essentially unlocalized electrons within the graphite structure (actually one electron per carbon atom). The appreciable electronic conductivity of graphite is apparently due to the mobility of these unlocalized electrons.

Charcoal, coke, and carbon black are usually considered amorphous because the graphitic lattices are broken, and the gross structure is porous (less dense than graphite). Finely divided carbon black has a tremendous surface area per unit mass; the attractive forces at this exposed surface strongly attract certain molecules. Carbon black (and charcoal) is useful in the adsorption of certain gases and of certain substances in liquid solutions. Two major uses of huge quantities of carbon black are in the manufacture of tires for motor vehicles to improve the rubber's resilience and resistance to abrasion, and as a pigment in printer's ink, paint, and the like.

Charcoal is made by pyrolysis (heating in the absence of oxygen) of wood; coke is usually produced by pyrolysis of soft coal; carbon black is made by the pyrolysis of natural gas (mostly methane). Petroleum coke, obtained as a solid residue during the distillation of crude petroleum, has practically no ash, whereas coke from soft coal may have as much as 12–14 per cent ash. Artificial graphite is usually made by heating petroleum coke to a high temperature in an electric furnace.

There are thousands of organic compounds whose molecular skeletons consist, at least in part, of a planar hexagonal carbon framework. These compounds that have certain structural aspects similar to graphite are called *aromatic (benzenoid) compounds*. Benzene, C_6H_6 (p. 684), is the simplest aromatic compound.

27.3 SOME BINARY COMPOUNDS OF CARBON

The simplest oxides of carbon are carbon dioxide, carbon monoxide, and carbon suboxide, C_3O_2. The most practical laboratory preparations of these oxides are given below.

a. *Carbon dioxide.* Treat an ionic carbonate (or hydrogen carbonate) with any Brönsted acid stronger than carbonic acid.

$$2H^+ + CO_3^{--} \leftrightarrows H_2CO_3 \leftrightarrows CO_2 \uparrow + HOH$$

b. *Carbon monoxide.* Gently heat formic acid, HCOOH, with concentrated sulfuric acid.

$$HCOOH + H_2SO_4 \rightarrow CO \uparrow + OH_3^+ + HSO_4^-$$

c. *Carbon suboxide.* Heat malonic acid, $H_2C(COOH)_2$, with phosphorus(V) oxide (*in vacuo*) at 140°–150°C. The product is a mixture of carbon suboxide and carbon dioxide, but the carbon suboxide can be liquefied at 6°C under 1 atm.

$$H_2C(COOH)_2 + 2P_2O_5 \xrightarrow{\Delta} C_3O_2 \uparrow + 4HPO_3$$

Also, $$H_2C(COOH)_2 \xrightarrow{\Delta} CO_2 \uparrow + CH_3COOH$$

The most common uses of carbon dioxide are (1) in extinguishing fires by smothering the flames; (2) in cooking (bubbles of carbon dioxide form in doughs and batters and cause the baked goods to "rise"); (3) in its solid state (dry ice) as a refrigerant; and (4) in the manufacture of sodium carbonate (washing soda), sodium hydrogen carbonate (baking soda), and "carbonated" beverages. Carbon monoxide is commercially used as a fuel and as a reducing agent.

Carbon disulfide (bisulfide), CS_2, is prepared by heating sulfur and carbon in an electric furnace. It is very volatile (boiling point, 47°C) and flammable, and it has an unusually low kindling temperature (well below 100°C).

Carbon tetrachloride, CCl_4 (boiling point, 77°C), is usually prepared by heating a mixture of carbon disulfide and chlorine to 40°–60°C (0.5 to 3 atm).

$$CS_2 + 3Cl_2 \rightarrow CCl_4 + S_2Cl_2$$

The two liquid products are separated by fractional distillation and the disulfur dichloride is then added to fresh carbon disulfide.

$$CS_2 + 2S_2Cl_2 \rightarrow CCl_4 + 6S$$

Carbon tetrachloride is nonflammable. It is an excellent solvent for fats, oils, and many nonpolar substances. Since it is rather toxic, prolonged inhalation of its vapor should be avoided.

Carbon tetrabromide, CBr_4 (boiling point, 189°C), is obtained by prolonged treatment of bromoform, $HCBr_3$, with sodium hypobromite, Na^+OBr^-, solution.

Carbon tetraiodide, CI_4, a red solid, is made by treating carbon tetrachloride with aluminum iodide. It is easily oxidized by oxygen, even in a benzene solution.

$$CI_4 + O_2 \rightarrow CO_2 + 2I_2$$

Tetrachloroethene, $Cl_2C{=}CCl_2$ (boiling point, 121°C), is nonflammable, is stable, and is a good solvent for dry cleaning and for degreasing of metals and fibers. It is less toxic than carbon tetrachloride.

There are several binary chlorides of carbon that are more complex than tetrachloroethene. Some are hexachloroethane, C_2Cl_6; octachloropropane, C_3Cl_8; octachlorobutene, C_4Cl_8; and hexachlorobenzene, C_6Cl_6.

The most prominent binary compounds of carbon, the hydrocarbons, will be described in the next sections.

27.4 THE SATURATED HYDROCARBONS (ALKANES)

The saturated hydrocarbons contain only carbon and hydrogen atoms held together by single covalent bonds. These hydrocarbons are often called *paraffin* (Latin, *little affinity*) *hydrocarbons* because under many conditions they are much less reactive than the unsaturated hydrocarbons. The names of all of the saturated hydrocarbons have the common suffix, *-ane;* collectively they are called the *alkanes.* These alkanes constitute a typical homologous series of compounds in which the members differ in composition by the increment CH_2. The general formula for the series is: C_nH_{2n+2}, where n is an integral number.

The normal alkanes are those hydrocarbons in which the molecular skeleton is a continuous chain of carbon atoms. Listed in Table 27.1 are the formulas and approximate normal boiling points and melting points of some normal alkanes.

TABLE 27.1   Some normal saturated (paraffin) hydrocarbons

Name	Formula	Boiling Point, °C	Melting Point, °C
Methane	CH_4	-162	-183
Ethane	C_2H_6	-89	-172
Propane	C_3H_8	-42	-187
Butane	C_4H_{10}	-0.5	-135
Pentane	C_5H_{12}	36	-130
Hexane	C_6H_{14}	69	-94
Heptane	C_7H_{16}	98	-90
Octane	C_8H_{18}	126	-57
Nonane	C_9H_{20}	151	-54
Decane	$C_{10}H_{22}$	174	-30
Undecane	$C_{11}H_{24}$	196	-25
Eicosane	$C_{20}H_{42}$	over 330	36
Triacontane	$C_{30}H_{62}$	over 330	66
Tetracontane	$C_{40}H_{82}$	over 330	81
Hexacontane	$C_{60}H_{122}$	over 330	99

The methane molecule, CH_4, is the simplest manifestation of the tetrahedral carbon atom. The carbon kernel resides in the center of an imaginary regular tetrahedron, with each of the four hydrogen kernels residing at a corner of the tetrahedron. The hydrogen kernels are equidistant from the carbon kernel and from each other. (See p. 196.) It is impossible by using a conventional two-dimensional electronic formulation to depict the methane molecule adequately, but the conventional graphic formula is

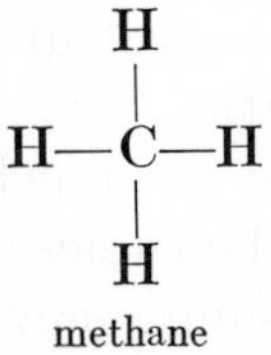

$$
\begin{array}{c}
\text{H} \\
| \\
\text{H}-\text{C}-\text{H} \\
| \\
\text{H}
\end{array}
$$

methane

The next homolog in the alkane series is ethane, which has a skeleton of two carbon atoms. Its graphic formula is

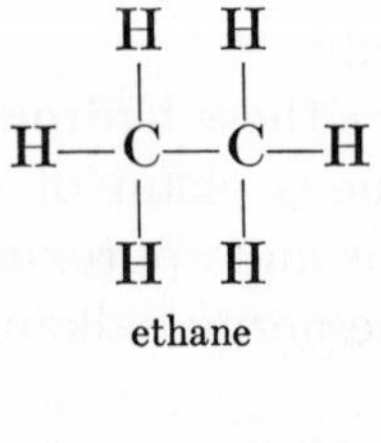

$$
\begin{array}{c}
\text{H} \quad \text{H} \\
| \quad | \\
\text{H}-\text{C}-\text{C}-\text{H} \\
| \quad | \\
\text{H} \quad \text{H}
\end{array}
$$

ethane

In the ethane molecule the two tetrahedrons share a common corner (see p. 197), and, as in the case of diamond, the C—C bond distance is 1.54 A.

The propane molecule, C_3H_8, has the structure

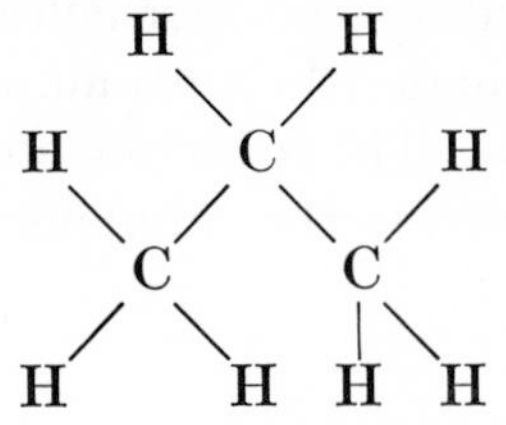

propane

The molecule is bent to indicate that the C—C bond angle is approximately 109.5° (the tetrahedral angle). For convenience it is customary to write the formulas of the large normal alkanes by placing the carbon atoms in a straight chain, although the bent or zig-zag formulation is more correctly descriptive.

27.5 STRUCTURAL ISOMERISM

Butane, C_4H_{10}, has a skeleton consisting of four carbon atoms, which may be arranged in two ways.

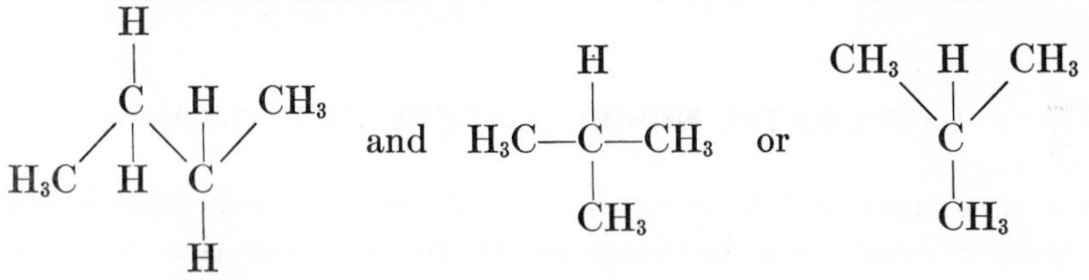

n-butane
(a continuous chain)

isobutane
(a branched chain)

Although n-butane (normal butane) and isobutane have identical compositions, they are structurally different and therefore have different physical and chemical properties. These two compounds are structural isomers in that they exhibit the phenomenon of *isomerism:* two or more compounds having identical compositions but different properties. It is evident that the compositional formula C_4H_{10} is inadequate to represent an alkane that has four carbon atoms because this formula is shared by two different molecules. A graphic structural formula must be used to differentiate the two. The correlation of structure and chemical and physical properties is eminently documented in organic chemistry.

The carbon atoms of the various alkanes are the building units of their molecular skeletons. We know that the more building units we have, the wider the variety of structures we can build. It should be expected, therefore, that the number of isomeric alkanes increases with the carbon content of the molecules. Table 27.2 lists the numbers of possible isomeric (skeletal) alkanes having the specified compositional formulas. The phenomenon of isomerism is obviously the main reason for the fabulous multiplicity of organic compounds.

TABLE 27.2 Number of possible isomeric (skeletal) alkanes

Compositional Formula	Number of Possible Isomers
C_5H_{12}	3
C_6H_{14}	5
C_7H_{16}	9
$C_{10}H_{22}$	75
$C_{12}H_{26}$	355
$C_{14}H_{30}$	1,858
$C_{20}H_{42}$	366,319
$C_{30}H_{62}$	4,111,846,763
$C_{40}H_{82}$	62,491,178,805,831

27.6 A SYSTEMATIC NOMENCLATURE FOR ALKANES

It is a difficult task to assign a name to each known organic compound; in some cases the names are far from systematic. Considering the 75 alkanes that have the same formula, $C_{10}H_{22}$, the chore of naming each of these would be formidable unless some logical system were used. An international systematic nomenclature, such as that adopted by the International Union of Chemistry (IUC system), is quite necessary. The essential aspects of this nomenclature as applied to alkanes are given below.

a. The stem of the name of an alkane is derived from its longest continuous carbon chain.

b. The carbon atoms in the longest continuous chain are consecutively numbered so that the positions of any attached groups are specified by using the smallest numbers possible.

c. The groups attached to the carbon chains of the alkanes are called *alkyl groups;* they are derived from the simpler alkanes. The methyl group, CH_3, is derived from methane; the ethyl group, CH_3CH_2, from ethane; the n-propyl group, $CH_3CH_2CH_2$, is related

$$CH_3—\overset{\displaystyle H}{\underset{\displaystyle |}{C}}—CH_3$$

to propane; and the isopropyl group, $CH_3—\overset{H}{\underset{}{C}}—CH_3$, is also related to propane. An alkyl group is often symbolized by using R.

To see how the systematic nomenclature is applied, let us examine the structural formulas and accepted names of a few typical alkanes.

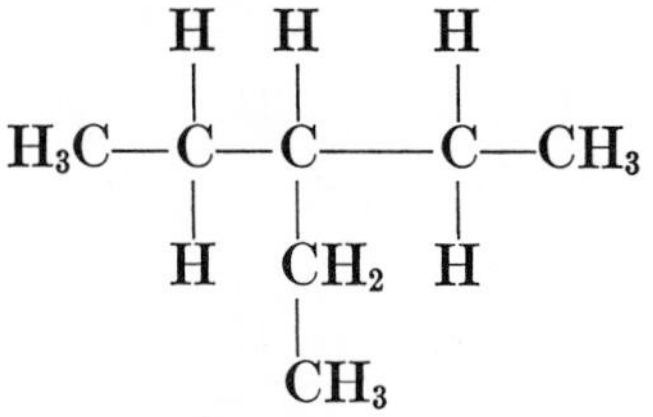

3-ethylpentane

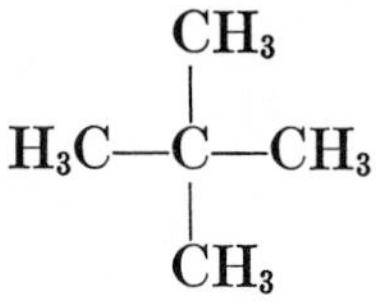

2,2-dimethylpropane

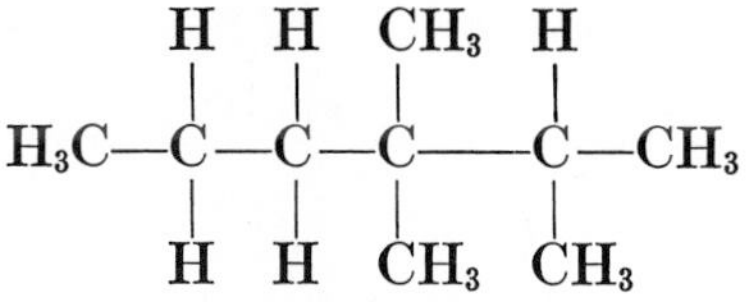

2,3,3-trimethylhexane

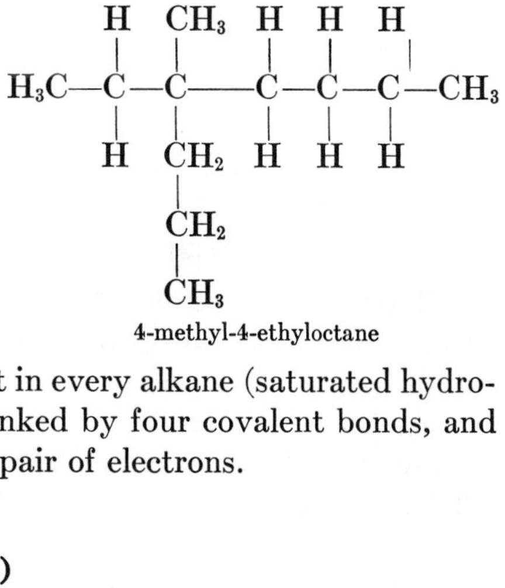

4-methyl-4-ethyloctane

You should keep in mind that in every alkane (saturated hydrocarbon) each carbon kernel is flanked by four covalent bonds, and each hydrogen kernel shares one pair of electrons.

27.7 THE ALKENES (OLEFINS)

Ethene (ethylene), C_2H_4, is the simplest stable member of the homologous series of *alkenes* or *olefins* (general formula: C_nH_{2n}). Since ethene has two hydrogen atoms less than ethane, it is called an *unsaturated hydrocarbon*. The structural formula of ethene is given below. (Review p. 197.)

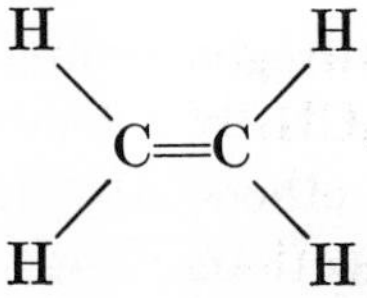

The double bond is characteristic of all olefins. The C=C bond length in ethene is 1.34 A. The two tetrahedral carbon atoms share a common edge. The names of all alkenes have the common suffix -*ene*.

To name an alkene, number the longest continuous carbon chain that *includes the double bond* so that *its location* is identified by the smallest number possible.

There is one propene (propylene), C_3H_6, but there are three structurally different (isomeric) compounds having the formula C_4H_8.

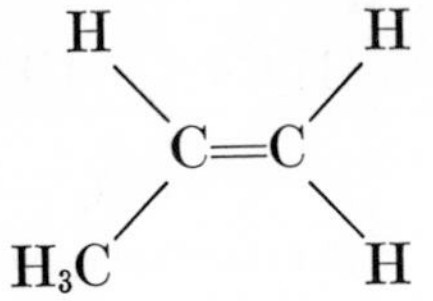

propene

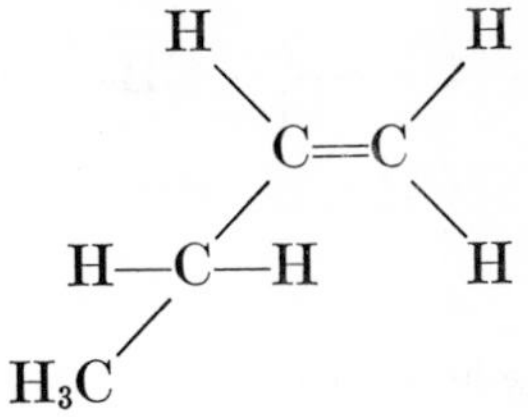

1-butene

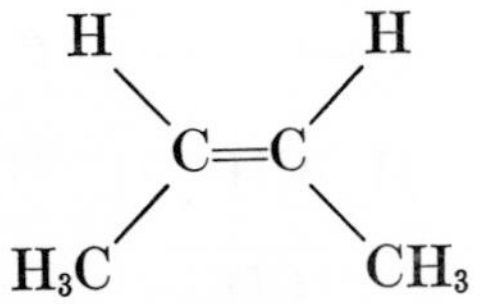

2-butene

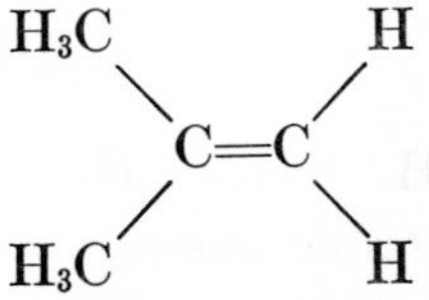

2-methylpropene

Two of the electrons at the double bond in an alkene molecule can be and often are rather unlocalized. They take part fairly readily in the formation of covalent bonds by interaction with entities that "add" at the double bond of an alkene. Bromine in the presence of a trace of moisture readily "adds" to ethene to yield 1,2-dibromoethane.

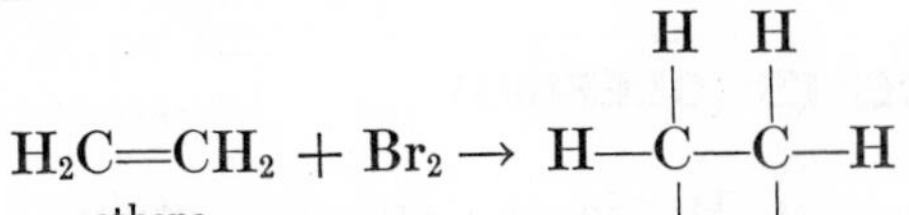

$H_2C=CH_2 + Br_2 \rightarrow$

ethene
(ethylene)

1,2-dibromoethane
(ethylene dibromide)

This is an oxidation-reduction reaction; the ethene is oxidized by bromine.

Ethene reacts with hydrogen bromide to yield a bromoalkane, called bromoethane, CH_3CH_2Br. Under correct conditions hydrogen chloride adds to ethene to yield chloroethane, whereas hydrogen iodide yields iodoethane.

$$\underset{\substack{H \\ |}}{H}C=\underset{\substack{H \\ |}}{C}\underset{\substack{H}}{H} + HBr \rightarrow H-\overset{\substack{H \\ |}}{\underset{\substack{| \\ H}}{C}}-\overset{\substack{H \\ |}}{\underset{\substack{| \\ H}}{C}}-Br$$

bromoethane (ethyl bromide)

Ethene readily "adds" sulfuric acid to yield ethyl hydrogen sulfate, an ester. This ester hydrolyzes in water to yield ethanol, an alcohol.

$$\underset{\text{ethene}}{\overset{\substack{H \\ \diagdown}}{\underset{\substack{/ \\ H}}{C}}=\overset{\substack{H \\ /}}{\underset{\substack{\diagdown \\ H}}{C}} + (HO)_2SO_2 \rightarrow H-\overset{\substack{H \\ |}}{\underset{\substack{| \\ H}}{C}}-\overset{\substack{H \\ |}}{\underset{\substack{| \\ O}}{C}}-H$$

$$\underset{\text{ethyl hydrogen sulfate}}{\diagdown SO_3H}$$

$$\underset{\text{ethanol}}{H_3C-\overset{\substack{H \\ |}}{\underset{\substack{| \\ H}}{C}}-OH} + OH_3^+ + HOSO_3^- \xleftarrow{\text{HOH}}$$

Most simple alkenes are readily oxidized by permanganate ion in acidic and basic solutions. An olefinic double bond can usually be reduced by catalytic hydrogenation.

$$\underset{\text{ethene}}{\overset{\substack{H \\ \diagdown}}{\underset{\substack{/ \\ H}}{C}}=\overset{\substack{H \\ /}}{\underset{\substack{\diagdown \\ H}}{C}} + H_2 \xrightarrow[\text{as catalyst}]{\text{Pt or Ni}} \underset{\text{ethane}}{H-\overset{\substack{H \\ |}}{\underset{\substack{| \\ H}}{C}}-\overset{\substack{H \\ |}}{\underset{\substack{| \\ H}}{C}}-H}$$

Alkenes that contain two double bonds per molecule are called *dienes*. An important diene is 1,3-butadiene, $H_2C=\overset{\substack{H \\ |}}{C}-\overset{\substack{H \\ |}}{C}=CH_2$, a substance commonly used in the manufacture of synthetic rubbers (elastomers). Isoprene, $H_2C=\overset{\substack{CH_3 \\ |}}{C}-\overset{\substack{H \\ /}}{C}=CH_2$ (2-methylbutadiene), plays an important role in the formation of natural rubber (a polymer). Isoprene fragments or isoprene skeletons are integral parts of many terpenes and their derivatives, which are found in many plants.

27.8 GEOMETRIC ISOMERISM

Essentially there are two major types of isomerism: structural (skeletal) isomerism and stereoisomerism, also called configurational isomerism (see p. 587). Some alkenes exhibit a type of stereoisomerism called *geometric isomerism:* the existence of spatially different unsaturated molecules. 2-Butene exists in two configurationally different forms: *cis* 2-butene and *trans* 2-butene. These two compounds differ with respect to the spatial arrangements of the methyl groups relative to the double bond. It is possible to differentiate these two geometric isomers by two-dimensional formulas. The *cis* form is the arrangement in which the two methyl groups, CH_3, are on the same side of the double bond; in the *trans* form the methyl groups are on opposite sides of the double bond.

$$
\begin{array}{cc}
H \qquad CH_3 & H \qquad CH_3 \\
\diagdown \quad \diagup & \diagdown \quad \diagup \\
C & C \\
\| & \| \\
C & C \\
\diagup \quad \diagdown & \diagup \quad \diagdown \\
H \qquad CH_3 & H_3C \qquad H \\
\textit{cis} \text{ 2-butene} & \textit{trans} \text{ 2-butene}
\end{array}
$$

Because the double bond greatly hinders rotation about itself, it is possible to isolate the two geometric isomers. Rotation about the central C—C bond (a single covalent bond) in butane is sufficiently free at ordinary temperature so that the two forms

$$
\begin{array}{ccc}
\quad H & & \quad H \\
\quad | & & \quad | \\
H{-}C{-}CH_3 & & H{-}C{-}CH_3 \\
\quad | & \text{and} & \quad | \\
H{-}C{-}CH_2 & & H_3C{-}C{-}H \\
\quad | & & \quad | \\
\quad H & & \quad H
\end{array}
$$

cannot be isolated because they are so readily interconvertible. 1-Butene does not exhibit geometric isomerism because one of the carbon kernels at the double bond has two identical entities (two hydrogen kernels) attached to it.

The two stereoisomeric forms of 1,2-dibromoethene are shown in Fig. 27.2.   1,1-Dibromoethene does not exhibit stereoisomerism.

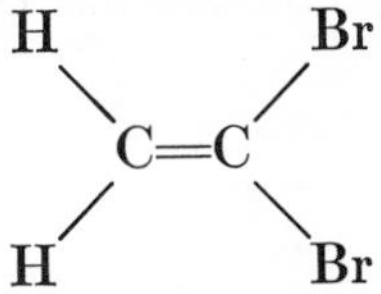

$$\begin{array}{ccc} H & & Br \\ & \diagdown C=C \diagup & \\ H & & Br \end{array}$$ (no *cis* and *trans* forms)

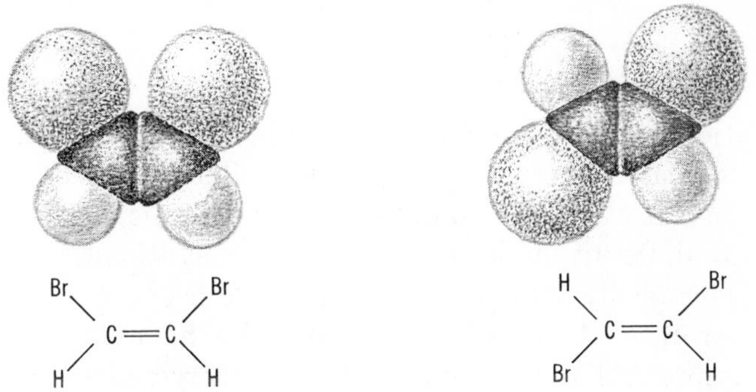

cis 1,2-dibromoethene	*trans* 1,2-dibromoethene

FIGURE 27.2 Forms of geometric isomerism. The two compounds differ in the spatial arrangement of their atomic kernels, although they have identical skeletons. In a pair of geometric isomers, the *trans* isomer is usually the more stable.

27.9 OPTICAL ISOMERISM

It seems logical to expect that the number of possible isomers of an alkene consisting of six carbon atoms would be larger than for an alkene having only five carbons.   Let us now consider two alkenes that have the compositional formula C_6H_{12}.

Inspection of the structural (graphic) formula of 3-methyl-2-pentene yields the conclusion that there are two stereoisomeric forms of this molecule, one *cis*, the other *trans*.

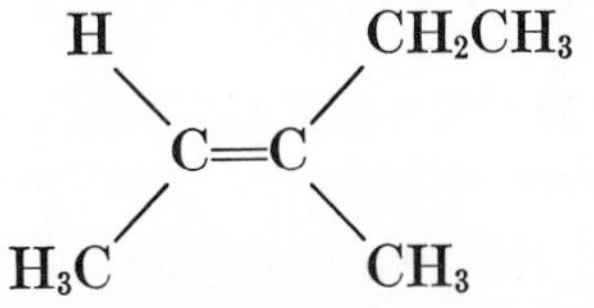

cis 3-methyl-2-pentene 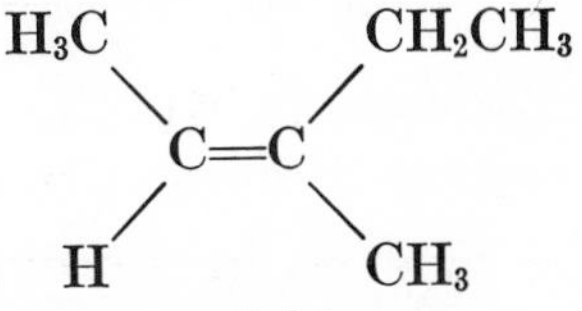   *trans* 3-methyl-2-pentene

However, an isomer of 3-methyl-2-pentene that has the double bond at carbon 1, called 3-methyl-1-pentene, does not exhibit geometric isomerism, because one carbon at the double bond has two identical entities.

$$H\diagdown C=C\diagup H \quad H \quad H$$

(no *cis* and *trans* forms)

3-methyl-1-pentene

Investigation of the compound 3-methyl-1-pentene reveals that it exhibits optical isomerism (see p. 587). The molecule is asymmetric; hence it exists in two optically active forms, *dextro* and *levo*. These two different molecules are called enantiomers; they are identical chemically and physically in all respects, except in their ability to rotate plane polarized light. Each enantiomer is the nonsuperimposable mirror image of the other, one being dextrorotatory, the other levorotatory.

Since optical activity is a property of all asymmetric molecules, we can predict optical isomerism if we can identify molecular asymmetry. One kind of molecular asymmetry that is easy to identify is that shown by 3-methyl-1-pentene, in which one of the carbon kernels that has a covalence of 4 has 4 different atomic kernels or groups of kernels attached to it. Such a carbon is at an asymmetric center (a center of asymmetry); hence it is called an *asymmetric carbon*. If an asymmetric carbon does not endow a specific molecule with either a center or a plane of symmetry, the molecule is optically active.

So that we can visualize the molecular asymmetry of the molecule in question, let us rewrite the graphic formula in a slightly different manner. The asymmetric center is at carbon 3, here identified by the asterisk.

$$H\diagdown C=C-C^*-C-CH_3$$

3-methyl-1-pentene

In order to show, in two dimensions, the two enantiomers of this compound, we must try to indicate that the enantiomers differ from each other in that each is the nonsuperimposable mirror image of the other. We must also try to show that the asymmetric carbon is at the imaginary center of a regular tetrahedron. Therefore we shall assume that the central carbon kernel is in the plane of the paper and that two of the attached groups are in a plane in front of the paper and bonded by solid lines to the central carbon, the other two in another plane in back of the paper and bonded to the central carbon by dotted lines.

$$\underset{\text{mirror}}{\text{H}_2\text{C}=\overset{\overset{\text{H}}{|}}{\text{C}}-\overset{\overset{\text{H}}{|}}{\underset{\underset{\text{CH}_3}{|}}{\text{C}}}-\text{CH}_2\text{CH}_3 \qquad \text{H}_3\text{CCH}_2-\overset{\overset{\text{H}}{|}}{\text{C}}-\overset{\overset{\text{H}}{|}}{\underset{\underset{\text{CH}_3}{|}}{\text{C}}}=\text{CH}_2}$$

These are the two optically active stereoisomers (enantiomers) of the compound 3-methyl-1-pentene. One is the *dextro* form, the other the *levo* form; both are plane projection diagrams.

If we review this brief discussion of 3-methyl-2-pentene and 3-methyl-1-pentene, the concept of stereoisomerism should merit our attention as we encounter more complicated organic compounds. For instance, if we should perform the relatively simple exercise of writing the formulas of all the alkenes that have the composition identified by the symbol C_6H_{12}, we consider all of the possible arrangements of the carbon skeleton and all of the different locations of the double bond in each specific skeletal arrangement. After all such isomers are identified, we must then inspect each to see whether it can exhibit stereoisomerism.

Let us recall an important aspect of optical isomerism, namely that it is a molecular phenomenon. That is, optical activity is a molecular property exhibited by asymmetric molecules. Therefore we should not be surprised to find hundreds of examples of optical isomerism even among the simple classes of compounds.

The simplest alkane that exhibits optical isomerism is 3-methylhexane. In this molecule, carbon 3 is the asymmetric center. The *dextro* and *levo* forms of 3-methylhexane are, according to the rules of nomenclature, enantiomeric stereoisomers because they are nonsuperimposable mirror images of each other.

The concept of optical isomerism becomes slightly more involved as we consider the compound 3,4-dimethylhexane.

$$H_3C-\overset{\overset{\displaystyle H}{|}}{\underset{\underset{\displaystyle H}{|}}{C}}-\overset{\overset{\displaystyle H}{|}}{\underset{\underset{\displaystyle CH_3}{|}}{C}}-\overset{\overset{\displaystyle H}{|}}{\underset{\underset{\displaystyle CH_3}{|}}{C}}-\overset{\overset{\displaystyle H}{|}}{\underset{\underset{\displaystyle H}{|}}{C}}-CH_3$$

A quick inspection of this formulation suggests that the molecule is symmetric; a plane of symmetry can be placed vertically in the middle of the molecule (between carbons 3 and 4). However, closer inspection reveals that carbons 3 and 4 are asymmetric, which leads us to suspect that a different spatial arrangement of the groups might yield molecular asymmetry. This is, indeed, the case. 3,4-Dimethylhexane exists in three stereoisomeric forms, a *dextro*, a *levo*, and a *meso*. The latter is optically inactive because it is a symmetric molecule. The *meso* form is, in fact, a nonenantiomeric stereoisomer of the *dextro* and of the *levo*. That is, the *dextro* and *levo* forms are enantiomeric, and the *meso* and *dextro* forms are nonenantiomeric. Since the *meso* form is not enantiomeric with the *dextro* and *levo* forms, it is different both chemically and physically from the *dextro* and *levo* forms. It is well to recall that enantiomeric molecules are chemically identical and differ physically only in regard to their effect on plane polarized light. In contrast, nonenantiomeric molecules are different both chemically and physically. The *meso* form is optically inactive, just as is every symmetric molecule. The optical inactivity of the *meso* form should not be unexpected.

levo	mirror	*dextro*	identical *meso* forms

An equimolar mixture of *dextro* and *levo* forms of a molecule such as 3,4-dimethylhexane is optically inactive and is called a *racemic mixture*. Since a racemic mixture consists of two different compounds, it can be resolved to yield each component. The resolution of a racemic mixture involves the conversion, by chemical means, of the enantiomers into two different compounds that are nonenantiomeric. The resultant nonenantiomeric compounds can be separated by physical means because they are different in many respects, both physical and chemical.

An optically inactive *meso* compound can be differentiated from a racemic mixture because the *meso* compound cannot be resolved into two different compounds, whereas a racemic mixture can be resolved.

Let us now for a moment consider an ordinary synthesis *in vitro* (in glass vessels) of a compound such as 3-methylhexane, say by the hydrogenation of 3-methyl-2-hexene. The alkene is optically inactive, whereas the alkane is optically active. The synthesis occurs in what seems to be a symmetric environment, and the product obtained is the racemic modification of the 3-methylhexane. That is, during the synthesis of the asymmetric compound both the *dextro* and *levo* forms are produced in equal amounts; hence the appearance of the racemic mixture. All evidence indicates that the synthesis of any asymmetric compound in an ordinary environment using ordinary organic solvents nearly always leads to the production of a racemic mixture. Also if a racemic mixture of an ordinary kind is used in an ordinary synthesis in a symmetric environment, both the *dextro* and *levo* forms react identically.

If an asymmetric compound is synthesized in an asymmetric environment, say in the presence of protein or in a protein molecule in a living organism, it is common to find that either the *dextro* or the *levo* form is produced almost exclusively. It seems, therefore, that a *dextro* or *levo* form can be recognized as such by participating molecules if the environment is asymmetric, whereas the *dextro* seems to appear identical to the *levo* form, molecularly speaking, in a symmetric environment. Syntheses in the presence of enzymes (catalyses) almost always yield either *dextro* or *levo*, but very rarely a racemic mixture. The enzymes are asymmetric because they are closely related to proteins (p. 434). *Dextro* forms and *levo* forms have quite different chemical properties in asymmetric environments.

27.10 THE ALKYNES

Acetylene (ethyne), C_2H_2, is the simplest homolog of the series of alkynes (general formula, C_nH_{2n-2}) (see p. 200). It is more unsaturated than ethene because each ethyne molecule has two hydrogen atoms less than an ethene molecule. The conventional structural formula of acetylene, or ethyne, is H—C≡C—H; the triple bond is characteristic of all alkynes. In acetylene the carbon tetrahedrons share a common face, and the C≡C bond length is 1.20 A. A hydrogen kernel attached to a carbon kernel that flanks a triple bond can, under appropriate conditions, easily leave as a positive ion; hence acetylene is a weak diprotic Brönsted acid (see p. 215). It is gaseous at ordinary temperatures.

There is one propyne, but there are two isomeric butynes. 1-Butyne can act as a Brönsted acid, but 2-butyne cannot.

$$H_3C—C≡C—H \qquad H_3C—\overset{\displaystyle H}{\underset{\displaystyle H}{\overset{|}{\underset{|}{C}}}}—C≡C—H \qquad H_3C—C≡C—CH_3$$

propyne   2-butyne
(methylacetylene)   (dimethylacetylene)

1-butyne
(ethylacetylene)

Acetylene readily "adds" many reagents, just as does ethene. For example, acetylene is readily hydrated in hot dilute sulfuric acid to which has been added mercury(II) oxide.

$$H—C≡C—H + HOH \xrightarrow[\text{Hg}^{++}]{42\% \text{ H}_2\text{SO}_4}$$

acetylene
(ethyne)

$$\left[H—\overset{\displaystyle H}{\overset{|}{C}}=\overset{\displaystyle H}{\overset{|}{C}}—OH \right] \xrightarrow{\text{(rearranges)}} H_3C—\overset{\displaystyle H}{\overset{|}{C}}=O$$

vinyl alcohol   acetaldehyde
(ethanal)

27.11 THE CYCLOALKANES

The cycloalkanes constitute a group of cyclic (ring-structure) hydrocarbons that are isomeric with certain mono-olefins but do not contain double bonds (general formula, C_nH_{2n}). The simplest stable cycloalkanes, cyclopropane (used in anesthesia) and cyclobutane, are molecules in which there is appreciable strain because the C—C bond angles are much less than the 109.5° of the open-chain alkanes. However, there is practically no strain in the cyclopentane and cyclohexane rings.

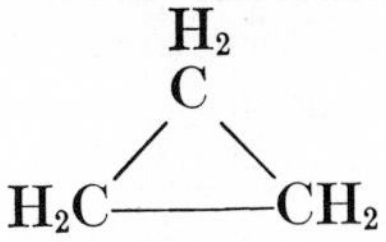

$$
\begin{array}{c}
H_2 \\
C \\
\diagup \quad \diagdown \\
H_2C \text{——} CH_2 \\
\text{cyclopropane}
\end{array}
\qquad
\begin{array}{c}
H_2C\text{—}CH_2 \\
\mid \qquad \mid \\
H_2C\text{—}CH_2 \\
\text{cyclobutane}
\end{array}
$$

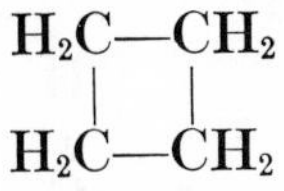

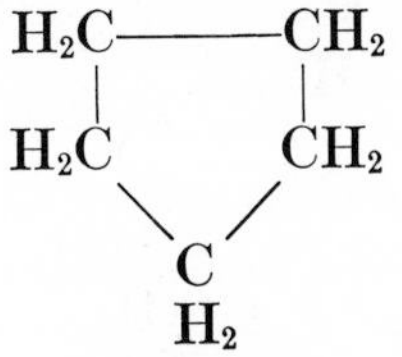

cyclopentane

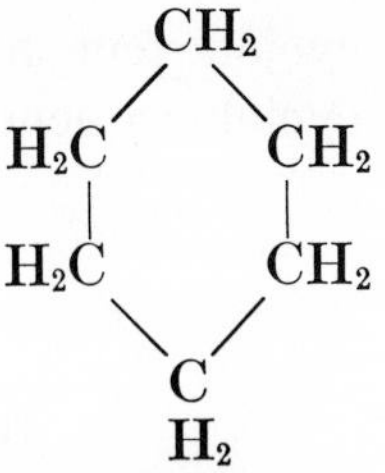

cyclohexane

The carbon kernels in the cyclohexane ring are not coplanar. In fact, there are two different conformations of the cyclohexane molecule. One is called the *boat form*, the other the *chair form*.

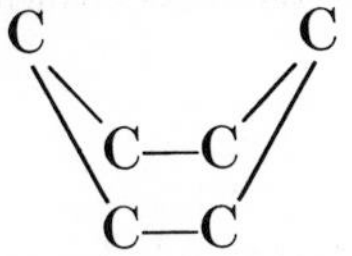

boat form

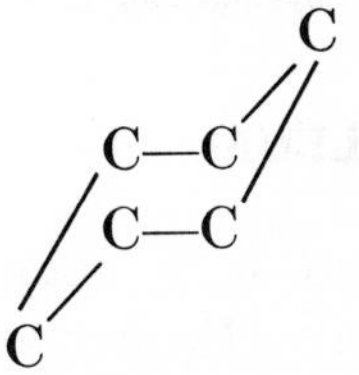

chair form

The cycloalkane rings can be alkylated to lead to a wider variety of compounds. For example, methylcyclopropane is isomeric with cyclobutane, while 1,1-dimethylcyclopropane, 1,2-dimethylcyclopropane, and ethylcyclopropane are all isomeric with cyclopentane.

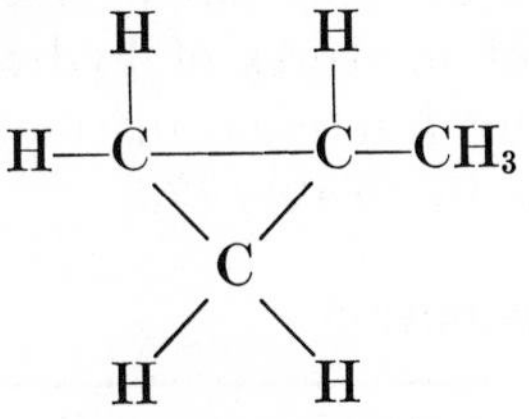

methylcyclopropane

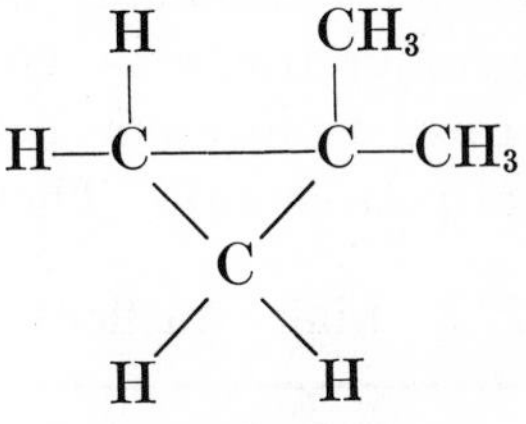

1,1-dimethylcyclopropane

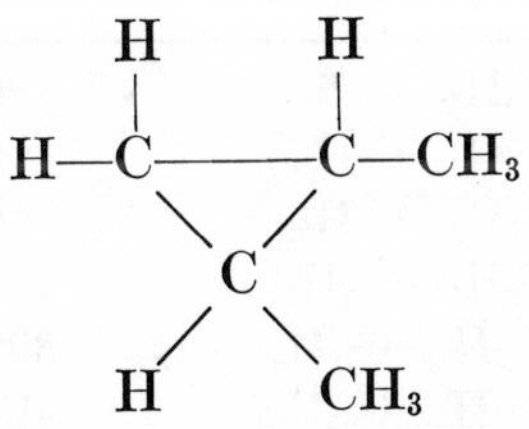

1,2-dimethylcyclopropane

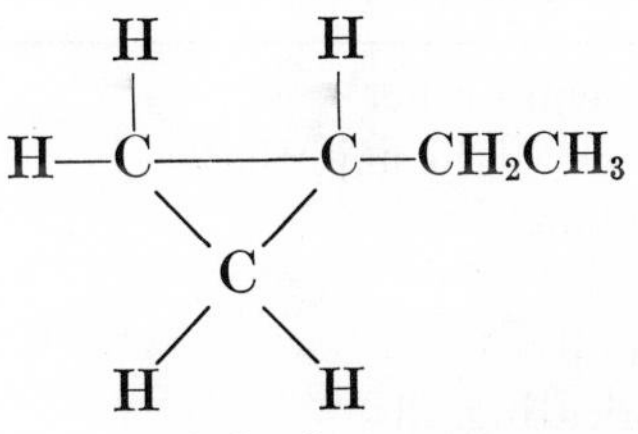

ethylcyclopropane

The cyclic monoenes are called *cycloalkenes*. They are isomeric with the alkadienes and the alkynes. Two examples are cyclohexene and cyclopentene. A typical cycloalkadiene is 1,3-cyclohexadiene.

cyclohexene   1,3-cyclohexadiene

27.12 PETROLEUM

Most petroleum is a complex mixture of hydrocarbons. The paraffin-base oils (Pennsylvania) contain mainly saturated open-chain hydrocarbons, whereas asphalt-base oils contain appreciable amounts of naphthenes (cyclopentane and cyclohexane and their alkyl derivatives). The Borneo crude oils contain considerable amounts of aromatic hydrocarbons (such as benzene and toluene).

Methane is the major constituent of natural gas, together with ethane, propane, butane, and isobutane. Carbon dioxide and nitrogen (and occasionally helium) are also present in natural gas.

The major fractions, consisting of mixtures of hydrocarbons, are separated from crude petroleum by fractional distillation (the refining of petroleum). They are noted in Table 27.3.

TABLE 27.3   Major fractions in crude petroleum

Fraction	Composition (Approximate)	Boiling Point Range, °C
Petroleum ether	C_5H_{12}–C_6H_{14}	20–60
Ligroin (light naphtha)	C_6H_{14}–C_7H_{16}	60–100
Gasoline	C_5H_{12}–C_9H_{20}	40–205
Kerosene	C_9H_{20}–$C_{16}H_{34}$	180–320
Fuel oil	$C_{15}H_{32}$–$C_{20}H_{42}$	300–375
Lubricating oils	$C_{20}H_{42}$–$C_{25}H_{52}$	above 300
Vaseline	above $C_{25}H_{52}$	above 300
Paraffin (wax)	above $C_{25}H_{52}$	above 300
Tar	above $C_{25}H_{52}$	above 300
Petroleum coke	above $C_{25}H_{52}$	above 300

Since the hydrocarbons in the gasoline fraction constitute not over 20–25 per cent of the hydrocarbons in most crude oils, it is necessary to produce more hydrocarbons in the gasoline range either by building them (by polymerization and/or alkylation) from smaller molecules or by thermal decomposition (cracking) of larger hydrocarbons. An example of the alkylation process is

$$\underset{\text{2-methylpropane}}{\text{H}_3\text{C}-\overset{\displaystyle\text{CH}_3}{\underset{\displaystyle\text{CH}_3}{\text{C}}}-\text{H}} + \underset{\text{2-methylpropene}}{\overset{\displaystyle\text{CH}_3}{\underset{\displaystyle\text{CH}_3}{\text{C}}}=\text{CH}_2} \rightarrow \underset{\substack{\text{2,2,4-trimethylpentane} \\ \text{(iso-octane)}}}{\text{H}_3\text{C}-\overset{\displaystyle\text{CH}_3}{\underset{\displaystyle\text{CH}_3}{\text{C}}}-\overset{\displaystyle\text{H}}{\underset{\displaystyle\text{H}}{\text{C}}}-\overset{\displaystyle\text{CH}_3}{\underset{\displaystyle\text{H}}{\text{C}}}-\text{CH}_3}$$

The 2-methylpropene may be obtained by cracking large paraffin hydrocarbons. There are two kinds of cracking processes, thermal and catalytic. During cracking, the larger, less volatile saturated hydrocarbons are decomposed to yield smaller paraffins and olefins. A large saturated hydrocarbon usually cracks to yield a molecule of a paraffin and a molecule of an olefin.

The hydrogenation of coal (Bergius process) and the formation of mixtures of hydrocarbons from water gas (Fischer-Tropsch process) are the most promising methods of substituting for petroleum refining when this becomes necessary because of shortage of petroleum supply. These processes were used as large-scale operations by Germany during World War II to produce gasoline from coal. The water gas needed for the Fischer-Tropsch process (200°C; 5 to 15 atm pressure; catalyst of nickel, iron, and cobalt with certain oxides as promoters) may be made from coke and steam or obtained by heating methane with a limited amount of oxygen at 1300°C.

$$\text{CH}_4 + \tfrac{1}{2}\text{O}_2 \rightarrow \text{CO} + 2\text{H}_2$$

Certain oil shales are sources of a petroleum-like liquid, which is obtained by heating the shales. Huge deposits of oil shales exist in some parts of the western United States.

During the development of fuels for internal combustion engines, it was noticed that branched-chain hydrocarbons and cyclic hydrocarbons (and to some extent the olefins) improved the antiknock character of gasoline. Iso-octane has high antiknock properties, whereas n-heptane knocks very badly. Pure iso-octane is given an octane rating (number) of 100; pure n-heptane is rated zero. The octane number of a gasoline is obtained by comparing its knock-

ing tendency with that of a known mixture of iso-octane and
n-heptane. A gasoline is assigned an octane rating (number) of
85 if it has the same knocking tendency as a mixture of 85 per
cent iso-octane and 15 per cent n-heptane. 2,2,3-Trimethylbutane
(triptane) has an octane rating of 125, which means its antiknock
properties are appreciably better than those of iso-octane. Knocking in a gasoline engine is due to explosively rapid combustion of
the fuel, probably because of certain chain reactions. Tetraethyl
lead, $Pb(C_2H_5)_4$, when added to gasoline (say, 2 ml per gallon to
produce ethyl gas), decreases the knocking tendency noticeably.

27.13 THE AROMATIC (BENZENOID) HYDROCARBONS

Benzene, C_6H_6, is the simplest *aromatic hydrocarbon* and it is the
prototype of a large group of cyclic hydrocarbons. The six carbon
kernels in benzene reside at the corners of a regular planar hexagon,
and there is a hydrogen kernel at each carbon. Since benzene has
six hydrogen atoms less than cyclohexane, C_6H_{12}, it would seem in
order to classify benzene as an unsaturated cyclic hydrocarbon.
Benzene, however, does not have the formal, somewhat localized
unsaturation of the cyclic monoenes and cyclic dienes. Since benzene is therefore not a cyclohexatriene, formulas I and II below are
invalid.

Actually, formula III is probably as descriptive and as valid as any.
Let us now discuss this point.

If we consider the conventional covalent bond approach to
molecular structure, we can, in trying to write a structure for the
benzene molecule, localize 12 pairs of electrons in ordinary covalent
bonding. This yields 12 sigma bonds (p. 199). Six of these bonds
are between the 6 carbon kernels, and 6 more hold the 6 hydrogen
kernels to the 6 carbon kernels. The actual number of valence

electrons in the constituent atoms of the benzene molecule is 30 (15 pairs).   The 6 carbon atoms bring 24 valence electrons, and the 6 hydrogen atoms bring 6.   Consequently, there are 6 electrons not used in sigma covalent bonding.   These electrons are pi (π) electrons (p. 200) that reside in two equivalent and uniform electron clouds that are in two planes, one above the plane of the hexagon that contains the atomic kernels, the other below.   This type of electronic structure with pi electrons which form pi bonds that augment sigma bonds is similar to that of ethene (p. 200).   (See Fig. 27.3.)

It is evident that by using conventional means it is impossible to write a valid electronic representation of the benzene molecule.

FIGURE 27.3   A crude depiction of the benzene molecule showing the regular planar hexagon composed by the atomic kernels.   The "loops" perpendicular to the plane at each carbon kernel represent the p orbitals.   Electrons in these orbitals overlap to yield a uniform pi electron cloud both above and below the plane of the carbon and hydrogen kernels.   Overlap of the p orbitals yields pi bonding that assists the sigma bonding in holding together the benzene molecule.   The bond angles at each carbon kernel are 120° because the sigma bonding is sp^2 (hybridized).

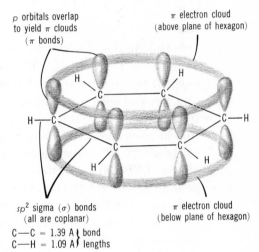

p orbitals overlap to yield π clouds (π bonds)

π electron cloud (above plane of hexagon)

π electron cloud (below plane of hexagon)

sp^2 sigma (σ) bonds (all are coplanar)

C—C = 1.39 A } bond
C—H = 1.09 A } lengths

A common method used currently is to write a simple regular hexagon with a circle inside (see formula III, p. 684).   The assumption is, of course, that a carbon kernel and a hydrogen kernel reside at each corner and the circle represents unlocalized electrons.   The circle also signifies incipient unsaturation.

You should keep in mind that the unsaturation in the benzene molecule cannot be localized because all C—C bonds appear to be equivalent.

Benzene and its homologs [such as toluene, $C_6H_5CH_3$; ethylbenzene, $C_6H_5CH_2CH_3$; the isomeric xylenes, $C_6H_4(CH_3)_2$] are called *aromatic* hydrocarbons because of their distinctive odors, in contrast with the pure saturated hydrocarbons, which are nearly odorless.

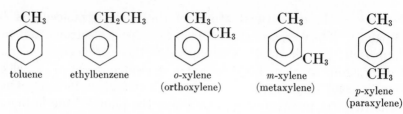

toluene   ethylbenzene   o-xylene (orthoxylene)   m-xylene (metaxylene)   p-xylene (paraxylene)

Among the other types of aromatic hydrocarbons containing one or more benzene ring systems are naphthalene, $C_{10}H_8$; anthracene, $C_{14}H_{10}$; phenanthrene, $C_{14}H_{10}$; diphenyl (biphenyl), $C_{12}H_{10}$; and pyrene, $C_{16}H_{10}$.

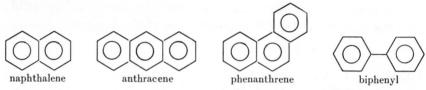

naphthalene   anthracene   phenanthrene   biphenyl

During the nineteenth century coal was the major source of the aromatic hydrocarbons. If bituminous coal is heated (absence of oxygen) to a temperature of 1000°–1300°C, coal gas, a black viscous coal tar, and coke are obtained. The coal gas contains benzene and toluene, and the coal tar (about 3 per cent of the coal) yields a mixture of more massive aromatic compounds having boiling points up to about 360°C. Since petroleum was relatively scarce during most of the nineteenth century, the pioneer organic chemical research predominantly involved syntheses of derivatives of aromatic hydrocarbons. During the twentieth century, a period in which petroleum has been plentiful, much research has been done on the nonaromatic (aliphatic) hydrocarbons and their derivatives.

The benzene ring (nucleus) is, in contrast with the alkenes, rather difficultly oxidized. Toluene and ethylbenzene are nearly quantitatively oxidized by alkaline potassium permanganate at 95°C to benzoic acid, C_6H_5COOH.

benzoic acid

27.14 HALOGEN DERIVATIVES OF THE HYDROCARBONS

The monohalogen derivatives of the saturated hydrocarbons (alkanes) are called the *alkyl halides*, whose general formula is *RX* (where R is any alkyl group, and X is any halogen). Among the methyl halides, CH_3X, methyl iodide (iodomethane), CH_3I, is the only liquid at room temperature and 1 atm. Ethyl bromide (bromoethane), CH_3CH_2Br, and ethyl iodide (iodoethane), CH_3CH_2I, are volatile liquids. There are two isomeric monochlorides that have a skeleton of three carbon atoms: n-propyl chloride (1-chloropropane), $CH_3CH_2CH_2Cl$; and isopropyl chloride (2-chloropropane),

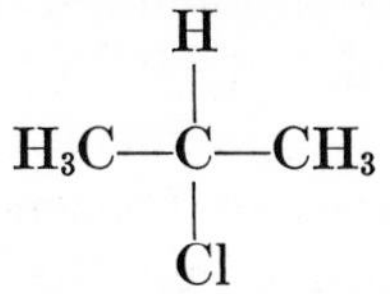

$$H_3C-\overset{\overset{\displaystyle H}{|}}{\underset{\underset{\displaystyle Cl}{|}}{C}}-CH_3$$

During most of the different reactions of the alkyl halides, the halogen is eliminated (usually displaced) as halide ion. The alkyl halides are fairly easily hydrolyzed (often best in basic aqueous solutions) to yield alcohols, the net result being the displacement of halide ion by hydroxide ion. Below are listed the four isomeric bromobutanes and their hydrolysis products.

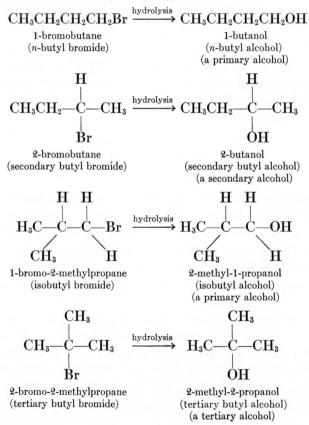

$$CH_3CH_2CH_2CH_2Br \xrightarrow{\text{hydrolysis}} CH_3CH_2CH_2CH_2OH$$

1-bromobutane
(n-butyl bromide)

1-butanol
(n-butyl alcohol)
(a primary alcohol)

2-bromobutane
(secondary butyl bromide)

2-butanol
(secondary butyl alcohol)
(a secondary alcohol)

1-bromo-2-methylpropane
(isobutyl bromide)

2-methyl-1-propanol
(isobutyl alcohol)
(a primary alcohol)

2-bromo-2-methylpropane
(tertiary butyl bromide)

2-methyl-2-propanol
(tertiary butyl alcohol)
(a tertiary alcohol)

Among the simplest halogen derivatives of the alkenes are vinyl chloride (chloroethene), $H_2C\!\!=\!\!\overset{\displaystyle H}{\overset{\displaystyle /}{C}}\!\!-\!\!Cl$; 1,1-dichloroethene, $H_2C\!\!=\!\!CCl_2$; and trichloroethylene, $Cl\!\!-\!\!\overset{\displaystyle H}{\overset{\displaystyle /}{C}}\!\!=\!\!CCl_2$. Among the hundreds of known saturated polyhalides, some of the simplest are chloroform, $HCCl_3$; bromoform, $HCBr_3$; iodoform, HCI_3; and dichlorodifluoromethane, Cl_2CF_2 (a Freon).

The halogen derivatives of benzene are called *aryl halides.* They are generally less reactive than the alkyl halides. Three aryl halides are bromobenzene (phenyl bromide), C_6H_5Br; *p*-dichlorobenzene, ClC_6H_4Cl (a moth repellent); and hexachlorobenzene, C_6Cl_6. A schematic drawing of a bromobenzene molecule and some other examples are shown in Fig. 27.4. The phenyl group is C_6H_5.

27.15 OXYGEN DERIVATIVES OF THE HYDROCARBONS

a. *Alcohols.* The simplest monohydroxyl (monohydric) alcohols (alkanols) are methanol (methyl alcohol or wood alcohol), CH_3OH; and ethanol (ethyl alcohol or grain alcohol), CH_3CH_2OH. The use of fermentation of starch and sugars to obtain ethanol is as old as antiquity.

$$\underset{\substack{\text{glucose} \\ \text{(a sugar)}}}{C_6H_{12}O_6} \xrightarrow[\substack{\text{(a complex} \\ \text{series of} \\ \text{enzymatic} \\ \text{reactions)}}]{\text{fermentation}} 2C_2H_5OH + 2CO_2$$

Methanol was formerly obtained as one of the products during the destructive distillation of wood; hence the name *wood alcohol.* The preparation of ethanol from ethene and of methanol from water gas $(CO + H_2)$ are now commercially important.

The alcohols are extensively used as solvents and in the syntheses of organic compounds, especially some of the simple oxy derivatives of the hydrocarbons.

Since there are thousands of alcohols (alkanols), a systematic nomenclature is essential. The rules are similar to those for the alkanes. Choose the longest continuous carbon chain that has in it the carbon holding the hydroxyl group. The stem of the name of the alcohol is then derived from the name of the alkane that has this number of carbon atoms. Use the smallest numbers possible to

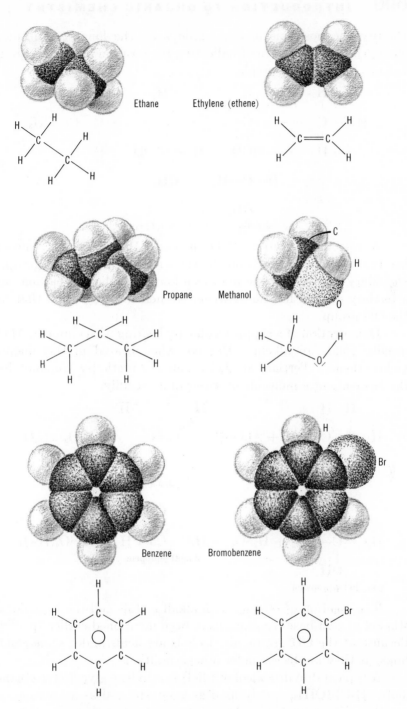

FIGURE 27.4 Some common organic compounds.

identify the positions of alkyl groups on the longest continuous chain, the smallest number indicating the position of the OH group. Let us consider an example.

$$H_3C-\underset{\underset{H}{|}}{\overset{\overset{H}{|}}{C}}-\underset{\underset{\underset{\underset{CH_3}{|}}{H-C-H}}{|}}{\overset{\overset{H}{|}}{\underset{HCH}{C}}}-\underset{\underset{\underset{CH_3}{|}}{H-C-OH}}{\overset{\overset{CH_3}{|}}{C}}-\underset{\underset{H}{|}}{\overset{\overset{H}{|}}{C}}-\underset{\underset{H}{|}}{\overset{\overset{H}{|}}{C}}-CH_3$$

3-methyl-3-*n*-propyl-4-ethyl-2-heptanol

A review of Section 27.14 indicates that a primary alcohol has two hydrogen kernels on the carbon that has the OH group, a secondary alcohol has one hydrogen kernel on the OH carbon, and a tertiary alcohol has no hydrogen kernels on the carbon that has the OH group.

Dehydration of a simple alcohol by heating with alumina, Al_2O_3, usually yields an alkene. Ethanol when heated in this manner yields ethene. Tertiary alcohols, such as 2-methyl-2-propanol, lose the elements of a molecule of water quite readily.

$$H-\underset{\underset{H}{|}}{\overset{\overset{H}{|}}{C}}-\underset{\underset{H}{|}}{\overset{\overset{H}{|}}{C}}-OH + Al_2O_3 \overset{\Delta}{\rightarrow} \overset{H}{\underset{H}{\diagdown}}C=C\overset{H}{\underset{H}{\diagup}} + Al_2O_3 \cdot xH_2O$$

ethanol   ethene

$$H_3C-\underset{\underset{OH}{|}}{\overset{\overset{CH_3}{|}}{C}}-CH_3 + H_2SO_4 \overset{\Delta}{\rightarrow} H_3C-\overset{\overset{CH_3}{|}}{C}=CH_2 + H_2SO_4(H_2O)$$

2-methyl-2-propanol   2-methylpropene

The reaction of ethanol with alkali metals and the behavior of ethanol in acid-base reactions have been mentioned earlier (p. 596). Because of the OH group, all alcohols are acids under some conditions, as they are bases under other conditions.

A typical dihydric alcohol (diol) is ethylene glycol (1,2-ethanediol), $(H_2C)_2(OH)_2$, widely used as a solvent and as a "permanent type" antifreeze in the cooling systems of internal combustion engines. A typical trihydric alcohol (triol) is glycerol or glycerine,

(1,2,3-propanetriol), a sweet, viscous, hygroscopic liquid. Glycerol is obtained as a by-product in the production of soap.

$$
\underset{\text{ethylene glycol}}{
\begin{array}{c}
\text{H} \quad\ \text{H} \\
| \qquad | \\
\text{H—C——C—H} \\
| \qquad | \\
\text{OH} \quad \text{OH}
\end{array}}
\qquad
\underset{\text{glycerol}}{
\begin{array}{c}
\text{H} \quad\ \text{H} \quad\ \text{H} \\
| \qquad | \qquad | \\
\text{H—C——C——C—H} \\
| \qquad | \qquad | \\
\text{OH} \quad \text{OH} \quad \text{OH}
\end{array}}
$$

Among the hydroxy derivatives of the hydrocarbons, a molecular arrangement in which two hydroxyl groups are attached to one carbon kernel seems to be very unstable because such a grouping is extremely rare, at least outside aqueous solutions. Chloral hydrate (melting point, 51.7°C), which has two hydroxyl groups on a carbon kernel, is a rather unusual compound. It is a hypnotic and an ingredient of "knockout drops."

$$
\underset{\text{chloral}}{
\begin{array}{c}
\text{H} \\
| \\
\text{Cl}_3\text{C—C}\!=\!\text{O}
\end{array}}
+ \text{HOH} \rightarrow
\underset{\text{chloral hydrate}}{
\begin{array}{c}
\text{H} \\
| \\
\text{Cl}_3\text{C—C—OH} \\
| \\
\text{OH}
\end{array}}
$$

Phenol, C_6H_5OH, is the simplest hydroxy derivative of an aromatic hydrocarbon and it is much more acidic (Brönsted) than the aliphatic alcohols. Phenol forms esters; in this respect it acts as an alcohol.

$$
\underset{\text{phenol}}{
\begin{array}{c}
\text{OH} \\
|\\
\bigcirc
\end{array}}
$$

b. *Aldehydes.* Primary alcohols can be gently oxidized to yield aldehydes.

$$
\underset{\substack{\text{any primary} \\ \text{alcohol}}}{
\begin{array}{c}
\text{H} \\
| \\
\text{R—C—OH} \\
| \\
\text{H}
\end{array}}
\xrightarrow[\text{oxidation}]{\text{gentle}}
\underset{\substack{\text{an aldehyde} \\ \text{(an alkanal)}}}{
\begin{array}{c}
\text{H} \\
| \\
\text{R—C}\!=\!\text{O}
\end{array}}
$$

The simplest aldehyde, $\text{H—}\overset{\displaystyle \text{H}}{\underset{\displaystyle}{\text{C}}}\!=\!\text{O}$, is usually called formaldehyde, but methanal is its more systematic name. It can be made by the gentle oxidation of methanol. The oxidation of formaldehyde yields formic acid; of acetaldehyde (ethanal), acetic acid; of propionaldehyde (propanal), propionic acid, CH_3CH_2COOH.

The systematic name of an aldehyde has the suffix -al. The stem of the name is derived from the longest continuous carbon chain that includes the aldehyde group. For example,

$$H_3C-\overset{\overset{\displaystyle H}{|}}{C}-CH_2-\overset{\overset{\displaystyle H}{|}}{C}=O$$
$$\underset{\underset{\displaystyle CH_3}{|}}{\overset{|}{C}H_2}$$

is 3-methylpentanal.

Since the aldehyde group has a seat of unsaturation, $C=O$ (the carbonyl group), aldehydes participate in many kinds of addition reactions (such as polymerizations), just as do the olefins. Aldehydes are easily oxidized to carboxylic acids and reduced to primary alcohols.

c. *Ketones.* Secondary alcohols can be oxidized to yield ketones.

$$R-\overset{\overset{\displaystyle H}{|}}{\underset{\underset{\displaystyle OH}{|}}{C}}-R \xrightarrow{\text{oxidation}} R-\overset{}{\underset{\underset{\displaystyle O}{||}}{C}}-R$$

any secondary   a ketone
alcohol   (an alkanone)

Acetone (dimethyl ketone), $H_3C-\overset{\overset{\displaystyle O}{||}}{C}-CH_3$, is the simplest ketone, propanone. The names and structures of the isomeric ketones having five carbon atoms are

$$H_3C-\overset{\overset{\displaystyle H}{|}}{\underset{\underset{\displaystyle H}{|}}{C}}-\overset{\overset{\displaystyle H}{|}}{\underset{\underset{\displaystyle H}{|}}{C}}-\overset{}{\underset{\underset{\displaystyle O}{||}}{C}}-CH_3 \quad H_3C-\overset{\overset{\displaystyle H}{|}}{\underset{\underset{\displaystyle H}{|}}{C}}-\overset{}{\underset{\underset{\displaystyle O}{||}}{C}}-\overset{\overset{\displaystyle H}{|}}{\underset{\underset{\displaystyle H}{|}}{C}}-CH_3 \quad H_3C-\overset{\overset{\displaystyle CH_3}{|}}{\underset{\underset{\displaystyle H}{|}}{C}}-\overset{}{\underset{\underset{\displaystyle O}{||}}{C}}-CH_3$$

(2-pentanone)   (3-pentanone)   (3-methyl-2-butanone)
methyl n-propyl ketone   diethyl ketone   methyl isopropyl ketone

Most ketones undergo addition reactions somewhat less readily than aldehydes of comparable molecular weight. Most, for instance, do not readily polymerize. Ketones are reduced to secondary alcohols; their oxidation yields a mixture of products because the ketone cleaves.

d. *Carboxylic acids.* The monocarboxylic acids, general formula R—$\overset{\displaystyle O}{\overset{\|}{C}}$—OH, may be prepared by oxidation of the appropriate aldehyde or primary alcohol.

$$\underset{\text{the primary alcohol}}{R-\overset{\displaystyle H}{\underset{\displaystyle H}{\overset{|}{\underset{|}{C}}}}-OH} \xrightarrow{\text{oxidation}} \underset{\text{the aldehyde}}{R-\overset{\displaystyle H}{\overset{|}{C}}=O} \xrightarrow{\text{oxidation}} \underset{\substack{\text{the carboxylic} \\ \text{(alkanoic) acid}}}{R-\overset{\displaystyle O}{\overset{\|}{C}}-OH}$$

The first four members of the homologous series of monocarboxylic acids are formic acid (methanoic acid), HCOOH; acetic acid (ethanoic acid), H_3C—COOH; propionic acid (propanoic acid), H_3C—CH_2—COOH; and butyric acid (butanoic acid),

$$H_3C-CH_2-CH_2-COOH$$

(Systematic names are in parentheses.)

Four long-chain saturated carboxylic acids found in nature are lauric acid (dodecanoic acid), $C_{11}H_{23}COOH$; myristic acid (tetradecanoic acid), $C_{13}H_{27}COOH$; palmitic acid (hexadecanoic acid), $C_{15}H_{31}COOH$; and stearic acid (octadecanoic acid), $C_{17}H_{35}COOH$. Oleic acid, $C_{17}H_{33}COOH$, is a naturally occurring unsaturated carboxylic acid. The saturated acids exist as their glyceryl esters primarily in animal fats, whereas oleic acid is found as its glyceryl ester predominantly in liquid fats, such as olive oil and cottonseed oil. These long-chain carboxylic acids are often called *fatty acids*.

The monocarboxylic acids are typical weak Brönsted acids. Except for formic acid and the unsaturated acids, they are rather difficultly oxidized. The saturated acids are rather difficultly reduced.

Oxalic acid, HOOC—COOH, is the simplest dicarboxylic acid. Others are

$$\underset{\text{succinic acid}}{\begin{array}{c} H \quad O \\ | \quad \| \\ H-C-C-OH \\ | \\ H-C-C-OH \\ | \quad \| \\ H \quad O \end{array}} \qquad \underset{\text{malic acid}}{\begin{array}{c} H \\ | \\ H-C-COOH \\ | \\ HO-C-COOH \\ | \\ H \end{array}}$$

$$
\begin{array}{cc}
\text{H} & \text{H} \\
| & | \\
\text{C—COOH} & \text{C—COOH} \\
\| & \| \\
\text{C—COOH} & \text{HOOC—C} \\
| & | \\
\text{H} & \text{H} \\
\text{maleic} & \text{fumaric} \\
\text{acid} & \text{acid} \\
cis & trans
\end{array}
$$

Note that maleic and fumaric acids are geometric isomers, and that malic acid shows optical isomerism.

Citric acid (in citrus fruits) is a tricarboxylic acid.

$$
\begin{array}{c}
\text{H} \\
| \\
\text{H—C—COOH} \\
| \\
\text{HO—C—COOH} \\
| \\
\text{H—C—COOH} \\
| \\
\text{H}
\end{array}
$$

e. *Esters.* Most common esters may be prepared by reacting an alcohol with an acid. The latter may be either organic or inorganic. The general formula of the esters of the monocarboxylic

acids is $R—C\!\!\overset{O}{\underset{}{\parallel}}\!\!—OR^1$, where R and R^1 may be identical or different. Let us use ethanol as a model alcohol to form certain ethyl esters.

$$C_2H_5OH + HBr \rightleftharpoons HOH + \underset{\text{ethyl bromide}}{C_2H_5Br}$$

$$C_2H_5OH + (HO)_2SO_2 \rightleftharpoons HOH + \underset{\text{ethyl hydrogen sulfate}}{C_2H_5OSO_2(OH)}$$

$$C_2H_5OH + HONO_2 \rightleftharpoons HOH + \underset{\text{ethyl nitrate}}{C_2H_5ONO_2}$$

$$C_2H_5OH + CH_3COOH \rightleftharpoons HOH + \underset{\text{ethyl acetate}}{CH_3COOC_2H_5}$$

In most of these reactions a small amount of concentrated sulfuric acid is commonly mixed with the reactants to supply protons, which catalyze the esterifications, and to tie up some of the product water, thereby shifting the equilibrium to favor the formation of ester.

Most of the liquid esters have rather pleasant odors.   Although only slightly soluble in water, they are good solvents for many organic compounds. Esters of carboxylic acids are rather easily hydrolyzed. Their hydrolyses are more nearly complete in aqueous solutions of alkali metal hydroxides because the carboxylate anions, $R\text{—}COO^-$, do not react readily with the alcohols. This alkaline hydrolysis of a carboxylic acid ester is called *saponification*. The hydrolysis of glyceryl esters of fatty acids yields soap.

$$R\text{—}\overset{\displaystyle O}{\overset{\|}{C}}\text{—}OR^1 + OH^- + HOH \rightarrow \left(R\text{—}\overset{\displaystyle O}{\overset{\|}{C}}\text{—}O\right)^- + R^1OH$$

Glyceryl trinitrate, a rather unusual ester, is obtained by treating glycerol with nitric acid and a small amount of concentrated sulfuric acid.

$$\begin{array}{c}
H \\
| \\
H\text{—}C\text{—}O\text{—}NO_2 \\
| \\
H\text{—}C\text{—}O\text{—}NO_2 \\
| \\
H\text{—}C\text{—}O\text{—}NO_2 \\
| \\
H
\end{array}$$

glyceryl trinitrate

Although this ester is often called *nitroglycerine*, the name is a misnomer. The chemist uses the prefix, nitro, to identify a compound in which the nitro group, NO_2, is attached to a carbon atom. For instance, nitromethane is $H_3C\text{—}NO_2$; its isomer is methyl nitrite, $H_3C\text{—}ONO$, an ester of nitrous acid, $HONO$. Nitrobenzene is $C_6H_5NO_2$, and trinitrotoluene (TNT) is $H_3CC_6H_2(NO_2)_3$.

nitrobenzene   2,4,6-trinitrotoluene

f. *Amides.* The carboxylic acid amides have the general formula, $R\text{—}\overset{\displaystyle O}{\overset{\|}{C}}\text{—}NH_2$. The simplest member of this family of organic compounds is formamide, the amide related to formic acid. Its formula is $H\text{—}\overset{\displaystyle O}{\overset{\|}{C}}\text{—}NH_2$; it is a liquid completely miscible with water. Its unusually high boiling point suggests that it is a highly associated liquid (hydrogen-bonding).

Other common amides are acetamide, propionamide, and butyramide.

$$
\underset{\text{acetamide}}{CH_3-\overset{\displaystyle O}{\overset{\|}{C}}-NH_2} \qquad \underset{\text{propionamide}}{CH_3CH_2\overset{\displaystyle O}{\overset{\|}{C}}-NH_2} \qquad \underset{\text{butyramide}}{CH_3CH_2CH_2\overset{\displaystyle O}{\overset{\|}{C}}-NH_2}
$$

The production of acetamide by the ammonolysis of acetyl chloride has been mentioned earlier (p. 233). Other amides can be produced by ammonolysis of the corresponding acyl chloride.

Amides hydrolyze in basic aqueous solutions to yield ammonia and the carboxylate ion of the corresponding carboxylic acid.

$$
CH_3\overset{\displaystyle O}{\overset{\|}{C}}-NH_2 + \text{aq } Na^+OH^- \xrightarrow{\Delta} \underset{\text{acetate ion}}{CH_3\overset{\displaystyle O}{\overset{\|}{C}}-O^-} + NH_3
$$

g. *Acyl chlorides.* The acyl chlorides of the carboxylic acids have the general formula, $R-\overset{\displaystyle O}{\overset{\|}{C}}-Cl$. The simplest stable member of the family of acyl chlorides of the carboxylic acids is acetyl chloride, $CH_3\overset{\displaystyle O}{\overset{\|}{C}}-Cl$. The hydrolysis of this compound has been mentioned earlier (p. 231), as has its alcoholysis (p. 233) and ammonolysis (p. 233).

Other simple acyl chlorides are propionyl chloride,

$$
CH_3CH_2\overset{\displaystyle O}{\overset{\|}{C}}-Cl
$$

butyryl chloride, $CH_3CH_2CH_2\overset{\displaystyle O}{\overset{\|}{C}}-Cl$; and oxalyl chloride, $\left(\overset{\displaystyle O}{\overset{\|}{C}}-Cl\right)_2$. These acyl chlorides undergo hydrolysis, alcoholysis, and ammonolysis, just as does acetyl chloride.

h. *Ethers.* The simple ethers have the general formula, $R-O-R$, an oxygen kernel flanked by two alkyl groups. The simplest ether is dimethyl ether, $H_3C-O-CH_3$, an isomer of ethanol. Each dialkyl ether is isomeric with one or more alcohols. The most common ether, diethyl ether, $H_5C_2-O-C_2H_5$, can be prepared by heating ethanol and sulfuric acid at 130–140°C.

$$C_2H_5OH + (HO)_2SO_2 \rightarrow C_2H_5OSO_2OH$$

ethanol sulfuric acid ethyl hydrogensulfate

$$C_2H_5OSO_2OH + C_2H_5OH \xrightarrow{\Delta} H_5C_2\text{—}O\text{—}C_2H_5$$

diethyl ether (ethoxyethane)

Diethyl ether is an anesthetic and it is used widely as a solvent in organic chemistry. It must be used with care because it is quite volatile (bp 35°C) and flammable.

Methyl ethyl ether, $H_3C\text{—}O\text{—}C_2H_5$, is the simplest mixed ether. Such ethers in which the alkyl groups are different, $R\text{—}O\text{—}R^1$, are prepared by the Williamson synthesis. In this process a sodium alkoxide, Na^+OR^-, is treated with an alkyl halide, RX.

$$Na^+OR^- + R^1X \rightarrow R^1\text{—}OR + Na^+X^-$$

an ether or
an alkoxyalkane

A specific synthesis is

$$Na^+OCH_3^- + C_2H_5I \rightarrow C_2H_5OCH_3 + Na^+I^-$$

sodium ethyl methyl ethyl ether sodium
methoxide iodide (methoxyethane) iodide

This is a typical displacement reaction in which the alkoxide ion, OR^-, displaces a halide ion on a carbon kernel.

Methyl phenyl ether, or anisole, is a typical alkyl aryl ether, and diphenyl ether is a diaryl ether.

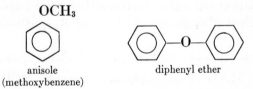

anisole
(methoxybenzene)

diphenyl ether

i. *Thiols, sulfides, and disulfides.* The simple thiols, RSH, are the sulfur analogs of the alcohols. The simplest alkanethiol is methanethiol, H_3CSH, more commonly called methyl mercaptan. The thiols were originally called *mercaptans* because they reacted readily with mercury(II) chloride or oxide to yield addition compounds. Since the thiols are monoalkyl derivatives of hydrogen sulfide, their unpleasant odor is expected. 1-Butanethiol is the main ingredient in "essence of skunk."

The alkyl mercaptans are often made by treating an alkyl halide with potassium hydrosulfide in alcoholic solution.

$$RX + K^+SH^- \rightarrow RSH + K^+X^-$$
$$C_2H_5I + K^+SH^- \rightarrow C_2H_5SH + K^+I^-$$

ethyl iodide potassium ethanethiol potassium
hydrosulfide (ethyl mercaptan) iodide

In this displacement reaction a hydrosulfide ion, SH^-, displaces a halide ion from an alkyl group. The SH group is often called the *sulfhydryl* group.

Cysteine is an amino acid that has a sulfhydryl (thiol) group. This acid is easily oxidized to cystine. The oxidation is reversible.

$$2\left\{\begin{array}{c} \underset{\underset{SH}{|}}{\overset{\overset{H}{|}}{H-C}}-\underset{\underset{NH_2}{|}}{\overset{\overset{H}{|}}{C}}-C\diagup^O_{OH} \end{array}\right. \xrightleftharpoons[\text{reduction}]{\text{oxidation}} \begin{array}{c} H-C-C-C\diagup OH \\ cystine \end{array}$$

cysteine

cystine

Benzenethiol, or thiophenol, C_6H_5SH, is the simplest aromatic (aryl) thiol. This is a stronger acid than phenol, C_6H_5OH.

Most thiols are very easily oxidized to disulfides, often if exposed to atmospheric air. The oxidation of an alkanethiol may be shown as $2RSH \rightarrow R-S-S-R$. This oxidation is reversible, that is, the disulfides are reduced to thiols. There are several thiol-disulfide oxidation-reduction systems that play important roles in certain biological phenomena, such as photosynthesis and cellular respiration.

The preparation of two typical disulfides is shown by

$$2CH_3SH + \text{air oxidation} \rightarrow CH_3S-SCH_3$$

methanethiol   dimethyl disulfide

$$2C_6H_5SH + \text{air oxidation} \rightarrow C_6H_5S-SC_6H_5$$

benzenethiol   diphenyl disulfide

Most disulfides can be oxidized to yield sulfonic acids that have the grouping SO_3H. The disulfides are much more stable than the analogous peroxides, $RO-OR$.

The alkyl sulfides, RSR, analogs of the ethers, are made by a process very similar to the Williamson synthesis of ethers.

$$2RSH + 2Na \rightarrow 2(RS^-Na^+) + H_2$$

alkanethiol   sodium salt
of the thiol

$$RS^-Na^+ + R^1X \rightarrow RSR^1 + Na^+X^-$$

alkyl   dialkyl
halide   sulfide

(R may be different from or identical to R^1)

Methyl phenyl sulfide, $CH_3SC_6H_5$, is a typical alkyl aryl sulfide and diphenyl sulfide, $C_6H_5SC_6H_5$, is the simplest diaryl sulfide.

27.16 FATS AND SOAP

Natural fats are carboxylic acid esters primarily of glycerol and certain long-chain carboxylic acids having an even number of carbon atoms per molecule. A typical solid fat is glyceryl stearate, also called tristearin or stearin.

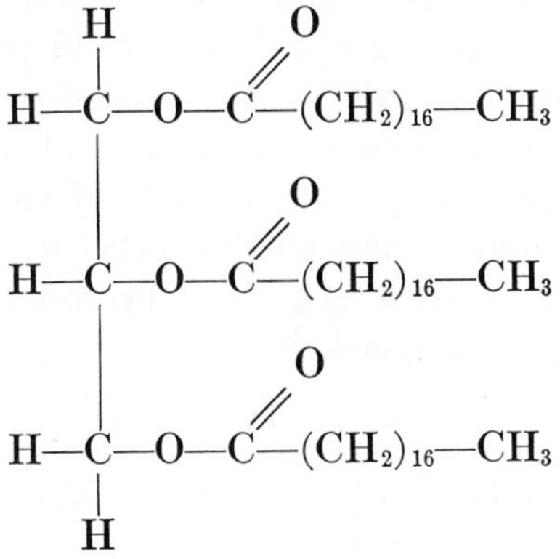

$$
\begin{array}{c}
H \qquad\qquad O \\
\mid \qquad\qquad \parallel \\
H-C-O-C-(CH_2)_{16}-CH_3 \\
\mid \qquad\qquad O \\
\qquad\qquad\quad \parallel \\
H-C-O-C-(CH_2)_{16}-CH_3 \\
\mid \qquad\qquad O \\
\qquad\qquad\quad \parallel \\
H-C-O-C-(CH_2)_{16}-CH_3 \\
\mid \\
H
\end{array}
$$

tristearin

(Note the three stearic acid fragments per glycerol fragment.)

Glyceryl oleate, or triolein, is a liquid fat. It is formulated using three oleic acid fragments per glycerol fragment.

Three different acids can combine with one glycerol molecule to form a fat, such as

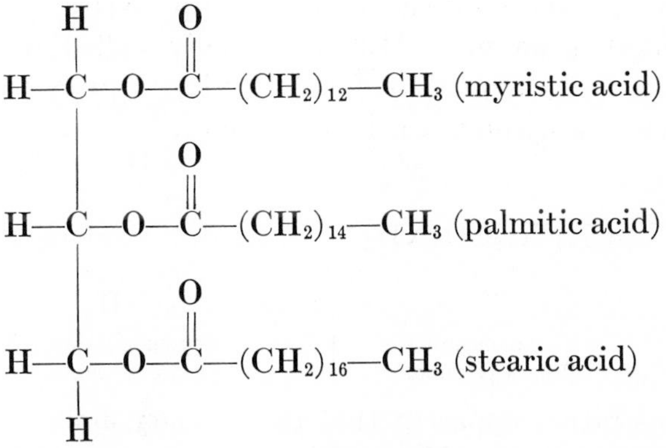

$$
\begin{array}{c}
H \qquad\qquad O \\
\mid \qquad\qquad \parallel \\
H-C-O-C-(CH_2)_{12}-CH_3 \text{ (myristic acid)} \\
\mid \qquad\qquad O \\
\qquad\qquad\quad \parallel \\
H-C-O-C-(CH_2)_{14}-CH_3 \text{ (palmitic acid)} \\
\mid \qquad\qquad O \\
\qquad\qquad\quad \parallel \\
H-C-O-C-(CH_2)_{16}-CH_3 \text{ (stearic acid)} \\
\mid \\
H
\end{array}
$$

If fats are hydrolyzed (saponified) by boiling aqueous sodium hydroxide, the sodium salts of the long-chain acids isolated from the reaction mixtures are the ordinary soaps. "Pure" soap is a mixture of sodium salts, including sodium stearate, sodium palmitate, sodium myristate, etc. Potassium soaps (potassium salts of the large fatty acids) are softer and more soluble than the common sodium soaps. Among the ordinary soaps the sodium salts of the C_{12} and C_{14} carboxylic acids seem to exhibit the most satisfactory detergency. Sodium salts of C_{20} and C_{22} acids are rather useless as detergents because they are only very slightly water-soluble at room temperature. The effective soaps reduce appreciably the surface tension of water in air-water systems, and reduce interfacial tension (aid emulsification) in many liquid-liquid systems.

The "synthetic" detergents do not yield precipitates in hard water as do the ordinary soaps, which cause the precipitation of the calcium and magnesium salts of the larger fatty acids. One kind of synthetic detergent is the sodium salt of the hydrogen sulfate ester of a long continuous-chain alcohol, cetyl alcohol. The formula of the detergent is $C_{16}H_{33}OSO_3^- Na^+$. Another detergent is the sodium salt of lauryl hydrogen sulfate.

$$CH_3(CH_2)_{10}-\overset{\displaystyle H}{\underset{\displaystyle H}{\overset{|}{\underset{|}{C}}}}-OSO_3^- Na^+$$

27.17 AMINES

The simplest amines are the primary amines which are characterized by the presence of the amino group, NH_2. The simplest amine is methaneamine, CH_3NH_2, usually called methylamine. Ethaneamine (ethylamine) is $CH_3CH_2NH_2$; 1-propaneamine and 2-propaneamine are isomeric primary amines.

$$CH_3CH_2CH_2NH_2 \qquad H_3C-\overset{\displaystyle H}{\underset{\displaystyle NH_2}{\overset{|}{\underset{|}{C}}}}-CH_3$$

1-propaneamine   2-propaneamine
(<i>n</i>-propylamine)   (isopropylamine)

It seems rather apparent that the primary amines are organic derivatives of ammonia, NH_3. Thus it is not surprising to learn that they can be made either directly or indirectly during reactions in which ammonia is a reactant. The ammonolysis of an alkyl halide does yield some primary amine, but other amines are produced also. These other amines are the secondary and tertiary amines. The simplest secondary amine is dimethylamine, $(CH_3)_2NH$, and trimethylamine, $(CH_3)_3N$, is the simplest tertiary amine. Treatment of methyl iodide, CH_3I, with ammonia yields all three kinds of methyl amines plus an ionic compound called tetramethylammonium iodide, $(CH_3)_4N^+I^-$. Such a compound is called a *quaternary ammonium salt*.

Since all amines are basic, they easily yield their conjugate acids in the presence of strong acids. The conjugate acid of each ordinary amine is a derivative of ammonium ion, just as the conjugate acid of ammonia is ammonium ion. The presence of an amino group (except in amides) always endows a molecule with a seat of basicity.

The simplest aromatic amine is aniline, $C_6H_5NH_2$, or phenylamine. Some aliphatic-aromatic amines are

$$CH_3$$
$$|$$
$$N—CH_3$$

N, N-dimethylaniline

$$H \quad CH_3$$
$$| \quad |$$
$$N—C—CH_3$$
$$|$$
$$H$$

N-isopropylaniline

The simplest alkanediamine is 1,2-ethanediamine, also called ethylenediamine. This compound has been mentioned earlier (p. 544) in connection with its action as a common ligand in complex ion formation. Another well-known diamine is 1,6-hexanediamine, or hexamethylenediamine (see p. 706).

$$H_2NCH_2CH_2NH_2$$
1,2-ethanediamine

$$H_2NCH_2CH_2CH_2CH_2CH_2CH_2NH_2$$
1,6-hexanediamine

The importance of the amino group in organic chemistry is manifested in the amino acids, in the proteins, and in many simple vital compounds. We shall mention it again before the end of this chapter.

Some amines have their nitrogen atoms within a ring system. Such amines are called nitrogen heterocycles; a few examples are pyrrole, pyrrolidine, pyridine, and pyrimidine.

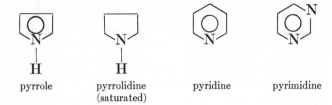

pyrrole   pyrrolidine   pyridine   pyrimidine
                 (saturated)

27.18 CARBOHYDRATES

The naturally occurring carbohydrates constitute an extremely important but complex branch of organic chemistry. This section is a very brief introduction to some of the simple aspects of some common carbohydrates. Sugars are simple carbohydrates.

The most common simple sugars are the hexoses: glucose (dextrose), fructose (levulose), mannose, and galactose. They all have the same formula, $C_6H_{12}O_6$, or $C_n(H_2O)_n$, where $n = 6$. Each sugar is an asymmetric (optically active) molecule. Glucose, mannose, and galactose are called *aldoses* because each contains an incipient aldehyde group. These three sugars are stereoisomers, but since they are not mirror-image isomers, they have different physical and chemical properties. Fructose is called a ketose because it contains an incipient ketone group.

The simple hexoses are called *monosaccharides*. Sugars having the compositional formula $C_{12}H_{22}O_{11}$ are called the *disaccharides*. The most common disaccharides are sucrose (cane sugar), lactose (milk sugar), and maltose. Each mole of a disaccharide yields, on hydrolysis, two moles of monosaccharide. For example, sucrose yields glucose and fructose, lactose yields galactose and glucose, and maltose yields two moles of glucose.

sucrose   hydrolysis   glucose   +   fructose

There are four aldopentoses that occur widely in plants. Their general formula is $C_5H_{10}O_5$, and each is a stereoisomer of the other three. Because they are asymmetric molecules, each exhibits optical isomerism. D-Xylose is also called wood sugar, L-arabinose is found as pentosans in vegetable gums, N-lyxose is closely related to D-xylose, and D-ribose is a constituent of certain nucleic acids, RNA. A ribose fragment is a major constituent of the riboflavin molecule, vitamin B_2.

The most common polysaccharides [general formula, $(C_6H_{10}O_5)_n$] are glycogen, the reserve carbohydrate in animals; starch, the reserve carbohydrate in most plants; and cellulose, the major structural material of plants. The polysaccharides (polymers) are huge molecules composed of many monosaccharide fragments (monomers). In glycogen, starch, and cellulose the monomer is glucose. Enzymatic hydrolysis of glycogen and of starch yields maltose, and the hydrolysis of maltose yields glucose. The acidic aqueous hydrolysis (*in vitro*) of cellulose yields cellobiose (a stereoisomer of maltose), $C_{12}H_{22}O_{11}$; the hydrolysis of cellobiose yields glucose. Starch and cellulose are identical with respect to the monosaccharide building block (glucose) of which each is constructed; yet the enzymes in the human organism are able to catalyze the hydrolysis of starch, but not of cellulose. That is, human beings can easily digest starch, but they cannot digest cellulose. The differences between starch and cellulose (and also between maltose and cellobiose) are due to the different spatial configurations of the attachments of the anhydro glucose units, $C_6H_{10}O_5$. The enzymes are asymmetric and the cellulose and starch molecules are asymmetric; hence it appears that stereochemical differences are readily recognized in an asymmetric environment.

Since cellulose is a polyhydric alcohol, it reacts with acids to yield polyesters, such as cellulose nitrate (gun cotton) and cellulose acetate (widely used as a plastic base for photographic emulsions).

27.19 POLYMERS OF MONO-OLEFINS

Simple olefins undergo many kinds of addition reactions because of the seat of unsaturation at the double bond. An olefin molecule usually can, under appropriate conditions, undergo polymerization to yield large molecules (polymers). (See p. 237.) During polymerization a single olefin molecule (the monomer) adds to itself an olefin molecule to form a dimer; the dimer adds a monomer to yield a trimer; the trimer adds a monomer to yield a tetramer, and so on, until a relatively huge polymer is formed. The polymers of the mono-olefins (monoenes) are usually called *thermoplastic resins,* or *plastics.* They are fairly rigid to quite rigid at room temperature, but soften and are rather pliable at elevated temperatures. If two different monomers polymerize, a copolymer is formed.

Ethylene polymerizes to yield polyethylene (polythene). A highly simplified representation of this is

$$2n \left(\begin{array}{c} H \quad H \\ | \quad | \\ H-C=C-H \end{array} \right) \rightarrow \cdots \left(\begin{array}{c} H \quad H \quad H \quad H \\ | \quad | \quad | \quad | \\ -C-C-C-C- \\ | \quad | \quad | \quad | \\ H \quad H \quad H \quad H \end{array} \right)_n \cdots$$

ethylene   polyethylene
(ethene)

Polyethylene is a rather chemically inert thermoplastic resin (similar to a large paraffin hydrocarbon in its chemical behavior). It is rather pliable at room temperature because its polymer chains are nonpolar and relatively free of cross-linkage, except after electronic radiation.

Most mono-olefins polymerize by following a pattern quite similar to that taken by ethylene. Let us mention a few olefins that yield useful polymers and copolymers.

a. Vinyl chloride, $H_2C=\overset{\displaystyle H}{\overset{\displaystyle /}{C}}-Cl$, is used as the monomer in the formulation of polyvinyl chloride (Koroseal).

b. Vinyl acetate, $H_2C=\overset{\displaystyle H}{\overset{\displaystyle /}{C}}-O-\overset{\displaystyle O}{\overset{\displaystyle \|}{C}}-CH_3$, polymerizes to yield polyvinyl acetate.

c. Vinyl chloride mixed with vinyl acetate yields copolymers, such as the Vinylites. The copolymer, Vinyon (a fiber), contains 88-95 per cent vinyl chloride and 5-12 per cent vinyl acetate.

d. Vinyl chloride and vinylidene chloride, $H_2C=CCl_2$, yield useful copolymers. Saran usually contains 90 per cent vinylidene chloride and 10 per cent vinyl chloride, which can be formulated as a fiber.

e. Acrylonitrile, $H_2C=\overset{\displaystyle H}{\overset{\displaystyle /}{C}}-C=N$, polymerizes to yield polyacrylonitrile. In the form of a fiber this is called Orlon.

f. Styrene, $C_6H_5-\overset{\displaystyle H}{\overset{\displaystyle /}{C}}=CH_2$ (phenylethylene), yields polystyrene on polymerization.

g. Tetrafluoroethylene, $F_2C\!=\!CF_2$, yields the extremely stable (up to 325°C), chemically inert polytetrafluoroethylene (Teflon).

h. Methyl methacrylate, $H_2C\!=\!\overset{\overset{\displaystyle CH_3}{|}}{C}\!-\!COOCH_3$, yields transparent plastics such as Lucite and Plexiglas.

27.20 POLYMERS OF DIENES

The polymers of the dienes are, at room temperature, more flexible and less rigid than most polymers of the monoenes; hence they are called the *elastomers*.   Natural rubber appears to be a polymer of isoprene, which is a derivative of butadiene.   Chemists have used butadiene and some of its derivatives to produce elastomers (synthetic rubbers).   Let us use the polymerization of isoprene as a model to represent a typical polymerization of a derivative of butadiene.

$$2n \; (H_2C\!=\!\overset{\overset{\displaystyle CH_3}{|}}{C}\!-\!\overset{\overset{\displaystyle H}{\diagup}}{C}\!=\!CH_2)$$

$$\longrightarrow \left\{ -\overset{\overset{\displaystyle H}{|}}{\underset{\underset{\displaystyle H}{|}}{C}}\!-\!\overset{\overset{\displaystyle CH_3}{|}}{C}\!=\!\overset{\overset{\displaystyle H}{|}}{C}\!-\!\overset{\overset{\displaystyle H}{|}}{\underset{\underset{\displaystyle H}{|}}{C}}\!-\!\overset{\overset{\displaystyle H}{|}}{\underset{\underset{\displaystyle H}{|}}{C}}\!-\!\overset{\overset{\displaystyle CH_3}{|}}{C}\!=\!\overset{\overset{\displaystyle H}{|}}{C}\!-\!\overset{\overset{\displaystyle H}{|}}{\underset{\underset{\displaystyle H}{|}}{C}}\!- \right\}_n$$

It should be noted that the raw polymer has many seats of unsaturation (double bonds).   Crude rubber (polyisoprene) is a rather sticky, unsuitable elastomer until vulcanized by heating with the appropriate amount of sulfur.   If during vulcanization not over 5 per cent of the long carbon chains in the rubber are cross-linked by sulfide bonds, the rubber has good elasticity and tensile strength. (Cross-linkage occurs at the double bonds as sulfur "adds" to the seats of unsaturation.)   Hard rubber may be made by vulcanizing with larger amounts of sulfur, thereby increasing the extent of cross-linkage.

Some of the more common synthetic elastomers are given below.

a. Polychloroprene (Neoprene) is prepared by the polymerization of chloroprene (2-chlorobutadiene), $H_2C\!=\!\overset{\overset{\displaystyle Cl}{|}}{C}\!-\!\overset{\overset{\displaystyle H}{|}}{C}\!=\!CH_2$.   This polymer is unaffected by liquid hydrocarbons (gasoline, fuel oil, etc.), whereas natural rubber swells badly in gasoline.

b. Buna-S (Gr-S) rubber is a copolymer of butadiene and styrene.

c. Perbunan (Gr-A) is a copolymer of butadiene and acrylonitrile.

d. Butyl rubber (Gr-I) is a copolymer of isoprene and 2-methylpropene (isobutylene).

27.21 SYNTHETIC FIBERS

We have already mentioned the synthetic fibers Vinyon, Saran, and Orlon, which are polymeric two-dimension molecules. These fibers are rather different from the natural, long-chain cellulose molecules in cotton, wood linen, etc., and the chainlike protein molecules in wool and silk. Let us now briefly consider some artificially produced fibers similar to cotton, linen, wool, and silk.

a. Viscose rayon is made by initially treating cellulose (either cotton or wood cellulose) with aqueous sodium hydroxide and carbon bisulfide. The colloid so produced is extruded through tiny holes into a solution of dilute acid in which the cellulose precipitates as a filament (fiber). If the viscose colloid is extruded through a narrow slit, the cellulose precipitates as a film (cellophane).

b. Acetate rayon is made by extruding, as filaments, a solution of cellulose acetate in acetone. The solvent acetone is removed from the filaments by evaporation; hence the fibers are a form of cellulose acetate.

c. One form of nylon (a polyamide) is prepared by reacting hexamethylene diamine, $H_2N-(CH_2)_6-NH_2$, with adipic acid, $HOOC-(CH_2)_4-COOH$.

$$n[H_2N-(CH_2)_6-NH_2] + n[HOOC-(CH_2)_4-COOH]$$

$$\left[\begin{array}{c} -N-(CH_2)_6-N-C-(CH_2)_4-\overset{\displaystyle O}{\underset{\displaystyle }{\overset{\|}{C}}}- \\ \underset{\displaystyle H}{|} \qquad \underset{\displaystyle H}{|} \overset{\|}{\underset{\displaystyle O}{}} \end{array} \right]_n \longleftarrow -HOH$$

a nylon

Nylon is called a *polyamide* because this polymer consists of many amide groupings (linkages), $-\overset{\displaystyle O}{\overset{\|}{C}}-\overset{\displaystyle H}{\overset{|}{N}}-$. These amide linkages abound in proteins such as silk, to which nylon is structurally similar.

d. Dacron (a polyester) forms during the progressive construction of ester linkages while terephthalic acid, $HOOC—C_6H_4—COOH$, reacts with ethylene glycol.   The initial step is

$$HOOC—\langle\bigcirc\rangle—COOH \; + \; HO—\overset{\overset{\displaystyle H}{|}}{C}—\overset{\overset{\displaystyle H}{|}}{C}—OH \rightarrow$$

terephthalic acid   ethylene glycol

$$HO—\overset{\overset{\displaystyle O}{\|}}{C}—\langle\bigcirc\rangle—\overset{\overset{\displaystyle O}{\|}}{C}—O—\overset{\overset{\displaystyle H}{|}}{C}—\overset{\overset{\displaystyle H}{|}}{C}—OH \leftarrow$$

—HOH

the Dacron "monomer"

The reaction continues because there is a free carboxyl group and a free alcoholic hydroxyl group on the "growing" molecule at all times.

27.22 PROTEINS

The proteins are the major cellular constituents in animals.   The animal body, excluding water and the inorganic portion of the skeleton, is mainly protein.   The proteins are extremely complex molecules, and until the last two decades relatively little was known about their structures.

The proteins are usually considered condensation polymers of the alpha amino acids.   Either acidic or basic hydrolysis of a protein yields amino acids, just as the hydrolysis of starch and of cellulose yields glucose.   There are 24 naturally occurring amino acids that appear to be the building units of the various natural proteins.

All of these amino acids have a common grouping, $—\overset{\overset{\displaystyle H}{|}}{\underset{\underset{\displaystyle NH_2}{|}}{C}}—COOH$.

A few of the simpler amino acids are

$$H—\overset{\overset{\displaystyle H}{|}}{\underset{\underset{\displaystyle NH_2}{|}}{C}}—COOH \qquad H_3C—\overset{\overset{\displaystyle H}{|}}{\underset{\underset{\displaystyle NH_2}{|}}{C}}—COOH \qquad H_5C_6—\overset{\overset{\displaystyle H}{|}}{\underset{\underset{\displaystyle H}{|}}{C}}—\overset{\overset{\displaystyle H}{|}}{\underset{\underset{\displaystyle NH_2}{|}}{C}}—COOH$$

glycine   alanine   phenylalanine

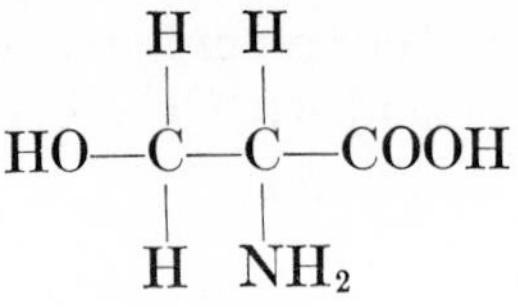

$$\begin{array}{cc} \overset{\displaystyle H}{\underset{\displaystyle H}{\overset{|}{\underset{|}{C}}}}\overset{\displaystyle H}{\underset{\displaystyle NH_2}{\overset{|}{\underset{|}{C}}}}\\ HO—C—C—COOH \end{array}$$

HO—C—C—COOH

serie

H₃C—S—(CH₂)₂—C—COOH

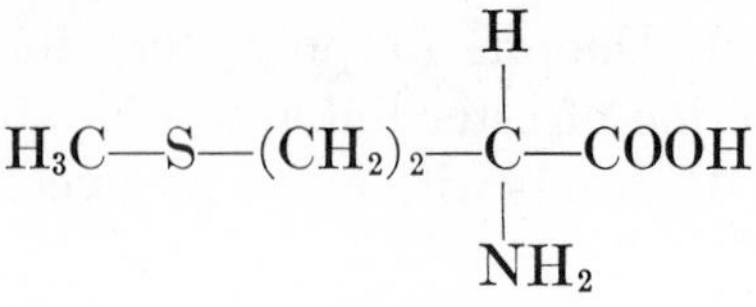

methionine

H₃C—C—C—COOH

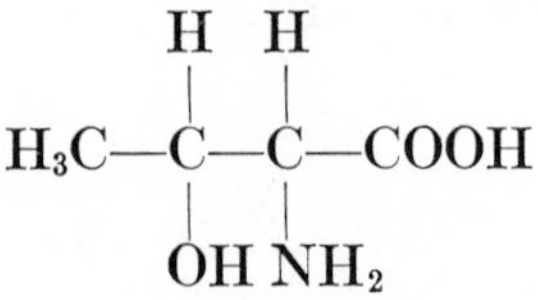

threonine

Since the amino group, NH_2, in each of these amino acids is on the carbon adjacent to the carboxyl group, the natural amino acids are called *alpha amino acids*. All of the 24 naturally occurring amino acids (except glycine) are optically active because the carbon atom adjacent to the carboxyl group is an asymmetric center. All proteins are asymmetric (optically active) because the constituent amino acids (except glycine) are asymmetric. (No protein contains only glycine.)

Using the appropriate amino acids, the human body can synthesize hundreds of different proteins, but it cannot synthesize 9 of the 24 natural amino acids. These 9 acids must be supplied to the body; they are therefore called the *essential amino acids*. They are lysine, leucine, isoleucine, phenylalanine, histidine, tryptophan, valine, threonine, and methionine. The proteins are in part built by successive condensation reactions between the constituent amino acids. Using glycine and alanine, let us represent a possible initial condensation reaction.

H—C—COOH + H₂N—C—CH₃ →

H—C—C—N—C—COOH + HOH

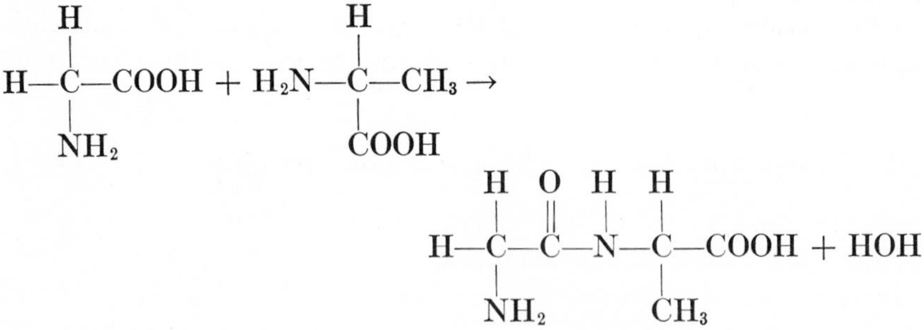

glycylalanine
(a dipeptide)

This dipeptide can react either with an alanine molecule or with a glycine molecule or any other amino acid to yield a tripeptide, etc., until a large polypeptide molecule is formed. Hydrogen-bonding seems to play an important role in holding together polypeptide fragments to create a large protein molecule. The smallest proteins have molecular weights around 10,000-15,000, whereas the plant viruses (proteins) have molecular weights around 15,000,000. The animal viruses seem to be much more massive than the plant viruses. Since there are so many different amino acids, a fantastic number of different protein molecules is possible.

Let us consider briefly certain stereochemical aspects of the amino acids. If one of the amino acids—say, alanine—is synthesized *in vitro*, the two optical isomers, D-alanine and L-alanine are produced in equal amounts. In the animal body, however, it appears that only L-alanine is formed because only this form is found in natural protein. It also appears that all the amino acids in natural proteins are L-amino acids. This means that the D-forms of the amino acids are worthless in the human body as building blocks to construct proteins. The asymmetric environment in the human body (proteins and carbohydrates are asymmetric) seems to play an important role in the differentiation of the optical isomers of an amino acid.

An activated enzyme (natural catalyst) is a complex substance that often consists of a specific protein to which is attached some nonprotein molecule, the prosthetic group. This prosthetic group is often called the *coenzyme*, and the specific protein, the *apoenzyme*. The coenzyme and the apoenzyme alone are each enzymatically inactive. The activated enzyme is the combination of the coenzyme with the apoenzyme. Several if not all of the vitamins are coenzymes or parts of coenzyme entities. Some of the vitamins and their related coenzymes are: riboflavin (vitamin B_2), cozymase; thiamine (vitamin B_1), cocarboxylase; niacin, coenzymes I and II; pantothenic acid, coenzyme A; and pyridoxine, coenzymes of transaminases.

Many enzymes have prosthetic groups in which a metal ion plays an important role in enzymatic activity. Many of the plant oxidases, for instance, contain copper ion. Hemoglobin, the oxygen carrier in red blood cells, is a complex substance consisting of a complex nonprotein fragment, hemin, plus a protein fragment, globin. Iron ion is present in the hemin.

Most enzyme systems are inactivated (usually due to structural changes in the protein portion of the enzyme) by acids and ionic hydroxides, by heat, by ultraviolet light, and x-radiation, and by certain chemical agents. Such effects are called the *denaturation of a protein*. If an aqueous solution of a protein (actually a colloidal system) is vigorously shaken, the protein is usually denatured. Denaturation of a protein usually causes a decrease in its solubility. Colloidal protein systems are frequently coagulated during denaturation. When an egg is cooked, the egg white, mainly ovalbumin (egg albumin), coagulates to yield denatured ovalbumin. This denaturation, as in most cases, is irreversible.

With respect to structure and solubility, there are two main types of proteins: fibrous and globular. The fibrous proteins are practically insoluble in water, whereas the globular proteins are soluble (form clear colloidal systems). The fibrous proteins and where they are found in nature include fibroin, silk; collagen, connective tissue; keratin, epithelial tissue (hair, feathers, wool, horn, nails); and elastin, elastic connective tissue. The globular proteins include globin, ovalbumin, casein (in milk) and the plasma proteins.

The nitrogen cycle in nature, in which proteins play a major role, is shown in Fig. 13.1 (p. 294).

27.23 STEROIDS

There is a large class of biologically important compounds that have a carbon skeleton that is classically called the perhydro-1,2-cyclopentenophenanthrene nucleus. All molecules that have this

perhydro-1,2-cyclopentenophenanthrene skeleton

skeleton are *steroids*. Among the steroids there are many that have a hydroxyl group at carbon 3; these are called *sterols*. The principal sterol of animal organisms is cholesterol, which occurs in all tissues of the animal body. This specific sterol is most abundant in the spinal cord, the brain, and gallstones. The relatively close relationship between cholesterol and vitamin D_2 is evident. Actually the irradiation of ergosterol, also a close relative of cholesterol, eventually yields vitamin D_2.

Female and male sex hormones have the steroid structure.

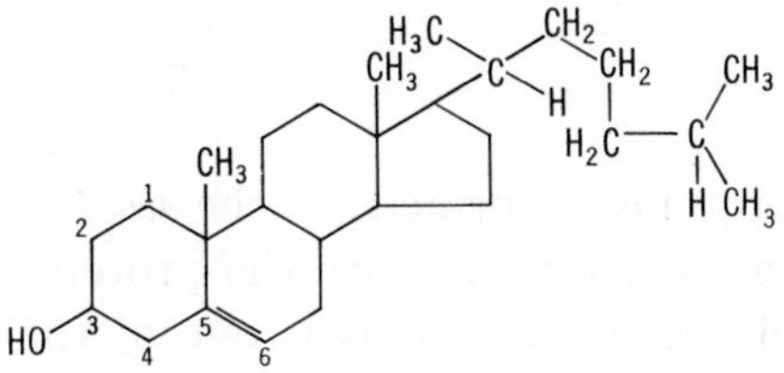

cholesterol

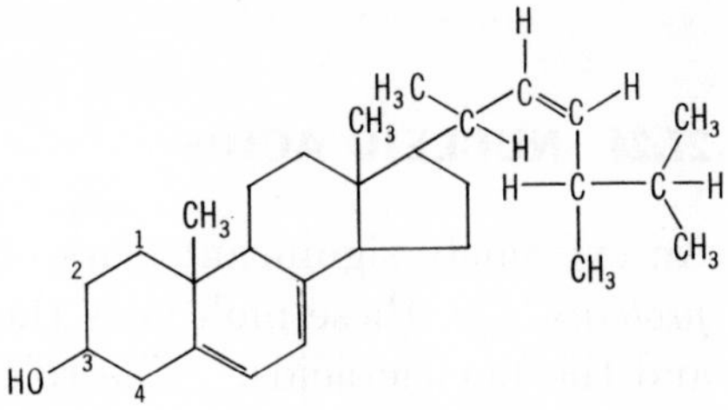

ergosterol

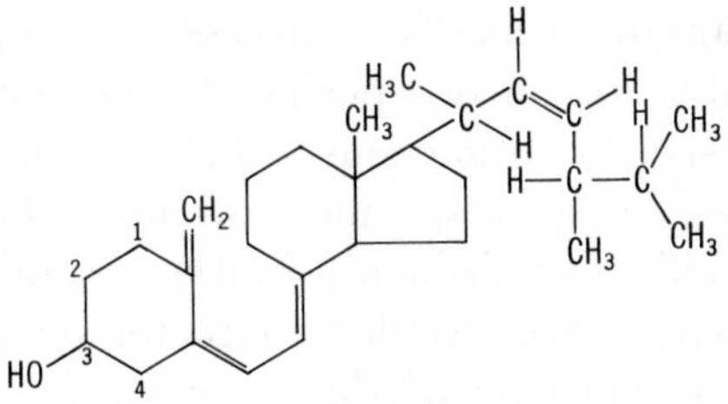

vitamin D$_2$

Typical female sex hormones are estradiol and progesterone; testosterone is a typical male sex hormone. The female sex hormones are called *estrogens*, the male hormones, *androgens*.

Cortisone is a typical adrenal cortical hormone.

Since the carbon skeleton of the steroids is, in essence, a series of condensed cyclohexane ring systems, the stereoisomerism is related to that of cyclohexane (boat and chair forms). Since this factor is rather complex, we shall not attempt to expand the concept here.

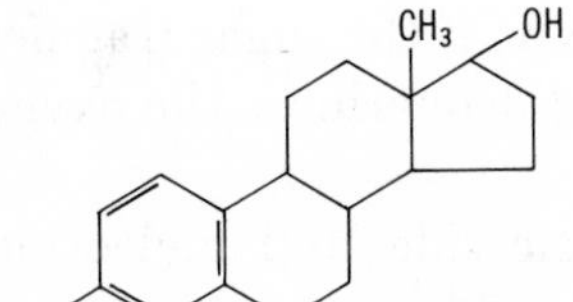

estradiol

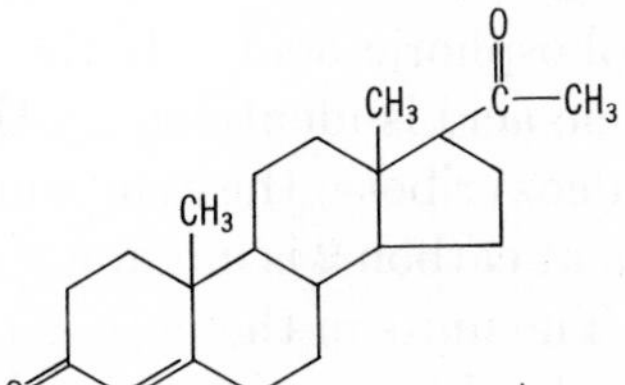

progesterone

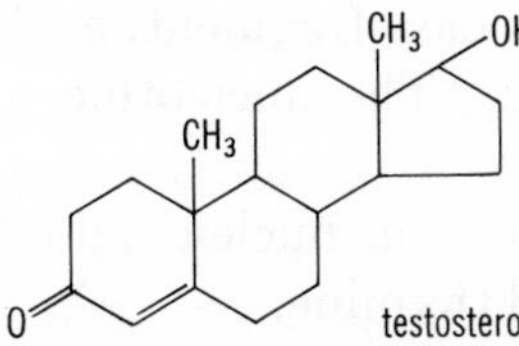

testosterone

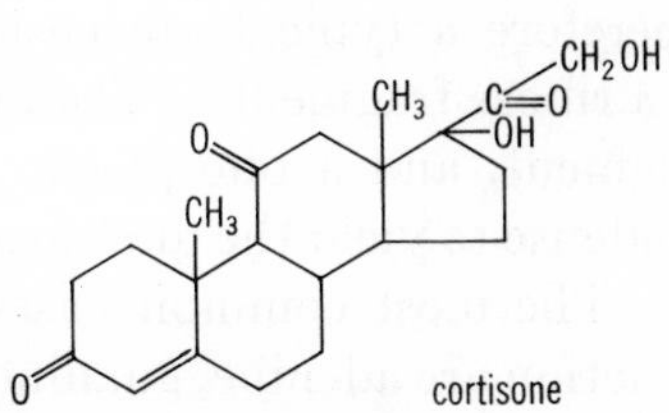

cortisone

27.24 NUCLEIC ACIDS

An extremely significant class of proteins is formed by the *nucleoproteins*. In these molecules the major fragments are the proteins and the nucleic acids. The role of the nucleic acids is one of the most vital because they apparently control at the molecular level what man calls heredity. The nucleic acids are able to direct the synthesis of molecules identical to themselves, so in this respect they yield duplication, or replication, of molecular species. While the nucleic acids are directing the syntheses of "new" nucleic acids, they seem to be able to control specifically the syntheses of particular proteins in specific organisms. That is, a given organism usually synthesizes its own specific proteins. This specificity is controlled by specific nucleic acids in the organism in question. As a matter of fact, the molecular character of a specific nucleic acid directs the construction of the organism in a given manner. Of course, there are many different nucleic acids in the various organisms; hence the variety in structures of the organisms.

It seems that the "backbones" of the nucleic acids are nearly the same, the differences between nucleic acids being mainly in the nature of the groups attached to the backbone chain.

The nucleic acids are long helical chains held together by hydrogen bonds. That is, the helixes are held to each other by hydrogen bonds, whereas each helix itself is held together by covalent bonds within the nucleotide units. The nucleic acids are, in a sense, condensation polymers in which the monomeric molecules are (1) some nitrogenous base, (2) either ribose or deoxyribose, (3) phosphoric acid. If the sugar fragment is ribose (p. 703), the nucleic acid is identified by the symbol RNA; if the sugar fragment is 2-deoxyribose, the symbol is DNA. In 2-deoxyribose the oxygen atom at carbon 2 is missing.

The units in the polymer are called nucleosides and nucleotides. A nucleoside consists of a base fragment and a sugar fragment. Therefore a typical nucleoside has an adenine fragment attached to a ribose fragment. The nucleotide has a base fragment, a ribose fragment, and a phosphoric acid fragment. The nucleotide units condense to yield the nucleic acid.

The most common bases that participate in nucleic acid construction are adenine, guanine, cytosine, and thymine.

adenine   2-deoxyribose   adenine   2-deoxyribose

a nucleoside   a nucleotide

phosphoric acid

adenine   guanine   cytosine   thymine

(Note that each has a pyrimidine nucleus [p. 702].)

The helical nucleic acid molecules have a conformation that attracts specific protein molecules having stereospecificity. In a sense, the nuclei acids serve as templates on which proteins of specific stereoisomeric forms are synthesized. Therefore the molecular structure of the nucleic acid dictates the character of the proteins synthesized. The proteins in turn dictate the nature of the organism—hence the role of nucleic acids in heredity.

Two helixes in a given nucleic acid are held together by hydrogen bonds either between adenine and thymine fragments or between guanine and cytosine fragments.

27.25   BIOCHEMISTRY

In this and in previous chapters we have discussed most of the major chemical principles. We have mentioned applications of these principles by describing specific chemical phenomena. Nearly every one of these principles is applied during investigations of vital phenomena that occur in plants and animals. These phenomena are of extreme importance to man's comfort and often to his very existence. The investigation of the many reactions that occur in plant and animal organisms and the isolation and identification of the participating substances are considered biochemistry. This branch of chemistry is relatively young because its complexity has deterred man's progress in it.

A meaningful discussion of biochemistry is far beyond the scope of this book. It would be presumptuous to mention a few vital compounds and reactions and then call it an introduction to biochemistry. Actually nearly everything in this book is in essence an introduction to biochemistry.

During the next 50 years, chemists and the medical scientists will discover many wonderful things that will greatly benefit mankind. The men and women who make these discoveries will apply sound logical reasoning based on principles such as those we have discussed in this book. You have used similar processes of reasoning while solving some of the problems and doing the exercises at the ends of the chapters. It is hoped that this experience will help you to realize that progress in chemistry, as in any other human endeavor, is based mainly on the courageous, logical application of valid ideas.

Problems

1. (a) Write the graphic structural formulas of all the compounds having formula C_7H_{16}. (b) Indicate the systematic name of each isomer by using the IUC system. (Be sure to include optical isomers.)

2. Write the graphic structural formula of each compound identified below.
(a) 2,3-dimethyl-4-ethylhexane
(b) 2,3,4,4-tetramethyl-2-heptene
(c) 3-methyl-3-ethyl-5-*n*-propyloctane
(d) 2-pentyne
(e) 2,3-dimethyl-1,3-pentadiene
(f) 2-methyl-3-ethyl-2-hexanol
(g) 2,3,3-trimethylbutanal
(h) 3,4-dimethyl-3,4-dichlorohexane
(i) methylcyclohexane
(j) 2,3,3-trimethyl-3-hexanone

3. Write the systematic name of each of the following compounds.

(a)
$$H_3C-CH_2-\underset{\underset{\displaystyle \underset{\underset{CH_3}{|}}{\overset{|}{CH_2}}}{\overset{\overset{CH_3}{|}}{\overset{|}{C}}}-\underset{\underset{H}{|}}{\overset{\overset{CH_3}{|}}{C}}-\underset{\underset{H}{|}}{\overset{\overset{H}{|}}{C}}-OH$$

(c)
$$H_3C-CH_2-\underset{\underset{\displaystyle \underset{CH_3}{\overset{|}{CH_2}}}{\overset{|}{C}}}{\overset{\overset{CH_3}{|}}{C}}-\overset{\overset{H}{|}}{C}=O$$

$$\text{(b)} \quad H_3C-\underset{\underset{CH_3}{|}}{\overset{\overset{CH_3}{|}}{C}}=\underset{\underset{CH_3}{|}}{\overset{\overset{H}{|}}{C}}-\overset{}{C}-CH_3$$

$$\text{(d)} \quad C_2H_5-C\equiv C-\underset{\underset{H}{|}}{\overset{\overset{CH_3}{|}}{C}}-CH_3$$

4. Write graphic formulations of the stereoisomeric forms of 1-chloro-1-butene. Which is the *cis* isomer?

5. What is the systematic name of chloral? (See p. 691.)

6. (a) What compound is formed when 2,3-dimethyl-2-pentene reacts with bromine? (b) Can the product yield optically active molecules?

7. Write the structural formulas of all the isomers having the formula C_5H_{10}. (Remember the cycloparaffins and include stereoisomers.)

8. (a) Write the structural formulas of all the alcohols having the formula $C_5H_{11}OH$. (b) How many are optically active?

9. (a) Write the structural formulas of the ethers, $R-O-R$, that are isomeric with the alcohols of Problem 8. (b) How many are optically active?

10. What is the major product formed by the gentle oxidation of 2,2-dimethylpropanol?

11. What is the major product formed by the oxidation of 2,3-dimethylbutanal?

12. What are the products of the saponification of (a) isopropyl propionate, (b) glyceryl tributyrate, (c) diethyl oxalate?

13. What is the major product of the hydrolysis of 3-bromo-3-methylpentane?

14. Starting with 1-propanol and any necessary inorganic reagents, suggest a practical preparation of *n*-propyl propionate.

15. Starting with methanol and ethyl iodide, prepare methoxyethane.

16. Write the graphic formulas of the two most stable isomers of methyl formate, $H-\overset{\overset{O}{\|}}{C}-OCH_3$. Name each compound.

17. Maleic acid (see p. 694) has a melting point of 130°C. Fumaric acid, the geometric isomer of maleic acid, has a melting point of 290°C. Interpret this marked difference.

18. What esters are isomeric with *n*-propyl propionate?

19. The saponification of a sample of fat yielded sodium stearate, sodium myristate, and glycerol. How many different glyceryl ester molecules might have been in the fat?

20. How many carboxylic acids are isomeric with hexanoic acid?

21. How many ethers are isomeric with ethyl *n*-propyl ether?

22. Write the graphic formulas of the two possible dipeptides containing one glycine fragment and one threonine fragment.

23. Two of the simplest optically active alcohols are D-2-butanol and L-2-butanol. Why are these substances optically active? How are their graphic formulations different? A handbook states that the boiling point of 2-butanol is 99.5°–100°C. To what substance or substances does this value refer?

24. Outline a series of reactions to convert (a) 2-bromobutane to butanone, (b) ethanol to ethyl acetate.

25. What alcohol, if oxidized, yields 3,3-dimethylbutanoic acid?

26. What is produced by the gentle oxidation of butanethiol?

27. What compound is produced by the reduction of dipropyl disulfide?

28. What is the formula of phenyl triphenylmethyl sulfide?

29. What are the molar weights of the following compounds?
    (a) diethylammonium bromide
    (b) 3,3-dimethyl-2,4-pentanediamine
    (c) N-ethylbutyramide
    (d) 1,4-cyclohexanediol
    (e) 3-bromocyclopentanone

30. Write the graphic formulas of all the stereoisomers that have a skeleton identical to that of 3,4-dimethyl-1,5-hexadiene.

31. How does the hydroxyl group at carbon 3 in estradiol differ from the OH group at carbon 3 in cholesterol?

32. Write the graphic formula of a noncyclic isomer of benzene.

33. How many grams of carbon dioxide are theoretically produced by the complete combustion in excess oxygen of 2.5 moles of 3,4,4-trimethyl-3-hexanol?

34. If 65 g of ethyl propionate is saponified completely, what is the theoretical yield of ethanol?

35. An alkenetriol has 12 carbon atoms. How many hydrogen atoms does it have?

APPENDIX

CONVERSION FACTORS

To Convert from	to	Multiply by
British thermal unit, Btu	calories (small), cal	252.
calories (small), cal	British thermal unit, Btu	3.97×10^{-3}
centimeters, cm	inches, in.	0.394
cubic centimeters, cu cm	cubic feet, cu ft	3.531×10^{-5}
cubic centimeters, cu cm	cubic inches, cu in.	0.06102
cubic centimeters, cu cm	gallons (U.S. liq), gal	2.642×10^{-4}
cubic centimeters, cu cm	milliliters, ml	0.999972
cubic centimeters, cu cm	ounces (U.S. liq), oz	0.03381
cubic feet, cu ft	cubic centimeters, cu cm	28317.
cubic inches, cu in.	cubic centimeters, cu cm	16.387
cubic inches, cu in.	milliliters, ml	16.387
feet, ft	centimeters, cm	30.48
gallons (U.S. liq), gal	cubic centimeters, cu cm	3785.
grains	grams, g	0.0648
grams, g	grains	15.43
grams, g	ounces (avoir.), oz	0.03527
inches, in.	centimeters, cm	2.54
kilograms, kg	pounds (avoir.), lb	2.205
liters, l	cubic feet, cu ft	0.0353
liters, l	cubic inches, cu in.	61.03
liters, l	gallons (U.S. liq), gal	0.2642
liters, l	quarts (U.S. liq), qt	1.0567
meters, m	feet, ft	3.281
meters, m	inches, in.	39.37
milliliters, ml	cubic centimeters, cu cm	1.000027
milliliters, ml	cubic inches, cu in.	0.06103
ounces (avoir.), oz	grams, g	28.35
ounces (U.S. liq), oz	cubic centimeters, cu cm	29.574
pounds (avoir.), lb	grams, g	453.6
quarts (U.S. liq), qt	cubic centimeters, cu cm	946.4
tons (metric)	kilograms, kg	1000.
tons (metric)	short tons	1.102
tons (short)	kilograms, kg	907.2
tons (short)	metric tons	0.9072

TABLE A.1 Vapor pressure of water

Temperature, in °C	Pressure, in mm of Hg	Temperature, in °C	Pressure, in mm of Hg
0	4.6	31	33.4
5	6.5	32	35.4
8	8.0	33	37.4
9	8.6	34	39.6
10	9.2	35	41.8
11	9.8	40	54.9
12	10.5	50	92.5
13	11.2	60	148.9
14	11.9	70	233.3
15	12.7	80	354.9
16	13.5	90	525.5
17	14.4	95	633.7
18	15.4	97	681.9
19	16.3	99	733.1
20	17.5	100	760.0
21	18.5	100.2	765.5
22	19.7	100.4	771.0
23	20.9	100.6	776.5
24	22.2	101	787.6
25	23.6	105	906.4
26	25.1	110	1075.4
27	26.5	114	1227.2
28	28.1	118	1397.2
29	29.8	150	3570.5
30	31.5	300	64432.8

TABLE A.2 Common alloys

Alloy	Composition in Per Cent
Bell metal	75–80 Cu, 25–20 Sn
Battery plate	94 Pb, 6 Sb
Brass (red)	90 Cu, 10 Zn
Brass (yellow)	67 Cu, 33 Zn
Bronze (aluminum)	90 Cu, 10 Al

TABLE A.2 (Continued)

Alloy	Composition in Per Cent
Bronze (bearing)	82 Cu, 16 Sn, 2 Zn
Bronze (gun metal)	90 Cu, 10 Sn
Bronze (hardware)	89 Cu, 9 Zn, 2 Pb
Bronze (manganese)	95 Cu, 5 Mn
Bronze (phosphor)	95.5 Cu, 4.3 Sn, 0.2 P (typical)
Babbitt metal	90 Sn, 7 Sb, 3 Cu
Britannia metal	90 Sn, 10 Sb
Chromel A	80 Ni, 20 Cr
Coinage gold	90 Au, 10 Cu
Coinage nickel (U.S.)	75 Cu, 25 Ni
Coinage silver	90 Ag, 10 Cu
Constantan	60 Cu, 40 Ni
Dentist amalgam	70 Hg, 30 Cu
Dowmetal A	91.8 Mg, 8 Al, 0.2 Mn
Duralumin	94.6 Al, 4.0 Cu, 0.8 Mg, 0.6 Mn
Duriron	84.3 Fe, 14.5 Si, 0.85 C, 0.35 Mn
German silver	60 Cu, 25 Zn, 15 Ni
Hastelloy A	60 Ni, 20 Fe, 20 Mo
Invar	63.8 Fe, 36 Ni, 0.2 C
Magnalium	90–95 Al, 10–5 Mg
Magnetic alloy	61 Cu, 26 Mn, 13 Al
Manganin	82 Cu, 15 Mn, 3 Ni
Manganese steel	86 Fe, 13 Mn, 1 C
Monel metal	60 Ni, 33 Cu, 7.0 Fe
Muntz metal	60 Cu, 40 Zn
Nichrome	60 Ni, 24 Fe, 16 Cr, 0.1 C
Nickel silver	55 Cu, 18 Ni, 27 Zn
Pewter (typical)	85 Sn, 7 Cu, 6 Bi, 2 Sb
Silver solder	63 Ag, 30 Cu, 7 Zn
Solder (plumber's)	67 Pb, Sn 33 (varies)
Speculum metal	67 Cu, 33 Sn
Stainless steel (typical)	70 Fe, 19 Cr, 9 Ni, 1 Cu, 1 Mo, 0.2 C
Steel (typical)	98–99.9 Fe, 0.1–2 C
Stellite No. 2	40 Co, 35 Cr, 9.2 W, 1.5 C, 1 Fe
Sterling silver	80 Ag, 18 Zn, 2 Cu
Type metal	82 Pb, 15 Sb, 3 Sn
Tin foil	88 Sn, 7.5 Pb, 4 Cu, 0.5 Sb
White gold	90 Au, 10 Pd; 60 Au, 40 Pt
Wood's metal	50 Bi, 25 Pb, 12.5 Sn, 12.5 Cd

TABLE A.3 Dissociation constants of weak acids (at room temperature)

Acid	K_a
Acetic, CH_3COOH	1.8×10^{-5}
Arsenic, $(HO)_3AsO$	2.5×10^{-4}
Dihydrogen arsenate ion, $(HO)_2AsO_2^-$	5.6×10^{-8}
Monohydrogen arsenate ion, $HOAsO_3^{--}$	3.0×10^{-13}
Benzoic, C_6H_5COOH	6.6×10^{-5}
Boric (meta), $HOBO$	6.0×10^{-10}
Carbonic, $(HO)_2CO$	4.2×10^{-7}
Hydrogen carbonate ion, $HOCO_2^-$	4.8×10^{-11}
Chlorous, $HOClO$	1.1×10^{-2}
Cyanic, $HOCN$	2.0×10^{-4}
Formic, $HCOOH$	2.1×10^{-4}
Hydrazoic, HN_3	1.9×10^{-5}
Hydrocyanic, HCN	4.0×10^{-10}
Hydrofluoric, HF	6.9×10^{-4}
Hydrogen peroxide, $HOOH$	2.4×10^{-12}
Hydrogen selenide, H_2Se	1.9×10^{-4}
Hydrogen sulfate ion, $HOSO_3^-$	1.3×10^{-2}
Hydrogen sulfide, H_2S	7.9×10^{-8}
Hydrosulfide ion, HS^-	2.0×10^{-15}
Hydrogen telluride, H_2Te	2.5×10^{-3}
Hydrotelluride ion, HTe^-	1.0×10^{-11}
Hypobromous, $HOBr$	2.0×10^{-9}
Hypochlorous, $HOCl$	3.2×10^{-8}
Nitrous, $HONO$	4.5×10^{-4}
Oxalic, $(HO)_2C_2O_2$	3.8×10^{-2}
Hydrogen oxalate ion, $HOC_2O_3^-$	5.0×10^{-5}
Phenol (carbolic acid), C_6H_5OH	1.0×10^{-10}
Phosphoric, $(HO)_3PO$	7.5×10^{-3}
Dihydrogen phosphate ion, $(HO)_2PO_2^-$	6.2×10^{-8}
Monohydrogen phosphate ion, $HOPO_3^{--}$	1.7×10^{-12}
Phosphorous, $(HO)_2HPO$	1.6×10^{-2}
Dihydrogen phosphite ion, $HOHPO_2^-$	7.0×10^{-7}
Propionic, CH_3CH_2COOH	1.4×10^{-5}
Sulfurous, $(HO)_2SO$	1.7×10^{-2}
Hydrogen sulfite ion, $HOSO_2^-$	5.6×10^{-8}
Tartaric, $C_2H_4O_2(COOH)_2$	1.1×10^{-3}
Hydrogen tartrate ion, $C_3H_4O_4COOH^-$	6.9×10^{-5}

TABLE A.4 Solubility-product constants (at room temperature)

Substances	Solubility Product Constant, K_{sp}
Silver acetate	4×10^{-3}
Silver bromate	6×10^{-5}
Bromides	
Lead bromide	4.6×10^{-6}
Mercury(I) bromide	1.3×10^{-22}
Silver bromide	5×10^{-13}
Carbonates	
Calcium carbonate	7×10^{-9}
Copper(II) carbonate	2.5×10^{-10}
Mercury(I) carbonate	9×10^{-17}
Silver carbonate	8.2×10^{-12}
Chlorides	
Lead chloride	1.7×10^{-5}
Silver chloride	1.7×10^{-10}
Mercury(I) chloride	1.1×10^{-18}
Fluorides	
Lead fluoride	4×10^{-8}
Strontium fluoride	7.9×10^{-10}
Calcium fluoride	1.7×10^{-10}
Hydroxides	
Aluminum hydroxide	5×10^{-33}
Chromium(III) hydroxide	7×10^{-31}
Cobalt(III) hydroxide	1×10^{-43}
Copper(II) hydroxide	1.6×10^{-19}
Iron(III) hydroxide	6×10^{-38}
Magnesium hydroxide	8.9×10^{-12}
Tin(II) hydroxide	3×10^{-27}
Zinc hydroxide	5×10^{-17}
Iodides	
Lead iodide	8.3×10^{-9}
Silver iodide	8.5×10^{-17}
Mercury(I) iodide	4×10^{-29}
Sulfates	
Calcium sulfate	2.4×10^{-5}
Barium sulfate	1.5×10^{-9}
Lead sulfate	1.3×10^{-8}
Sulfides	
Manganese(II) sulfide	8×10^{-14}
Iron(II) sulfide	4×10^{-17}
Zinc sulfide	1×10^{-20}
Cobalt(II) sulfide	5×10^{-22}

TABLE A.4 (Continued)

Substances	Solubility Product Constant, K_{sp}
Nickel(II) sulfide	1×10^{-22}
Lead sulfide	4×10^{-26}
Cadmium sulfide	6×10^{-27}
Bismuth sulfide	1×10^{-70}
Copper(II) sulfide	4×10^{-36}
Silver sulfide	1×10^{-50}
Mercury(I) sulfide	1×10^{-45}
Mercury(II) sulfide	1×10^{-50}

TABLE A.5 Covalent and ionic radii

Element	Covalent Atomic Radius, in A	Ion	
		Symbol	Radius, in A
Hydrogen	0.30	H^-	2.08
Helium	0.93		
Lithium	1.52	Li^+	0.60
Beryllium	1.11	Be^{++}	0.31
Boron	0.88		
Carbon	0.77		
Nitrogen	0.70		
Oxygen	0.66	O^{--}	1.40
Fluorine	0.64	F^-	1.36
Neon	1.12		
Sodium	1.86	Na^+	0.95
Magnesium	1.60	Mg^{++}	0.65
Aluminum	1.43	Al^{3+}	0.50
Silicon	1.17		
Phosphorus	1.10		
Sulfur	1.04	S^{--}	1.84
Chlorine	0.99	Cl^-	1.81
Argon	1.54		
Potassium	2.31	K^+	1.33
Calcium	1.97	Ca^{++}	0.99
Scandium	1.60	Sc^{3+}	0.81
Titanium	1.46		
Vanadium	1.31		

TABLE A.5 (Continued)

Element	Covalent Atomic Radius, in A	Ion Symbol	Ion Radius, in A
Chromium	1.25		
Manganese	1.29	Mn++	0.80
Iron	1.26	Fe++	0.75
Cobalt	1.25	Co++	0.72
Nickel	1.24	Ni++	0.70
Copper	1.28	Cu+	0.96
Zinc	1.33	Zn++	0.74
Gallium	1.22	Ga³+	0.62
Germanium	1.22	Ge⁴+	0.53
Arsenic	1.21		
Selenium	1.17	Se--	1.98
Bromine	1.14	Br-	1.95
Krypton	1.69		
Rubidium	2.44	Rb+	1.48
Strontium	2.15	Sr++	1.13
Yttrium	1.80	Y³+	0.93
Zirconium	1.57		
Silver	1.44	Ag+	1.26
Cadmium	1.49	Cd++	0.97
Indium	1.62	In³+	0.81
Tin	1.40	Sn⁴+	0.71
Antimony	1.41		
Tellurium	1.37	Te--	2.21
Iodine	1.33	I-	2.16
Xenon	1.90		
Cesium	2.62	Cs+	1.69
Barium	2.17	Ba++	1.35
Lanthanum	1.87	La³+	1.15
Cerium	1.82	Ce³+	1.01
Neodymium	1.82	Nd³+	0.99
Europium	2.04	Eu³+	0.97
Gadolinium	1.79	Gd³+	0.96
Holmium	1.76	Ho³+	0.93
Lutetium	1.74	Lu³+	0.89
Gold	1.44	Au+	1.37
Mercury	1.55	Hg++	1.10
Thallium	1.71	Tl³+	0.95
Lead	1.75	Pb⁴+	0.84
Uranium	1.40	U³+	1.11

TABLE A.6 Naturally radioactive families*

Uranium-238 Series

Nuclide	Half-life
^{238}U	4.5×10^9 yr
^{234}Th	24.1 days
^{234}Pa	1.14 min
^{234}U	2.4×10^5 yr
^{230}Th	8.0×10^4 yr
^{226}Ra	1620 yr
^{222}Rn	3.8 days
^{218}Po	3.0 min
^{218}At	2 sec
^{214}Pb	26.8 min
^{214}Bi	19.7 min
^{214}Po	1.5×10^{-4} sec
^{210}Tl	1.32 min
^{210}Pb	22 yr
^{210}Bi	5 days
^{210}Po	140 days
^{206}Tl	4.23 min
^{206}Pb	

Uranium-235 Series

Nuclide	Half-life
^{235}U	7.1×10^8 yr
^{231}Th	24.6 hr
^{231}Pa	3.2×10^4 yr
^{227}Ac	21.7 yr
^{227}Th	18.9 days
^{223}Fr	21 min
^{223}Ra	11.2 days
^{219}Rn	3.9 sec
^{215}Po	2×10^{-3} sec
^{215}At	10^{-4} sec
^{211}Pb	36.1 min
^{211}Bi	2.16 min
^{211}Po	5×10^{-3} sec
^{207}Tl	4.76 min
^{207}Pb	

Thorium-232 Series

Nuclide	Half-life
^{232}Th	1.39×10^{10} yr
^{228}Ra	6.7 yr
^{228}Ac	6.13 hr
^{228}Th	1.9 yr
^{224}Ra	3.64 days
^{220}Rn	54.5 sec
^{216}Po	0.16 sec
^{216}At	3×10^{-4} sec
^{212}Pb	10.6 hr
^{212}Bi	60.5 min
^{212}Po	3×10^{-7} sec
^{208}Tl	3.1 min
^{208}Pb	

* Half-life of each nuclide is shown in parentheses.

TABLE A.7 Ground state electronic configurations of atoms of elements 31–101*
(Subgroups 1s, 2s, 2p, 3s, 3p, and 3d are complete.)

Atomic No.	Element	Number of Electrons in Subgroups											
		4s	4p	4d	4f	5s	5p	5d	5f	6s	6p	6d	7s
31	Ga	2	1										
32	Ge	2	2										
33	As	2	3										
34	Se	2	4										
35	Br	2	5										
36	Kr	2	6										
37	Rb	2	6			1							
38	Sr	2	6			2							
39	Y	2	6	1		2							
40	Zr	2	6	2		2							
41	Nb	2	6	4		1							
42	Mo	2	6	5		1							
43	Tc	2	6	6		1							
44	Ru	2	6	7		1							
45	Rh	2	6	8		1							
46	Pd	2	6	10									
47	Ag	2	6	10		1							
48	Cd	2	6	10		2							
49	In	2	6	10		2	1						
50	Sn	2	6	10		2	2						
51	Sb	2	6	10		2	3						
52	Te	2	6	10		2	4						
53	I	2	6	10		2	5						
54	Xe	2	6	10		2	6						
55	Cs	2	6	10		2	6			1			
56	Ba	2	6	10		2	6			2			
57	La	2	6	10		2	6	1		2			
58	Ce	2	6	10	2	2	6			2			
59	Pr	2	6	10	3	2	6			2			
60	Nd	2	6	10	4	2	6			2			
61	Pm	2	6	10	5	2	6			2			
62	Sm	2	6	10	6	2	6			2			
63	Eu	2	6	10	7	2	6			2			
64	Gd	2	6	10	7	2	6	1		2			

*Electronic configurations of atoms of elements 1 through 20 are on page 113; of elements 21 through 30, page 123.

TABLE A.7 (Continued)

Atomic No.	Element	4s	4p	4d	4f	5s	5p	5d	5f	6s	6p	6d	7s
65	Tb	2	6	10	9	2	6			2			
66	Dy	2	6	10	10	2	6			2			
67	Ho	2	6	10	11	2	6			2			
68	Er	2	6	10	12	2	6			2			
69	Tm	2	6	10	13	2	6			2			
70	Yb	2	6	10	14	2	6			2			
71	Lu	2	6	10	14	2	6	1		2			
72	Hf	2	6	10	14	2	6	2		2			
73	Ta	2	6	10	14	2	6	3		2			
74	W	2	6	10	14	2	6	4		2			
75	Re	2	6	10	14	2	6	5		2			
76	Os	2	6	10	14	2	6	6		2			
77	Ir	2	6	10	14	2	6	9					
78	Pt	2	6	10	14	2	6	9		1			
79	Au	2	6	10	14	2	6	10		1			
80	Hg	2	6	10	14	2	6	10		2			
81	Tl	2	6	10	14	2	6	10		2	1		
82	Pb	2	6	10	14	2	6	10		2	2		
83	Bi	2	6	10	14	2	6	10		2	3		
84	Po	2	6	10	14	2	6	10		2	4		
85	At	2	6	10	14	2	6	10		2	5		
86	Rn	2	6	10	14	2	6	10		2	6		
87	Fr	2	6	10	14	2	6	10		2	6		1
88	Ra	2	6	10	14	2	6	10		2	6		2
89	Ac	2	6	10	14	2	6	10		2	6	1	2
90	Th	2	6	10	14	2	6	10		2	6	2	2
91	Pa	2	6	10	14	2	6	10	2	2	6	1	2
92	U	2	6	10	14	2	6	10	3	2	6	1	2
93	Np	2	6	10	14	2	6	10	5	2	6		2
94	Pu	2	6	10	14	2	6	10	6	2	6		2
95	Am	2	6	10	14	2	6	10	7	2	6		2
96	Cm	2	6	10	14	2	6	10	7	2	6	1	2
97	Bk	2	6	10	14	2	6	10	9	2	6		2
98	Cf	2	6	10	14	2	6	10	10	2	6		2
99	Es	2	6	10	14	2	6	10	11	2	6		2
100	Fm	2	6	10	14	2	6	10	12	2	6		2
101	Md	2	6	10	14	2	6	10	13	2	6		2

TABLE A.8 Stable nuclides (isotopes) occurring in nature

Element	Atomic Number	Mass Numbers of the Nuclides* (Approx. At. Wts. on Physical Scale)
Hydrogen	1	1, 2
Helium	2	4, 3
Lithium	3	7, 6
Beryllium	4	9, 8
Boron	5	11, 10
Carbon	6	12, 13
Nitrogen	7	14, 15
Oxygen	8	16, 18, 17
Fluorine	9	19
Neon	10	20, 22, 21
Sodium	11	23
Magnesium	12	24, 25, 26
Aluminum	13	27
Silicon	14	28, 29, 30
Phosphorus	15	31
Sulfur	16	32, 34, 33
Chlorine	17	35, 37
Argon	18	40, 36, 38
Potassium	19	39, 41, 40 (radioactive; *long* half-life)
Calcium	20	40, 44, 42, 43
Scandium	21	45
Titanium	22	48, 46, 47, 50, 49
Vanadium	23	51
Chromium	24	52, 53, 50, 54
Manganese	25	55
Iron	26	56, 54, 57, 58
Cobalt	27	59, 57
Nickel	28	58, 60, 62, 61, 64
Copper	29	63, 65
Zinc	30	64, 66, 68, 67, 70
Gallium	31	69, 71
Germanium	32	74, 72, 70, 73, 76
Arsenic	33	75
Selenium	34	80, 78, 76, 82, 77, 74
Bromine	35	79, 81
Krypton	36	84, 86, 82, 83, 80, 78
Rubidium	37	85, 87 (radioactive; *long* half-life)
Strontium	38	88, 86, 87, 84
Yttrium	39	89
Zirconium	40	90, 92, 94, 91, 96
Niobium	41	93

* Listed in decreasing order of abundance.

TABLE A.8 (Continued)

Element	Atomic Number	Mass Numbers of the Nuclides* (Approx. At. Wts. on Physical Scale)
Molybdenum	42	98, 96, 95, 92, 94, 100, 97
Ruthenium	44	102, 101, 104, 100, 99, 96
Rhodium	45	103, 101
Palladium	46	106, 108, 105, 110, 104, 102
Silver	47	107, 109
Cadmium	48	114, 112, 110, 111, 113, 116, 106, 108
Indium	49	115, 113
Tin	50	120, 118, 116, 119, 117, 124, 122, 112, 114, 115
Antimony	51	121, 123
Tellurium	52	130, 128, 126, 125, 124, 122, 123, 120
Iodine	53	127
Xenon	54	132, 129, 131, 134, 136, 130, 128, 124, 126
Cesium	55	133
Barium	56	138, 137, 136, 135, 134, 130, 132
Lanthanum	57	139
Cerium	58	140, 142, 138, 136
Praseodymium	59	141
Neodymium	60	142, 144, 146, 143, 145, 148, 150
Samarium	62	152, 154, 147, 149, 148, 150, 144
Europium	63	151, 153
Gadolinium	64	156, 158, 155, 157, 160
Terbium	65	159
Dysprosium	66	164, 163, 162, 161
Holmium	67	165
Erbium	68	166, 168, 167, 170
Thulium	69	169
Ytterbium	70	174, 172, 173, 176, 171
Lutetium	71	175
Hafnium	72	180, 178, 177, 179, 176
Tantalum	73	181
Wolfram (Tungsten)	74	184, 186, 182, 183, 180
Rhenium	75	187, 185
Osmium	76	192, 190, 189, 188, 187, 186, 184
Iridium	77	193, 191
Platinum	78	195, 194, 196, 198, 192
Gold	79	197
Mercury	80	202, 200, 199, 201, 198, 204, 196
Thallium	81	205, 203
Lead	82	208, 206, 207, 204
Bismuth	83	209
Thorium	90	232 (radioactive but long half-life)
Uranium	92	238, 235 (both radioactive but long half-life)

TABLE A.9 Physical constants of the common elements

Element	Mp, °C	Bp, °C	Sp. Gr.	Form Color	Radioactive Nuclides	Major Oxid. States
Aluminum	660	2057	2.7	cub. silv.	24, 25, 26, 28, 29	+3
Antimony	631	1380	6.68	hex. silv.	116, 120, 122, 124–134	−3, +3, +5
Argon	−189	−185.7	1.40(liq)	col.	35, 37, 39, 41, 42	0
Arsenic	814(b)	615(s)	5.7 4.7 2.0	hex. blk. amor. blk. cub. yel.	68–74, 76–80	−3, +3, +5
Barium	850	1140	3.5	yel. silv.	126–129, 131, 133, 137, 139–144	+2
Beryllium	1280	2970	1.85	hex. gray	7, 8, 10	+2
Bismuth	271	1560	9.8	hex. silv. wh. red	198–208, 210–215	−3, +3, +5
Boron	2300	2550	3.34 2.34	monocl. yel. amor. brown	8, 9, 12	+3
Bromine	−7.2	58.8	2.93	red liq.	74–78, 80, 82–85, 87–89	−1, +1, +5
Cadmium	321	767	8.64	hex. silv. wh.	104, 105, 107, 109, 111, 113, 115, 117, 118	+2
Calcium	844	1240	1.55	cub. silv. wh.	39, 41, 45, 47, 49	+2
Carbon	3652+ 3652+ >3500	4200 4200 4200	1.8–2.0 2.25 3.51	amor. blk. graphite diamond	10, 11, 14, 15	−4 to +4

TABLE A.9 (Continued)

Element	Mp, °C	Bp, °C	Sp. Gr.	Form Color	Radioactive Nuclides	Major Oxid. States
Cerium	640	1400	6.9 6.7	cub. hexag. gray	133–135, 137, 139, 141, 143–146	+3, +4
Cesium	28.5	670	1.87	hex. silv.-wh.	123, 125–132, 134–144	+1
Chlorine	−103	−34.6	1.56(liq)	gas, grn.-yel.	32–34, 36, 38–40	−1, +1, +3, +5, +7
Chromium	1890	2200	7.20	cub. gray	46, 48, 49, 51, 55	+2, +3, +6
Cobalt	1495	2900	8.9	cub. silv.-gray	54–58, 60–62	+2, +3
Copper	1083	2336	8.92	cub. redsh.	58–62, 64, 66–68	+1, +2
Fluorine	−223	−188	1.11(liq)	gas, grn.-yel.	17, 18, 20, 21	−1
Gallium	29.8	1983	5.9–6.1	rhomb. gray-blk.	64–68, 70, 72, 73	+3
Germanium	958.5	2700	5.35	cub. gray-wh.	66–69, 71, 73, 75, 77, 78	−4, +2, +4
Gold	1063	2600	19.3	cub. yel.	191–203, 187, 188, 189	+1, +3
Hafnium	2207	3200	13.3	gray	170–173, 175, 179, 180, 181	+4
Helium	−272	−269	0.15(liq)	gas	5, 6	0
Hydrogen	−259.1	−252.8	0.07(liq)	gas	3	+1, −1
Indium	156.4	2000	7.30	tetr. silv.-wh.	107–119	+1, +2, +3
Iodine	113.7	184.4	4.93	rhomb. blk.-vlt.	119–126, 128–139	−1, +1, +5, +7

	Melting point	Boiling point	Density	Form / color	Isotopes	Valence
Niobium	1950	2900	8.55	rhomb. gray	89–99	+3, +5
Nitrogen	−209.9	−195.8	.81(liq)	gas	12, 13, 16, 17	−1, −2, −3, +1 to +5
Osmium	2700	5300	22.48	hex. gray	182, 183, 185, 187, 190, 191, 193, 194	+3, +4, +6, +8
Oxygen	−218.4	−183	1.14(liq)	gas	14, 15, 19	−2, −1
Palladium	1549	2540	11.4	cub. silv.-wh.	98–101, 103, 105, 107, 109, 111–113	+2, +4
Phosphorus	44.1 590 593	280 — —	1.82 2.20 2.36 2.70	yel. red vlt. blk.	28, 29, 30, 32, 33, 34	−3, +1, +3, +5
Platinum	1774	4300	21.45	cub. silv.	187, 188, 189, 191, 193, 195, 197, 199	+2, +4, +6
Potassium	62.3	760	0.86	cub. soft silv.	38, 40, 42, 43, 44, 45	+1
Radium	960	1140	5+	silv.-wh.	213, 219–230	+2
Radon	−110	−61.8	4.4(liq)	gas	206–212, 215–222	0
Rubidium	38.5	700	1.53(liq) 1.48(liq)	silv.-wh. soft met.	81–84, 86–95, 97	+1
Selenium	(220) —	688 —	4.82 4.2	amor. red vitr. blk.	70, 72, 73, 75, 77, 79, 81, 83, 84	−2, +4, +6
Iridium	2454	4800	22.4	cub. silv.-wh.	187–192, 194–198	+3, +4, +6

TABLE A.9 (Continued)

Element	Mp, °C	Bp, °C	Sp. Gr.	Form Color	Radioactive Nuclides	Major Oxid. States
Iron	1535	3000	7.86	cub.	52, 53, 55, 59, 60, 61	+2, +3
Krypton	−156.6	−152.9	2.16(liq)	gas	76, 77, 79, 81, 83, 85, 87–95, 97	0, +4
Lanthanum	826	1800	6.15	gray	131–138, 140–144	+3
Lead	327.4	1620	11.34	cub.	197–205, 207, 214, 209–212	+2, +4
Lithium	186	1335	0.534	cub. silv.-wh.	5, 8, 9	+1
Magnesium	651	1107	1.74	hex. silv.-wh.	23, 27, 28	+2
Manganese	1260	1900	7.20	cub. or tetr. gray-pink	50–54, 56, 57	+2, +4, +6, +7
Mercury	−38.87	356.6	13.6	silv. liq.	189–195, 197, 199, 203, 205	+1, +2
Molybdenum	2620	5560	10.2	cub. silv.-wh.	90, 91, 93, 99, 101, 102, 105	+3, +4, +5, +6
Neodymium	840	—	6.9	yel. met.	138–141, 144, 147, 149, 151	+3, +4
Neon	−248.7	−246	1.20(liq)	gas	18, 19, 23, 24	0
Nickel	1455	2900	8.90	cub. silv.	56, 57, 59, 63, 65, 66	+2, +3
Silicon	1400	2600 2600 2600	2.42 2.00 2.4	cub. gray amor. brown blk.	26, 27, 31, 32	−4, +4
Silver	960.8	1950	10.5	cub. wh.	102–115	+1

Element						
Sodium	97.5	880	0.97	cub. silv.	20, 21, 22, 24, 25	+1
Strontium	(800)	1150	2.6	cub. silv. pa. yel.	81, 82, 83, 85, 87, 89–95, 97	+2
Sulfur	112.8 / 119.3 / 120	445 / 445 / 445	2.07 / 1.96 / 1.92	rhomb. yel. / monocl. yel. / amor. pa. yel.	31, 35, 37	−2, +2, +4, +6
Tantalum	3027	(4100)	16.6	cub. gray-blk.	176–186	+5
Tellurium	452 / 452	1390 / 1390	6.25 / 6.00	rhomb. silv. / amor. blk.	116–119, 121, 123, 125, 127, 129, 131–134	−2, +2, +4, +6
Thallium	302	1457	11.85	tetr. blk.	195–202, 204, 206–210	+1, +3
Thorium	1845	>3000	11.2	cub. gray	223–235	+4
Tin	231.9 (stab)	2260 / 2270 / 2270	5.75 / 7.28 / 6.54	cub. gray / tetr. wh. / rhomb. wh.	108–111, 113, 117, 119, 123, 125–127, 130–132, 121	+2, +4
Titanium	1800	>3000	4.5	hex. or cub. / silv. gray	43, 44, 45, 51	+2, +3, +4
Tungsten	3370	5900	19.3	cub. gray blk.	176–181, 183, 185, 187, 188	+3, +6
Uranium	(1133)	ignite	18.7	cub. blk. silv.-wh.	227–223, 236, 237, 239, 240	+3, +4, +6
Vanadium	1710	3000	5.96	cub. gray	45–49, 52, 53, 54	+2, +3, +4, +5
Zinc	419.5	907	7.14	hex. blue-wh.	60–63, 65, 69, 71, 72	+2
Zirconium	1900	>2900	6.4	cub. silv. wh.-gray	86–90, 93, 95, 97	+4

TABLE A.10 Table of logarithms

N	0	1	2	3	4	5	6	7	8	9
10	0000	0043	0086	0128	0170	0212	0253	0294	0334	0374
11	0414	0453	0492	0531	0569	0607	0645	0682	0719	0755
12	0792	0828	0864	0899	0934	0969	1004	1038	1072	1106
13	1139	1173	1206	1239	1271	1303	1335	1367	1399	1430
14	1461	1492	1523	1553	1584	1614	1644	1673	1703	1732
15	1761	1790	1818	1847	1875	1903	1931	1959	1987	2014
16	2041	2068	2095	2122	2148	2175	2201	2227	2253	2279
17	2304	2330	2355	2380	2405	2430	2455	2480	2504	2529
18	2553	2577	2601	2625	2648	2672	2695	2718	2742	2765
19	2788	2810	2833	2856	2878	2900	2923	2945	2967	2989
20	3010	3032	3054	3075	3096	3118	3139	3160	3181	3201
21	3222	3243	3263	3284	3304	3324	3345	3365	3385	3404
22	3424	3444	3464	3483	3502	3522	3541	3560	3579	3598
23	3617	3636	3655	3674	3692	3711	3729	3747	3766	3784
24	3802	3820	3838	3856	3874	3892	3909	3927	3945	3962
25	3979	3997	4014	4031	4048	4065	4082	4099	4116	4133
26	4150	4166	4183	4200	4216	4232	4249	4265	4281	4298
27	4314	4330	4346	4362	4378	4393	4409	4425	4440	4456
28	4472	4487	4502	4518	4533	4548	4564	4579	4594	4609
29	4624	4639	4654	4669	4683	4698	4713	4728	4742	4757
30	4771	4786	4800	4814	4829	4843	4857	4871	4886	4900
31	4914	4928	4942	4955	4969	4983	4997	5011	5024	5038
32	5051	5065	5079	5092	5105	5119	5132	5145	5159	5172
33	5185	5198	5211	5224	5237	5250	5263	5276	5289	5302
34	5315	5328	5340	5353	5366	5378	5391	5403	5416	5428
35	5441	5453	5465	5478	5490	5502	5514	5527	5539	5551
36	5563	5575	5587	5599	5611	5623	5635	5647	5658	5670
37	5682	5694	5705	5717	5729	5740	5752	5763	5775	5786
38	5798	5809	5821	5832	5843	5855	5866	5877	5888	5899
39	5911	5922	5933	5944	5955	5966	5977	5988	5999	6010
40	6021	6031	6042	6053	6064	6075	6085	6096	6107	6117
41	6128	6138	6149	6160	6170	6180	6191	6201	6212	6222
42	6232	6243	6253	6263	6274	6284	6294	6304	6314	6325
43	6335	6345	6355	6365	6375	6385	6395	6405	6415	6425
44	6435	6444	6454	6464	6474	6484	6493	6503	6513	6522
45	6532	6542	6551	6561	6571	6580	6590	6599	6609	6618
46	6628	6637	6646	6656	6665	6675	6684	6693	6702	6712
47	6721	6730	6739	6749	6758	6767	6776	6785	6794	6803
48	6812	6821	6830	6839	6848	6857	6866	6875	6884	6893
49	6902	6911	6920	6928	6937	6946	6955	6964	6972	6981
50	6990	6998	7007	7016	7024	7033	7042	7050	7059	7067
51	7076	7084	7093	7101	7110	7118	7126	7135	7143	7152
52	7160	7168	7177	7185	7193	7202	7210	7218	7226	7235
53	7243	7251	7259	7267	7275	7284	7292	7300	7308	7316
54	7324	7332	7340	7348	7356	7364	7372	7380	7388	7396

TABLE A.10 (Continued)

N	0	1	2	3	4	5	6	7	8	9
55	7404	7412	7419	7427	7435	7443	7451	7459	7466	7474
56	7482	7490	7497	7505	7513	7520	7528	7536	7543	7551
57	7559	7566	7574	7582	7589	7597	7604	7612	7619	7627
58	7634	7642	7649	7657	7664	7672	7679	7686	7694	7701
59	7709	7716	7723	7731	7738	7745	7752	7760	7767	7774
60	7782	7789	7796	7803	7810	7818	7825	7832	7839	7846
61	7853	7860	7868	7875	7882	7889	7896	7903	7910	7917
62	7924	7931	7938	7945	7952	7959	7966	7973	7980	7987
63	7993	8000	8007	8014	8021	8028	8035	8041	8048	8055
64	8062	8069	8075	8082	8089	8096	8102	8109	8116	8122
65	8129	8136	8142	8149	8156	8162	8169	8176	8182	8189
66	8195	8202	8209	8215	8222	8228	8235	8241	8248	8254
67	8261	8267	8274	8280	8287	8293	8299	8306	8312	8319
68	8325	8331	8338	8344	8351	8357	8363	8370	8376	8382
69	8388	8395	8401	8407	8414	8420	8426	8432	8439	8445
70	8451	8457	8463	8470	8476	8482	8488	8494	8500	8506
71	8513	8519	8525	8531	8537	8543	8549	8555	8561	8567
72	8573	8579	8585	8591	8597	8603	8609	8615	8621	8627
73	8633	8639	8645	8651	8657	8663	8669	8675	8681	8686
74	8692	8698	8704	8710	8716	8722	8727	8733	8739	8745
75	8751	8756	8762	8768	8774	8779	8785	8791	8797	8802
76	8808	8814	8820	8825	8831	8837	8842	8848	8854	8859
77	8865	8871	8876	8882	8887	8893	8899	8904	8910	8915
78	8921	8927	8932	8938	8943	8949	8954	8960	8965	8971
79	8976	8982	8987	8993	8998	9004	9009	9015	9020	9025
80	9031	9036	9042	9047	9053	9058	9063	9069	9074	9079
81	9085	9090	9096	9101	9106	9112	9117	9122	9128	9133
82	9138	9143	9149	9154	9159	9165	9170	9175	9180	9186
83	9191	9196	9201	9206	9212	9217	9222	9227	9232	9238
84	9243	9248	9253	9258	9263	9269	9274	9279	9284	9289
85	9294	9299	9304	9309	9315	9320	9325	9330	9335	9340
86	9345	9350	9355	9360	9365	9370	9375	9380	9385	9390
87	9395	9400	9405	9410	9415	9420	9425	9430	9435	9440
88	9445	9450	9455	9460	9465	9469	9474	9479	9484	9489
89	9494	9499	9504	9509	9513	9518	9523	9528	9533	9538
90	9542	9547	9552	9557	9562	9566	9571	9576	9581	9586
91	9590	9595	9600	9605	9609	9614	9619	9624	9628	9633
92	9638	9643	9647	9652	9657	9661	9666	9671	9675	9680
93	9685	9689	9694	9699	9703	9708	9713	9717	9722	9727
94	9731	9736	9741	9745	9750	9754	9759	9763	9768	9773
95	9777	9782	9786	9791	9795	9800	9805	9809	9814	9818
96	9823	9827	9832	9836	9841	9845	9850	9854	9859	9863
97	9868	9872	9877	9881	9886	9890	9894	9899	9903	9908
98	9912	9917	9921	9926	9930	9934	9939	9943	9948	9952
99	9956	9961	9965	9969	9974	9978	9983	9987	9991	9996

SUGGESTED BIBLIOGRAPHY

A complete list of specific articles in periodicals and chemical journals and of specific sections and chapters in books that could be read profitably by the student of introductory chemistry would be enormous. Even if such a list were available, the choice of when, what, and how much to read would be, to say the least, arbitrary.

Below is a brief list of some of the more obvious sources of information and interpretations that students who are using this book may find useful as means to supplement and complement what is in the text. The list is prepared on the assumption that many students enjoy browsing and that the wise student appreciates the value of an index.

PERIODICALS AND JOURNALS
> *Journal of Chemical Education; Chemical and Engineering News; Science News Letter; Scientific American.*

BOOKS ON PROBLEMS AND CALCULATIONS
> Anderson, H. V., *Chemical Calculations*, 6th ed., McGraw-Hill, New York, 1955.
> Benson, S. W., *Chemical Calculations*, Wiley, New York, 1952.
> Babor, J. A., and Kremer, C. B., *How to Solve Problems in General Chemistry*, 2nd ed., Crowell, New York, 1950.
> Frey, Paul R., *Chemistry Problems and How to Solve Them*, 5th ed., Barnes and Noble, New York, 1958.
> Pierce, C., and Smith, R. N., *General Chemistry Workbook*, 2nd ed., Freeman, San Francisco, 1958.
> Sackheim, G. I., *Chemical Calculations*, Stipes, Champaign, Ill., 1958.
> Schaum, D., *Theory and Problems of College Chemistry*, 4th ed., Schaum, New York, 1958.
> Sorum, C. H., *How to Solve General Chemistry Problems*, 2nd ed., Prentice-Hall, Englewood Cliffs, N.J., 1958.

MORE ADVANCED TEXTS
> Brewster, R. A., and McEwen, W. E., *Organic Chemistry: A Brief Course*, 2nd ed., Prentice-Hall, Englewood Cliffs, N.J., 1959.
> Day, M. C., and Selbin, J., *Theoretical Inorganic Chemistry*, Reinhold, New York, 1962.
> Emeleus, H. J., and Anderson, J. S., *Modern Aspects of Inorganic Chemistry*, 3rd ed., Van Nostrand, Princeton, N.J., 1960.
> Fieser, L. F., and Fieser, Mary, *Basic Organic Chemistry*, Heath, Boston, 1959.

Gilreath, E., *Fundamental Concepts of Inorganic Chemistry*, McGraw-Hill, New York, 1958.

Gould, E. S., 2nd ed., *Inorganic Reactions and Structure*, Holt, Rinehart and Winston, New York, 1962.

Hart, H., and Schuetz, R. D., *A Short Course in Organic Chemistry*, 2nd ed., Houghton Mifflin, Boston, 1959.

Kruyt, H. R., and Overbeek, J. T. G., *An Introduction to Physical Chemistry*, Holt, Rinehart and Winston, New York, 1962.

Leffler, J. E., *A Short Course of Organic Chemistry*, Macmillan, New York, 1959.

Moeller, T., *Inorganic Chemistry*, Wiley, New York, 1952.

Morrison, R., and Boyd, R., *Organic Chemistry*, Allyn and Bacon, Boston, 1959.

Wallwork, S. C., *Physical Chemistry for Students of Pharmacy and Biology*, Wiley, New York, 1960.

BOOKS ON SPECIFIC TOPICS

Brown, G. I., *A Simple Guide to Modern Valency Theory*, Longmans, Green, New York, 1957.

Dyson, G. M., *A Short Guide to Chemical Literature*, 2nd ed., Longmans, Green, New York, 1958.

Gamow, G., *Mr. Tompkins Explores the Atom*, Macmillan, New York, 1945.

Harrow, B., and Mazur, A., *Textbook of Biochemistry*, 8th ed., Saunders, Philadelphia, 1962.

Hogness and Johnson, *Qualitative Analysis and Chemical Equilibrium*, 4th ed., Holt, New York, 1954.

Kieffer, W. F., *The Mole Concept in Chemistry*, Reinhold, New York, 1962 (paperbound).

Kittel, C., *Elementary Solid State Physics*, Wiley, New York, 1962.

Lewis, G. N., *Valence and the Structure of Atoms and Molecules*, Chemical Catalog Co., New York, 1923.

Li Ch'iao-Píng, *The Chemical Arts of Old China*, Chemical Education Publishing Co., Easton, Pa.

Meyer, L. H., *Food Chemistry*, Reinhold, New York, 1960.

Overman, R. T., *Basic Concepts of Nuclear Chemistry*, Reinhold, New York, 1962 (paperbound).

Partington, J. R., *A History of Chemistry*, vols. 2 and 3, St. Martin's Press, New York, 1961.   (Volumes 1 and 4 are in preparation.)

Pauling, L., *The Nature of the Chemical Bond*, 3rd ed., Cornell University Press, Ithaca, N.Y., 1960.

Ryschkewitsch, G. E., *Electronic Structure, Bonding, and Molecular Shape*, Reinhold, New York, 1962 (paperbound).

Sanderson, R. T., *Chemical Periodicity*, Reinhold, New York, 1960.

Seaborg, G. T., *The New Elements*, Chemical Education Publishing Co., Easton, Pa., 1959.

Seaborg, G. T., and Valens, E. G., *Elements of the Universe*, Dutton, New York, 1962.

Sisler, H. H., *Chemistry in Non-Aqueous Solvents*, Reinhold, New York, 1961 (paperbound).

VanderWerf, C. A., *Acids, Bases, and the Chemistry of the Covalent Bond*, Reinhold, New York, 1961 (paperbound).

Weeks, Mary Elvira, and Leicester, H. M., *Discovery of the Elements*, 6th ed., Chemical Education Publishing Co., Easton, Pa., 1956.

ANSWERS TO PROBLEMS

CHAPTER 1

1. (a) 743,480 mg; (b) 26.27 oz; (c) 1.638 lb; (d) 0.74348 kg. **2.** (a) 3700 ml; (b) 22 g; (c) 0.041 l. **3.** 3.9 l. **4.** 149°F. **6.** (a) 4.6 ml; (b) 131 g; (c) 5 ml of Bi; (d) Bi; (e) 4900 mg; (f) 220 ml; (g) 27 ml; (h) 2600 g. **7.** 130 ml. **8.** 0.5. **9.** 45 ml. **10.** (a) On ordinary 2-pan chemical balance; (b) on 1-pan, single-spring device. **11.** (a) c; (b) p; (c) p; (d) c; (e) p; (f) p; (g) p; (h) p. **12.** (a) p; (b) c; (c) c; (d) p; (e) neither; (f) c; (g) c.

CHAPTER 2

1. 110 g. **2.** 23 g. **3.** 126,000 mg. **4.** 2.7 g. **5.** (a) 5.0 g of boron; (b) 10 g of sodium. **6.** 120 g. **7.** 3.33 moles. **8.** 16 g-atoms. **9.** 35 g. **10.** 460 g. **11.** 37 g. **12.** 4.9 g. **13.** 34 ml. **14.** 92 ml. **15.** 38. **16.** 1.5×10^{23} atoms. **17.** 193. **18.** 0.055 cal/g°C.

CHAPTER 3

1. 34,000 mg. **2.** 190 g. **3.** 86 g. **4.** (a) $H_2S_2O_7$; (b) $H_2S_2O_7$; **5.** HN_3. **6.** C_8H_{18}. **7.** Ta_2O_4. **8.** C_6H_{12}. **9.** NH_2. **10.** 3.3 g-atoms. **11.** (a) 12 g-atoms; (b) 77.5 g; (c) 19 g; (d) 0.31 mole. **12.** K_2GeF_6. **13.** C_3H_8. **14.** Z_2M_6. **15.** (a) 92.25% C, 7.75% H; (b) 97.66% N, 2.34% H; (c) 26.58% K, 35.35% Cr, 38.07% O; (d) 40% C, 53.3% O, 6.7% H. **16.** 32.6 tons. **17.** (a) BaSe; (b) Al_2S_3; (c) $MnCl_3$; (d) $RaBr_2$; (e) $Cd(NO_3)_2$; (f) $Mg(ClO_4)_2$; (g) $NaNO_2$; (h) K_3PO_4; (i) $LiMnO_4$; (j) $Ca(HCO_3)_2$; (k) $CaSO_3$; (l) $PbCrO_4$; (m) $Co(OH)_2$; (n) $FeCl_3$; (o) $NaBrO_3$; (p) Ag_2SO_4; (q) NiO; (r) Cr_2O_3; (s) $(NH_4)_2SO_4$; (t) N_2O_5. **18.** (a) sodium chlorite; (b) cesium hydrogen carbonate; (c) manganese(III) hydroxide; (d) potassium perchlorate; (e) calcium carbide; (f) potassium cyanate; (g) zinc chromate; (h) sodium monohydrogen phosphate; (i) barium cyanide; (j) sodium dichromate; (k) calcium hydrogen carbonate; (l) barium hypochlorite; (m) potassium thiosulfate; (n) sulfur hexafluoride; (o) strontium iodide; (p) magnesium selenide; (q) calcium silicate; (r) potassium hydrogen sulfate; (s) sodium hydrogen sulfite; (t) ammonium bromide.

CHAPTER 4

1. (a) 13 moles; (b) 420 g; (c) 6 moles; (d) 690 tons; (e) 195 tons; (f) 206×10^4 g. **2.** (a) 110 kg; (b) 60 l; (c) 2.5×10^4 l; (d) 18 g. **3.** (a) 14 g;

(b) 78%; (c) 3.13 g; (d) 27 g. **4.** 40 g of C_3H_8, 150 g of O_2. **5.** (a) 32 g; (b) 10 moles; (c) 1.6 l; (d) 420 l; (e) 28 l. **6.** (a) 250 g; (b) 50; (c) 65 g. **7.** (a) 40; (b) 240 g; (c) 24 g; (d) 71. **8.** 3.4 g. **9.** 5.6×10^5 cal. **10.** (a) 0.4 mole; (b) 37,000 cal.

CHAPTER 5

1. $^{136}_{58}Ce$. **2.** (a) $^{142}_{58}Ce$; (b) 55 electrons; (c) $^{136}_{54}Xe$. **3.** (a) Ba; (b) 56 protons. **4.** 8. **5.** 40. **6.** (a) $^{116}_{48}Cd$; (b) 78; (c) $^{116}_{52}Te$. **7.** 50%. **8.** Have differing numbers of protons and neutrons. **9.** Zinc 64, 66, 67, 68, 70. **10.** Selenium 80, 78, 76, 82, 77, 74. **11.** 63.6. **12.** Radioactive alpha emitter. **13.** (a) $^{106}_{48}Cd$; (b) cadmium 106; (c) 48 electrons; (d) 46 electrons; (e) 48 protons. **14.** (a) $^{104}_{44}Ru$; (b) ruthenium 104; (c) 44 (positive); (d) palladium 104; (e) ruthenium 102, 101, 100, 99, 96; (f) 44.

CHAPTER 6

1. (a) 18; (b) 18; (c) 30; (d) 50; (e) 16; (f) 12; (g) 14; (h) 30. **2.** (a) 0 or 8; (b) 1; (c) 5; (d) 6; (e) 7; (f) 4; (g) 6; (h) 2. **3.** (a) 0 or 4; (b) none; (c) 1; (d) 2; (e) 3; (f) 1; (g) 2; (h) 1. **4.** (a) 0; (b) 1; (c) 3; (d) 2; (e) 1; (f) 2; (g) 2; (h) 0. **5.** (a) 36; (b) 54; (c) 78; (d) 28; (e) 46; (f) 28; (g) 46; (h) 28; (i) 46; (j) 78. **6.** (a) 19; (b) 27; (c) 40; (d) 15; (e) 26; (f) 16; (g) 24; (h) 15; (i) 24; (j) 42. **7.** (a) $Sr|$; (b) $Cs\cdot$; (c) $\overline{Pb}\cdot$; (d) $\cdot\overline{As}\cdot$; (e) $|\underline{I}\cdot$; (f) $|\underline{Se}\cdot$; (g) $\cdot\overline{Sb}\cdot$; (h) $\overline{Ge}\cdot$; (i) $\overline{In}\cdot$; (j) $|\overline{At}\cdot\cdot$. **8.** (a) ++; (b) +; (c) 4+; (d) 5+; (e) 7+; (f) 6+; (g) 5+; (h) 4+; (i) 3+; (j) 7+. **9.** (a) Concept of chemical periodicity; (b) I, Br, Cl; (c) solid, dark. **10.** Concept of periodicity. **12.** Inert gases. **13.** Cs and Ba. **14.** Rb^+, Kr, Br^-, Se^{--}, Y^{3+}. **15.** Br^-, Kr, Rb^+, Sr^{++}, Y^{3+}. **16.** As, Se, Ge, Ga, Kr. **17.** Po, Se, S, O. **18.** K^+, Ar, Cl^-, S^{--}. **19.** 32. **20.** 10, omitting $8a$ elements. **21.** Oxygen-17 and oxygen-18. **22.** 2.6.

CHAPTER 7

1. SrI_2. **2.** $TeCl_6$. **3.** (a) CsH, SrS, MgI_2, Mg_3N_2, K_3PO_4, $LiClO_4$; (b) AsH_3, BrCl, SO_2, CBr_4. **4.** All those in Problem 3(a). **5.** Cl^-, Ar, K^+, Ca^{++}. **6.** Cl^-, S^{--}. **7.** Na^+F^-, $Mg^{++}O^{--}$ or $(Na^+)_2O^{--}$, $Mg^{++}(F^-)_2$, or K^+Cl^-, $Ca^{++}S^{--}$, etc. **8.** All can be grouped as indicated—one group is ClO_3^-, SO_3^{--}, PO_3^{3-}; another is BrO_3^-, SeO_3^{--}, AsO_3^{3-}; another is NO_3^-, CO_3^{--}. **9.** Ne, F^-, O^{--}, N^{3-}, C_4^-, Na^+, Mg^{++}, Al^{3+}. **10.** Yes, sodium ions (+ charged molecules) and chloride ions (− charged molecules). **11.** In Na^+ 11 protons attract 10 electrons; in F^- 9 protons attract 10 electrons. **12.** K, Ca, Sc, Ti, V, Cr, Mn. **13.** (a) H_2Se; (b) AsH_3; (c) $Sr^{++}(Cl^-)_2$;

(d) $Mg^{++}S^{--}$; (e) K^+I^-; (f) $(Cs^+)_2Te^{--}$; (g) $(Li^+)_2Se^{--}$; (h) $BeBr_2$; (i) Al_2S_3; (j) $(Mg^{++})_3(N^{3-})_2$. **14.** (a) Sn; (b) Rb; (c) Cs; (d) I; (e) N; (f) Te; (g) Al; (h) P; (i) C; (j) Bi. **15.** (a) Br; (b) P; (c) Cl; (d) F; (e) F; (f) I; (g) C; (h) S; (i) Se; (j) N. **16.** F_2. **17.** (a) c, d, e, f, g, j; (b) a, b, h, i.

CHAPTER 8

1. Ionic—a, d, f, h, i; covalent—b, c, e, g, j. **2.** (a) C—O; (b) H—O; (c) H—O; (d) Si—F; (e) S—F; (f) P—Cl; (g) P—O; (h) P—Cl; (i) C—H; (j) H—F. **3.** C—S or N—Cl. **4.** Si—F. **5.** C—S or N—Cl. **7.** (a) Resorcinol; (b) toluene; (c) resorcinol; (d) toluene; (e) toluene; (f) resor-

cinol. **8.** (a) D—$\overline{O}$—D; (b) D—$\overline{Cl}$|; (c) $Na^+D|^-$; (d) D—$\overset{\overset{\displaystyle D}{|}}{\underset{\underset{\displaystyle D}{|}}{C}}$—D;

(e) D—$\overset{}{\underset{\underset{\displaystyle D}{|}}{N}}$| (f) $\left[D—\overset{\overset{\displaystyle D}{|}}{\underset{\underset{\displaystyle D}{|}}{N}}—D \right]^+$; (g) D—$\overset{}{\underset{\underset{\displaystyle D}{|}}{As}}$|; (h) D—$\overline{Se}$—D. **9.** (a) Planar,

bent; (b) linear; (d) tetrahedral; (e) triangular pyramidal; (f) tetrahedral; (g) pyramidal; (h) planar, bent (90°). **11.** (a) 4 or 5; (b) 12; (c) 10; (d) 1; (e) 12; (f) 18; (g) 2; (h) 10; (i) 6; (j) 9. **12.** b, e, j. **13.** b, e, j. **14.** (a) Linear; (b) tetrahedral; (c) pyramidal; (d) pyramidal; (e) tetrahedral; (f) octahedral; (g) planar, 90°; (h) pyramidal; (i) linear; (j) tetrahedral. **15.** BrCl. **16.** a, d, f, h, i. **17.** (a) Tetrahedral, sp^3; (b) octahedral, sp^3d^2; (c) planar, sp^2, 120°; (d) linear, 180°, sp; (e) tetrahedral, sp^3; (f) planar, 120°, sp^2. **18.** (a) Potassium oxide; (b) barium sulfide; (c) calcium chloride; (d) phosphorus pentabromide; (e) rubidium fluoride. **19.** (a) Ionic (inter); (b) ionic (inter), covalent in C_2^{--} (intra); (c) covalent (intra), van der Waals (inter); (d) covalent (intra), hydrogen bonds, and van der Waals (inter); (e) ionic (inter), covalent (intra) in nitrate ion; (f) covalent (intra), van der Waals (inter). **21.** Cl. **22.** 17%. **23.** (a) Resorcinol; (b) toluene.

CHAPTER 9

1. (a) C_2H_2 (O); (b) Br_2 (O); (c) H_2 (O); (d) CH_3OH (O); (e) H_2O (O); (f) Cl_2 (O); (g) O_2 (O); (h) F_2 (O); (i) Br_2 (O); (j) O_2 (O). **2.** (a) Cs^+Br^-; (b) $Ca^{++}S^{--}$; (c) Ga_2O_3; (d) TeO_3; (e) PCl_5; (f) AsF_5; (g) SF_6; (h) Rb^+I^-; (i) $Ba^{++}S^{--}$; (j) $(Mg^{++})_3(N^{3-})_2$. **3.** (a) 22.5 moles; (b) 75 moles; (c) 360 moles; (d) 39 g. **4.** 1×10^{-9} M. **5.** 1×10^{-9} M, acidic. **6.** (a) 1×10^{-12} M; (b) HOH, OH_3^+, OH^-, HEN, EN^-; (c) EN^- acts as a base, HOH acts as an acid; (d) basic; (e) HOH, OH_3^+, HEN; (f) HOH, OH^-, EN^-; (g) HOH; (h) HOH; (i) $HEN + HOH \leftrightarrows EN^- + OH_3^+$; (j) $EN^- + HOH \leftrightarrows HEN + OH^-$. **7.** Symmetry (molecular and electronic) of the resultant ions that enhances stability. **8.** (a) $CH_3NH_2 + CO_2 \rightarrow CH_3NH_2CO_2$; (b) $HCO_3^- + NH_3 \rightarrow NH_4^+ + CO_3^{--}$; (c) $CrO_3 + H_2O \leftrightarrows (HO)_2CrO_2$, $(HO)_2CrO_2 + HOH \leftrightarrows HOCrO_3^- + OH_3^+$, $HOCrO_3^- + HOH \leftrightarrows CrO_4^{--} + OH_3^+$; (d) $SOCl_2 + 2HOH \rightarrow 2HCl + SO(OH)_2$; (e) $SO_2 + OH^- \leftrightarrows HOSO_2^-$; (f) $H_2 + Br_2 \rightarrow 2HBr$; (g) $BiCl_3 + HOH \leftrightarrows BiOCl + 2HCl$; (h) $ClCOCl + 2C_2H_5OH \rightarrow H_5C_2OCOOC_2H_5 + 2HCl$; (i) $HO^- + PbO \leftrightarrows HOPbO^-$; (j) $CuCl_2 + 4NH_3 \leftrightarrows [Cu(NH_3)_4]^{++} + 2Cl^-$; (k) $CH_3COBr + CH_3NH_2 \rightarrow CH_3CONHCH_3 + HBr$; (l) $CH_3COO^- + HOH \leftrightarrows CH_3COOH + OH^-$; (m) $HOClO_3 + HONO_2 \leftrightarrows H_2ONO_2^+ + OClO_3^-$; (n) $H_2PO_4^- + HOH \leftrightarrows HPO_4^{--} + OH_3^+$; (o) $C_2H_4 + HI \rightarrow C_2H_5I$; (p) $HgI_2 + I^- \leftrightarrows HgI_3^-$, also HgI_4^{--}.

CHAPTER 10

2. (a) Smallest mol wt; (b) no. **3.** Se^{--} is a less able proton acceptor than S^{--} because of lower charge density. **4.** $PH_4^+ + NH_3 \rightarrow NH_4^+ + PH_3$. **5.** AgN_3, $N_2H_5^+(HSO_4)^-$, HSe^-, $Na^+BH_4^-$. **6.** Larger gravitational attraction of larger bodies. **7.** 15 l. **8.** Sulfur, paraffin wax (hydrocarbons), and inert solids. **9.** Basic solution causes oxidation of Al metal. **10.** 259.3 kcal. **11.** 848 lb.

CHAPTER 11

1. (a) HgO, NO, O_2; (b) $HOSeO_3^-$; (c) Cl^-, SO_4^{--}; (d) SO_3^{--}, NH_4^+, Cl^-; (e) SrO, CO_2; (f) $[Cr(OH)_4]^-$; (g) VO_4^{3-}, $HOVO_3^-$; (h) $Ba^{++}(OH^-)_2$; (i) Na^+, OH^-; (j) $[Zn(OH)_3]^-$; (k) SeO_4^{--}. **2.** H_2O. **3.** Yellow to orange. **5.** $S^{--} \rightarrow S^\circ$, $S^{--} + 2H^+ \leftrightarrows H_2S$. **6.** 150 tons. **7.** 6.6 moles. **8.** OH^-, O_2. **10.** Excess OH_3^+ yields $Be(OH_2)_4^{++}$, excess OH^- yields $[Be(OH)_4]^{--}$. **11.** Changes to crystalline rhombic. **12.** Fe(III) reduced by S^{--}. **13.** Zn^{++}. **14.** (a) Lithia; (b) alumina; (c) alumina; (d) all; (e) lithia. **15.** No. **16.** The dissociation of O_3 is exothermic. **18.** Ag and O_2, products. **19.** PtO_2.

CHAPTER 12

1. Water at 10°. **2.** 0.1 M Na^+OH^-. **3.** Add Fe^{3+} ions; if I^- is present, I_2 is produced. **4.** (a) 4240 tons; (b) 2220 tons. **5.** 112 kg. **6.** The Br_2 is oxidized to colorless BrO^-. **8.** ClO_3^-. **10.** Basic. **11.** Br_2. **12.** (a) AgI; (b) yellow; (c) $[AgI_2]^-$ (soluble); (d) add water to dilute. **13.** Displacement of air from glass vessel. **14.** Add I^- for Cl_2, add Ag^+ for Cl^-.

CHAPTER 13

2. NO and NO_2 (N_2O_3), N_2O_5. 3. Acid-base. 5. A precipitate appears, then disappears. 7. 18 moles. 8. 81 tons. 9. $Al + OH^-$. 10. $4NH_3 + 5O_2 \rightarrow 4NO + 6H_2O$. $2NO + O_2 \rightarrow 2NO_2$; $3NO_2 + H_2O \rightarrow 2HNO_3 + NO$. 11. $N_2O_5 + H_2O \rightarrow 2HNO_3$, acid-base. 12. NO; NO_2. 13. 1400 tons. 14. Nonradical has less color. 15. Bi(III) is oxidized. 16. $(Na^+)_4(P_2O_7)^{4-}$; $K^+PO_3^-$ (the empirical formula); $Rb^+H_2PO_2^-$; $Na^+H_2AsO_3^-$; $(Ca^{++})_3(PO_4^{3-})_2$; $(Mg^{++})_2(P_2O_7)^{4-}$.

CHAPTER 14

1. 3.5 times greater. 2. 120 g. 3. 8 atm. 4. 46 cm. 5. 13.4 g. 6. 0.14 g. 7. 84 g. 8. $-136°C$. 9. 160 g. 10. (a) Z; (b) X; (c) 110 g; (d) 1.6 moles. 11. $68°C$. 12. 33 g. 13. 3.1 g. 14. 45,000 ml. 15. X, 46 cm; Y, 68 cm; Z, 21 cm. 16. (a) 0.05 g; (b) 260 ml; (c) 730 mm; (d) 0.009 g. 17. 2 l. 18. (a) 39 ml; (b) 110 cu ft; (c) 78 ml of X_2Q_2, 130 ml of Z_2Q_2, 4 ml of X_3Z_5. 19. 200 l. 20. N_2, 8 atm; O_2, 1.6 atm. 21. $-86°C$. 22. 33.6 l. 23. 6 atm. 24. (a) 1.25 g/l; (b) 70 g. 25. Hydrogen chloride. 26. Carbon dioxide. 27. $-10°C$. 28. Stronger intermolecular attractive forces in chlorine. 29. $-147°C$. 30. Much lower temperature. 31. No. 32. No. 33. Decrease.

CHAPTER 15

1. Carbon bisulfide. 2. Heptane. 3. $100°C$. 4. $50°C$. 5. Collect near $40°C$. 6. The gaseous pressure on liquid's surface. 7. At least equal to pressure on water's surface. 8. $61.3°C$. 9. 24,000 cal. 10. 24 kcal. 11. 13 eu. 12. Same as. 13. Ice at $30°F$ slowly vaporizes. 14. Weaker intermolecular attractive forces in ether. 15. Sublimation. 16. Plot vapor pressures vs. temperatures to find temperature at which vapor pressure is 760 mm. 18. 2.7 kg. 19. (a) Y; (b) yes; (c) X; (d) $-170°C$. 20. A. 21. Same as. 22. (a) Tom; (b) Dick; (c) Tom; (d) Tom; (e) T. 23. (a) 150 ml; (b) 29.8 cm; (c) A; (d) B; (e) CS_2; (f) C_6H_6; (g) 840 mm; (h) B; (i) 91 mg; (j) CS_2.

CHAPTER 16

1. 8.75 g. 2. 3.6 g. 3. 0.19 M. 4. 0.13 M. 5. 360 ml. 6. 244 ml. 7. 400 g. 8. 130 g. 9. (a) 10 M; (b) 36 m; (c) 0.39; (d) $-67°C$; (e) $120°C$. 10. 300. 11. 0.045 g. 12. X dissociates to yield 2 moles of entities per mole. 13. Unsaturated. 14. 95 g. 15. Precipitation of Na^+Cl^-. 16. Na^+Cl^- precipitates. 17. No precipitation observed. 18. $60°C$. 19. $NH_4^+Cl^-$. 20. $K^+NO_3^-$. 21. K^+Cl^-. 22. 320 g. 23. 0.8 g.

24. 15 g. **25.** Of HOH, 0.85. **26.** 9.7 m. **27.** 6.1 M. **28.** A. **29.** By fractional distillation. **31.** −360 cal/mole. **32.** (a) Increase; (b) no. **33.** $K_d = 2$ for X/Y.

CHAPTER 17

1. (a) CH_3OH; (b) C_2H_5OH; (c) $(CH_2)_2(OH)_2$; (d) CH_3COOH; (e) $(C_2H_5)_2O$; (f) CH_3CONH_2; (g) NH_3. **2.** (a) C_3H_7OH; (b) C_3H_7COOH; (c) $C_2H_5CONH_2$; (d) CH_3OH; (e) C_2H_5OH. **3.** CH_3I. **4.** 90 g. **5.** Water molecules decrease lattice energy. **6.** Hydration of ions in water, no solvation in hexane; water has a much higher dielectric constant. **7.** Hydrated cobalt(II) ions impart pink color; unhydrated ions impart blue color. **8.** (a) $MnSO_4 \cdot 3H_2O$; (b) manganese(II) sulfate-3-water; (c) 26.3%; (d) 1.15 M. **9.** (a) Less soluble; (b) differences in sizes of ions. **10.** CsOH. **11.** Deliquescent implies absorption of water to yield a liquid. **13.** (a) CsCl; (b) RbCl; (c) RbOH; (d) $Ba(OH)_2$; (e) Cs_2CO_3; (f) NaI; (g) Rb_2CO_3; (h) $Ca(NO_3)_2$; (i) NH_4I; (j) Cs_2SO_4. **14.** $LiI \cdot 3H_2O$; lithium iodide-3-water. **15.** Dark brown is anhydrous form; yellow solid is hydrated form. **16.** 6.9×10^{-9}. **17.** 9×10^{-4} g. **18.** CaF_2. **19.** AgI. **20.** 2.5×10^{-11} mole. **21.** (a) 1.5×10^{-7} M; (b) 1.2×10^{-5} mole. **22.** AgBr. **23.** Precipitation of $PbCl_2$. **24.** N_2 expels H_2S, thereby upsetting equilibrium to favor dissolution of CdS. **25.** Common-ion effect in saturated solution of $PbCl_2$.

CHAPTER 18

1. Six-fold increase. **2.** Activation and/or reaction occurs on interior walls. **3.** Liters^2/mole^{2}min. **4.** Second-order. **5.** First-order. **6.** (a) Third-order; (b) $r = k[NO]^2[O_2]$. **7.** 0.033 min^{-1}. **8.** 21 min. **9.** Plot log k vs. $1/T$; slope of line equals $-E_a/2.3R$, where $R = 1.98$ cal/mole deg. **10.** No; ΔF is positive. **11.** Since ΔS is positive, $T \Delta S$ can exceed ΔH in $\Delta F = \Delta H - T \Delta S$, if T is large enough. **12.** (a) −213 kcal; (b) −311 kcal/mole of C_2H_2, or −622 kcal for reaction as written; (c) −41.7 kcal; (d) −74.4 kcal; (e) +17.9 kcal. **13.** −5 kcal. **14.** −84 kcal. **15.** 541 kcal. **16.** 10.1 g. **17.** No; it is nonspontaneous under these conditions, but a change in conditions would alter value of ΔF, perhaps to yield a negative value of ΔF. **18.** (a) −57.6 eu; (b) −28.8 eu; (c) +42.9 eu; (d) −47.4 eu; (e) −77.6 eu. **19.** (a) −195 kcal; (b) −24.1 kcal; (c) −65.62 kcal; (d) −7.96 kcal; (e) −113.1 kcal. **20.** (a) −213 kcal; (b) −32.7 kcal; (c) −52.8 kcal; (d) −22.06 kcal; (e) −136.3 kcal.

CHAPTER 19

1. (a) More M_2X_2 and ZT; (b) favors endothermic reaction; (c) increases equally the rates of the two reactions; (d) favor formation of T_4 and MXZ_2;

(e) equilibrium essentially unchanged; slight tendency to favor exothermic reaction; (f) exothermic reaction; (g) $P_{T_4} \times P^2_{MXZ_1}/P^4_{ZT} \times P_{M_2X_2}$. **2.** $P^2_{NO_2}/P_{N_2O_4} = K$. **3.** Endothermic reaction. **4.** (a) 4; (b) 0.3 M; (c) 1 M. **5.** 808. **6.** 1.24×10^{-3}. **7.** (a) $[SO_3]^2/[SO_2]^2[O_2]$; (b) increased; (c) no. **8.** Approach the system from the two opposite directions. **9.** Exothermic. **10.** None. **11.** 0.67 mole of X; 0.35 mole of Y. **12.** 1.3×10^{-3} M. **13.** 1.8×10^{-5} M. **14.** 2.3×10^{-7}. **15.** 1 g. **16.** $K = 1$; reaction proceeds halfway to completion. **17.** $+1.16$ kcal/mole. **18.** (a) No; (b) 1.7×10^{-28}.

CHAPTER 20

1. (a) In order; $-3, +5, -3, +3, -1, -2, -2, +2, 0, -1$ (total), $-3, -1, +4, -3, +5$; (b) all but K_3N, NH_4Cl, $CsNH_2$, NH_3; (c) all but KNO_3, $HONO_2$; (d) KNO_3, $HONO_2$; (e) K_3N, NH_4Cl, $CsNH_2$, NH_3; (f) KNO_2, NH_2OH, N_2H_4, NO, N_2, NH_3, $NH_2OH_2^+$, $N_2H_5^+$, N_2O_4. **2.** (a) He, Sr^{++}, Li^+, F_2; (b) Ca, He, Rb, O^{--}, Se^{--}, H^-, I^-, F^-, N^{3-}; (c) O_2, H_2, O_2^{--}, Sr^{++}, P_4, C_2^{--}, Li^+, F_2; (d) all but He, Sr^{++}, Li^+, F_2, F^-; (e) O_2, H_2, O_2^{--}, P_4, C_2^{--}; (f) Sr^{++}, Li^+, F_2. **3.** (a) Rb; (b) N; (c) Bi; (d) As. **4.** (a) Fe^{++}; (b) Fe^{++}; (c) Fe; (d) Fe^{3+}; (e) yes; (f) no; (g) yes; (h) no; (i) yes. **5.** (a) Tl_2S_3; (b) Tl; (c) 20 moles; (d) -2; (e) 350 g. **6.** 65 g. **7.** 125 g-atoms. **8.** (a) 6; (b) 64; (c) 96; (d) 13; (e) 0.8 mole. **9.** (a) 48; (b) 1.94; (c) 8; (d) 2.5; (e) 7.3 moles. **10.** 1.2. **11.** 79.2 g. **12.** $+3$. **13.** N_2O_3. **14.** 210 g. **15.** Oxidizing agents are (a) CO; (b) SO_2; (c) NO_2; (d) H_2; (e) none; (f) Br_2; (g) none; (h) C_2H_2; (i) S; (j) none. **16.** (a) BaI_2; (b) Rb_3P; (c) $SnCl_4$; (d) AsF_5; (e) GeO_2; (f) $FeBr_3$; (g) Cs_3N; (h) $InCl_3$; (i) SeO_3; (j) ZnI_2. **19.** (a) 28 g; (b) 56 g; (c) 21 g; (d) 62 g; (e) 14 g. **20.** 43.3 g. **21.** 4.4. **22.** 5.

CHAPTER 21

1. 48,250. **2.** 90 g. **3.** 6.2×10^{19}. **4.** 43 min. **5.** 169 g. **6.** (a) Br_2, H_2, and Rb^+OH^- from solution near cathode; (b) metallic Ba, Cl_2; (c) Cl_2, H_2, and K^+OH^- from solution near cathode; (d) Li metal, Br_2; (e) D_2, O_2. **7.** (a) 1.384 g; (b) 7720 coulombs; (c) 0.08 mole; (d) 12.9 min. **8.** (a) 4.48 l; (b) 2.76 g; (c) 14,200 mg. **9.** (a) 20 g; (b) 5 moles. **10.** 104 g. **11.** Deposition of silver on iron. **12.** Droplets of elemental mercury. **13.** Nothing. **14.** $+1.53$ volts. **15.** (a) Z; (b) X; (c) oxidation of $Sn°$ to Sn^{++}; (d) reduction of Ag^+ to $Ag°$. **16.** (a) Yes; (b) no; (c) yes; (d) yes; (e) yes; (f) yes; (g) yes. **17.** (a) $+1.04$ volts; (b) 1.16 volts; (c) 1.10 volts. **18.** $1 \times 10^{+37}$. **19.** $1 \times 10^{+1.27}$, or 18.6.

CHAPTER 22

1. (a) $H_2Se + HOH \leftrightarrows OH_3^+ + HSe^-$, $HSe^- + HOH \leftrightarrows OH_3^+ + Se^{--}$; (b) OH_3^+ and HSe^-; (c) HOH, HSe^-; (d) HOH, H_2Se, OH_3^+, HSe^-; (e) HOH, HSe^-, Se^{--}, OH^-; (f) OH_3^+; (g) nothing remains; (h) $OH_3^+ + OH^- \leftrightarrows 2HOH$; $H_2Se + OH^- \leftrightarrows HOH + HSe^-$; $HSe^- + OH^- \leftrightarrows Se^{--} + HOH$; $HOH + OH^- \leftrightarrows HOH + OH^-$; (i) HSe^-; (j) less acidic. 2. (a) Ammonium ions act as acids; (b) sulfite ions act as bases; (c) amide ions act as bases; (d) CO_2 acts as acid with NH_3 molecules (initially); (e) acetate ion, as base, decreases OH_3^+ concentration (common ion effect); (f) piperidine acts as a base; (g) methyl violet acts as a base; (h) phosphate ions act as bases; (i) methylammonium ions act as acids; (j) hydride ions act as bases. 3. (a) $C_2H_5NH_3^+$; (b) HNO_2; (c) H_3PO_4; (d) HCO_3^-; (e) $H_3NSO_3H^+$; (f) H_2SO_3; (g) H_2Br^+. 4. HOP. 5. Hydroxide ion and dimethylammonium ion. 6. OH_3^+, HOH, NH_4^+. 7. (a) Less than; (b) $0.25 \times 10^{-5} M$; (c) HAT and OH^-. 8. (a) $4 \times 10^{-3} M$; (b) $8.5 \times 10^{-3} M$; (c) $1.25 \times 10^{-2} M$; (d) basic. 9. One-third. 10. (a) Weak acid; (b) diprotic; (c) $1 \times 10^{-13} M$; (d) HOH, $C_2H_5O_4^-$; (e) HOH; (f) $C_2H_5O_4^-$, $C_2H_4O_4^{--}$, HOH, OH^-; (g) OH^-. 11. H_2S, HOH, OH^-, OH_3^+, HS^-, S^{--}; (a) H_2S; (b) S^{--}; (c) increase the pH; (d) bubbles of H_2S appear (effervescence). 12. $1 \times 10^{-7} M$. 13. (a) Less than; (b) 42 ml; (c) $1 \times 10^{-3} M$. 14. Add NH_4^+ in some ammonium salt. 15. 64 g. 16. Rb^+OH^-. 17. 55.8. 18. $6.97 \times 10^{-2} M$. 19. (a) 3890 mg; (b) 0.12 M; (c) 1640 ml; (d) 366 mg. 20. 64.4 mg. 21. (a) X used 30 ml, Y used 45 ml; (b) 0.1 N. 22. (a) HAMP; (b) HUMP; (c) H_2AMP^+. 23. (a) Red; (b) purple; (c) acid and base forms of Congo red and ions of water; (d) either $1 \times 10^{-5} M$ or less.

CHAPTER 23

2. (a) A precipitate appears and eventually disappears; (b) $[Al(OH)_4]^- + OH_3^+ \leftrightarrows [Al(OH)_3(OH_2)] + HOH$; (c) trihydroxoaquoaluminum III. 3. Heat in strongly basic solution, test for NH_3. 4. Loosely bound protons and unshared pairs of electrons. 5. NH_2^- in some alkali metal amide or excess NH_3. 7. (a) $CO_2 + H^- \rightarrow HCO_2^-$, $CO + OH^- \rightarrow HCO_2^-$; (b) $H^- + SO_3 \rightarrow HSO_3^-$, $HO^- + SO_2 \rightarrow HOSO_2^-$; (c) $H_2S_2O_7 + HCl \rightarrow H_2Cl^+ + HS_2O_7^-$; (d) $H_2SO_4 + Cl^-$ (in solid Na^+Cl^-) $\rightarrow HCl + HSO_4^-$; (e) $CO_2 + O^{--} \rightarrow CO_3^{--}$; (f) $HCOOH + H_2SO_4 \rightarrow OH_3^+ + CO + HSO_4^-$; (g) $SO_3 + NH_2^- \rightarrow SO_3NH_2^-$, $SO_3 +$ excess $NH_3 \rightarrow NH_4^+SO_3NH_2$; (h) $NH_2^- + CH_3OH \rightarrow CH_3O^- + NH_3$. 8. Dissolve salt in water; then add enough $3M$ HCl to change half the monohydrogen phosphate ions to dihydrogen phosphate ions. 9. (a) $NH_4^+ + OC_2H_5^- \leftrightarrows NH_3 + HOC_2H_5$; (b) $HO^- + SO_2 \rightarrow HOSO_2^-$; (c) $H_2SO_4 + HCl \leftrightarrows H_2Cl^+ + HSO_4^-$; (d) $C_2H_5NH_3^+ + HOH \leftrightarrows OH_3^+ + C_2H_5NH_2$; (e) $Br^- + H_2SO_4 \leftrightarrows HBr +$

HSO_4^-; (f) $CH_3O^- + HOH \leftrightarrows CH_3OH + OH^-$; (g) $SOCl_2 + $ excess $HOH \rightarrow$ $2OH_3^+ + 2Cl^- + SO_2 + H_2SO_3$ (initially); (h) $NH_2^- + CH_3OH \rightarrow NH_3 +$ CH_3O^-; (i) $O^{--} + HOH \leftrightarrows 2OH^-$; (j) $H_2SO_4 + Cl^- \leftrightarrows HCl + HSO_4^-$. **10.** (a) 0.1 M HBr, 0.1 M HI, 0.1 N $HClO_4$; (b) 0.1 M H_2SO_4; (c) 0.1 M H_2SO_4; (d) 0.25 M HCN; (e) 0.25 M HCN; (f) 0.25 M HCN. **11.** 4×10^{-10} M. **12.** 3×10^{-11} M. **13.** 5×10^{-6}. **14.** 1.6×10^{-3} M. **15.** 1.1×10^{-3} M. **16.** Very nearly 0.1 M. **17.** 0.3— M. **18.** 0.4— M. **19.** OAc^-/HOAc ratio (molarities) must be 0.036; i.e., to 1 l of 0.1 M acetic acid solution add 3.6 mmoles of sodium acetate. **20.** $[M(OH)_6]^{--}$. **21.** Monohydrogen phosphate ion. **22.** Nitrogen and hydrogen. **23.** Carbamic acid, H_2NCOOH. **24.** (a) Linear; (b) tetrahedral; (c) square planar; (d) linear; (e) octahedral; (f) octahedral; (g) octahedral; (h) octahedral; (i) square planar; (j) tetrahedral. **25.** (a) $(Na^+)[Co(NH_3)_2Cl_4]^-$; (b) $[Co(NH_3)_4Br_2]^+Cl^-$; (c) $[Pt(NH_3)_5Cl]^{3+}(Cl^-)_3$; (d) $[Fe(CN)_5(NO)]^{--}$; (e) $[Co(C_5H_5N)_2(H_2N(CH_2)_2NH_2)_2]^{3+}$; (f) $[Fe(SCN)_2(OH_2)_4]^+$; (g) $[Cu(NH_3)_4]^{++}(SO_4)^{--} \cdot H_2O$; (h) $(Na^+)_2[ZnO_2]^{--}$; (i) $Co(NH_3)_3(Br)_3$; (j) $[Al(OH)_2(OH_2)_4]^+Cl^-$. **26.** (a) Geometric; (b) geometric and optical; (c) optical; (d) geometric; (e) geometric.

CHAPTER 24

1. Cs^+, La^{3+}, Ce^{4+}, I^-, Te^{--}. **2.** Unpaired loosely held electrons. **3.** Cs. **4.** Al. **5.** SO_2. **6.** Most K compounds are quite soluble in water. **7.** (a) 8.3 tons; (b) 6750 l. **8.** Less soluble in H_2O. **9.** Br^-, Se^{--}, As^{3-}. **10.** Hg, Cs, Ga. **11.** Bp of Li is too high. **12.** $K \rightarrow K^+ + 1e^-$. **13.** 1.3 g. **14.** $HCO_3^- + H_2PO_4^- \leftrightarrows HPO_4^{--} + H_2CO_3 \leftrightarrows CO_2 + H_2O$. **15.** Effervescence, CO_2. **16.** 100,000. **17.** 72,000 cal. **18.** Sublimation. **19.** Precipitate appears, then disappears. **20.** $Pb(OH)_2 + OH^- \leftrightarrows [Pb(OH)(O)]^- + HOH$ (unhydrated formulation). **21.** Bubbles of H_2S and precipitate of SnS_2. **22.** $Pb(OH)_2$ less soluble than $PbCrO_4$, and $Pb(OH)_2$ dissolves (amphoteric). **23.** Precipitate of $PbCl_2$. **24.** Add CrO_4^{--} and acetic acid; if precipitate, Ba^{++} present. **25.** Add OH^-; if precipitate, Mg^{++} present. **26.** Mg^{++} smallest ion (except Be), so hydrogen-bonding in crystal lattice is extensive; Mg^{++} largest charge density and tendency to hydrate, so in chromate this factor predominates.

CHAPTER 25

1. MnO, Mn_2O_3, MnO_2, MnO_3, Mn_2O_7. **2.** Unpaired electrons. **3.** Ti^{4+}, Ca^{++}, K^+, Cl^-, S^{--}. **4.** Ni, Ag, Cu, etc. **5.** 518 g. **6.** 66 tons. **7.** Precipitate appears, then disappears. **8.** H^+ tie up S^{--} in H_2S. **10.** 14.2%. **11.** Color. **12.** $FeCl_2 \cdot 4H_2O$. **13.** 4. **14.** Yields soluble $[Zn(NH_3)_4]^{++}$. **15.** In order: tetramminecopper(II) ion, tetrachlorocuprate(II) ion, diamminesilver(I) ion, tetracyanonickelate(II) ion, diaquodiamminecopper(II) ion, tetraquozinc(II) ion, tetrahydroxozincate(II) ion, trichloromercurate(II) ion, hexacyanomanganeseate(II) ion, dioxozincate(II) ion. **16.** Add aq HCl and detect either presence or absence of odor of H_2S. **17.** NO_3^-. **18.** Add S^{--} to aqueous suspension; if yellow solid appears, CdS present. **19.** Planar square.

CHAPTER 26

1. (a) ^{138}Ce; (b) ^{251}Cf; (c) ^{62}Cu; (d) ^{115}In; (e) ^{216}Po; (f) ^{45}Sc; (g) ^{75}Se; (h) ^{21}Ne; (i) ^{208}Bi; (j) ^{104}Ag. **2.** 0.3 mg. **3.** 0.02 mg. **4.** 4 P.M., Thursday. **5.** Iron-57; cobalt-57; rubidium-87, strontium-87; molybdenum-100, ruthenium-100; cadmium-113, indium-113; antimony-123, tellurium-123; neodymium-144, samarium-144; rhenium-187, osmium-187. **6.** Iron-57, cobalt-57; rubidium-87, strontium-87; ruthenium-101, rhodium-101; cadmium-113, indium-113; indium-115, tin-115; antimony-123, tellurium-123; rhenium-187, osmium-187. **7.** Over a dozen pairs of isobars. **9.** First-order. **10.** 6.16×10^{23}. **11.** (a) ^{21}Ne; (b) ^{24}Na; (c) ^{24}Na; (d) ^{36}Ar; (e) ^{59}Fe; (f) ^{231}Np; (g) ^{257}Lw; (h) ^4He. **12.** ^{10}B. **13.** Alpha particle. **14.** ^{130}Te. **15.** All elements represented in the naturally radioactive ^{238}U series (family). **16.** 4×10^7. **19.** No.

CHAPTER 27

3. (a) 2,3-Dimethyl-3-ethyl-1-hexanol; (b) 2,3,4-trimethyl-2-pentene; (c) 2-methyl-2-ethylbutanal; (d) 2-methyl-3-hexyne. **5.** Trichloroethanal. **6.** (a) 2,3-Dibromo-2,3-dimethylpentane; (b) yes. **7.** Nine. **8.** (a) Eight; (b) 2. **9.** (a) Six; (b) one. **10.** 2,2-Dimethylpropanal. **11.** 2,3-Dimethylbutanoic acid. **12.** (a) Sodium propionate and 2-propanol; (b) glycerol and sodium butyrate; (c) ethanol and sodium oxalate. **13.** 3-Methyl-3-pentanol. **14.** Oxidize 1-propanol to propanoic acid; then esterify acid with 1-propanol. **15.** Treat methanol with Na to get $Na^+OCH_3^-$; then do Williamson with C_2H_5I to get ether. **16.** Acetic acid and hydroxyethanal. **17.** Intramolecular hydrogen-bonding in maleic, intermolecular in fumaric to yield larger molecular aggregates. **18.** Thirteen. **19.** Twelve. **20.** Seven. **21.** Five. **23.** Asymmetric molecules; each is the nonsuperimposable mirror image of the other; the racemic mixture. **24.** (a) Hydrolyze bromide to alcohol; then oxidize alcohol to ketone; (b) oxidize ethanol to acetic acid; then esterify acid with ethanol. **25.** 3,3-Dimethyl-1-butanol. **26.** Dibutyl disulfide. **27.** 1-Propanethiol. **28.** $C_6H_5SC(C_6H_5)_3$. **29.** (a) 154 g; (b) 130 g; (c) 115 g; (d) 116 g; (e) 163 g. **30.** Dextro, levo, and meso. **31.** Hydroxyl in estradiol is as in phenol (acidic); that in cholesterol is as in cyclohexanol (secondary alcohol). **32.** $C \equiv C-C-C-C \equiv C$ or $C-C \equiv C-C \equiv C-C$. **33.** 990 g. **34.** 29 g. **35.** 24.

INDEX